THEORY OF STRUCTURES

THEORY OF STRUCTURES

BY

ARTHUR MORLEY
O.B.E., D.Sc., Hon.M.I.Mech.E.

*Formerly Professor of Mechanical
Engineering in University College
Nottingham*

WITH DIAGRAMS AND PLATES

LONGMANS, GREEN AND CO
LONDON · NEW YORK · TORONTO

LONGMANS, GREEN AND CO. LTD
6 & 7 CLIFFORD STREET, LONDON W.1

LONGMANS, GREEN AND CO. INC.
55 FIFTH AVENUE, NEW YORK 3

LONGMANS, GREEN AND CO.
215 VICTORIA STREET, TORONTO 1

ALSO AT MELBOURNE AND CAPE TOWN

ORIENT LONGMANS LTD
BOMBAY, CALCUTTA, MADRAS

FIRST EDITION . . . . *August* 1912
SECOND EDITION . . . . . *January* 1918
NEW IMPRESSIONS . . . . . . *May* 1919,
February 1920, *December* 1921, *October* 1923,
March 1927
THIRD EDITION . . . . . *June* 1929
NEW IMPRESSION . . . . . *June* 1931
FOURTH EDITION . . . . . *November* 1934
NEW IMPRESSIONS . . . . . *January* 1937,
November 1938, *August* 1940, *September* 1941,
March 1942, *August* 1942, *April* 1943,
July 1944, *May* 1946
FIFTH EDITION . . . . . . *November* 1948
NEW IMPRESSION . . . . *April* 1950

Printed in Great Britain by William Clowes & Sons, Limited, Beccles

PREFACE TO FIFTH EDITION

FOR this edition the type has been re-set and new diagrams have been made. The opportunity has been used to re-write several sections of the book. Those on properties of materials and fundamental statics have been curtailed and others relating to later developments of stress analysis have been added. In particular, room has been found for an introduction to the methods of moment distribution, tension coefficients, the Williott-Mohr deflection diagram, wider use of elastic strain energy methods and a fuller treatment of reinforced concrete.

In the preparation of the diagrams I have had the assistance of Mr. G. F. Rodmell, M.I.Struct.E., to whom I am indebted for the design in Plate I. For this and for his valued co-operation in several sections I here express my thanks.

A. M.

BATH,
1948.

PREFACE TO FIRST EDITION

THE object of the following pages is mainly to set forth the theory of the simpler structures so far as it relates to strength, stiffness, and stability. The subject is largely based upon statics and the elastic properties of material, and has much in common with that called Strength of Materials. Consequently I have taken a considerable amount of matter in seven chapters out of the first nine, without great modification from my earlier book, " Strength of Materials," to which the present volume forms a companion.

Worked-out examples form an important feature of the text, and are generally essential to obtaining a sound knowledge of the subject. I have not hesitated to use examples which may be called academic, because they are simplified to illustrate particular points without unnecessary arithmetic complication ; this is particularly the case with statically indeterminate structures and secondary stresses on which little more than the principle is given as an introduction to the larger treatises.   Students are apt to forget how many stress computations in structural design are necessarily of a conventional nature, and the attempt has been made to point out when this is specially the case.   In some instances more exact estimates have been made to indicate the nature and degree of possible error involved by conventional assumptions.

Fairly free use has been made of influence lines, which form such clear and instructive means of understanding the stresses arising from moving loads.

The practical design of structures involves so much outside of what may reasonably be called theory that it can only be thoroughly learned in the drawing office, but a few examples have been included to illustrate the application of the theory to practice.

Reinforced concrete structures are becoming so important as to demand a complete volume for their treatment, and no attempt has been made to deal with this subject except incidentally as an example of a beam of composite cross-section.

I take this opportunity of thanking numerous friends who have generously assisted me in reading proofs, preparation of designs or diagrams, and checking examples; particularly Messrs. S. W. Budd, R. T. McCallum, B.Sc., and W. N. Thomas, B.Sc.   I also thank Sir Wm. Arrol & Co., Ltd., Messrs. Dorman Long & Co., Ltd., and Messrs. R. A. Skelton & Co., for the use of tables, diagrams, and technical information; and Mr. H. S. Prichard for much information regarding American practice relating to the treatment of live loads.

I should be grateful for intimation of any errors which readers may observe in the book.

ARTHUR MORLEY.

UNIVERSITY COLLEGE,
  NOTTINGHAM.
    April, 1912.

CONTENTS

CHAPTER V

STRESSES IN BEAMS

CHAPTER VI

MOVING LOADS

CHAPTER VII

DEFLECTION OF BEAMS

CHAPTER VIII

CONSTRAINED BEAMS

CHAPTER IX

FLEXURAL STRAIN ENERGY

CHAPTER X

DIRECT AND BENDING STRESSES

CHAPTER XI

FRAMED STRUCTURES

CHAPTER XII

STRESSES IN FRAMES

CHAPTER XIII

MOVING LOAD STRESSES IN FRAMES

CHAPTER XIV

SELECTED TYPICAL FRAMED STRUCTURES

CHAPTER XV

DEFLECTION AND INDETERMINATE FRAMES

CHAPTER XVI

SOME INDETERMINATE COMBINATIONS

CHAPTER XVII

FRAME MEMBERS AND STRUCTURAL CONNECTIONS

CHAPTER XVIII

PLATE GIRDERS AND BRIDGES

CHAPTER XIX

SUSPENSION BRIDGES AND METAL ARCHES

CHAPTER XX

EARTH PRESSURE, FOUNDATIONS, MASONRY STRUCTURES

PLATES

THEORY OF STRUCTURES

CHAPTER I

STRESS AND STRAIN

1. Introductory. The subject generally known as the *Theory of Structures* or *Mechanics of Structures* includes the study of the forces carried by structures and by the individual members of structures. It is largely an application of the subject of statics, but frequently the complexity of a structure or the uncertainty of the conditions of loading prevent anything like an exact mathematical analysis of the stresses, and assumptions have to be made which it is necessary to test by experiment and practical experience. It is important to realise the limits of much of our theory and the extent to which stress computations are frequently quite conventional rather than representing an actual physical state; *e.g.* the maximum intensity of stress in a flat bar axially pulled is not known within wide limits if the bar is perforated by a single hole.

The mechanics of structures is fundamental to structural design, but successful design involves commercial questions, such as cost and durability, which are not treated as theory, and which cannot well be taken into account except as the result of practical experience.

The " Theory of Structures " is closely related to the subject of the " Strength of Materials," and any boundary between the two is necessarily an arbitrary one. " Strength of Materials " has been treated in a separate volume, but to make this book serviceable to the reader who is concerned with structures only and not with machines, sufficient of the theory of stresses and strains in single pieces has been included to make it complete in itself.

2. Stress. The equal and opposite action and reaction which take place between two bodies, or two parts of the same body, transmitting forces constitute a stress. If we imagine a body which transmits a force to be divided into two parts by an ideal surface, and interaction takes place across this surface, the material there is said to be stressed or in a state of stress. The constituent forces, and therefore the stress itself, are distributed over the separating surface either uniformly or in some other manner. The *intensity of the stress* at a surface, generally referred to with less exactness as merely the stress, is estimated by the force transmitted per unit of area in the case of uniform distribution; if the distribution is not uniform, the stress intensity at a point in the surface must be looked upon as the limit of the ratio of units of force to units of area when each is decreased indefinitely.   The intensity of stress is also sometimes called the unit stress.

3. Simple Stresses.   There are two specially simple states of stress which may exist within a body.   More complex stresses may be split into component parts.

(1) *Tensile stress* between two parts of a body exists when each draws the other towards itself.   The simplest example of material subject to tensile stress is that of a tie-bar sustaining a pull.   If the

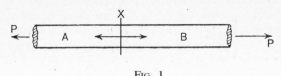

FIG. 1

pull on the tie-bar is say P lb., and we consider any imaginary plane of section X perpendicular to the axis of the bar, of area a sq. in., dividing the bar into two parts A and B (Fig. 1), the material at the section X is under a tensile stress.   The portion B, say, exerts a pull on the portion A which just balances P, and is therefore equal and opposite to it.   The average force exerted per square inch of section is

$$p = P/a$$

and this value p is the mean intensity of tensile stress at this section.

(2) *Compressive stress* between two parts of a body exists when each pushes the other from it.

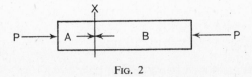

FIG. 2

If a bar (Fig. 2) sustains an axial thrust of P tons at each end, at a transverse section X of area a sq. in., dividing the bar into two parts A and B, the material is under compressive stress.   The portion A, say, exerts a push on the portion B equal and opposite to that on the far end of B.   The average force per square inch of section is

$$p = P/a$$

and this value p is the mean intensity of compressive stress at the section X.

Shear stress exists between two parts of a body in contact when the two parts exert equal and opposite forces on each other laterally in a direction tangential to their surface of contact.　As an example, there is a shear stress at the section XY of a pin or rivet (Fig. 3) when the two plates which it holds together sustain a pull P in the plane of the section XY.　If the area of section XY is *a* sq. in., and the pull is P tons, the total shear at the section XY is P tons, and the average force per square inch is

$$q = P/a$$

This value *q* is the mean intensity of shear stress at the section XY.

4. Strain.　Strain is the alteration of shape or dimensions resulting from stress.

(1) Tensile strain is the stretch, and often results from a pull which causes a condition of tensile stress to be set up.　It is in the direction of the tensile stress, and is measured by the fractional

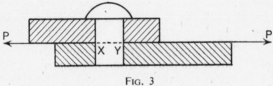

P　　　　　　　　　　　　　　　　　　　　　　　P

FIG. 3

elongation.　Thus, If a length *l* units is increased to *l*+δ*l*, the strain is

$$\delta l / l$$

The strain is obviously equal numerically to the stretch per unit of length.

(2) Compressive strain is the contraction which is often due to compressive stress, and is measured by the ratio of the contraction to the original length.　If a length *l* contracts to *l*−δ*l*, the compressive strain is

$$\delta l / l$$

Tensile stress causes a contraction perpendicular to its own direction, and compressive stress causes an elongation perpendicular to its own direction.

(3) Distortional or shear strain is the angular displacement produced by shear stress.　If a piece of material be subjected to a pure shear stress in a certain plane, the change in inclination (estimated in radians) between the plane and a line originally perpendicular to it, is the numerical measure of the resulting shear strain (see Art. 10).

5. Elastic Limits.　The limits of stress for a given material within which the resulting strain completely disappears after the removal of the stress are called the elastic limits.   If a stress beyond an elastic limit is applied, part of the resulting strain remains after the removal of the stress; such a residual strain is called a permanent set.   The determination of an elastic limit will evidently depend upon the detection of the smallest possible permanent set, and gives a lower stress when instruments of great precision are employed than with cruder methods.   In some materials the time allowed for strain to develop or to disappear will affect the result obtained.

Elastic strain is that produced by stress within the limits of elasticity; but the same term is often applied to the portion of strain which disappears with the removal of stress even when the elastic limits have been exceeded.

Hooke's Law states that within the elastic limits the strain produced is proportional to the stress producing it.   The law refers to all kinds of stress.

This law is not exactly true for all materials, but is approximately so for many.

6. Modulus of Elasticity.   Assuming the truth of Hooke's Law, we may write

intensity of stress α strain

or   stress intensity $=$ strain $\times$ constant

The constant in this equation is called the modulus or coefficient of elasticity, and will vary with the kind of stress and strain contemplated, there being for each kind of stress a different kind of modulus. Since the strain is measured as a mere number, and has no dimensions of length, time, or force, the constant is a quantity of the same kind as a stress intensity, being measured in units of force per unit of area, such as pounds or tons per square inch.   We might define the modulus of elasticity as the intensity of stress which would cause unit strain, if the material continued to follow the same law outside the elastic limits as within them, or as the intensity of stress per unit of strain.

7. Components of Oblique Stresses.   When the stress across any given surface in a material is neither normal nor tangential to that surface, we may conveniently resolve it into rectangular components, normal to the surface and tangential to it.   The normal stresses are tensile or compressive according to their directions, and the tangential components are shear stresses.

A simple example will illustrate the method of resolution of stress. If a parallel bar of cross-section a square inches be subjected to a pull of P tons, the intensity of tensile stress p is P/a in the direction of the length of the bar, or, in other words, normal to a surface, AB (Fig. 4), perpendicular to the line of pull.

Let p_n and p be the component stress intensities, normal and tangential respectively, to a surface, CD, which makes an angle θ with the surface AB.   Resolving the whole force P normal to CD, the component is

$$P_n = P \cos \theta$$

and the area of the surface CD is $a \sec \theta$, hence

$$p_n = \frac{P \cos \theta}{a \sec \theta} = \frac{P}{a} \cos^2 \theta = p \cos^2 \theta$$

and resolving along CD, the tangential component of the whole force is

$$P_t = P \sin \theta$$

$$p = \frac{P \sin \theta}{a \sec \theta} = \frac{P}{a} \sin \theta \cos \theta = p \sin \theta \cos \theta, \text{ or } \frac{p}{2} \sin 2\theta$$

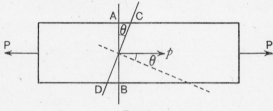

FIG. 4

Evidently p_t reaches a maximum value $\frac{1}{2}p$ when $\theta = 45°$, so that all surfaces, curved or plane, inclined 45° to AB (and therefore also to the axis of pull) are subjected to maximum shear stress.   In testing materials in tension or compression, it often happens that fracture takes place by shearing at surfaces inclined at angles other than 90° to the axis of pull.

Example.   The material of a tie-bar has a uniform tensile stress of 5 tons per sq. in.   What is the intensity of shear stress on a plane the normal of which is inclined 40° to the axis of the bar? What is the intensity of normal stress on this plane, and what is the resultant intensity of stress?

Considering a portion of the bar, the section of which is 1 square inch normal to the axis, the pull is 5 tons.   The area on which this load is spread on a plane inclined 40° to the perpendicular cross-section is

$$(1 \times \sec 40°) \text{ sq. in.}$$

and the amount of force resolved parallel to this oblique surface is

$$(5 \times \sin 40°) \text{ tons}$$

hence the intensity of shearing stress is

$$5 \sin 40° \div \sec 40° = 5 \sin 40° \cos 40° = 5 \times 0{\cdot}6428 \times 0{\cdot}7660$$
$$= 2{\cdot}462 \text{ tons per sq. in.}$$

The force normal to this oblique surface is 5 cos 40°, hence the intensity of normal stress is

$$5 \cos 40° \div \sec 40° = 5 \cos^2 40° = 5 \times 0.766 \times 0.766$$
$$= 2.933 \text{ tons per sq. in.}$$

The resultant stress is in the direction of the axis of the bar, and its intensity is

$$5 \div \sec 40° = 5 \cos 40° = 3.83 \text{ tons per sq. in.}$$

8. Complementary Shear Stresses. State of Simple Shear. A shear stress in a given direction cannot exist without a balancing shear stress of equal intensity in a direction at right angles to it.

If we consider an infinitely small [1] rectangular block, ABCD, of material (Fig. 5) under shear stress of intensity q, we cannot have equilibrium with merely equal and opposite tangential forces on the

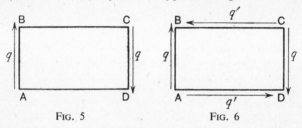

Fig. 5   Fig. 6

parallel pair of faces AB and CD: these forces constitute a couple, and alone exert a turning moment. Statical considerations of equilibrium show that in this case no additional system of forces can balance the couple and produce the equilibrium unless they result in a couple contrary to the previous one; hence there must be tangential components along AD and CB, such as to balance the moments of the forces on AC and CD whether there are in addition normal forces or not. If there is a tangential stress exerting force along AD and CB (Fig. 6), and its intensity be q', and the thickness of the block ABCD perpendicular to the figure be l, the forces on AB, BC, CD, and DA are

$$\text{AB} . l . q, \quad \text{BC} . l . q', \quad \text{CD} . i . q, \quad \text{and} \quad \text{DA} . l . q'$$

respectively, and equating the moments of the two couples produced

$$\text{AB} . l . q \times \text{BC} = \text{BC} . l . q' \times \text{AB}$$

hence $q = q'$

That is, the intensities of shearing stresses across two planes at right angles are equal; this will remain true whatever normal stresses may act, or, in other words, whether q and q' are component or resultant stresses on the perpendicular planes.

[1] On a block of finite size normal stress which is not of uniform intensity may produce a couple.

Simple Shear. The state of stress shown in Fig. 6, where there are only the shear stresses of equal intensity q, is called simple shear. To find the stress existing in other special directions, take a small block ABCD (Fig. 7), the sides of the square face ABCD

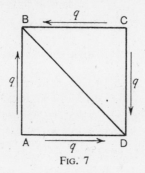

FIG. 7

being each s and the length of the block perpendicular to the figure being l. Considering the equilibrium of the piece BCD, resolve the forces q perpendicularly to the diagonal BD, and we must have a force

$$2 . q . s . l \cos 45°, \text{ or } 2\frac{qsl}{\sqrt{2}}$$

acting on the face BD.

The area of BD is $BD \times l = \sqrt{2} . s . l$

Therefore, if p_n is the intensity of normal stress on the face BD,

$$p_n \times \sqrt{2} . s . l = \frac{2}{\sqrt{2}} . q . s . l$$

hence $$p_n = q$$

and p_n is evidently compressive.

Similarly the intensity of *tensile* stress on a plane AC is evidently equal numerically to q.

Further by resolving along BD or AC the intensity of the tangential stress on such planes is evidently zero. Hence a state of simple shear produces pure tensile and compressive stresses across planes inclined 45° to those of pure shear, and the intensities of these direct stresses are each equal to the intensities of the pure shear stress.

9. Three Important Elastic Constants. Three moduli of elasticity (Art. 6) corresponding to three simple states of stress are important.

Young's Modulus, also called the Stretch or Direct Modulus, is the Modulus of Elasticity for pure tension with no other stress acting; it has in most materials practically the same value for compression; it is always denoted by the letter E. This direct modulus of elasticity is equal to the tensile (or compressive) stress per unit of linear strain (Art. 6). If a tensile stress p tons per sq. in. cause a tensile strain e (Art. 4), intensity of tensile stress = tensile strain × E

or $$p = e \times E$$

hence $$E = \frac{p}{e} = \frac{\text{tensile stress intensity}}{\text{tensile strain}}$$

and is expressed in the same units (tons per square inch here) as the stress p.

The value of E for steel or wrought iron is about 13,000 tons per sq. in.

Example 1. Find the elongation in a steel tie-bar 10 ft. long and 1·5 in. diameter, due to a pull of 12 tons.

Area of section = 1·5 × 1·5 × 0·7854 = 1·767 sq. in.

$$\text{Stress intensity} = \frac{12}{1·767} = 6·79 \text{ tons per sq. in.}$$

$$\text{Strain} = \frac{6·79}{13,000}$$

$$\text{Elongation} = \frac{6·79}{13,000} \times 10 \times 12 = 0·0627 \text{ in.}$$

Example 2. A copper and a steel wire, both the same length, the former 0·1 and the latter 0·2 sq. in. in cross-sectional area, are joined together at their ends and are then stretched by a force W. Find the tension taken by each wire, taking E as 6,000 for copper and 13,000 for steel in tons per square inch.

The essential fact is that the stretch of the two wires must be the same. Let P be the pull in the steel; then W − P is the pull borne by the copper. Then, if l = length of both wires

$$\text{Stretch of the steel} = l \times \frac{\text{unit stress}}{E} = l \times \frac{P}{0·2 \times 13,000}$$

$$\text{Stretch of the copper} = l \times \frac{W - P}{0·1 \times 6,000}$$

Equating the two stretches

$$\frac{P}{26} = \frac{W - P}{6}$$

hence $$P = \tfrac{13}{16}W \text{ and } W - P = \tfrac{3}{16}W$$

10. Modulus of Rigidity. Modulus of Transverse Elasticity, or Shearing Modulus, is the modulus expressing the relation between the intensity of shear stress and the amount of shear strain. It is denoted by the letter N, also sometimes by C or G. If the shearing strain (Art. 4) is φ (radians) due to a shear stress of intensity q tons per sq. in., then

$$\text{shear stress} = \text{shear strain} \times N$$

or
$$q = \varphi \times N$$

$$N \text{ (tons per square inch)} = \frac{q}{\varphi} = \frac{\text{shear stress}}{\text{shear strain}}$$

The value of N for steel is about $\frac{2}{5}$ of the value of E.

Strains in Simple Shear. A square face, ABCD (Fig. 8), of a piece of material under simple shear stress, as in Art. 8, will suffer a

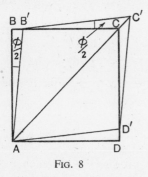

FIG. 8

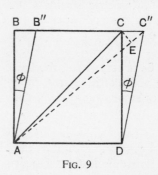

FIG. 9

strain such as is indicated, by taking the new shape AB'C'D'. For expressing the strain it is slightly more convenient to consider the side AD, say, fixed, and the new shape accordingly, as in Fig. 9, AB"C"D. The strains being extremely small quantities, the straight line BB" practically coincides with an arc struck with centre A, and a line CE drawn perpendicular to AC" is substantially the same as an arc centred at A. The shear strain (Art. 4) φ radians is (Fig. 9)

$$\frac{BB''}{AB} \text{ or } \frac{CC''}{CD}, \text{ and is equal to } \frac{q}{N} \text{ as above.}$$

The elongation of the diagonal AC is equal to EC", and the linear strain is

$$\frac{EC''}{AC} = \frac{CC'' \times \frac{1}{\sqrt{2}}}{CD \times \sqrt{2}} = \frac{1}{2} \cdot \frac{CC''}{CD} = \frac{1}{2}\varphi \text{ or } \frac{1}{2} \cdot \frac{q}{N}$$

That is, the strain in this direction is numerically half the amount of the shear strain. Similarly, the strain along the direction BD is $\frac{1}{2}\varphi$, but dimensions in this direction are shortened. These are the strains corresponding to the direct stresses of intensities equal to q produced across diagonal planes, as in Art. 8, by the shear stresses. Note that the strain along AC is *not* simply p_n/E, because in addition to the tensile stress p_n there is a compressive stress of equal intensity at right angles to it.

11. Bulk Modulus is that corresponding to the volumetric strain resulting from three mutually perpendicular and equal direct

B*

stresses, such as the slight reduction in bulk a body suffers, for example, when immersed in a liquid under pressure: this modulus is generally denoted by the letter K.

If the intensities of the equal normal stresses are each p,

$$\frac{p}{K} = \text{volumetric strain} = \frac{\text{change in volume}}{\text{original volume}}$$

The volumetric strain is three times the accompanying linear strain, for if we consider a cube of side a strained so that each side becomes

$$a \pm \delta a,$$

where δa is very small, the linear strain is $\delta a/a$.

The volumetric change is $(a \pm \delta a)^3 - a^3$, or $\pm 3a^2\delta a$ to the first order of small quantities. The strain then is

$$3a^2\delta a/a^3 = 3 \cdot \delta a/a$$

which is three times the linear strain $\delta a/a$, or, in other words, the linear strain is one-third of the volumetric strain.

12. Poisson's Ratio. Direct stress produces a strain in its own direction and an opposite kind of strain in every direction perpendicular to its own. Thus a tie-bar under tensile stress extends longitudinally and contracts laterally. Within the elastic limits the ratio

$$\frac{\text{lateral strain}}{\text{longitudinal strain}}$$

generally denoted by $1/m$, is a constant for a given material. The value of m is usually from 3 to 4, the ratio $1/m$ being about $\frac{1}{4}$ for many metals. This ratio, which was formerly suggested as being for all materials $\frac{1}{4}$, is known as *Poisson's Ratio*.

13. Relations between the Elastic Constants. Some relations between the above quantities E, N, K, and m may be simply deduced. The strain of the diagonal of a square block of material in simple shear of intensity q or p was (Art. 10) found to be $\frac{1}{2}\frac{q}{N}$,

which by Art. 8 may be replaced by $\frac{1}{2}\frac{p}{N}$, where p is the intensity of the equal and opposite direct stresses across diagonal planes.

The resulting direct stress p (Art. 8) in the direction of a diagonal would, if acting alone, cause a strain p/E in the direction of that diagonal, and the opposite kind of direct stress in the direction of the diagonal perpendicular to the first would, acting alone, cause a similar kind of strain to the above one, amounting to $\frac{1}{m} \cdot \frac{p}{E}$ in the direction of the first-mentioned diagonal.

Hence, the total strain of the diagonal is

$$\tfrac{1}{2}\frac{p}{N}=\frac{p}{E}\left(1+\frac{1}{m}\right)$$

from which

$$\frac{1}{2N}=\frac{1}{E}\left(1+\frac{1}{m}\right)$$

or

$$E=2N\left(1+\frac{1}{m}\right)\qquad\text{. . . . . (1)}$$

Note that if $m=4$, $E/N=5/2$.

Again, consider a cube of material under a direct normal stress p, say compressive, in each of the three perpendicular directions parallel to its edges (Fig. 10). Each edge is shortened by the action of the forces parallel to that edge, and the amount of such strain is

$$p/E$$

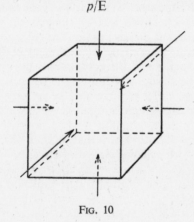

Fig. 10

Again each edge is lengthened by the action of the two pairs of forces perpendicular to that edge and the amount of such strain is

$$2\times\frac{1}{m}\cdot\frac{p}{E}$$

The total linear strain of each edge is then

$$\frac{p}{E}(1-2/m)$$

and the volumetric strain is therefore

$$3\cdot\frac{p}{E}(1-2/m)\quad\text{(Art. 11)}$$

which is also by definition

$$p/K$$

where K is the bulk modulus.

Therefore $\dfrac{p}{K} = 3\dfrac{p}{E}(1 - 2/m)$ or $\dfrac{1}{K} = \dfrac{3}{E}(1 - 2/m)$

$$E = 3K(1 - 2/m) \quad . \quad . \quad . \quad . \quad . \quad . \quad (2)$$

Hence from (1) and (2)

$$E = 2N(1 + 1/m) = 3K(1 - 2/m)$$

Eliminating E, this gives

$$\dfrac{1}{m} = \dfrac{3K - 2N}{6K + 2N} \quad . \quad . \quad . \quad . \quad . \quad (3)$$

also, eliminating m,

$$E = \dfrac{9KN}{N + 3K} \quad . \quad . \quad . \quad . \quad . \quad . \quad (4)$$

14. Compound Stresses. When a body is under the action of several forces which cause wholly normal or wholly tangential stresses across different planes in known directions, we may find the state of stress across other planes by adding algebraically the various tangential components and the components normal to such planes, and combining the sums according to the rules of statics.

Principal Planes. Planes through a point within a material such that the resultant stress across them is wholly a normal stress are called *Principal Planes*, and the normal stresses across them are called the *Principal Stresses* at that point: the direction of the principal stresses are called the axes of stress.

However complex the state of stress at a point within a body, there always exist three mutually perpendicular principal planes, and stresses at that point may be resolved wholly into the three corresponding normal stresses: further, the stress intensity across one of these principal planes is, at the point, greater than in any other direction, and another of the principal stresses is less than the stress in any other direction.

In many practical cases there is a plane perpendicular to which there is practically no stress, or in other words, one of the principal stresses is zero or negligibly small; in these cases resolution and compounding of stresses becomes a two-dimensional problem as in co-planar statics. We now proceed to investigate a few simple cases.

15. Two Perpendicular Normal Stresses. If there be known normal stresses across two mutually perpendicular planes and no stress across the plane perpendicular to both of them, it is required to find the stress across any oblique interface perpendicular to that plane across which there is no stress. Let p_x and p_y be the given stress intensities normal to the mutually perpendicular planes, say in directions OX and OY. If p_x and p_y vary along the directions OX and OY, we might consider the equilibrium of an indefinitely small element of material. If not, however, we may take a piece such as EGFH (Fig. 11), of unit thickness perpendicular to the figure.

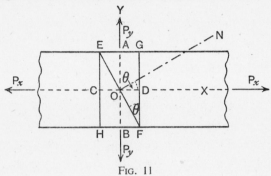

FIG. 11

Our problem is to find the magnitude and direction of the resultant stress on a plane face EF, inclined θ to all planes which are perpendicular to the axis OX, or the normal ON of which is inclined θ to OX, $\left(\dfrac{\pi}{2}-\theta\right)$ to OY and in the plane of the figure, perpendicular to which the stress is *nil*. The stresses p_x and p_y are here shown alike, but for unlike stresses the problem is not seriously altered.

The whole normal force on the face FG is $P_x = p_x \times \mathrm{FG}$, the area being FG × unity.

The wholly normal force on EG is $P_y = p_y \times \mathrm{EG}$.

Let p_n and p_t be the normal and tangential stress intensities respectively on the face EF reckoned positive in the directions ON and OF. Then considering the equilibrium of the wedge EGF, resolving forces in the direction ON,

$$p_n \times \mathrm{EF} = P_x \cos\theta + P_y \cos\left(\frac{\pi}{2}-\theta\right)$$
$$= p_x \cdot \mathrm{FG} \cdot \cos\theta + p_y \cdot \mathrm{EG} \cdot \sin\theta$$

dividing by EF

$$p_n = p_x \cos^2\theta + p_y \sin^2\theta \quad \cdots \quad (1)$$

Resolving in direction OF

$$p_t \times \mathrm{EF} = P_x \sin\theta - P_y \cos\theta$$
$$= p_x \cdot \mathrm{FG} \cdot \sin\theta - p_y \cdot \mathrm{EG} \cdot \cos\theta$$

dividing by EF

$$p_t = (p_x - p_y)\sin\theta\cos\theta = \frac{p_x - p_y}{2}\sin 2\theta \quad \cdots \quad (2)$$

If $\theta = 45°$, the shear stress intensity

$$p_t = \tfrac{1}{2}(p_x - p_y) \quad \cdots \cdots \quad (2\text{A})$$

and is a maximum.

Across the same plane the direct (tensile) stress intensity is

$$p_n = p_x \cos^2 45° + p_y \sin^2 45° = \frac{p_x + p_y}{2}$$

Combining (1) and (2), if p is the intensity of the resultant stress, since the two forces P_x and P_y are equal to the rectangular components of the force $p \times EF$,

$$p \cdot EF = \sqrt{(P_x^2 + P_y^2)}$$
$$= \sqrt{\{(p_x \cdot FG)^2 + (p_y \cdot EG)^2\}}$$
$$= EF \sqrt{(p_x^2 \cos^2 \theta + p_y^2 \sin^2 \theta)}$$
$$p = \sqrt{(p_x^2 \cos^2 \theta + p_y^2 \sin^2 \theta)} = \sqrt{(p_n^2 + p_t^2)} \quad . \quad . \quad (3)$$

and since the component forces in directions OX and OY on unit area of the plane EF are $p_x \cos \theta$ and $p_y \sin \theta$, p evidently makes an angle a with OX such that

$$\tan a = \frac{p_y \sin \theta}{p_x \cos \theta} = \frac{p_y}{p_x} \cdot \tan \theta \quad . \quad . \quad . \quad . \quad (4)$$

And p makes an angle β with the plane EF, across which it acts, such that

$$\tan \beta = \frac{p_n}{p_t} \text{ or } \frac{p_x \cos^2 \theta + p_y \sin^2 \theta}{(p_x - p_y) \cos \theta \sin \theta} = \cot \varphi \quad . \quad . \quad (5)$$

where φ is the angle which the resultant stress makes with the normal to the plane EF.

Example. Find the plane across which the resultant stress is most inclined to the normal.

Let φ be the maximum inclination to the normal. Then

$$\tan \varphi = \frac{p_t}{p_n} = \frac{(p_x - p_y) \cos \theta \sin \theta}{p_x \cos^2 \theta + p_y \sin^2 \theta} \quad . \quad . \quad . \quad (6)$$

When φ is a maximum, $\tan \varphi$ is a maximum, and

$$\frac{d(\tan \varphi)}{d\theta} = 0$$

Therefore, differentiating and dividing out common factors,

$$(p_x \cos^2 \theta + p_y \sin^2 \theta) \cos 2\theta + (p_x - p_y) \sin \theta \cos \theta \times \sin 2\theta = 0$$
$$p_n \cos 2\theta + p_t \sin 2\theta = 0$$

$$\tan 2\theta = -\frac{p_n}{p_t} = -\cot \varphi = \tan \left(\frac{\pi}{2} + \varphi\right)$$

$$2\theta = \frac{\pi}{2} + \varphi$$

$$\theta = \frac{\pi}{4} + \frac{\varphi}{2} \quad . \quad . \quad . \quad . \quad . \quad . \quad (7)$$

Substituting this value of θ in equation (6) we get

$$\tan \varphi = \frac{(p_x - p_y) \cos \varphi}{p_x(1 - \sin \varphi) + p_y(1 + \sin \varphi)}$$

hence

$$\frac{p_y}{p_x} = \frac{1 - \sin \varphi}{1 + \sin \varphi} \quad \cdots \cdots \quad (8)$$

a result used in the theory of earth pressure.

Also

$$\sin \varphi = \frac{p_x - p_y}{p_x + p_y} \quad \cdots \cdots \quad (9)$$

Equation (9) gives the maximum inclination to the normal, and equation (7) gives the inclination of the normal to the axis of the direct stress p_x.

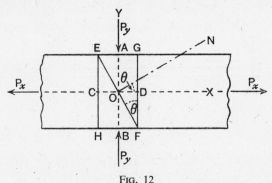

FIG. 12

Unlike Stresses.　If the two given stresses p_x and p_y are unlike, say, p_x tensile and p_y compressive, we have the slight modifications

$$p_n = p_x \cos^2 \theta - p_y \sin^2 \theta \text{ (tensile)}$$
$$p_t = (p_x + p_y) \sin \theta \cos \theta = \tfrac{1}{2}(p_x + p_y) \sin 2\theta$$

These results might be obtained just as before, but using Fig. 12. The maximum shear is again when $\theta = 45°$, and its value is

$$\frac{p_x + p_y}{2}$$

In the special case of unlike stresses, where p_x and p_y are numerically equal, the values for $\theta = 45°$ are

$$p_t = \tfrac{1}{2}(p_x + p_y) = p_x = p_y$$
$$p_n = 0$$

These correspond exactly with the case of pure shear in Art. 8.

16. Ellipse of Stress.　In the last article we supposed two principal stresses p_x and p_y given, and the third to be zero, *i.e.* no stress perpendicular to Figs. 11 and 12.　In this case, using the same notation and like stresses, the direction and magnitude of the resultant stress on any plane can easily be found graphically by the following means.

Describe, with O as centre (Fig. 13), two circles, CQD and ARB, their radii being proportional to p_x and p_y respectively. Draw OQ normal to the interface EF (Art. 15) to meet the larger circle in Q and the smaller in R. Draw QN perpendicular to OX and RP perpendicular to OY to meet QN in P. Then OP represents the resultant stress p both in magnitude of intensity and in direction.

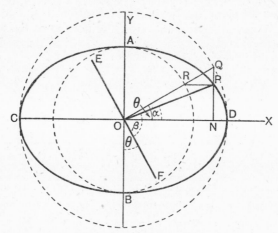

FIG. 13.—Ellipse of stress

The locus of P for various values of θ, *i.e.* for different oblique inter-faces, is evidently an ellipse, for the co-ordinate ON along OX is

$$OQ \cos \theta \text{ or } p_x \cos \theta$$

and PN, the co-ordinate along OY, is

$$OR \sin \theta \text{ or } p_y \sin \theta$$

The axes of the ellipse are the axes of stress (Art. 14).

Also that

$$\tan \alpha = \frac{p_y \sin \theta}{p_x \cos \theta} = \frac{p_y}{p_x} \tan \theta$$

is obvious from the figure.

In the second case where, say, p_y is negative and p_x is positive, OP (Fig. 14) will represent the stress in magnitude and direction: here $\tan \alpha$ is negative and β is obviously less than β in Fig. 13.

Example. A piece of material is subjected to tensile stresses of 6 tons per sq. in., and 3 tons per sq. in., at right angles to each other. Find fully the stresses on a plane, the normal of which makes an angle of 30° with the 6-ton stress.

The intensity of normal stress on such a plane is
$$p_n = 6 \cos^2 30° + 3 \sin^2 30°$$
$$= 6 \times \tfrac{3}{4} + 3 \times \tfrac{1}{4} = 4\tfrac{1}{2} + \tfrac{3}{4} = 5\tfrac{1}{4} \text{ tons per sq. in.}$$

And the intensity of tangential stress is
$$p_t = 6 \sin 30° \cos 30° - 3 \sin 30° \cos 30°$$
$$= 3 \times \tfrac{1}{2} \times \sqrt{3}/2 = 3\sqrt{3}/4 = 1 \cdot 299 \text{ tons per sq. in.}$$

The resultant stress then has an intensity,
$$p = \sqrt{\{(21/4)^2 + (3\sqrt{3}/4)^2\}} = \tfrac{1}{4}\sqrt{(441 + 27)} = 5 \cdot 41 \text{ tons per sq. in.}$$

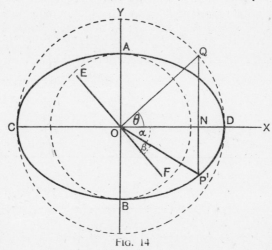

FIG. 14

and makes an angle α with the direction of the 6-ton stress, such that

$$\tan \alpha = \frac{3 \sin 30°}{6 \cos 30°} = \tfrac{1}{2} \tan 30° = 0 \cdot 288$$

which is the tangent of 16° 4′.

This is the angle which the resultant stress makes with the 6-ton stress.   It makes, with the normal to the plane across which it acts, an angle
$$30° - 16° 4′ = 13° 56′$$

To check this, the cotangent of the angle the resultant stress makes with the normal, or the tangent of that it makes with the plane, is
$$p_n/p_t = 5 \cdot 25/1 \cdot 299 = 4 \cdot 035$$
which is tangent of 76° 4′, and therefore the cotangent of 13° 56′.

17. Circular Diagram of Stress.   The main points relating to the analysis of two-dimensional stress demonstrated in Arts. 15 and 16 may conveniently be summarised in a simple geometrical construction sometimes known as the " Mohr " circle or " stress circle."

Referring to Fig. 11, across a face the normal of which is inclined θ to the axis OX, the normal stress as found at (1) of Art. 15 may alternatively be written

$$p_n = \tfrac{1}{2}(p_x + p_y) + \tfrac{1}{2}(p_x - p_y)\cos 2\theta \quad . \quad . \quad . \quad (1)$$

also as in (2) of Art. 15,

$$p_t = \tfrac{1}{2}(p_x - p_y)\sin 2\theta \quad . \quad . \quad . \quad . \quad . \quad (2)$$

It will be noticed that p_t and the part of p_n which varies with the angle θ may be represented by the two rectangular projections of a radius vector of length $\tfrac{1}{2}(p_x - p_y)$ and making an angle 2θ with OX,

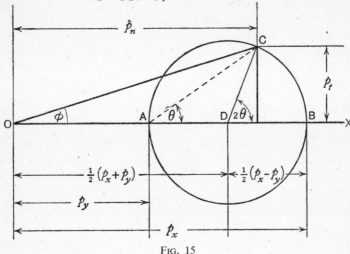

FIG. 15

which immediately suggests a simple graphical construction for finding the component and resultant stresses on the plane under consideration (*i.e.* the plane the normal to which is inclined θ to OX).

If along an axis OX, Fig. 15, a distance OB be set off to represent to scale the magnitude of p_x and OA similarly to represent p_y, then if AB be bisected in D, $OD = \tfrac{1}{2}(p_x + p_y)$ and $AD = DB = \tfrac{1}{2}(p_x - p_y)$. If a circle ACB be described with D as centre and $AD = DB$ as radius, then the stress on the plane under consideration is found by drawing the radius vector DC inclined 2θ to DB (*i.e.* to the direction OX). For $DE = DC\cos 2\theta = \tfrac{1}{2}(p_x - p_y)\cos 2\theta$, hence

$$OE = OD + DE = \tfrac{1}{2}(p_x + p_y) + \tfrac{1}{2}(p_x - p_y)\cos 2\theta \quad . \quad . \quad (3)$$

and therefore represents p_n,

and $EC = DC\sin 2\theta = \tfrac{1}{2}(p_x - p_y)\sin 2\theta \quad . \quad . \quad . \quad (4)$

and therefore represents p_t.

Hence OC, the vector sum of the two rectangular components OE and EC, gives the magnitude of p, the resultant stress, and the angle φ or CÔE gives the angle of inclination of the resultant stress to the normal.

An inspection of the circular diagram of stress (Fig. 15) immediately brings out clearly certain points, *e.g.* that the maximum values of p_t, viz. $\frac{1}{2}(p_x-p_y)$, occur when $2\theta=90°$ or $270°$, *i.e.* where $\theta=45°$ or $135°$, that the maximum value of φ, the obliquity of the resultant stress to the normal of the plane across which it acts, occurs where OC touches the stress circle, *i.e.* when

$$\sin \varphi = \frac{p_x - p_y}{p_x + p_y} \qquad . \qquad . \qquad . \qquad . \qquad . \qquad (5)$$

as in (9) of Art. 15.

The case of the circle illustrated in Fig. 15 is that of two like stresses, and in this case the point O falls outside the circle. But it is evident that as p_y, say, diminishes to zero the points O and A approach one another so that when $p_y=0$, O and A coincide, and when p_y is of opposite sign to p_x, O will fall within the circle, *i.e.* between A and D if p_x is (irrespective of sign) of greater magnitude than p_y.

The circular stress diagram offers an easy solution of some problems which might offer difficulties in mathematical manipulation by other methods. If sufficient data are given, the circle is easily determined and then the stresses on any plane are easily found. For example, if the normal and tangential stresses on two planes are given, two points on the circle can be plotted by co-ordinates along and perpendicular to an axis OX corresponding to Fig. 15, and then a bisector of the chord terminated by the two plotted points intersects the axis OX in the centre (D) of the circle which can then be drawn. The principal stresses and stresses on any other plane are then easily found. The solution of a problem may be obtained entirely by drawing lines to scale or by trigonometrical calculation from the diagram.

A rather important case occurs when the normal and tangential stresses are known on two planes at right angles. If the angles of the planes to that of the major principal stress p_x be θ_1 and $\theta_1+90°$, then the corresponding radii vectors on the circle of stress are inclined $2\theta_1$ and $2\theta_1+180°$ to OX (Fig. 15), that is, they are in the same straight line and constitute a diameter of the circle. It follows, from inspection of the diagram, that not only are the tangential stresses p_t on the two planes of equal magnitude, but that the projections on OX of the two radii vectors are of equal length, so that one normal component, or value of p_n, say p_1, exceeds

$\frac{1}{2}(p_x+p_y)$ being as much as the other, say, p_2, is in defect of $\frac{1}{2}(p_x+p_y)$, or in other words

$$p_1+p_2=p_x+p_y \quad . \quad . \quad . \quad . \quad . \quad (6)$$

A relation which is obvious from an inspection of equation (1), when θ_1 and $\theta_1+90°$ are substituted in turn for θ.

A further treatment of the Stress Circle is given in Art. 19.[1]

18. Principal Stresses. When bodies are subjected to known stresses in certain directions, and these are not all wholly normal stresses, the stresses on various planes may be found by the methods of the two previous articles, provided we first find the principal planes and principal stresses (see Art. 14). It is also often important in itself, in such cases, to find the principal stresses, as one of these is, as previously stated, the greatest stress to which the material is subjected. We proceed to find principal stresses and planes in a few simple, two-dimensional cases where the stress perpendicular to the figure is *nil*.

As a very simple example, we have found in Art. 8 that the two shear stresses of equal intensity, on two mutually perpendicular planes, with no stress on planes perpendicular to the other two, give principal stresses of intensity equal to that of the shear stresses, on planes inclined $\pi/4$ to the two perpendicular planes to which the pure shear stresses are tangential.

As a second example, let there be, on mutually perpendicular planes, normal stresses, one of intensity p_1 and the other of intensity p_2, in addition to the two equal shear stresses of intensity q, as in Fig. 19, which represents a rectangular block of the material unit thickness perpendicular to the plane of the figure, across all planes parallel to which there is no stress; we may imagine the block so small that the variation of stress intensity over any plane section is negligible. The stresses p_1, p_2, and q may be looked upon as independent known stresses arising from several different kinds of external straining actions, or as rectangular components, normal and tangential (Art. 7), into which oblique stresses, on the faces perpendicular to the figure, have been resolved.

It is required to know the direction of the principal planes and the intensity of the (normal) principal stresses upon them. Fig. 16 represents the given normal stresses as tensions: the work is practically the same in the case of compressive stresses, or if one stress be compressive and the other tensile.

Let θ be the inclination of one principal plane to the face BC. Then an interface, AB, is a principal plane, and the stress p upon it

---

[1] A different method of approach and some applications are to be found in an article by Dr. H. W. Swift on " A Graphical Analysis of Stress," in *The Engineer*, Aug. 26, 1927.

is wholly normal to AB. Consider the equilibrium of a wedge, ABC (Figs. 16 and 17), cut off by such a plane.

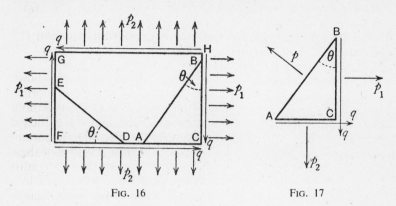

FIG. 16   FIG. 17

Resolving forces parallel to AC

$$p . AB \times \cos \theta = p_1 . BC + q . AC$$
$$= p_1 . AB \cos \theta + q . AB \sin \theta$$

hence

$$(p - p_1) \cos \theta = q \sin \theta$$
$$p - p_1 = q \tan \theta \quad . . . . (1)$$

Resolving parallel to BC

$$p . AB \times \sin \theta = p_2 . AC + q . BC$$
$$= p_2 . AB \sin \theta + qAB \cos \theta$$
$$(p - p_2) \sin \theta = q \cos \theta$$
$$p - p_2 = q \cot \theta \quad . . . . (2)$$

Subtracting equation (1) from equation (2)

$$p_1 - p_2 = q(\cot \theta - \tan \theta) = 2q/\tan 2\theta$$
$$\tan 2\theta = 2q/(p_1 - p_2) \quad . . . . (3)$$

From which two values of θ differing by a right angle may be found, *i.e.* the inclinations to BC of two principal planes which are mutually perpendicular.

Further, multiplying (1) by (2)

$$(p - p_1)(p - p_2) = q^2 \quad . . . . . (4)$$
$$p^2 - p(p_1 + p_2) - (q^2 - p_1 p_2) = 0$$
$$p = \tfrac{1}{2}(p_1 + p_2) \pm \sqrt{\{\tfrac{1}{4}(p_1 + p_2)^2 + (q^2 - p_1 p_2)\}} \quad . . (5)$$

or

$$p = \tfrac{1}{2}(p_1 + p_2) \pm \sqrt{\{\tfrac{1}{4}(p_1 - p_2)^2 + q^2\}}$$

These two values of p are the values of the (normal) stress intensities on the two principal planes. The larger value (where the upper sign is taken) will be the stress intensity on such a plane as AB (Figs. 16 and 17), and will be of the same sign as p_1 and p_2;

the smaller value, say p', will be that on such a plane as ED (Figs. 16 and 18) perpendicular to AB, and will be of opposite sign to p_1 and p_2 if q^2 is greater than $p_1 p_2$.

The planes on which there are maximum shear stresses are inclined 45° to the principal planes found, and the maximum intensity of shear stress from (2A) of Art. 15 is $\frac{1}{2}(p-p')$ and

$$\tfrac{1}{2}(p-p') = \sqrt{\{\tfrac{1}{4}(p_1+p_2)^2+q^2-p_1 p_2\}} = \sqrt{\{\tfrac{1}{4}(p_1-p_2)^2+q^2\}} . \quad (6)$$

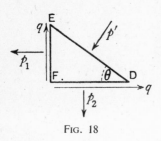

FIG. 18

The modifications necessary in (3) and (4), if p_1 or p_2 is of negative sign, are obvious. If, say, p_2 is zero, the results from substituting this value in (3) and (4) are simple. This special case is of sufficient importance to be worth setting out briefly by itself.

Principal Planes and Stresses when complementary shear stresses are accompanied by a normal stress on the plane of one shear stress. Fig. 19 shows the forces on a rectangular block, GHCF, of unit thickness perpendicular to the figure, and of indefinitely small dimensions parallel to the figure, unless the stresses are uniform. Let θ be the inclination of a

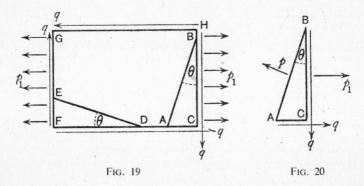

FIG. 19   FIG. 20

principal plane AB to the plane BC, which has normal stress of intensity p_1 and a shear stress of intensity q acting on it, and let p be the intensity of the wholly normal stress on AB. The face FC has only the shear stress of intensity q acting tangentially to it.

Consider the equilibrium of the wedge ABC; resolving the forces as before but omitting all terms in which p_2 is a factor, which simplifies the analysis

$$(p-p_1) = q \tan \theta \quad . \quad . \quad . \quad . \quad (1\text{A})$$

$$\tan \theta = q/p \quad . \quad . \quad . \quad . \quad . \quad (2\text{A})$$

Substituting for $\tan \theta$ in (1A)

$$(p-p_1)=q^2/p$$
$$p^2-p_1p-q^2=0$$
$$p=\tfrac{1}{2}p_1\pm\sqrt{(\tfrac{1}{4}p_1^2+q^2)}. \quad . \quad . \quad . \quad (5\text{A})$$

and the values of θ may be found by substituting these values of p in (2A). The two values differ by a right angle, the principal planes being at right angles. AB (Fig. 20) shows a principal plane of greatest stress corresponding to

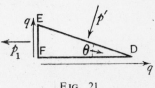

FIG. 21

$$p=\tfrac{1}{2}p_1+\sqrt{(\tfrac{1}{4}p_1^2+q^2)}$$

and ED (Fig. 21) shows the other principal plane on which the normal stress is

$$p'=\tfrac{1}{2}p_1-\sqrt{(\tfrac{1}{4}p_1^2+q^2)}$$

of opposite sign to p_1.

The planes of greatest shear stress are (Art. 15) those inclined 45° to the principal planes, and the intensity of shear stress upon them is

$$\tfrac{1}{2}(p-p')=\sqrt{(\tfrac{1}{4}p_1^2+q^2)} \quad . \quad . \quad . \quad . \quad (6\text{A})$$

Example. At a point in material under stress the intensity of the resultant stress on a certain plane is 4 tons per sq. in. (tensile) inclined 30° to the normal of that plane. The stress on a plane at right angles to this has a normal tensile component of intensity $2\tfrac{1}{2}$ tons per sq. in. Find fully (1) the resultant stress on the second plane, (2) the principal planes and stresses.

(1) On the first plane the tangential stress is

$$q=4 \sin 30°=2 \text{ tons per sq. in.}$$

Hence on the second plane the tangential stress is 2 tons per sq. in. (Art. 8). And the resultant stress is

$$p=\sqrt{(2\cdot5^2+2^2)}=\tfrac{1}{2}\sqrt{41}=3\cdot2 \text{ tons per sq. in.}$$

(2) The intensity of stress normal to the first plane is

$$4 \cos 30°=3\cdot464 \text{ tons per sq. in.}$$

Hence the principal stresses are (Art. 18 (5))

$$p=\tfrac{1}{2}(3\cdot464+2\cdot5)\pm\sqrt{\{\tfrac{1}{4}(3\cdot462-2\cdot5)^2+2^2\}}$$
$$=2\cdot982\pm2\cdot06$$
$$=5\cdot042 \text{ tons per sq. in. tension and } 0\cdot922 \text{ ton per sq. in. tension.}$$

If θ be the angle made by a principal plane with the first-mentioned plane, by Art. 18 (3),

$$\tan 2\theta = \frac{2 \times 2}{3 \cdot 464 - 2 \cdot 5} = \frac{4}{0 \cdot 964} = 4 \cdot 149$$
$$2\theta = 76° 27'$$
$$\theta = 38° 13 \cdot 5$$

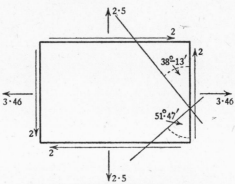

FIG. 22.—Direction of principal planes

The principal planes and stresses are then one plane inclined 38° 13·5′ to the first given plane, and having a tensile stress 5·042 tons per sq. in. across it, and a second at right angles to the other

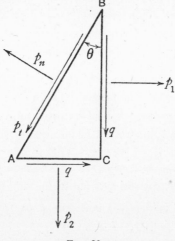

FIG. 23

or inclined 51° 46·5′ to the first given plane, and having a tensile stress 0·922 ton per sq. in. across it. The planes are shown in Fig. 22.

19. More General Case of Circular Stress Diagram.   As graphical methods make a strong appeal to some minds an alternative method of approach to the analysis of the three preceding articles may be considered.   In order to find the component stresses in any direction in a material subject to stresses all of which have no component to one plane, let ABC (Fig. 23) represent an indefinitely small prismatic element of material, the normal stress intensities being p_1 and p_2, on two mutually perpendicular faces BC and AC, both normal to the plane of the diagram, perpendicular to which there is no stress.

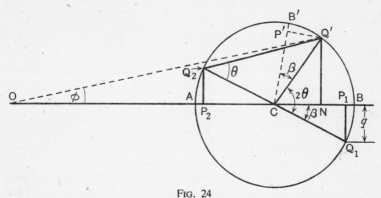

FIG. 24

Then taking the faces of the prism as unit length perpendicular to the diagram and resolving perpendicular to the face AB,

$$p_n \cdot AB = p_1 \cdot BC \cdot \cos \theta + p_1 AC \sin \theta + q \cdot BC \cdot \sin \theta + q \cdot AC \cdot \cos \theta$$

$$p_n = p_1 \cos^2 \theta + p_2 \sin^2 \theta + 2q \sin \theta \cos \theta$$

or $$p_n = \tfrac{1}{2}(p_1 + p_2) + \tfrac{1}{2}(p_1 - p_2) \cos 2\theta + q \sin 2\theta \quad \ldots \quad (1)$$

and resolving along the face AB

$$p_t \cdot AB = p_1 BC \sin \theta - p_2 AC \cos \theta + q AC \sin \theta - q BC \cos \theta$$

$$p_t = p_1 \sin \theta \cos \theta - p_2 \sin \theta \cos \theta + q (\sin^2 \theta - \cos^2 \theta)$$

or $$p_t = \tfrac{1}{2}(p_1 - p_2) \sin 2\theta - q \cos 2\theta \quad \ldots \ldots \quad (2)$$

These two component stresses and their resultant are conveniently represented by a simple diagram known as the Circular Diagram of Stress.   To construct this set off from O (Fig. 24) along a base line OP, lengths OP_1 to represent p_1 and OP_2 to represent p_2 to scale. From P_1 set off at right angles to the base line a length P_1Q_1 to represent q to the selected scale.   Then if P_1P_2 be bisected in C, evidently OC represents $\tfrac{1}{2}(p_1 + p_2)$ and $CP_1 = CP_2$ represents $\tfrac{1}{2}(p_1 - p_2)$.

If a circle be described with C as centre passing through Q_1, this is the circle of stress from which may be found the component and resultant stresses on any plane, perpendicular to the plane of Fig. 23, through the point at which the given stresses $p_1 p_2$ and q act. To find the stresses across a plane (perpendicular to the plane of Fig. 23) inclined θ to the plane across which p_1 is the normal stress, from C set off an angle $Q_1 \hat{C} Q'$ equal to 2θ (or from Q_2, the extremity of a diameter $Q_1 C Q_2$, set off an angle $C \hat{Q}_2 Q'$ equal to θ) which determines the point Q' on the circumference of the circle. Then if a perpendicular $Q'N$ be drawn from Q' to the base line OB, the length, $ON = OC + CN$

$$= \tfrac{1}{2}(p_1 + p_2) + \tfrac{1}{2}(p_1 - p_2) \cos 2\theta = q \sin 2\theta \quad . \quad . \quad (3)$$

which is the value of p_n given at (1); and the length

$$Q'N = \tfrac{1}{2}(p_1 - p_2) \sin 2\theta - q \cos 2\theta \quad . \quad . \quad . \quad (4)$$

which is the value of p_t given at (2).

These two relations (3) and (4) will easily be realised [1] by conceiving the radius vector CQ_1 turned through an angle 2θ carrying with it CB and $P_1 Q_1$ to the positions CB' and $P'Q'$ respectively, and then projecting the length CP', which represents $\tfrac{1}{2}(p_1 - p_2)$, and P'O', which represents q to the base line and perpendicular to it. It is then clear that ON and NQ' represent the components p_n and p_t respectively, and consequently OQ' represents the resultant stress p across the plane considered.

It is easy to study from Fig. 24 the variations of p_n, p_t, and p. Remembering that the radius R of the circle is

$$R = \sqrt{(CP_1{}^2 + P_1 Q_1{}^2)} = \sqrt{\{\tfrac{1}{4}(p_1 - p_2)^2 + q^2\}} \quad . \quad . \quad (7)$$

it is evident that, for this case of p_1 and p_2 positive:

(a) The value of p_n varies between the upper limit

$$\tfrac{1}{2}(p_1 + p_2) + \sqrt{\{\tfrac{1}{4}(p_1 - p_2)^2 + q^2\}}$$

when $2\theta = \beta$ or $\tan 2\theta = 2q \dfrac{2q}{p_1 - p_2}$

i.e. when Q' falls on B, and the lower limit (when Q' falls on A)

$$\tfrac{1}{2}(p_1 + p_2) - \sqrt{\{\tfrac{1}{4}(p_1 - p_2)^2 + q^2\}}$$

when $2\theta = \beta + 180°$ or $\theta = \tfrac{1}{2}\beta + 90°$,

i.e. on a plane at right angles to that for which p_n reaches its upper limit.

---

[1] Or alternatively, if R is the radius of the stress circle, by substituting R cos β for CP_1, i.e. for $\tfrac{1}{2}(p_1 - p_2)$ and R sin β for $P_1 Q_1$, i.e. for q, in equation (1) we have

$$p_n = \tfrac{1}{2}(p_1 + p_2) + R \cos 2\theta \cos \beta + R \sin 2\theta \sin \beta$$
$$= OC + R \cos (2\theta - \beta) = OC + CN = ON$$

and from (2)

$$p_t = R \sin 2\theta \cos \beta - R \cos 2\theta \sin \beta$$
$$= R \sin (2\theta - \beta) = Q'N$$

(*b*) For these two values of θ corresponding to the limits of critical values of p_n, the value of p_t is zero.

(*c*) The value of p_t varies between the limit

$$\sqrt{\{\tfrac{1}{4}(p_1-p_2)^2+q^2\}}$$

when $2\theta=\beta+90°$ or $\theta=\tfrac{1}{2}\beta+45°$; and

$$-\sqrt{\{\tfrac{1}{4}(p_1-p_2)^2+q^2\}}$$

when $2\theta=\beta+270°$ or $\theta=135°$, the planes giving extreme values of p_t being at 45° to the planes, giving extreme values of p_n.

(*d*) The resultant stress reaches its limits with the limits of p_n for $2\theta=\beta$ and $2\theta=\beta+180°$ and has the same values as p_n on these planes, since p_t is there zero. These values are therefore principal stresses and may be designated, say

$$p_x=\tfrac{1}{2}(p_1+p_2)+\sqrt{\{\tfrac{1}{4}(p_1-p_2)^2+q^2\}}$$

when $2\theta=\beta$, and

$$p_y=\tfrac{1}{2}(p_1+p_2)-\sqrt{\{\tfrac{1}{4}(p_1-p_2)^2+q^2\}}$$

when $2\theta=\beta+180°$

(*e*) Since $\tan\theta=p_t/p_n$ the angle φ or $\mathrm{Q'\hat{O}N}$ gives the inclination of the resultant stress (p) to the normal of the plane across which it acts, and the maximum value of φ occurs when the vector OQ′ giving the values of p is a tangent to the stress circle and then

$$\sin\theta=\frac{2\sqrt{\{\tfrac{1}{4}(p_1-p_2)^2+q^2\}}}{(p_1+p_2)}\text{ or }\frac{p_x-p_y}{p_x+p_y}.$$

If the stresses p_1 and p_2 are of opposite signs, say p_2 is negative, it is only necessary to use the appropriate sign in the foregoing conclusions. But it will be instructive for the reader to sketch the stress circle for this case and draw the important conclusions. Evidently the point O will fall within the circle, between P_1 and P_2. In this case the following conclusions are of some importance, and will be obvious from a sketch of the stress circle.

(*f*) There will be two planes subject to pure shear stress, the normal stress being zero (when the point N falls on the fixed point O).

(*g*) In the case of simple tension in the direction of p_1, p_2 is zero and O coincides with P_2 at one end (A) of the diameter AB (Fig. 24). The maximum shear stress then has a magnitude $\tfrac{1}{2}p_1$.

(*h*) If $p_2=-p_1$ and $q=0$, *i.e.* p_1 and p_2 are principal stresses, O coincides with C and the maximum shear stress has a magnitude equal to p_1, the radius of the circle, and occurs on planes inclined 45° to the principal planes ($2\theta = 90°$).

20. Principal Strains.   In a bar of material within limits of perfect elasticity a (say tensile) stress intensity p_1 alone will produce a strain e_1, in its own direction such that

$$e_1 = p_1/E$$

where E is Young's modulus of elasticity or the stretch modulus, provided there is freedom of lateral contraction.   The contraction in all directions at right angles to the axis of the stress p_1 will be represented by a strain

$$p_1/(mE)$$

where $1/m$ is Poisson's ratio.

In an isotropic material, *i.e.* one having the same elastic properties in all directions, the effect of a stress p_2 acting alone at right angles to the direction of p_1 would be to produce a strain in its own direction, e_2, such that

$$e_2 = p_2/E$$

and at right angles to this, including the direction of the strain p_1/E, a contraction strain

$$p_2/(mE)$$

Similarly a stress p_3, the direction of which is perpendicular to both the previously mentioned stresses, will produce in addition to its longitudinal strain a contraction strain

$$p_3/(mE)$$

in all directions perpendicular to its direction, including the direction of the stress p_1.

If we have at a point in isotropic material three principal stresses of intensities p_1, p_2, and p_3, each will independently produce the same strains which it would cause if acting alone.   Taking all the stresses of the same sign the total strain produced in the direction of the stress p_1 will then be

$$e_1 = \frac{p_1}{E} - \frac{p_2 + p_3}{mE} \quad \ldots \ldots \quad (1)$$

In the direction of p_2 the strain

$$e_2 = \frac{p_2}{E} - \frac{p_1 + p_3}{mE} \quad \ldots \ldots \quad (2)$$

and in the direction of p_3 the strain

$$e_3 = \frac{p_3}{E} - \frac{p_1 + p_2}{mE} \quad \ldots \ldots \quad (3)$$

If any one of the above stresses is of opposite kind, *i.e.* compressive in this case, the strains will be found by changing the sign of that stress in each of the above equations.

Example. The intensities of the three principal stresses in a boiler-plate are at a certain point 4 tons per sq. in. tensile in one direction, 3 tons per sq. in. tensile in a second, and zero in a third. Find what stress acting alone would produce the same strain in the direction of the 4-ton stress, given the ratio of Young's modulus to the modulus of rigidity is $\frac{5}{2}$.

By Art. 13 (1)

$$\frac{1}{m} = \frac{E}{2N} - 1$$

$$= \tfrac{5}{4} - 1 = \tfrac{1}{4}$$

Hence, in the direction of the 4-ton stress,

$$\text{Strain} = \frac{4}{E} - 1\tfrac{1}{4}\frac{3}{E} = \frac{13}{4} \times \frac{1}{E}$$

If p is the stress intensity to produce this strain when acting alone

$$\frac{p}{E} = \frac{13}{4} \cdot \frac{1}{E}$$

or, $\qquad\qquad p = \tfrac{13}{4} = 3\tfrac{1}{4}$ tons per sq. in.

21. Elastic Distribution of Loads. If a load P is jointly supported or resisted by two elastic elements A and B so that they suffer a common deformation or deflection, it is often of importance to know in what proportion A and B share the load which they jointly carry. (They may be so joined as to form a composite body, or be two parts of a single body or they may be separate.)

Let the load be P and let P_A be the part carried by A and P_B that carried by B such that

$$P_A + P_B = P \quad . \quad . \quad . \quad . \quad . \quad . \quad (1)$$

P, P_A, and P_B may be forces or may be moments (torques). Let R_A and R_B be the elastic forces, or *resistances* we may call them, exerted by A and B respectively, to loads so applied, per unit of deformation or deflection. Let δ be the common deflection of A and B due to the joint load P. Then if A and B remain elastic, by Hooke's Law the force P_A for a deflection δ is δ times that for a unit deflection or

$$P_A = R_A \times \delta \quad . \quad . \quad . \quad . \quad . \quad . \quad (2)$$

$$P_B = R_B \times \delta \quad . \quad . \quad . \quad . \quad . \quad . \quad (3)$$

And $\qquad\qquad \dfrac{P_A}{P_B} = \dfrac{R_A}{R_B} \quad . \quad . \quad . \quad . \quad . \quad . \quad (4)$

Hence
$$\frac{P_A}{P_A + P_B} = \frac{P_A}{P} = \frac{R_A}{R_A + R_B} \quad \ldots \quad (5)$$

Similarly
$$\frac{P_B}{P} = \frac{R_B}{R_A + R_B} \quad \ldots \quad \ldots \quad (6)$$

And evidently if P is borne by three or more elements, A, B, C, D, etc.

$$\frac{P_A}{P} = \frac{R_A}{R_A + R_B + R_C + R_D + \text{etc.}} \quad \ldots \quad (7)$$

or
$$P_A/P = R_A/\Sigma(R_n) \quad \ldots \quad \ldots \quad (8)$$

where
$$\Sigma(R_n) = \Sigma(R_A + R_B + R_C + R_D + \text{etc.}) \quad \ldots \quad (9)$$

We shall find this general law of elastic distribution of use later. R_A, R_B, R_C, etc., are to be calculated according to the type of elastic body and the mode of support; they may be tensile or they may be forces (or moments) exerted by bent beams or twisted shafts.

It may be noted that R_A, R_B, etc., the resistances per unit deflection, are the reciprocals of the deflections per unit load on A, B, etc., respectively, quantities which may be rather more familiar. The method of calculating R_A, R_B, etc., depends on the sort of straining action to which A, B, etc., are subjected; it may be stretching, or it may be bending or twisting, forms which will be investigated later.

We have already had a simple example in Example 2 of Art. 9 of elastic elements A and B which were wires jointly supporting a load by the elastic tensile resistance which they exert.

For the steel, say, body A, R_A = stress intensity × area of section = E × strain × area = E × (1/*l*) × a_A (where a_A is the area of cross-section of wire A), or

$$R_A = 13{,}000 \times 0 \cdot 2 \times 1/l \text{ tons, where } l \text{ is length of}$$
wire in inches.

Similarly
$$R_B = 6{,}000 \times 0 \cdot 1 \times 1/l \text{ tons.}$$

Hence
$$P_A/P_B = R_A/R_B \quad 2{,}600/600 = \tfrac{13}{3}$$
$$P_A = \tfrac{13}{16}W, \quad P_B = \tfrac{3}{16}W, \text{ as in Example 2, Art. 9.}$$

More generally for tensile joint support of a load P, if a_B is the area of cross-section of B

$$\frac{P_A}{P_B} = \frac{R_A}{R_B} = \frac{E_A \times a_A \times l_B}{E_B \times a_B \times l_A} \quad \ldots \quad \ldots \quad (10)$$

and
$$\frac{P_A}{P} = \frac{E_A a_A/l_A}{\Sigma(Ea/l)} \quad \ldots \quad \ldots \quad (11)$$

EXAMPLES 1

1. A round tie-bar of mild steel, 18 ft. long and $1\frac{1}{2}$ in. diameter, lengthens $\frac{1}{16}$ in. under a pull of 7 tons. Find the intensity of tensile stress in the bar, the value of the stretch modulus, and the greatest intensity of shear stress on any oblique section.

2. A rod of steel is subjected to a tension of 3 tons per sq. in. of cross-section. The shear stress across a plane oblique to the axis is 1 ton per sq. in. What is the inclination of the normal of this plane to the axis? What is the intensity of the normal stress across the plane, and what is the intensity of the resultant stress across it? Of the two possible solutions, take the plane with normal least inclined to the axis of the rod.

3. On a plane oblique to the axis of the bar in Problem No. 1, the intensity of shear stress is 1·5 ton per sq. in. What is the intensity of normal stress across this plane? Also what is the intensity of resultant stress across it? Take the plane most inclined to the axis.

4. A hollow cylindrical cast-iron column is 10 in. external and 8 in. internal diameter and 10 ft. long. How much will it shorten under a load of 60 tons? Take E as 8,000 tons per sq. in.

5. The stretch modulus of elasticity for a specimen of steel is found to be 28,500,000 lb. per sq. in., and the transverse modulus is 11,000,000 lb. per sq. in. What is the modulus of elasticity of bulk for this material, and how many times greater is the longitudinal strain caused by a pull than the accompanying lateral strain?

6. The tensile (principal) stresses at a point within a boiler-plate across the three principal planes are 0, 2, and 4 tons per sq. in. Find the component normal and tangential stress intensities, and the intensity and direction of the resultant stress, at this point, across a plane perpendicular to the first principal plane, and inclined 30° to the plane having a 4-ton principal stress.

7. With the same data as Problem No. 6, find the inclination of the normal, to the axis of the 4-ton stress, of a plane on which the resultant stress is inclined 15° to the normal. What is the intensity of this resultant stress?

8. At a point in strained material the principal stresses are 0, 5 tons per sq. in. tensile, and 3 tons per sq. in. compressive. Find the resultant stress in intensity and direction on a plane inclined 60° to the axis of the 5-ton stress, and perpendicular to the plane which has no stress. What is the maximum intensity of shear stress in the material?

9. If a material is so strained that at a certain point the intensities of normal stress across two planes at right angles are 5 tons and 3 tons per sq. in., both tensile, and if the shear stress across these planes is 4 tons per sq. in., find the maximum direct stress and the plane to which it is normal.

10. Solve Problem No. 9 if the stress of 3 tons per sq. in. is compressive.

11. At a point in a cross-section of a girder there is a tensile stress of 4 tons per sq. in. normal to the cross-section; there is also a shear stress of 2 tons per sq. in. on that section. Find the principal planes and stresses.

12. In a shaft there is at a certain point a shear stress of 3 tons per sq. in. in the plane of a cross-section, and a tensile stress of 2 tons per sq. in. normal to this plane. Find the greatest intensities of direct stress and of shear stress.

13. In a boiler-plate the tensile stress in the direction of the axis of the shell is $2\frac{1}{2}$ tons per sq. in., and perpendicular to a plane through the axis the tensile stress is 5 tons per sq. in. Find what intensity of tensile stress acting alone would produce the same maximum tensile strain if Poisson's ratio is $\frac{1}{4}$.

14. A cylindrical piece of metal undergoes compression in the direction of

its axis. A well-fitted metal casing, extending almost the whole length, reduces the lateral expansion by half the amount it would otherwise be. Find in terms of " m " the ratio of the axial strain to that in a cylinder quite free to expand in diameter. (Poisson's ratio $= 1/m$.)

15. Three long parallel wires, equal in length and in the same vertical plane, jointly support a load of 3,000 lb. The middle wire is steel, and the two outer ones are brass, and each is $\frac{1}{4}$ sq. in. in section. After the wires have been so adjusted as to each carry $\frac{1}{3}$ of the load a further load of 7,000 lb. is added. Find the stress in each wire, and the fraction of the whole load carried by the steel wire. E for steel 30×10^6 lb. per sq. in., and for brass 12×10^6 lb. per sq. in.

CHAPTER II

WORKING STRESSES

22. Elasticity. A material is said to be perfectly elastic if the whole of the strain produced by a stress disappears when the stress is removed. Within certain limits (Art. 5) many materials exhibit practically perfect elasticity.

Plasticity. A material may be said to be *perfectly* plastic when no strain disappears when it is relieved from stress.

In a plastic state, a solid shows the phenomenon of " flow " under unequal stresses in different directions, much in the same way as a liquid. This property of " flowing " is utilised in the " squirting " of lead pipe, the drawing of wire, the stamping of coins, forging, etc.

Ductility is that property of a material which allows of its being drawn out by tension to a smaller section, as for example when a wire is made by drawing out metal through a hole. During ductile extension, a material generally shows a certain degree of elasticity, together with a considerable amount of plasticity. *Brittleness* is lack of ductility.

When a material can be beaten or rolled into plates, it is said to be malleable; malleability is a very similar property to ductility.

23. Tensile Strain of Ductile Methods. If a ductile metal be subjected to a gradually increasing tension, it is found that the resulting strains, both longitudinal and lateral, increase at first proportionally to the stress. When the elastic limit is reached, the tensile strain begins to increase more quickly, and continues to grow at an increasing rate as the load is augmented. At a stress a little greater than the elastic limit some metals, notably soft irons and steels, show a marked breakdown, the elongation becoming many times greater than previously with little or no increase of stress. The stress at which this sudden stretch occurs is called the " yield point " of the material.

Fig. 25 is a " stress-strain " curve for a round steel bar 10 in. long and 1 in. diameter, of which the ordinates represent the stress intensities and the abscissæ the corresponding strains. The limit of elasticity occurs about A, the line OA being straight. The point B marks the " yield point," AB being slightly curved. After the yield-point stress is reached, the ductile extensions take place, the strains increasing at an accelerating rate with greater stresses as indicated by the portion of the curve between C and D. Strains produced at

C

loads above the yield point do not develop in the same way as those below the elastic limit.   The greater part of the strain occurs very quickly, but this is followed without any further loading by a small additional extension which increases with time but at a diminishing rate.   At D, just before the greatest load is reached, the material is almost perfectly plastic, the tensile strain increasing greatly for very slight increase of load.   It should be noted that in this diagram both stress intensity and strain are reckoned on the original dimensions of the material.

After the maximum load is reached, a sudden local stretching takes place, extending over a short length of the bar and forming a

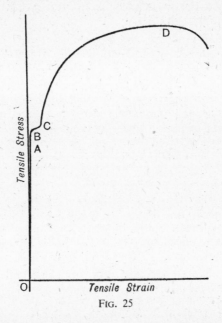

FIG. 25

" waist."   The local reduction in area is such that the load necessary to break the bar at the waist is considerably less than the maximum load on the bar before the local extension takes place. Nevertheless the breaking load divided by the reduced area of section shows that the " actual stress intensity " is greater than at any previous load.   If the load be divided by the original area of cross-section, the result is the " nominal intensity of stress," which is less, in such a ductile material as soft steel, at the breaking load than at the maximum load sustained at the point D on Fig. 25.

Elastic Limit and Yield Point.   The elastic limit (Art. 5) in tension is the greatest stress after which no permanent elongation remains when all stress is removed.   In nearly all metals, and particularly in soft and ductile ones, instruments of great precision will reveal slight permanent extensions resulting from very low stresses, and particularly in material which has never before been subjected to such tensile stress. In many metals, however, notably wrought iron and steel, if we neglect permanent extensions less than, say, $\frac{1}{100000}$ of the length of a test-bar (*i.e.* strains less than 0·00001), stresses up to a considerable proportion of the maximum cause purely elastic and proportional elongation. The proportionality of the strain to the stress in Fig. 25 is indicated by OA being a straight line. For such metals as wrought iron and steel, the proportionality holds good up to the elastic limit—that is, the end of the straight line at A indicates the elastic limit, or in other words, Hooke's Law (Art. 5) is substantially true.

Commercial Elastic Limit. In commercial tests of metals exhibiting a yield point, the stress at which this marked breakdown occurs is often called the elastic limit; it is generally a little above the true elastic limit.

There are, then, three noticeable limits of stress:

    (1) The elastic limit, as defined in Art. 5.
    (2) The limit of proportionality of stress to strain.
    (3) The stress at yield point—the commercial elastic limit.

In wrought iron and steel the first two are practically the same, and the third is somewhat higher.

24. Ultimate and Elastic Strength and Factor of Safety. The maximum load necessary to rupture a specimen in simple tension or shear, divided by the *original area* of section at the place of fracture, gives the nominal maximum stress necessary for fracture, and is called the ultimate strength of the material under that particular kind of stress. It is usually reckoned in pounds or tons per square inch. The ultimate strength in tension is also called the *Tenacity*. The greatest calculated stress to which a part of a machine or structure is ever subjected is called the working stress, and the ratio ultimate strength to working stress is called the Factor of Safety. But in structural work it is common to replace ultimate strength by the stress at the yield point in this ratio.

It is, of course, usual to ensure that the working stress shall be below the elastic limit of the material ; but this is not sufficient, and designers, when allowing a given working stress, generally specify or assume, amongst other properties, an ultimate strength (or sometimes a stress at yield point) for the material, greater than the working stress in the ratio of a reasonable factor of safety. The factor of safety varies very greatly according to the nature of the stresses, whether constant, variable or alternating, simple or compound, it is frequently made to cover an allowance for straining actions, such as shocks, no reliable estimate of which can in some instances be made, diminution of section by corrosion, and other contingencies.

The factor of safety is here defined with reference to the estimated maximum intensity of stress produced by a load. And generally such a factor of safety of say *n* would provide for one *n*th part of the load which would cause breakdown in the material. But not in all cases. We shall see in Chapter x that a long rod (or strut) in compression will collapse for a load much less than that which would cause failure by yielding in a very short length. Hence, for a corresponding margin of safety we should limit the load on the long piece to one *n*th part of that which would cause yielding. A factor then is applicable to the load rather than to the stress.

Elastic Strength. If it is desired to limit working stresses to values that leave a certain margin within the elastic limit it becomes important to know how the limit of elasticity changes (in one and the same metal) with the ratio of the principal stresses. It has long been recognised, for example, that the stress at the elastic limit is lower for equal and opposite principal stresses than for simple tension. Several hypotheses have been advanced from time to time and have been the subject of much experimental research. Some account of the conclusions drawn may be in the Author's *Strength of Materials* (9th edition).

For practical purposes in ductile materials like structural steel the conclusion is that for static stress perfect elasticity ceases and more or less plastic yielding begins when a certain limit is reached by the greatest shear stress. This is given by (2A) of Art. 15, where p_x is the greatest and p_y the least principal stress or by (6) of Art. 18 in a common case of compound stress. The greatest intensity of shear stress is in any case equal to half the greatest difference in the principal (direct) stresses.

25. Importance of Ductility. In a machine or structure it is usual to provide such a section as shall prevent the stresses within the material from reaching the elastic limit. But the elastic limit can, in manufacture, by modification of composition or treatment be made high, and generally such treatment will reduce the ductility and cause greater brittleness or liability to fracture from vibration or shock. Ductile materials, on the other hand, are not brittle, and a lower elastic limit is usually found with greater ductility. Local ductile yielding in a complex structure will relieve a high local stress, due to imperfect workmanship or other causes thereby preventing a member accidentally stressed beyond its elastic limit from reaching a much higher stress such as might be produced in a less plastic material. Thus in many applications the property of ductility is of equal importance to that of strength.

It is the practice of some engineers to specify that the steel used in a structure shall have an ultimate tensile strength between certain limits; the reason for fixing an upper limit is the possibility that greater tensile strength may be accompanied by a decrease in ductility or in power to resist damage by shock.

The usual criteria of the ductility of a metal are the percentages of elongation and contraction of sectional area in a test piece

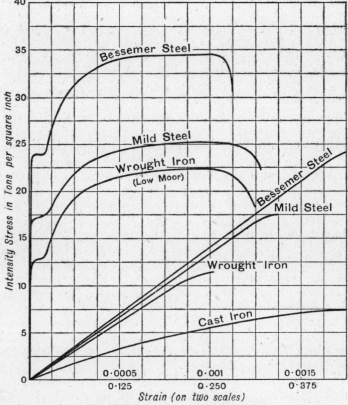

FIG. 26.—Tensile stress-strain curves

fractured by tension. Probably the percentage elongation is the better one; smaller elongation is sometimes accompanied by greater contraction of area.

26. Tenacity and Other Properties of Various Metals. The behaviour of a typical ductile metal has been described fully in Art. 23. Stress-strain curves for two varieties of steel and a very good quality of wrought iron are shown in Fig. 26; all of these refer to round pieces of metal 1 in. diameter, and extensions are measured on a length of 8 in. The straight line representing the elastic stage of extension has been plotted on a scale 250 times larger than that for the later stages of strain.

Cast iron is a brittle material, *i.e.* it breaks with very little elongation or lateral contraction, and at a rather low stress. The stress-strain curve for a sample of good cast iron is shown on the large scale of Fig. 26, the ultimate strength or tenacity being just over 10 tons per sq. in., and the strain being then just above $\frac{1}{400}$.

The ultimate strength of cast iron in tension is usually from 7 to 10 tons per sq. in.; in compression it is often about 50 tons per sq. in.

Owing to the liability to porosity, initial stress in cooling, etc., the working strength allowable in cast iron does not usually exceed about 1 ton per sq. in. in tension and 8 tons per sq. in. in compression.

Wrought Iron. Wrought iron is a typical ductile metal, and contains over 99 per cent. of pure iron, and only about one-tenth per cent. of carbon. It comes from the puddling furnace in a spongy or pasty state (not liquid), and subsequent hammering and rolling do not expel all traces of slag, which may be traced in layers in the finished product. The structure appears from a fractured specimen to be fibrous or laminated: this results from the rolling and working up of the crude product, but the metal itself, when examined under the microscope, is found to consist of crystalline grains. Both the tenacity and ductility are greater in the direction of the fibres than across them. The mechanical properties differ considerably in different qualities; those of a high quality are represented in Fig. 26; lower qualities have a lower ultimate strength and smaller elongation (see Table at end of chapter).

The composition of wrought iron varies in different qualities. It is desirable to keep phosphorus below $\frac{1}{4}$ per cent. and sulphur below 0·05 per cent. Phosphorus makes the metal brittle when it is cold, and sulphur causes brittleness at a red heat.

Steel. Steel was the term formerly applied to various qualities of iron which hardened by being cooled quickly from a red heat. Such material contained over $\frac{1}{2}$ per cent. of carbon chemically combined with the iron. The tenacity and ductility of these steels is not of so much interest as that of the softer varieties. The high-carbon steels are not ductile, but have a high tensile strength.

Now, much more ductile materials, having a lower tensile strength, are produced by the Bessemer, Siemens, and other processes, and are classed as mild steels. The mild steels have for many purposes replaced wrought iron, being stronger, more uniform, and more ductile; unlike wrought iron they can be cast, and when required for bars, etc., they are first cast in ingots and then rolled; the ingot being obtained from the liquid state no fibre is produced in the subsequent rolling or forging, and the metal is more homogeneous than wrought iron, and often has as little carbon present, but it is not so reliable for (non-fusion) welding, and when a weld is necessary good wrought iron is used. These steels contain less than ½ per cent. of carbon, the quantity varying according to the purpose for which the steel is required. Thus steel rails may have from 0·3 to 0·4 per cent., structural steel about 0·25 per cent., and rivet steel about 0·1 per cent. of carbon.

Other constituents even in small quantities also greatly modify the properties of steels, and apart from chemical composition the mechanical and thermal treatment which the metal receives will greatly modify the strength and ductility. Comparatively recently, steels containing small quantities of nickel, chromium, vanadium, or manganese have been produced, having very high tensile strengths combined with a considerable degree of ductility.

The qualities desirable in steel for structural ship-building and machine purposes are indicated by the Standard Specifications drawn up by the British Standards Institution and published for them. The chief requirements with respect to tensile tests and composition (when specified) are shown in the following Table. All the strengths and elongations are to be measured on test pieces of standard dimensions (see complete specifications), and other mechanical tests are specified.

Material and use	Composition		Tenacity in tons per sq. in.		Minimum elongation on 8 in. (per cent.)	Remarks
	Maximum sulphur per cent.	Maximum phosphorus per cent.	Minimum	Maximum		
Structural steel for bridges and general building construction, plates, angles, etc.	0·06	{0·06* / 0·07†}	28	32	20	* Open-hearth process.
Rivet bars for above	—	—	26	30	25	† Besse-mer.
Ship plates	—	—	28	32	20‡	‡ 16 per cent. for plates below ⅜ in.
Angles, bulb angles, channel sections, etc., for ship-building	—	—	28	33	20	
Rivet bars for ships	—	—	25	30	25	
Railway axles	0·035	0·035	35 to 40	—	{25 / 20}	

The strength and ductility of steel forgings and castings is dependent upon many circumstances, and varies considerably in different parts of large pieces of material. Some idea of the values is given in the table at the end of the chapter.

27. Stress due to Change of Temperature. It is well known that metals, when free to do so, change their dimensions with change of temperature. If, however, such change of dimensions is resisted and prevented, stress is induced in the material corresponding to the strain or change of dimension prevented. Thus if a long bar is lengthened by heat, and then its ends firmly held to rigid supports, so as to prevent contraction to its original length, the bar on cooling will be in tension, and will exert a pull on the supports. Numerous applications of this means of applying a pull are to be found, such as tie-bars holding two parallel walls together, and tyres shrunk on to wheels.

The linear expansion under heat is for moderate ranges of temperature closely proportional to the increase of temperature. The proportional extension, or extension per unit of length per degree of temperature, is called the coefficient of linear expansion. Thus if α is the coefficient of expansion, a length l of a bar at t_1° becomes

$$l\{1+\alpha(t_2-t_1)\}$$

at a temperature t_2°.

If subsequently the bar is cooled to t_1° and contraction is wholly prevented, a proportional strain

$$\alpha(t_2-t_1)$$

remains, and the corresponding tension and pull on the constraints is

$$E\alpha(t_2-t_1)$$

per unit area of cross-section of the bar, where E is Young's modulus for the material.

The following are the approximate linear coefficients of expansion for Fahrenheit degrees:

Wrought iron	0·0000067
Steel	0·0000062
Copper	0·000010
Cast iron	0·0000060

For steel the tensile strain per degree Fahrenheit if contraction is prevented will be 0·0000062, and taking the stretch modulus as 13,000 tons per sq. in., this corresponds to a stress intensity of

$$13{,}000 \times 0\cdot0000062, \text{ or } 0\cdot0806 \text{ ton per sq. in.}$$

Thus the cooling necessary to cause a stress of 1 ton per sq. in. would be

$$\frac{1}{0\cdot0806} \text{ or about } 12^\circ \text{ F.}$$

The different amounts of expansion in different metals in a machine may cause serious stresses to be set up due to temperature changes. Occasionally use is made of the different expansions of two parts.

Example 1. If a bar of steel 1 in. diameter and 10 ft. long is heated to 100° F. above the temperature of the atmosphere, and then firmly gripped at its ends, find the tension in the bar when cooled to the temperature of the atmosphere if during cooling it pulls the end fastenings $\frac{1}{40}$ in. nearer together. Assume that steel expands 0·0000062 of its length per degree Fahrenheit, and that the stretch modulus is 13,000 tons per sq. in.

The final proportional strain of the bar is

$$0 \cdot 0000062 \times 100 - \tfrac{1}{40} \div 120$$

or $\qquad 0 \cdot 00062 - 0 \cdot 00021 = 0 \cdot 00041$

Intensity of stress $= 13,000 \times 0 \cdot 00041$

$$= 5 \cdot 33 \text{ tons per sq. in.}$$

and total pull on a bar 1 in. diameter is

$$5 \cdot 33 \times 0 \cdot 7854 = 4 \cdot 18 \text{ tons.}$$

28. Elastic Strain Energy. The work done in producing an elastic strain is stored as *strain energy* in the strained material and reappears in the removal of the load. In materials which follow Hooke's Law, the elastic portion of the load-extension diagram being a straight line, the amount of work stored as strain energy for loads not exceeding the elastic limit in tensile straining is equal to

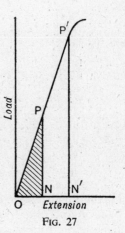

Fig. 27

$$\tfrac{1}{2} \cdot \text{load} \times \text{extension}$$

In Fig. 27 the work stored when the load reaches an amount PN is represented by the shaded area OPN, or by $\frac{1}{2} \cdot \text{PN} \cdot \text{ON}$, which is proportional to

$$\tfrac{1}{2} \cdot \text{load} \times \text{extension}$$

In a piece of metal under *uniform* intensity of tensile stress p, below the elastic limit, if A is the area of cross-section and l the length, the load is

$$p \cdot \text{A}$$

and the extension is

$$l \times \text{proportional strain, or } l \times \frac{p}{\text{E}} \text{ (Art. 9)}$$

C*

where E is the stretch modulus. Hence the elastic strain energy (or resilience) is

$$\tfrac{1}{2} \cdot p\text{A} \cdot l\frac{p}{\text{E}} = \tfrac{1}{2} \cdot \frac{p^2}{\text{E}} \cdot l\text{A} = \tfrac{1}{2}\frac{p^2}{\text{E}} \times \text{volume of piece}$$

or $\qquad \tfrac{1}{2}\dfrac{p^2}{\text{E}}$ per unit volume of the material.

Where the tension is not uniform the expression is of similar form, but the factor is less than $\tfrac{1}{2}$ if p is the maximum intensity of stress. Some particular cases will be noticed later.

Proof Resilience. The greatest strain energy which can be stored in a piece of material without permanent strain is sometimes called its proof resilience. If f is the (uniform) intensity of stress at the elastic limit or proof stress, the proof resilience is then

$$\tfrac{1}{2}\frac{f^2}{\text{E}} \times \text{volume}$$

This is represented in Fig. 27 by the area OP′N′ for a material obeying Hooke's Law.

The proof resilience is often stated as a property of a material, and is then stated per unit volume, viz.

$$\tfrac{1}{2}f^2/\text{E}$$

29. Live Tensile Loads within the Elastic Limit. If a tensile load is suddenly applied to a bar and does not cause a stress beyond the limit of elasticity, the bar behaves like any other perfect spring, and makes oscillations in the tension, the amplitude on either side of the equilibrium position being equal to the extension which would be produced by the same load gradually applied. Hence the maximum instantaneous strain produced is double that which would be produced by the same load applied gradually.

Suppose, for example, that a tensile load W is suddenly applied to a bar of cross-sectional area A. The instantaneous strain produced is

$$e = 2(\text{W}/\text{A}) \div \text{E}$$

and the instantaneous intensity of stress produced is

$$p = \text{E}e = 2 \cdot \text{W}/\text{A}$$

which is twice that for a static or gradually applied load W. It is here assumed that the stress-strain curve (or value of Young's modulus) within the elastic limit is independent of the rate of loading, which is probably nearly true.

The instantaneous stress-strain diagram is shown in Fig. 28. Its area is proportional to

$$\tfrac{1}{2}\text{E}e^2 \text{ or } \tfrac{1}{2}(\text{E}e)^2/\text{E}$$

which is the work for unit volume of material.

If a bar already carries, say, a " dead " tensile load W_0, and another " live " load W of the same kind is applied, the greatest stress reached, provided the elastic limit is not exceeded, will be

$$W_0/A + 2W/A$$

or

$$\frac{W_0 + W}{A} + \frac{\text{change of load}}{A}$$

If, on the other hand, the live load W causes a stress of opposite kind (say compressive) to that already operating, the instantaneous stress would be

$$W_0/A - 2W/A$$

or

$$\frac{W_0 - W}{A} - \frac{\text{change in load}}{A}$$

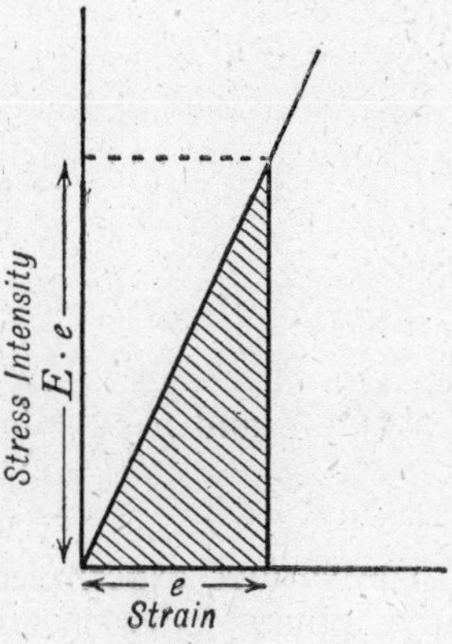

FIG. 28 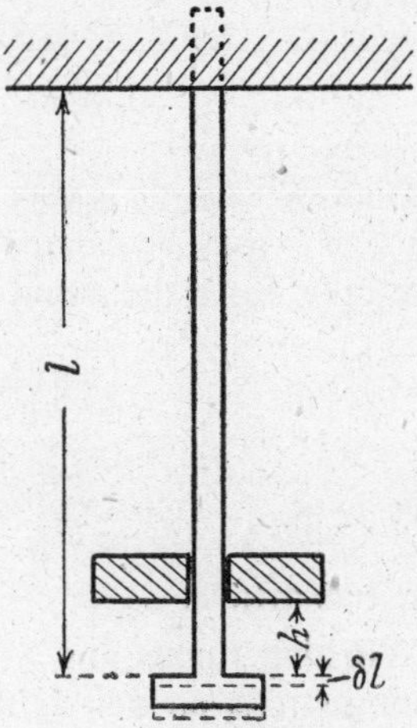   FIG. 29

Example. Find the statical load which would produce the same maximum stresses as (*a*) a tensile dead load of 40 tons and a tensile live load of 10 tons; (*b*) a tensile dead load of 20 tons and a compressive live load of 30 tons.

(*a*) Equivalent static load $= 50 + 10 = 60$ tons tension.

(*b*) Equivalent static load $= 20 - 30 - 30 = -40$ tons, *i.e.* 40 tons compression.

30. Impacts producing Tension. If an impulsive tensile load, such as that of a heavy falling weight, is applied axially to a light bar and the limits of proportionality of stress to strain are not exceeded, the strain energy instantaneously taken up by the bar is nearly equal to the kinetic energy lost by the falling weight if all the connections except the bar are *infinitely rigid*.

If a heavy weight W lb. (Fig. 29) falls through a height h in.

on to a stop in such a way as to bring a purely axial tensile stress on a bar of length l in. and cross-section A sq. in., causing a stretch $\delta l = pl/E$, strain e, and an instantaneous tensile stress of intensity p, then, if the stop, the falling weight, and the supports of the bar be supposed infinitely rigid, *neglecting the small loss in impact*,

$$W(h+\delta l) = \tfrac{1}{2}Ee \times A \times \delta l \text{ or } \tfrac{1}{2}F \,.\, \delta l$$

where F is the equivalent statical load on the bar in pounds, and E is the stretch modulus of elasticity in pounds per sq. in.; hence

$$W(h+\delta l) = \tfrac{1}{2}Fe \times A \times el$$
$$= \tfrac{1}{2}Ee^2 \times \text{volume of bar}$$

or, since $\dfrac{p}{E} = e$ $\quad W(h+\delta l) = \tfrac{1}{2}\dfrac{p^2}{E} \times \text{volume of bar}$

and $\qquad\qquad p^2 = \dfrac{2E \times W(h+\delta l)}{\text{volume of bar}} \text{ or } \dfrac{2EWh}{\text{volume}}$

approximately when δl is very small compared to the fall h.

From this p may be calculated if E is known. If, as a particular case, we take $h=0$, the equation

$$p^2 = \frac{2EW(h+\delta l)}{\text{volume of bar}}$$

becomes $p^2 = \dfrac{2EW\delta l}{A \,.\, l} = 2 \,.\, \dfrac{W}{A} \,.\, E \,.\, \dfrac{\delta l}{l} = 2 \,.\, \dfrac{W}{A} \,.\, p$, and $p = 2 \,.\, \dfrac{W}{A}$ as in the previous article.

31. Working Loads and Stresses. The various experiments on fluctuating stress, as well as the results of general experience in the design and use of structures and machines, point to the use of different working stresses according to the nature of the straining action to be endured. If a factor of safety or ratio of ultimate statical strength to maximum working stress of, say, 3 be sufficient for mild steel to cover accidental and uncalculated straining actions, errors of workmanship, for a steady, unvarying or dead load, a similar factor might be applied when the maximum stress is calculated to allow for the effects of live or varying loads as in Arts. 29 and 30 or otherwise.

Equivalent Dead Load. One method of proportioning members of structures is to use a constant working stress, viz. that applicable to a dead load, and to increase the maximum load by some amount to allow for the effect of a live load. The allowance may be the whole or some fraction of the extreme variation or range of load. If there is a sudden fluctuation of the load from the minimum to the maximum, the elastic vibrations would produce the same straining effect as twice that alteration occurring very gradually (see Art. 29), so that in this case

Equivalent dead load=min. load +2(max. load −min. load)

=max. load+(max. load−min. load) . . (1)

or   max. load+variation in load

Impact Allowances. Sometimes the equivalent dead load is taken as the dead load and the live load plus some fraction of the variation in load, so that

Equivalent dead load=max. load +k(range or variation in load) . . . (2)

where k is a coefficient dependent on circumstances such as the suddenness or otherwise of the change in stress. For example, in a girder traversed by a moving load the change of stress is not sudden, but occurs much more quickly in some parts than in others, as is evident from Arts. 73, 74, and 75.

The formula (1) is equivalent to taking $k=1$ in (2) or to taking an equivalent dead load equal to minimum load plus twice the range of load; this is a sufficient allowance for both fatigue (if any) due to repetitions of load and impact or dynamical action in producing a stress higher than that resulting from a static load. They represent something like ordinary British practice although the actual empirical formulæ used vary in form.

The American Railway Engineering and Maintenance of Way Association's specification 1905, known as the Pencoyd formula, is

$$k=\frac{300}{L+300} . . . . . . (3)$$

where L is the loaded length of the track in feet producing the maximum stress; the value (3) varies for chord members from 1 to 0·5 as the span increases from 0 to 300 ft. These are generally considered a sufficient margin for both fatigue and impact. Whether the two effects should be included in a common allowance or be treated separately is a matter on which opinions differ. The allowance for impact is based upon the fact shown by actual deflection measurements that rolling loads (including imperfectly balanced wheels) produce greater effects than stationary ones and effects which increase with increased speeds. The dynamic effect is naturally greater in short spans than in long ones where the greater inertia of the structure permits of smaller strains from a given impact, provided such effects do not accumulate due to a coincidence of vibration periods with a periodic disturbance.

The work of the Bridge Stress Committee [1] has gone far to confirm that on railway bridges any stress due to impact arises from the dynamical effect of the live load, notably the " hammer blow " of locomotives using reciprocating engines, and not from the imposition of the moving load which, at practicable speeds, is applied far too gradually to produce any significant dynamical effects. The magnitudes of the impact stresses are therefore, it is argued, in no way proportional to the moving load and should be allowed for separately. No formula of the Pencoyd class which treats impact effect as proportional to the moving load can be theoretically valid, and it is suggested that its use is illogical.

The frequency of rhythmically repeated blows, arising from the unbalance of the moving parts of locomotives or from jolts given by rail joints may approach the natural frequency of vibration of loaded bridges. The blows may then become important and involve considerable increases in stresses and strains in bridges.

A bridge may thus be subject to two types of variation of stress arising from (a) rhythmically repeated blows during the passage of a travelling load, and (b) the imposition and removal of the weight of the travelling load: the (British) Bridge Stress Committee appears to doubt whether either variation is of a type to produce " fatigue," but it appears to the author that the chances of fatigue occurring are far from being disproved, nor is it clear that there have not been fatigue failures in bridges although bridge failure of any kind is very rare in Great Britain. Whether entirely logical or not, convenient impact formulæ of the Pencoyd type making higher allowances of impact stress for short than for long spans and making some provision against possible fatigue are not likely to be entirely displaced for a long time. The British Standard impact factor for railways given in B.S.S. No. 153 is

$$k = 120/\{90 + (n+1)L/2\} \qquad . \quad . \quad . \quad (4)$$

where L is the loaded length of track in feet, and n is the number of tracks. For a road bridge the factor is two-thirds of this with a maximum of 0·70.

The Bridge Stress Committee for certain standard loads,[2] and impact stresses due to definite hammer blows, allowing for resonant effects, have prepared tables of equivalent uniformly distributed loads appropriate to British railway practice. These are published in their report. For design purposes the actual loading is replaced by a dead load which includes an allowance for impact effect, and so no question of variable stress allowance arises. In arriving at their conclusions they considered a great amount of experimental

---

[1] See Report (H.M. Stationery Office, 1928).
[2] See B.S.S. No. 153, which gives the standard loadings and equivalents. See also Art. 175.

data in which stresses were estimated from known loadings by means of strain measurements.

Alternative Methods. The reader should realise that the alternatives of using a variable unit stress in connection with the maximum straining action or using a constant (or dead load) unit stress with a dynamically increased equivalent dead load is largely a matter of individual choice, and that one system can always be expressed in terms of the other, and that in either case the rules in common use are empirical. Thus, illustrating from the simple case of tension, let M = maximum load, R = range of load, then for a tie bar

$$\text{sectional area} = \frac{M}{\text{variable unit stress}} = \frac{M+kR}{\text{dead load unit stress}} \quad . \quad (5)$$

hence

$$\text{variable unit stress} = \frac{\text{dead load unit stress}}{1+kR/M} \quad . \quad (6)$$

Thus writing $k = 1$ we get what is called the dynamic formula, viz.

$$\text{(variable) working stress} = \frac{\text{dead load stress}}{1+R/M} \quad . \quad (7)$$

An example will make clear the use of the formulæ of the present article.

Example. Taking a dead load stress of 6 tons per sq. in., find the cross-sectional area for a tie bar subject to a tensile dead load of 4 tons and live loads which vary from 1 ton compression to 2 tons tension.

maximum tensile = 4 + 2 = 6 tons
minimum load = 4 − 1 = 3 tons. Range of load = 3 tons.

Using (1)

equivalent dead load = minimum + twice range
= 3 + 2 × 3 = 9 tons
area required = 9 tons/6 tons per sq. in.
= 1·5 sq. in.

Alternatively, from dynamic formula (7)

working stress = 6 tons per sq. in./(1 + 3/6)
= 4 tons per sq. in.

area required = maximum load/working stress
= (4 + 2) tons/4 tons sq. in.
= 6/4 = 1·5 sq. in.

Unwin gives the following table of factors of safety for different materials and circumstances:

TABLE OF FACTORS OF SAFETY

Material	Factors of safety for			
	Dead load	Live or varying load		Structure subject to shock
		Stress of one kind only	Reversed stresses	
Cast iron	4	6	10	15
Wrought iron and steel .	3	5	8	12
Timber	7	10	15	20
Brickwork and masonry .	20	30	—	—

For a dead load on structural steel the factor of safety is commonly 4.

TABLE OF ULTIMATE STRENGTHS

(*The following are average and not extreme values*)

Material	Tenacity in tons per sq. in.	Shearing strength in tons per sq. in.
Cast iron	7 to 10	9 to 11
Wrought-iron bars	20 to 24	15 to 18
,, plates (with fibre). .	21	16
,, ,, (across fibre) . .	19	14
[1]Steel, mild structural	28 to 33	21 to 24
,, ,, for rivets	26 to 29	—
,, for rails	30 to 40	—
,, castings and forgings	25 to 35	—
,, wire	70 to 90	—
Brass	8	8 to 10
Manganese-bronze	35	—
Aluminium, cast	3 to 5	—
,, rolled.	7 to 10	6
Aluminium-bronze (10 per cent. copper)	40	25
Oak (British)	4 to 8	$\frac{1}{3}$
Ash	2 to 7	$\frac{1}{4}$
Elm	2 to 6	Along
Teak	2 to 7	the
Yellow pine	1 to 2	$\frac{1}{8}$ grain.
Red pine	2 to 6	
Spruce	2 to 3	$\frac{1}{8}$

[1] See Table in Art. 26.

Note.—Tables of Ultimate Compression or Crushing Strength, Elastic Modulus, and Working Stresses are given in the Appendix.

EXAMPLES II

1. The following figures give the observations from a tensile test of a round piece of mild steel 1 in. diameter and 10 in. between the gauge points:

Load in tons	5	10	15	16	17	18	19	20	20·5	21	21·5
Extension in inches	0·0047	0·0096	0·0145	0·0155	0·16	0·21	0·26	0·32	0·36	0·39	0·43

Load in tons	22	22·5	23	23·5	24	24·5	25	25·45	25·1	23·1	21·7
Extension in inches	0·49	0·53	0·60	0·69	0·78	0·89	1·08	2·13	2·13	2·30	2·35

Plot separate stress-strain diagrams for the elastic and ductile extensions and find the ultimate tensile strength, intensity of stress at yield point, the percentage elongation on 10 in., and the stretch modulus for the metal.

2. Two parallel walls, 25 ft. apart are stayed together by a steel bar 1 in. diameter, passing through metal plates and nuts at each end. The nuts are screwed up to the plates while the bar is at a temperature of 300° F. Find the pull exerted by the bar after it has cooled to 60° (*a*) if the ends do not yield; (*b*) if the total yielding at the two ends is $\frac{1}{4}$ in. Steel expands 0·0000062 of its length per degree Fahrenheit, and E = 13,500 tons per sq. in.

3. Find the work done per cu. in. of material in the static test to fracture given in Problem No. 1.

4. Find the total elastic strain energy or resilience of a bar of mild steel 1 in. diameter and 10 ft. long, carrying a tensile load of 7 tons. E = 13,500 tons per sq. in.

5. Find the total proof resilience of a bar of steel 1$\frac{1}{2}$ in. diameter and 8 ft. long, the tensile elastic limit being 14 tons per sq. in. and the stretch modulus (E) 13,500 tons per sq. in. Find also the proof resilience per cu. in.

6. Find the intensity of stress and extension produced in a bar 10 ft. long and 1·5 sq. in. in section, by the sudden application of a tensile load of 6 tons. What suddenly applied load would produce an extension of $\frac{1}{20}$ of an in.? Take E = 13,000 tons per sq. in.

7. Estimate the dead loads equivalent to the following: (*a*) A dead load (tensile) of 15 tons and a live load of 20 tons. (*b*) A dead load (compressive) of 15 tons and a live tensile load of 20 tons. If the strain is not to exceed 0·001, find the area of section required in each case, E being 13,500 tons per sq. in.

8. A load of 560 lb. falls through $\frac{1}{2}$ in. on to a stop at the lower end of a vertical bar 10 ft. long and 1 sq. in. in section. If the stretch modulus (E) is 13,000 tons epr sq. in., find the stress produced in the bar.

9. Find the greatest height from which the load in Problem No. 6 may fall before beginning to stretch the bar in order not to produce a greater stress than 14 tons per sq. in.

10. What is a suitable value for the working stress for a bar carrying a dead load of 7 tons tension and subject also to a load which fluctuates between 3 tons tension and 2 tons compression if the safe stress for dead loads is 5 tons per sq. in.

11. Find a suitable area of cross-section for a tie bar the tension in which varies from 10 tons to 8 tons. the safe stress for a dead load being 7 tons per sq. in.

CHAPTER III

STATICS

32. Systems of Forces in Equilibrium. In estimating the stresses on parts of a structure, it will frequently be necessary to consider the equilibrium of the structure regarded as a rigid body under the action of a system of forces, some of which (the loads) may be known, and others, the supporting forces or reactions, may be unknown and require to be found by the principles of statics. Or again, it is often necessary to consider in the same way a portion of a structure, and very frequently the equilibrium of the system of concurrent forces meeting at some point in the structure. Mainly graphical methods are used, but the algebraic ones are also employed. The foundation of graphical statics is the principle of geometrical or vector addition of forces. The rules relating to coplanar systems are frequently sufficient for estimating the forces on a structure, but extensions to other cases are occasionally used.

Graphical Methods. When statical problems are solved by graphical methods, it is usually necessary first to draw out a diagram, showing correctly the inclinations of the lines of action of the various known forces to one another, and to some scale, their relative positions. Such a diagram is called a diagram of positions, or *space diagram*; this is not to be confused with the vector diagram of forces, which gives magnitudes and directions, but not positions of forces.

Bow's Notation. In this notation the lines of action of each force in the *space diagram* are denoted by two letters placed one on each side of its line of action. Thus the spaces rather than the lines or intersections have letters assigned to them, but the limits of a space having a particular letter to denote it may be different for different forces.

The corresponding force in the *vector diagram* has the same two letters at its ends as are given to the spaces separated by its line of action in the space diagram. We shall use capital letters in the space diagram, and the corresponding small letters to indicate a force in the vector diagram.

It will be assumed that the reader is familiar with the conditions of equilibrium, with the polygon of forces and with the link or funicular polygon used in connection with non-concurrent forces all in one plane.[1]

---

[1] See the Author's *Mechanics for Engineers* or *Applied Mechanics*.

Conditions of Equilibrium. For a rigid body acted upon by forces all in one plane the conditions of equilibrium may usefully be summarised as follows:

(1) The algebraic total horizontal component of the forces is zero.
(2) The algebraic total vertical component of the forces is zero.
(3) The algebraic total of the moments of all the forces about one point in the plane is zero.

These are sufficient but it follows (3A) that the total moment about *every* point in the plane is zero. In terms of graphical methods the conditions are that (1) the polygon of forces is a closed figure; (2) that the link or funicular polygon is a closed figure.

33. Moments of Parallel Forces from Funicular Polygon.

Let AB, BC, CD, DE, EF (or W_1, W_2, W_3, W_4, and W_5) (Fig. 30) be

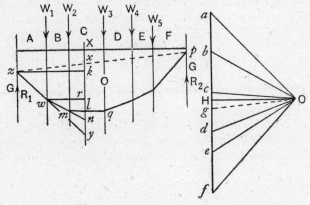

Fɪɢ. 30.—Moments of parallel forces from funicular polygon

five parallel (vertical) forces balanced by two equilibrants *fg* and *ga* (or R_1 and R_2). Let the funicular polygon for any pole *o*, starting, say, from *z*, be drawn, *og* being drawn parallel to *zp* or GO, the closing line of the funicular, so that R_1, the left-hand equilibrant, is represented by the vector *ga* and R_2 by *fg*, while the loads W_1, W_2, W_3, W_4, and W_5 are represented by the vectors *ab*, *bc*, *ce*, *de*, and *ef* respectively. Consider any vertical line through X, at which the height of the link polygon is *xl*. Produce *xl* and the side *zw* to meet in *y*. Also produce the side *wm* of the funicular polygon to meet *xy* in *n*, and let the next side *mq* of the funicular meet *xy* in *l*. The sides *zw*, *wm*, and *mq* (or AO, BO, and CO) are parallel to *ao*, *bo*, and *co* respectively. Draw a horizontal line, *zk*, through *z* to meet *xy* in *k*, a horizontal line through *w* to meet *xy* in *r*, and a horizontal *o*H through *o* in the vector polygon to meet the line *abcdef* in H. Then in the two triangles *xyz* and *gao* there are three sides in either parallel respectively to three sides in the other, hence the triangles are similar, and

$$\frac{xy}{ag} = \frac{zk}{o\text{H}}, \text{ or } xy \cdot o\text{H} = ag \times zk, \text{ or } xy = \frac{ag \cdot zk}{o\text{H}}$$

Therefore, since *ag* is proportional to R_1, and *zk* is equal or proportional to the distance of the line of action of R_1 from X, $ag \cdot zk$ is proportional to the moment of R_1 about X, and *o*H being an arbitrarily fixed constant, *xy* is proportional to the moment of R_1 about X.

Similarly

$$yn = \frac{ab \cdot wr}{o\text{H}}$$

and therefore represents the moment of W_1 about X to the same scale that *xy* represents the moment of R_1 about X. Hence *xn* or *xy*−*ny* represents to the same scale the moment of the two forces R_1 and W_1 about X (or of their algebraic sum acting at their intersection of *xz* and *wn*). Similarly *nl* represents the moment of W_2 about X to the same scale and

$$xl = xy - ny - ln$$

represents the moment about X of the three forces R_1, W_1, and W_2, or of their resultant (the algebraic sum) acting at the intersection of the lines *xz* and *lm*. For any point in the plane, and for any number of parallel forces the proper intercept between the sides of the funicular polygon represents the moment and always to the same scale, since the distance from *o* to any side of the vector polygon *abcdefg* is the same, viz. *o*H. For different pole distances (*o*H) the depth of closed link polygon will be inversely proportional to the pole distance.

Scales. If the scale of forces in the vector diagram is

1 in. to *p* lb.

and the scale of distance in the space diagram is

1 in. to *q* ft.;

and if *o*H is made *h* in. long, the scale on which the intercepts *xl*, *xn*, *xy*, *ny*, etc., represent the moments about X is

1 in. to $p \cdot q \cdot h$ lb.-feet.

34. Moments, Centroids, and Second Moments (or Moments of Inertia) of Plane Areas. The moment of a plane area about a line in its plane is the limit of the sum of products of small elements of the area and their perpendicular distances from that line. If δA represents any element of a plane area A distant y from a given line in its plane, the moment of the area is the limiting value of

$$\Sigma(y \,.\, \delta A) \text{ or } \int y d A$$

The *centroid* of a plane area (also called the centre of gravity of the area), may be defined as a point in its plane such that the moment of the area about any line in the plane passing through that point is zero.   Or for any line in the plane, through the centroid the product sum

$$\Sigma(y\delta A)=0 \quad . \quad . \quad . \quad . \quad . \quad . \quad (1)$$

Central Axis. Such a line through the centroid is called a *central axis* of the figure.   The distance $\bar{y}$ of the centroid from any other line in the plane is given by the equation

$$\bar{y}=\Sigma(y \,.\, \delta A)\div A \quad . \quad . \quad . \quad . \quad (2)$$

The position of the centroid of simple geometrical figures is dealt with in books on elementary mechanics.[1]

Second Moment or Moment of Inertia of a Plane Area. The second moment or moment of inertia (I) of the area about any axis in its plane is defined by the relation

$$I = \Sigma(y^2 \,.\, \delta A) \quad . \quad . \quad . \quad . \quad . \quad (3)$$

where values of y are the distances of elements of area δA from the axis about which the quantity I is to be estimated.

The calculation of the quantity I for various simple geometrical figures about various axes will now be briefly considered.   The summation denoted by $\Sigma(y^2 \,.\, \delta A)$ can often be easily carried out by ordinary integration.   If A be the area of any plane figure and I its moment of inertia about an axis in its plane, the radius of gyration (k) of the area about that axis is defined by the relation

$$k^2 A = I = \Sigma(y^2 \,.\, \delta A) \quad . \quad . \quad . \quad . \quad (4)$$

or k is that value of y at which, if the area A were concentrated, the moment of inertia would be the same as that of the actual figure. Two simple theorems are very useful in calculating moments of inertia of plane figures made up of a combination of a number of parts of simple figures such as rectangles and circles.

Theorem (1).   The moment of inertia of any plane area about any axis in its plane exceeds that about a parallel line through its centre of gravity (or centroid) by an amount equal to the product of the area and the square of the distance of the centroid from the axis.

Otherwise, if I is the moment of inertia of an area A about any axis in the plane of the figure, and I_G is the moment of inertia about

---

[1] Such as the Author's *Mechanics for Engineers*.

a parallel central axis, *i.e.* a parallel axis through the centroid, and l is the distance between the two axes

$$I = I_G + l^2 A \quad \ldots \quad \ldots \quad (5)$$

or, dividing each term by A

$$k^2 = k_G^2 + l^2 \quad \ldots \quad \ldots \quad (6)$$

where k is the radius of gyration about any axis distance l from the centroid and k_G that about a parallel axis through the centroid. The proof of the theorem may be briefly stated as follows:

$$I = \Sigma\{(l+y)^2 \delta A\} = \Sigma\{(l^2 + 2ly + y^2)\delta A\}$$
$$= l^2 \Sigma(\delta A) + 2l\Sigma(y \cdot \delta A) + \Sigma(y^2 \delta A)$$
$$= l^2 \cdot A + 0 + I_G$$

when y is measured from an axis through the centroid.

Theorem (2). The sum of the moments of inertia of any plane figure about two perpendicular axes in its plane is equal to the moment of inertia of the figure about an axis perpendicular to its plane passing through the intersection of the other two axes. Or, if I_Z, I_X, and I_Y are the moments of inertia about three mutually perpendicular axes OZ, OX, and OY intersecting in O, OX, and OY being in the plane of the figure

$$I_Z = I_X + I_Y \quad \ldots \quad \ldots \quad \ldots \quad (7)$$

or $\quad \Sigma(r^2 \cdot \delta A) = \Sigma(y^2 \cdot \delta A) + \Sigma(x^2 \delta A)$ or $\Sigma\{(x^2 + y^2)\delta A\}$. (8)

where r, y, and x are the distances of any element of area δA from OZ, OX, and OY respectively, since $r^2 = x^2 + y^2$.

Rectangular Area. The moment of inertia of the rectangle ABCD, Fig. 31, about the axis XX may be found as follows, using the notation given in the figure, by taking strip elements of area $b \cdot dy$ parallel to XX

$$I_{XX} = \int_{-\frac{d}{2}}^{\frac{d}{2}} y^2 \cdot b \, dy = \tfrac{1}{3} b \left[y^3 \right]_{-\frac{d}{2}}^{\frac{d}{2}} = \tfrac{1}{12} b d^3$$

Similarly about YY

$$I_{YY} = \tfrac{1}{12} d b^3$$

About DC, by theorem (1) above

$$I_{DC} = I_{XX} + bd \cdot \left(\frac{d}{2}\right)^2 = bd^3(\tfrac{1}{12} + \tfrac{1}{4}) = \tfrac{1}{3} bd^3$$

which might also be obtained by integrating thus

$$I_{DC} = \int_0^d by^2 \, dy = \tfrac{1}{3} bd^3$$

y being measured from DC.

Hollow Rectangular Area and Symmetrical **I** *Section.* The moment of inertia about the axes XX of the two areas shown in Fig. 32 are equal, for the difference of distribution of the areas in a direction parallel to XX does not alter the moment of inertia about that line. In either case

$$I_{XX} = \tfrac{1}{12}(BD^3 - bd^3)$$

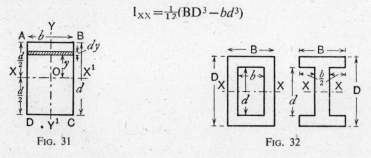

FIG. 31   FIG. 32

Triangular Area. For any of the triangles shown in Fig. 33 about the base *b*

$$I_{XX} = \int_0^h b \times \frac{h-y}{h} y^2 dy = \frac{b}{h}\int_0^h (hy^2 - y^3)dy = \tfrac{1}{12}bh^3$$

and using theorem (1), about a parallel axis GG through the centroid

$$I_{GG} = I_{XX} - \tfrac{1}{2}bh(\tfrac{1}{3}h)^2 = \tfrac{1}{36}bh^3$$

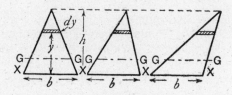

FIG. 33

Circular Area. The moment of inertia I_0 about an axis perpendicular to the circular surface and through its centre (Fig. 34) is found by taking circular strips of radius *r* and width *dr*.

$$I_0 = \int_0^R r^2 \cdot 2\pi r dr = 2\pi \frac{R^4}{4} = \tfrac{1}{2}\pi R^4 \text{ or } \frac{\pi}{32}D^4$$

Using theorem (2)

$$I_0 = I_{XX} + I_{YY}$$

where I_{XX} and I_{YY} are the moments of inertia about two perpendicular diameters XX and YY; and since by symmetry $I_{XX} = I_{YY}$

$$I_0 = 2I_{XX} = 2I_{YY}$$

and

$$I_{XX} = I_{YY} = \tfrac{1}{4}\pi R^4 \text{ or } \frac{\pi}{64}D^4$$

which might easily be established by taking straight strips parallel to XX or YY.

Circular Ring Area.   Evidently, from the above result, if I_0 is the moment of inertia about a central axis perpendicular to the plane of Fig. 35

$$I_0 = \frac{\pi}{2}(R^4 - r^4) \text{ or } \frac{\pi}{32}(D^4 - d^4)$$

and $$I_{XX} = I_{YY} = \frac{\pi}{4}(R^4 - r^4) \text{ or } \frac{\pi}{64}(D^4 - d^4)$$

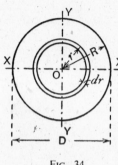

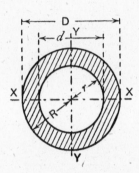

FIG. 34   FIG. 35

I-*Shaped Sections.*   The moment of inertia, etc., of a rolled **I** section such as that in Fig. 36 may generally be calculated by dividing it into rectangles, triangles, circular sections, and sprandrils as shown, and applying theorem (1), but such a process is very laborious and leads to a result of perhaps needless exactness, for all the dimensions, though specified with great precision, could scarcely be adhered to in manufacture with similar exactness.   The moments of inertia of the sections recommended by the British Standards Institution have been worked out by the exact method and tabulated (see Appendix).   A graphical method suitable for any kind of section is given in the next article.

T *Sections*, etc.   These sections will usually have rounded corners, and if they are known exactly, the moment of inertia may be calculated by division, as in Fig. 36.   If, however, the rounding is neglected and the section regarded as consisting of rectangles, as in Fig. 37, we may proceed as follows.   Find the distance h of the centre of gravity or centroid from the edge PQ by the methods of moments, thus

$$h\{(B.T) + (b.d)\} = (B.T.\tfrac{1}{2}T) + (b.d)(T + \tfrac{1}{2}d)$$

from which h can be found.

Then find the moment of inertia I_{PQ} about PQ, taking the rectangles PRSQ and VWUT

$$I_{PQ} = \tfrac{1}{3}B \cdot T^3 + \tfrac{1}{12}b \cdot d^3 + b \cdot d(T + \tfrac{1}{2}d)^2$$

or taking the rectangles VWNM and twice RTMP

$$I_{PQ} = \tfrac{1}{3}(B - b)T^3 + \tfrac{1}{3}b(T + d)^3$$

Having found I_{PQ}, apply theorem (1), whence

$$I_{XX} = I_{PQ} - (BT + bd)h^2$$

Another alternative would be to find I_{XX} directly by subdivision into rectangles and application of theorem (1); as h will not generally be so simple a number as the main dimensions, this will

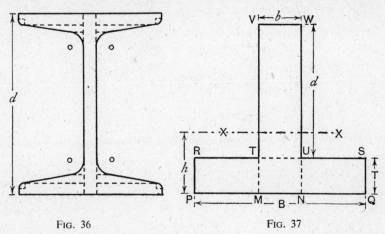

FIG. 36 FIG. 37

generally involve multiplications of rather less simple figures than in the above methods.

Yet another plan would be to find the moment of inertia about VW, thus

$$I_{VW} = \tfrac{1}{3}B(d + T)^3 - \tfrac{1}{3}(B - b)d^3$$

and then apply theorem (1), to find I_{XX}.

Precisely similar principles may be applied to find the moment of inertia of any section divisible into rectangles and not symmetrical about the neutral axis, *e.g.* that in Fig. 70.

35. Centroids and Second Moments (or Moments of Inertia) of Irregular Plane Areas. To determine the moment and moment of inertia (or second moment) of sections which are not made up of simple geometrical figures, some approximate form of estimation must be employed, generally either graphical or tabular. Of graphical methods, probably the following is the simplest, a planimeter being used to measure the areas.

To find the moment and moment of inertia of any plane figure APQB (Fig. 38), about any axis XX, and the moment of inertia about a parallel axis through the centroid. Draw any line SS parallel to XX and distance d from it; choose any pole O in XX, preferably the point nearest to the figure APQB. Draw a number of lines, such as PQ and AB across the figure parallel to XX. From the extremities P and Q, etc., project lines perpendicular to SS, meeting it in N and M, etc. Join such points as N and M to O by lines meeting PQ in P_1 and Q_1, AB in A_1 and B_1, etc. Through

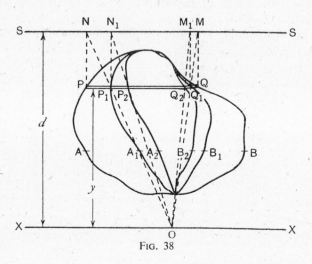

Fig. 38

the points so derived, draw in the modified or first derived area $P_1Q_1B_1A_1$. Repeat the process on this figure, projecting P_1Q_1 at N_1M_1 and obtaining P_2Q_2 and a second modified figure or derived area $P_2Q_2B_2A_2$.

Let the areas PQBA, $P_1Q_1B_1A_1$ and $P_2Q_2B_2A_2$ be represented by A, A_1, and A_2 respectively, and their width at any distance y from XX be denoted by z, z_1, and z_2 respectively. Then elementary strips PQ, P_1Q_1, and P_2Q_2, or δA, δA_1, and δA_2 of area are respectively equal to $z \cdot dy$, $z_1 \cdot dy$, and $z_2 \cdot dy$, and

$$\delta A_1 = \delta y \cdot z \cdot y/d, \quad \delta A_2 = \delta A \times z \times y^2/d^2$$

$$A_1 = \Sigma(\delta A_1) = \Sigma(y \delta A)/d \text{ or } \Sigma(yz\delta y)/d \quad \cdots \quad (1)$$

$$A_2 = \Sigma(\delta A_2) = \bar{z}(y^2 \delta A)/d^2 \text{ or } \Sigma(y^2 z \delta y)/d^2 = I_{XX}/d^2. \quad (2)$$

Hence

$$I_{XX} = A_2 d^2 \quad \cdots \quad \cdots \quad (3)$$

which may be found by measuring A_2 by a planimeter or otherwise.

Also if $\bar{y}$ is the distance of the centroid from XX

$$\bar{y} = \Sigma(y\delta A)/A = d \times A_1/A \quad . \quad . \quad . \quad . \quad (4)$$

which may be found by measuring the areas A_1 and A.

And from (5), Art. 34, the moment of inertia about an axis through the centroid and parallel to XX is

$$I_G = I_{XX} - A(\bar{y})^2$$

or

$$I_G = A_2 d^2 - d^2 A_1{}^2/A = d^2(A_2 - A_1{}^2/A) \quad . \quad . \quad . \quad (5)$$

An approximate value of the second moment can be found by dividing an area into small parts and finding the sum of the second moments of the parts. The methods will be exemplified by finding the second moment about its axis of the area bounded by a parabola and a line perpendicular to its axis, as this will allow of the degree of accuracy of the method being judged. The area ABCD is shown in Fig. 39. Either of the halves into which it is divided by its axis AD can be divided into, say, 10 strips of equal width either horizontally or vertically. In the former case the width δy of a strip is 0·1 in. and in the latter the width δx is 0·4 in.

The most obvious method, but not necessarily the best, is to take horizontal strips of width δy, length $z = 4 - x$ with their horizontal centre lines distant y from the axis AD. The values of y and z are set out in Table I and the values of y^2 and $y^2 z$ are calculated and entered in the table.

TABLE I   TABLE II

y	y^2	z	$y^2 z$	x	y	y^3
0·05	0·0025	3·99	0·010	0·2	0·224	0·011
0·15	0·0225	3·91	0·088	0·6	0·387	0·058
0·25	0·0625	3·75	0·234	1·0	0·500	0·125
0·35	0·1225	3·5	0·430	1·4	0·592	0·207
0·45	0·2025	2·19	0·646	1·8	0·671	0·302
0·55	0·3025	2·79	0·844	2·2	0·742	0·408
0·65	0·4225	2·31	0·976	2·6	0·806	0·523
0·75	0·5625	1·75	0·984	3·0	0·866	0·649
0·85	0·7225	1·11	0·802	3·4	0·922	0·784
0·95	0·9025	0·39	0·352	3·8	0·975	0·927

$\Sigma(y^2 z) = 5\cdot366$ (in.)^3　　　　　　$\Sigma(y^3) = 3\cdot994$ (in.)^3

The sum of the ten quantities $y^2 z$ from the table is 5·366 (inches)^3 for half the area or 10·732 (inches)^3 for the whole area, hence $\Sigma(y^2 z \delta y)$ or $I_x = 10\cdot73$ (inches)$^3 \times 0\cdot1$ in. $= 1\cdot073$ (inch)^4.

An alternative method is to take, say, 10 vertical strips of length y and width $\delta x = 0\cdot4$ in. The second moment of such a strip about XX by Art. 34 is $y^3 \delta x/3$ and we have only to add the 10 such products and double the sum for the whole area to get I_{XX}. The values of x, y, and y^3 are shown in Table II, from which $\Sigma(y^3) = 3\cdot994$ (inch)^3 and $I_{XX} = 2\Sigma(y\delta x)/3 = \frac{2}{3} \times 3\cdot994$ (inch)$^3 \times 0\cdot4$ (inch) $= 1\cdot065$ (inch)^4, which differs by less than 1 per cent. from the previous result. The actual value of the second moment is

$$\tfrac{4}{15} \times 4 \text{ in.} \times 1^3 \text{ (inch)}^3 = \tfrac{16}{15} \text{ (inches)}^4 = 1\cdot067 \text{ (inches)}^4$$

A closer approximation to this true value could have been found by smaller subdivision of the area.

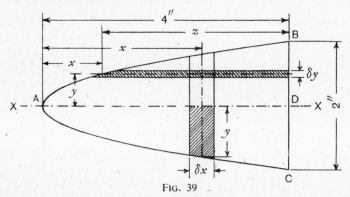

FIG. 39

36. Ellipse of Inertia, or Momental Ellipse. *Principal Axes of a Section.*

The principal axes OX and OY of a plane area may be defined as the rectangular axes in its plane, and through the centroid such that the sum $\Sigma(xy \cdot \delta A)$, called the *product of inertia* (or product moment), is zero, x and y being the rectangular co-ordinates of an element δA of the area with reference to OX and OY.

Let
$$\Sigma(y^2 \cdot \delta A) = I_x = k_x^2 \cdot \Sigma(\delta A)$$
$$\Sigma(x^2 \cdot \delta A) = I_y = k_y^2 \Sigma(\delta A)$$

Then the moment of inertia of the area about any perpendicular axes OX' and OY' in its plane when OX' is inclined at an angle α to OX may be found by writing from the right-hand side of Fig. 40 for the co-ordinates (x', y') of any point P,

$$OM = x' = x \cos\alpha + y \sin\alpha$$
$$PM = y' = y \cos\alpha - x \sin\alpha$$

hence
$$I_{y'} = \Sigma(x'^2 \cdot \delta A) = \cos^2\alpha\, \Sigma(x^2\delta A) + \sin^2\alpha\, \Sigma(y^2\delta A) + 2\sin\alpha\cos\alpha\, \Sigma(xy\delta A)$$

or
$$\left.\begin{array}{l} I_{y'} = I_y \cos^2\alpha + I_x \sin^2\alpha \\ k_{y'}^2 = k_y^2 \cos^2\alpha + k_x^2 \sin^2\alpha \end{array}\right\} \text{since } \Sigma(xy\delta A) = 0 \quad . \quad . \quad (1)$$

Also similarly
$$\left.\begin{array}{l} I_{x'} = I_x \cos^2\alpha + I_y \sin^2\alpha \\ k_{x'} = k_x^2 \cos^2\alpha + k_y^2 \sin^2\alpha \end{array}\right\} \quad . \quad . \quad . \quad (2)$$

Adding (1) and (2)

$$\left.\begin{array}{l} I_{x'} + I_{y'} = I_x + I_y \\ k_x^2 + k_{y'}^2 = k_x{}^2 + k_y{}^2 \end{array}\right\} = \text{constant} \quad . \quad . \quad . \quad (3)$$

A result which follows directly from theorem (2) Art. 34.

If OA=OA', Fig. 40, be set off to represent k_y and OB=OB' to represent k_x and an ellipse ABA'B' be drawn with OA and OB as semi-principal axes, then $k_{y'}$ is represented by OC, the perpendicular distance from the centre O to the tangent parallel to OY' when OX' and OY' are inclined as shown at an angle α to OX and OY respectively. For a property of the ellipse is

$$OC^2 = OA^2 \cos^2 \alpha + OB^2 \sin^2 \alpha$$

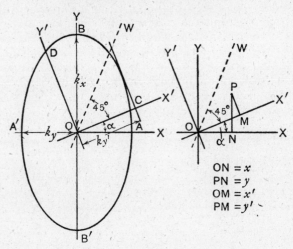

ON = x
PN = y
OM = x'
PM = y'

FIG. 40

which is the relation given by (1). This *momental ellipse* then shows the radius of gyration about any axis, such as OY' by the length of the perpendicular from O on the tangent parallel to OY'. Also since the product OD . OC is constant in an ellipse (viz. equal to OA . OB), the radius of gyration about any axis such as OY' is inversely proportional to the radius vector OD in that direction. Its value is

$$k_{y'} = \frac{k_x \cdot k_y}{OD}$$

If a curve be drawn such that every radius vector measured from O is proportional to the square of k, *i.e.* proportional to I about that radius vector, it is called an *inertia curve* for the given section. The radius vector in the direction OX', for example, would be given by equation (2), and others might be found similarly.

It is evident by differentiating (1) with respect to α, or by inspection of the ellipse, that k has maximum and minimum values, k_x and k_y, the values of k about the two principal axes. It is often important to find the minimum value of k (and I) of a given section, and therefore to find the principal axes. If the section has an axis of symmetry that is evidently one principal axis, for from the symmetry the sum $\Sigma(xy \cdot \delta A)$ must be zero. The other principal axis is then at right angles to the first, and through the centroid of the section; a case in point is an angle section with equal sides.

If a plane figure (such as a circular or square section) has more than two axes of symmetry, its momental ellipse becomes a circle, and its moment of inertia about every axis in its plane and through the centroid is the same. If a section has not an axis of symmetry the principal axis and the principal or maximum and minimum moments of inertia may be found from the moments of inertia about two perpendicular axes OX' and OY', say, and the moment of inertia about a third axis OW, Fig. 40, inclined 45° to each of the other two; these three moments of inertia may be found by the methods described in the preceding articles. Let I_w be the moment of inertia about OW. Then applying (2)

$$I_w = I_x \cos^2{(\alpha + 45°)} + I_y \sin^2{(\alpha + 45°)} = \tfrac{1}{2}I_x(1 - \sin 2\alpha)$$
$$+ \tfrac{1}{2}I_y(1 + \sin 2a) \quad \ldots \ldots \quad (4)$$

$$2I_w = I_x + I_y + (I_y - I_x)\sin 2\alpha \quad \ldots \ldots \ldots \quad (5)$$

Hence by (3)
$$(I_y - I_x)\sin 2a = 2I_w - (I_{x'} + I_{y'}) \quad \ldots \quad (6)$$

and subtracting (2) from (1)

$$(I_y - I_x)\cos 2\alpha = I_{y'} - I_x \quad \ldots \ldots \quad (7)$$

Dividing (6) by (7)

$$\tan 2\alpha = \frac{2I_w - (I_{x'} + I_{y'})}{I_{y'} - I_{x'}} \quad \ldots \ldots \quad (8)$$

which determines the directions of the principal axes, α to be measured from OX' in the direction opposite to OW.

Also from (3) and (7)

$$I_x = \tfrac{1}{2}\{I_{x'} + I_{y'} + (I_{x'} - I_{y'})\sec 2\alpha\} \quad \ldots \quad (9)$$
$$I_y = \tfrac{1}{2}\{I_{x'} + I_{y'} - (I_{x'} - I_{y'})\sec 2\alpha\} \quad \ldots \quad (10)$$

which gives the principal moments of inertia in terms of the three known moments of inertia.

37. Moments and Products of Inertia. It is sometimes convenient to be able to calculate the principal moments of inertia of an area from the moments and products of inertia about two perpendicular (but not principal) axes. Let OX and OY to the right-hand side of Fig. 40 represent *any* two perpendicular axes through the centroid O of a plane figure, for which $\Sigma(xy\delta A)$ is not generally zero, and let OX′ and OY′ be any other pair of rectangular axes through O.　Then (1) of Art. 36 becomes

$$I_{y'} = I_y \cos^2 \alpha + I_x \sin^2 \alpha + \Sigma(xy\delta A) \sin 2\alpha \quad . \quad . \quad (1)$$

and (2) becomes

$$I_{x'} = I_y \sin^2 \alpha + I_x \cos^2 \alpha - \Sigma(xy\delta A) \sin 2\alpha \quad . \quad . \quad (2)$$

Differentiating with respect to α,

$$dI_{x'}/d\alpha = -(I_x - I_y) \sin 2\alpha - 2\Sigma(xy\delta A) \cos 2\alpha \quad . \quad (3)$$

which vanishes when

$$\tan 2\alpha = -2\Sigma(xy\delta A)/(I_x - I_y) \quad . \quad . \quad . \quad (4)$$

$dI_{y'}/d\alpha$ has the same value as (3) but is of opposite sign and becomes zero for the same values of α, viz. those shown in (4).　Also the values of the second differential coefficients of $I_{x'}$ and $I_{y'}$ are of opposite sign.　Hence $I_{x'}$ and I_y reach turning value for the same values of α, 90° apart, but when one is a maximum the other is a minimum.　Subtracting (1) from (2) and reducing

$$I_{x'} - I_{y'} = (I_x - I_y) \cos 2\alpha - 2\Sigma(xy\delta A) \sin 2\alpha \quad . \quad . \quad (5)$$

and for a maximum or minimum value of $I_{x'}$, substituting for $\Sigma(xy\delta A)$ in (5) its value from (4) and reducing we obtain

$$I_{x'} - I_{y'} = (I_x - I_y) \sec 2\alpha \quad . \quad . \quad . \quad . \quad (6)$$

The value of $I_{x'}$ and $I_{y'}$, the maximum and minimum values of I, can now be found from (2) and (1) by substituting the value of α given by (4) if I_x, I_y, and product of inertia $\Sigma(xy\delta A)$ are known, or can be easily calculated from given dimensions (*e.g.* in a figure divisible into rectangles).

By adding (1) and (2) and (6), we should obtain

$$I_{x'} = \tfrac{1}{2}\{I_x + I_y + (I_x - I_y) \sec 2\alpha\} \quad . \quad . \quad . \quad (7)$$

and
$$I_{y'} = \tfrac{1}{2}\{I_x + I_y - (I_x - I_y) \sec 2\alpha\} \quad . \quad . \quad . \quad (8)$$

where α has the value given by (4) for critical values of I.

If the product of inertia $\Sigma(x'y'\delta A)$ be found in terms of I_x, I_y, and $\Sigma(xy\delta A)$ by writing the values of x', and y' from Art. 36 and reducing

$$\Sigma(x'y'\delta A) = \Sigma\{\tfrac{1}{2}(y^2 - x^2) \sin 2\alpha + xy \cos 2\alpha\}\delta A$$
$$= \tfrac{1}{2}(I_x - I_y) \sin \alpha + \Sigma(xy\delta A) \cos 2\alpha \quad . \quad . \quad . \quad (9)$$

But under the condition (4) for maximum and minimum values of $I_{x'}$ and $I_{y'}$ substitution in (9), say, for sin 2α from (4) shows that

$$\Sigma(x'y'\delta A) = 0$$

That is, for the principal axes the product of inertia is zero, a point assumed as a definition in Art. 36.

Graphical Method.　If I_x, I_y, and $\Sigma(xy\delta A)$ are given, equations (6) and (4) provide for a simple graphical construction for finding the principal moments of inertia and position of the principal axes. In Fig. 41, make $BC=I_x$, $AC=I_y$ to scale. Bisect AB in O and describe the circle AEBF. Set off $CD = \Sigma(xy\delta A)$ perpendicular to

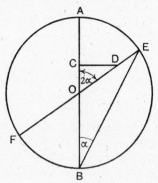

FIG. 41

AB, join OD, and complete the diameter FODE. Then $OC=\frac{1}{2}(BC-AC)=\frac{1}{2}(I_x-I_y)$; hence the angle

$$COD = \tan^{-1}\{2\,\Sigma(xy\delta A)/(I_x-I_y)\} = 2\alpha$$

and $OD = OC \sec 2\alpha = \frac{1}{2}(I_x-I_y) \sec 2\alpha = \frac{1}{2}(I_{x'}-I_{y'})$

Hence, to scale, $FD=I_{x'}$, and $ED=I_{y'}$, the maximum and minimum values of I respectively.

Examples III

1. An I-section of a girder is made up of three rectangles, viz. two flanges having their long sides horizontal, and one web connecting them having its long side vertical. The top flange section is 6 in. by 1 in., and that of the bottom flange is 12 in. by 2 in. The web section is 8 in. deep and 1 in. broad. Find the height of the c.g. of the area of cross-section from the bottom of the lower flange.

2. Find the c.g. of a **T** section, the height over all being 8 in., and the flange width 6 in., the metal being $\frac{7}{8}$ in. thick in the vertical web, and 1 in. thick in the horizontal flange.

3. A girder of I-shaped cross-section has two horizontal flanges, 5 in. broad and 1 in. thick, connected by a vertical web 9 in. high and 1 in. thick. Find the moment of inertia of the area of the section about a horizontal axis in the plane of the section and through its c.g. or centroid.

4. Find the moment of inertia and radius of gyration of the area of the section in Problem No. 2 about an axis through the c.g. of the section and parallel to the flange.

Numerous examples on centroids, and moments of inertia, etc., of plane areas may be found in the tables of standard sections (see tables in the Appendix).

CHAPTER IV

BENDING MOMENTS AND SHEARING FORCES

38. Beams and Bending. A bar of material acted on by external forces (including loads and supporting forces) oblique to its longitudinal axis is called a beam, and the components perpendicular to the axis cause the straining called flexure or bending. This and the following four chapters deal only with beams which are straight or nearly straight. As beams are frequently horizontal, and the external forces are weights, it will be convenient to speak always of the beams as being horizontal and the external forces as vertical, although the same conclusions would hold in other cases. Members of structures are often beams as well as struts or ties; that is, there

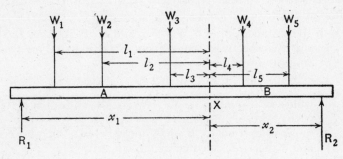

Fig. 42

are some transverse forces acting upon them in addition to longitudinal ones.

39. Straining Actions on Beams. Shearing Force and Bending Moment. Before investigating the stresses and strains set up in bending, the straining actions resulting from various systems of loading and supporting beams will be considered.

If we consider a beam carrying a number of transverse loads, as in Fig. 42, the whole beam is in equilibrium under the action of the loads W_1, W_2, W_3, etc., and the supporting forces or reactions R_1 and R_2; further, if we divide the beam into two parts A and B by an ideal plane of section X, each part is in equilibrium. The system which keeps A in equilibrium consists of the forces W_1, W_2, W_3, and R_1, together with the forces exerted on A by B across the section X in virtue of the state of stress in the beam. We may conveniently consider these latter forces by estimating their total

D

horizontal and vertical components and their moments. Applying the ordinary conditions of equilibrium, Art. 32, we conclude:

(1) Since there are no horizontal forces acting on the piece A except those across the section X, the algebraic total horizontal component of those forces is zero.

(2) Since the algebraic sum of the vertical *downward* forces on A is

$$W_1 + W_2 + W_3 - R_1$$

the total or resultant *upward* vertical force exerted by B on A is $W_1 + W_2 + W_3 - R_1$, which is also equal to an upward force

$$R_2 - (W_4 + W_5)$$

Shearing Force.   The resultant vertical force exerted by B on A is then equal to the algebraic sum of the vertical forces on either side of the plane of section X; the action of A on B is equal and opposite.   This total vertical component is the *shearing force* on the section in question.

(3) If the distances of W_1, W_2, W_3, and R_1 from X be l_1, l_2, l_3, and x_1 respectively the moment of the external forces on A about the section X is

$$M = R_1 x_1 - W_1 l_1 - W_2 l_2 - W_3 l_3$$

which is also equal to $W l_4 + W_5 l_5 - R_2 x_2$, and is of clockwise sense if the above expressions are positive.   The moment exerted by B on A must balance the above sum, and is therefore of equal magnitude.

Bending Moment.   The above quantity M is the algebraic sum of the moments of all the forces on either side of the section considered, and is called the *bending moment*.   The balancing moment which B exerts on A is called the *moment of resistance* of the beam at that section.   The statical conditions of equilibrium show that the moment of resistance and the bending moment are numerically equal.

40. Diagrams of Shearing Force and Bending Moment.   Both shearing force and bending moment will generally vary in magnitude from point to point along the length of a loaded beam; their values at any given cross-section can often be calculated arithmetically, or general algebraic expressions may give the bending moment and shearing force for any section along the beam.   The variation may also be shown graphically by plotting curves the bases of which represent to scale the length of the beam, and the vertical ordinates the bending moments or shearing forces, as the case may be.   Some simple typical examples of bending moment and shearing force curves follow in Figs. 43 to 52, inclusive.   In each case M represents bending moment, F shearing force, and R reactive or supporting force, with appropriate suffixes to denote the position to which the letters refer. Other cases of bending-moment and shearing-force diagrams will be dealt with later (see Arts. 85 to 92).

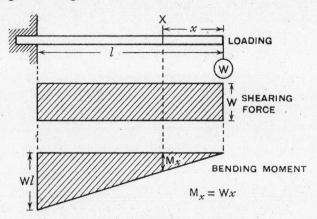

Fig. 43.—Cantilever with end load

$$M_x = Wx$$

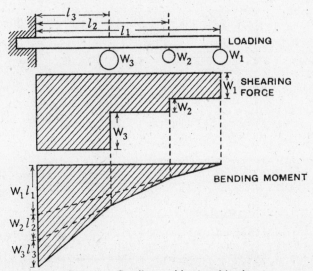

Fig. 44.—Cantilever with several loads

In the case of moving loads the straining actions change with the position of the load; such cases are dealt with in Chapter VI. When a beam carries several different concentrated or distributed loads the bending moment at any and every cross-section is the algebraic sum of the bending moments produced by the various loads acting separately. In plotting the diagrams it is sometimes convenient to add the ordinates of diagrams for two separate loads

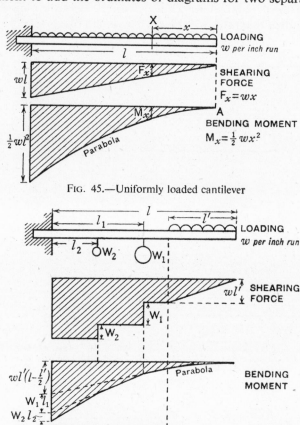

FIG. 45.—Uniformly loaded cantilever

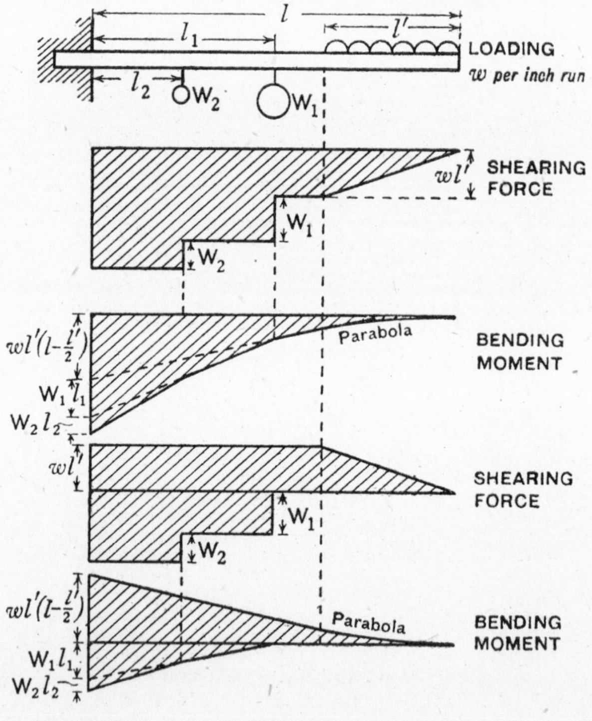

FIG. 46

and plot the algebraic sum, or to plot the two curves on opposite sides of the same base-line, and measure resultant values (vertically) directly from the extreme boundaries of the resultant diagram.

The two methods are illustrated in order in Fig. 46. Figs. 43,
44, 45, and 46 represent cantilevers, *i.e.* beams firmly fixed in position and direction at one end and free at the other.   Figs 47, 48,
49, 50 represent beams resting freely on supports at each end, and
carrying various loads as shown.   In calculating the shearing force
or bending moment at any given point, or obtaining a symbolic

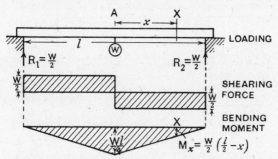

Fɪɢ. 47.—Freely supported beam with central load

expression for either quantity for every point over part or all the
length of the beam, the first step is usually to find the value of the
unknown supporting forces (R_1 and R_2).   These can conveniently
be found by considering the moments of all external forces about
either support, and equating the algebraic sum to zero.   When all
the external forces are known, the shearing force and bending

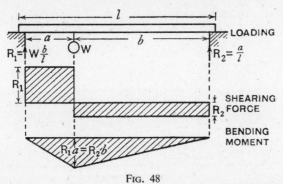

Fɪɢ. 48

moment are easily obtained for any section, the former being the
algebraic sum of the external transverse forces to either side of the
section, and the latter being the algebraic sum of the moments of
the external forces to either side of the section.

The question of positive or negative sign of the resulting sums is
arbitrary and not very important; it is dealt with in Art. 42, but in
a diagram it is well to show opposite forces and moments on

opposite sides of the base-line. Take the case in Fig. 50 fully as an example. The load is uniformly spread at the rate of w per inch run over a length c of the beam. The distances of the centre of gravity of the load from the left- and right-hand supports of the

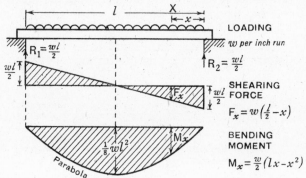

FIG. 49.—Freely supported beam with uniformly distributed load

beam are a and b respectively, so that $a+b=l$, the span of the beam between the supports.

Taking moments about the right-hand support

$$R_1 \times l = w \cdot c \times b$$
$$R_1 = w \cdot c \cdot b/l \qquad R_2 = wc \cdot a/l$$

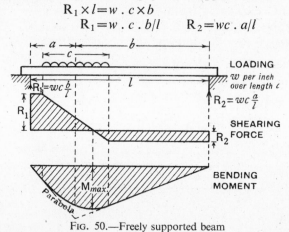

FIG. 50.—Freely supported beam

The shearing force (F) from the left support to the beginning of the load is equal to R_1.

Over the loaded portion, at a distance x from the left support, *i.e.* from $x = a - c/2$ to $x = a + c/2$,

$$F_x = R_1 - w\{x - (a - c/2)\} = wcb/l - wx + w(a - c/2)$$
or
$$w(cb/l + a - x - c/2)$$

which equals zero when $x = cb/l + a - c/2$.

For the remainder of the length to the right-hand support the shearing force is numerically equal to R_2, or algebraically to $R_1 - wc$, *i.e.*

$$F = w(cb/l - c) \text{ or } wc(b - l)/l \text{ or } -wca/l$$

The bending moment (M) at a section distant x from the left-hand end to the beginning of the load, *i.e.* if x is less than $a - c/2$, estimating moments on the left of the section, is

$$M_x = R_1 \cdot x = wcbx/l \text{ (a straight line)}$$

Over the loaded portion, *i.e.* if x is greater than $a - c/2$ and less than $a + c/2$

$$M_x = R_1 \cdot x - \{x - (a - c/2)\} \times w \cdot \tfrac{1}{2}\{x - (a - c/2)\}$$
$$= wcbx/l - \tfrac{1}{2}w(x - a - c/2)^2$$

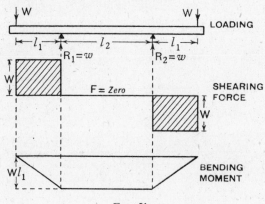

Fig. 51

The first term is represented by the left-hand dotted straight line, and the second by the distance between the curve and the straight line, and the value M_x by the vertical ordinate of the shaded diagram.

To the right of the load, *i.e.* when x is greater than $a + c/2$, estimating to the left

$$M_x = R_1 \cdot x - wc(x - a) = wcbx/l - wc(x - a)$$
or $\quad M_x = wca - wcx(1 - b/l) \text{ or } wca - wcax/l = wca(l - x)/l$
$$= R_2(l - x) \text{ (a straight line)}$$

which is much more simply found by taking the moments of the sole force R_2 to the right of any section in the range considered.

Fig. 51 represents a beam symmetrically placed over supports of shorter span, l_2, than the length of the beam, $l_2 + 2l_1$, and carrying equal end loads. Between the supports the shearing force is zero and the bending moment is constant. The magnitudes are unaffected if the positions of the loads and reactions are interchanged.

Fig. 52 shows a beam of length l_2+2l_1, with a uniformly spread load placed on supports l_2 apart and overhanging them by a length l_1 at each end. The bending moment at the supports is

$$M = wl_1 \times l_1/2 = wl_1^2/2$$

Within the span at a distance x from either support the bending moment is

$$M_x = w(l_1+x) \times \tfrac{1}{2}(l+x) - R_1 x = \tfrac{1}{2}w(l_1+x)^2 - wx(l_1+l_2/2)$$
$$= \tfrac{1}{2}wl_1^2 - \tfrac{1}{2}wx(l_2-x)$$

the first term of which is the bending moment at the supports, and the second is bending moment for a uniformly loaded span of length l_2 (see Fig. 49). The two terms are of opposite sign, and,

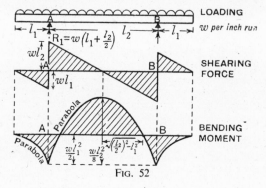

Fig. 52

provided l_2 is long enough, the bending moment will be zero and change sign at two points within the span, viz. when $M_x=0$, or

$$\tfrac{1}{2}w \,.\, l_1^2 - \tfrac{1}{2}wx(l_2-x)=0, \quad x^2-l_2x+l_1^2=0$$
$$x=\tfrac{1}{2}l_2 \pm \sqrt{\{(\tfrac{1}{2}l_2)^2-l_1^2\}}$$

i.e. at two points distant $\sqrt{[\{(\tfrac{1}{2}l_2)^2-l_1^2\}]}$ on the other side of mid-span; the two points are coincident (at mid-span) if $l_2=2l_1$, and do not exist if l_2 is less than $2l_1$, when the bending moment does not change sign.

Points of Contraflexure. Bending moments of opposite sign evidently tend to produce bending of opposite curvature. In a continuous curve of bending moments change of sign involves passing through a zero value of bending moment, and this point of zero bending moment and change of sign is called a point of inflexion or contraflexure, or a virtual hinge. The positions of the points of contraflexure for Fig. 52 have just been determined above from the equation $M_x=0$.

Actual Reactions and Effective Span. The foregoing diagrams are somewhat conventional as regards the application of the loads and reactions. These will actually be more or less distributed forces and not concentrated in lines (or rather planes perpendicular to the diagrams). The kind of modification which such distribution will produce in the diagrams of shearing force and bending moment is illustrated in Fig. 53, where the load W and both supporting forces are assumed to be uniformly distributed over short lengths of the beam: a comparison with Fig. 48 shows the effect of such distribution. The three curved portions of the bending moment diagram would be in this case parabolic (as in Fig. 50). The intensity of loading will usually be less at the boundary of the

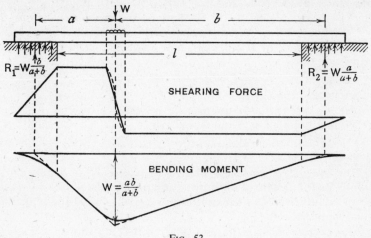

FIG. 53

short loaded lengths, and in this case the change of shearing force will be as indicated by the steep dotted curve instead of the uniform rate of change. When the ends of such a beam rest on seatings of finite length, the bending moments everywhere will be greater than if the beam were supported at the ends of the span *l*. The distance $(a+b)$ from centre to centre of the two seatings may be called the *effective span*, which is greater than the *clear span l.*

Example 1. A concentrated load of 1 ton is carried 3 ft. from the abutment of a beam having a clear span of 9 ft. Calculate the maximum bending moment first if the beam is only 9 ft. long and is just supported at its ends; secondly, if it is 11 ft. long and rests on seatings 1 ft. long at each end and the pressure is uniformly distributed along the seatings.

In the first case the reaction more distant from the load is

$$1 \times \tfrac{3}{9} = \tfrac{1}{3} \text{ ton}$$

D*

And the maximum bending (moment under the load) is

$$\tfrac{1}{3} \times 6 = 2 \text{ ton-ft.}$$

In the second case the more distant supporting force found by taking moments about the centre of the near seating is

$$1 \times 3 \cdot 5/10 = 0 \cdot 35 \text{ ton}$$

And the bending moment under the load is

$$0 \cdot 35 \times 6 \cdot 5 = 2 \cdot 275 \text{ ton-ft.}$$

Example 2. A girder of 40 ft. effective span supported at its ends has a total load of 56·5 tons uniformly distributed along its length. The load is not carried directly, but is transferred to the girder at its ends and at four consecutive points *a*, *b*, *b'*, *a'* (cross girders) placed 8, 16, 24, and 32 ft. respectively, from the left-hand support. Assuming that each load point *a*, *b*, *b'*, and *a'* carries the load for 8 ft. length, find the bending moment at each point.

Load at each point $= \tfrac{8}{40} \times 56 \cdot 5 = 11 \cdot 3$ tons
effective reactions at each end $= \tfrac{1}{2} \times 4 \times 11 \cdot 3 = 22 \cdot 6$ tons
bending moment at *a* and *a'* $= 22 \cdot 6 \times 8 = 180 \cdot 8$ ton-ft.
bending moment at *b* and *b'* $= 22 \cdot 6 \times 16 - 11 \cdot 3 \times 8 = 271 \cdot 2$ ton-ft.

A bending-moment diagram for this girder but with greater load is shown in Fig. 259.

Example 3. A girder of 11·25 ft. effective span carries a uniformly distributed load of 1 ton total and 2 loads of 30·8 tons each 2½ ft. on either side of the centre of the span. Find the maximum bending moment.

This corresponds to the two types of loading shown in Figs. 49 and 51 (reversed) acting together, consequently since the concentrated loads are $11 \cdot 25/2 - 2 \cdot 5 = 3 \cdot 125$ ft. from the supports, the total bending moment at the centre of the span will be

$$(30 \cdot 8 \times 3 \cdot 125) + \frac{1 \times 11 \cdot 25}{8} = 97 \cdot 7 \text{ ton-ft.}$$

41. Bending Moments and Shearing Forces from Link and Vector Polygons. The vertical breadths of a funicular or link polygon for a system of vertical forces on a horizontal beam represent to scale the bending moments at the corresponding sections. This has already been proved in Art. 33, and is illustrated in Fig. 54, where the link polygon has been drawn on a horizontal base by making the vector *fo* in the vector polygon horizontal, *i.e.* by choosing a pole *o* in the same horizontal line as the point *f*, which divides the load-line *abcde* in the ratio of the supporting forces. The position of *f* can be calculated or found by means of a trial link polygon with any pole. The scale of bending moment as explained in Art. 33 is

$p \cdot q \cdot h$ lb.-in. to 1 in. where the scale force is p lb. to 1 in., of distance q in. to 1, and the pole distance fo measures h in.   It is not necessary to draw the diagram on a horizontal base, but the distance h must be estimated horizontally, and the ordinates of bending moment must be measured vertically.

The shearing-force diagram is shown projected from the vertical load-line of the vector polygon.

The same method of drawing the bending-moment diagram to as close approximation as is desired is applicable to loads distributed either uniformly or otherwise by dividing the load into a number of sections along the length of the beam, and treating each part as a load concentrated at its centre of gravity.   The resulting funicular

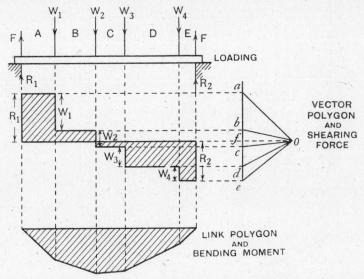

FIG. 54

polygon will be a figure with straight sides, and the curve of bending moments is the *inscribed* (not *circumscribed*) curve touching the sides of the polygon, for the polygon evidently gives excessive ordinates at the points of concentration and correct ones at the junctions of the parts into which the loaded lengths are divided. Consideration with a sketch of an extreme case, say a uniform load throughout the span and only two equal divisions, will make this clear.   It is also illustrated in Fig. 55.

Fig. 55 shows the bending-moment diagram for a beam with overhanging ends. The reactions are found by closing the funicular polygon and drawing og parallel to the closing line, the most convenient order of lettering and setting off the forces on the vector

polygon being consecutively round the beam.   Care is then required
in projecting the shearing-force diagram, as the forces do not follow
in consecutive order across the paper.   It will be found instructive
to redraw the vector polygon in such consecutive order and project
a shearing-force diagram from it.   The choice of signs in Fig. 55 is
arbitrary, and those given are in accordance with a convention given
in Art. 42.   Fig. 56 shows the case of a beam overhanging at one
end, and shows how to deal with a uniformly distributed load which
here extends over the length between the supports.   Only four
divisions have been taken, but a curve through *v, w, x, y, z,* gives the

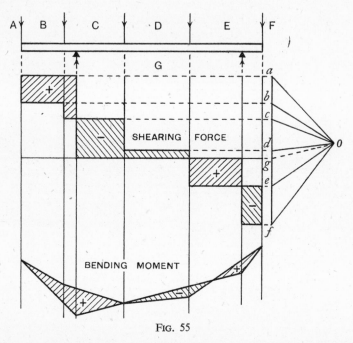

FIG. 55

curve of bending moments, and a straight line through *v′, w′, x′,*
y′, z′ gives the correct shearing-force diagram in place of the stepped
figure.   A caution is again required in projecting the shearing-force
diagram unless the load-line is redrawn.

Fig. 57 represents a cantilever carrying three loads; if *o* were
chosen in the same horizontal line as *a* the bending moment diagram becomes exactly like that already drawn in Fig. 44.   The link
polygon for the three given forces is not closed, and for equilibrium
an upward force *da* together with a moment M_w at the wall is
required; these are supplied by upward and lesser downward
reactions on the clamped end.

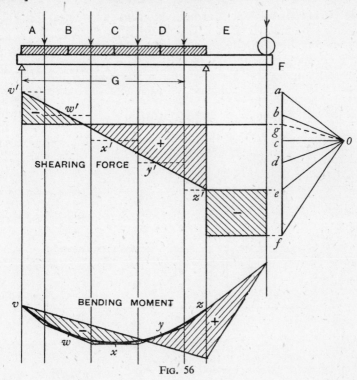

Fig. 56

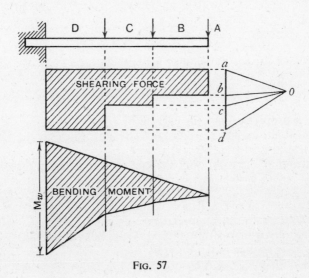

Fig. 57

42. Relation between Bending Moment and Shearing Force.
Consider a small length δx of a beam (Fig. 58) carrying a continuous distributed load w per unit of length, where w is not necessarily constant, but δx is sufficiently small to take w as constant over that length. Let F and F$+\delta$F be the shearing forces, M and M$+\delta$M the bending moments at either end of the length δx as shown in Fig. 58.

Equating upward and downward vertical forces on length δx

$$F+\delta F=F+w\delta x$$
$$\delta F=w\,.\,\delta x$$

and
$$\frac{dF}{dx}=w \qquad \qquad \text{. . . . .} \quad (1)$$

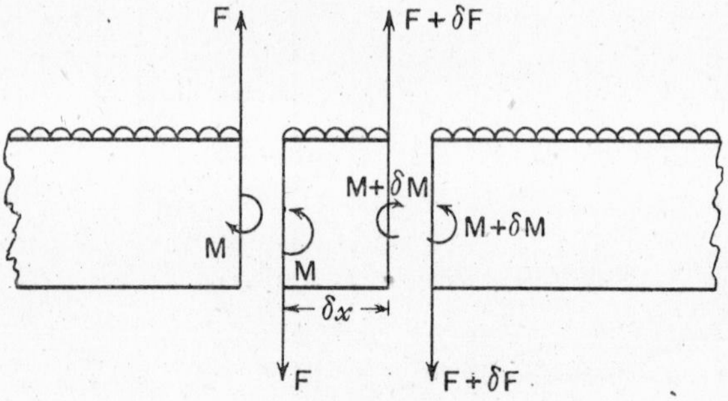

FIG. 58

i.e. the rate of change of shearing force (represented by the slope of the shearing-force curve) is numerically equal to the intensity of loading.

Or integrating between two sections $x-x_0$ apart

$$F-F_0 \text{ (the total change in shearing force)}=\int_{x_0}^{x} w\,.\,dx$$

or
$$F=F_0+\int_{x_0}^{x} w\,.\,dx$$

taking appropriate signs for each term.

These relations for $w=$constant, are illustrated in the shearing-force diagrams of Figs. 43, 49, and 52.

Equating moments of opposite kinds, of all external forces on the piece of length δx, about any point in the left-hand section

$$M+(F+\delta F)\delta x-w\,.\,\delta x \times \frac{\delta x}{2}=M+\delta M$$

$\delta M=F\delta x$, to the first order of small quantities

and
$$\frac{dM}{dx}=F \qquad \text{. . . . .} \quad (2)$$

i.e. the rate of change of bending moment is equal to the shearing force.

Hence, integrating, the total change of bending moment from x_0 to x is $\int_{x_0}^{x} F dx$, which is proportional to the area of the shearing-force diagram between the ordinates at x_0 and x. For example, this area is zero between the ends of the beam in Figs. 47 to 56 inclusive, there being as much area positive as negative.

The relation (2) indicates that the ordinates of the shearing-force diagram are proportional to the slopes or gradients of the bending-moment curve. Where the shearing force passes through a zero value and changes sign, the value of the bending moment is a (mathematical) maximum or minimum, a fact which often forms a convenient method of determining the greatest bending moment to which a beam is subjected, as in Figs. 49, 50, and 52. In Fig. 50, the section at which the shearing force is zero evidently divides the length c in the ratio R_1/R_2; or, using the expression given in Art. 40, F is zero at a distance

$$cb/l + a - c/2$$

from the left support. At this point the bending moment is a maximum, and its value is easily calculated.

Signs. It is to be noted that x being taken positive to the right and w positive downwards, F has been chosen as positive in (1) when its action is upwards to the left and downwards to the right of the section considered. Hence, taking account of sign forces being reckoned positive downwards, the shearing force is equal to the downward internal force exerted to the right of any section, or to the algebraic sum of the *upward external forces* to the *right* of the section, or to the algebraic sum of the *downward external forces* to the *left* of the section. Also M has been chosen as positive in (2) when its action is clockwise on the portion of the beam to the left of the section and contra-clockwise to the right of the section. Hence the bending moment is equal to the *clockwise moment* of the *external forces* to the right of a section or to the contra-clockwise moment of the external forces to the left of the section. It is evident that a positive bending moment will produce convexity upwards and a negative bending moment convexity downwards.

Concentrated Loads. In the case of loads concentrated (more or less) at fixed points along the span, the curve of shearing force (see Figs. 44, 46, 47, 48, 51, 53, 54, 55, 56, and 57) is discontinuous, and so also is the gradient of the bending-moment curve. Between the points of loading, however, the above relations hold, and the section at which the shearing-force curve crosses the base-line is a section having a maximum bending moment (see Figs. 47, 48, 51, 54, 55, and 56). A concentrated load in practice is, as stated in Art. 40, usually a load distributed (but not necessarily uniformly) over a very short distance, and the vertical lines shown in the shear diagrams at the loads should really be slightly inclined to the vertical, there being at any given section only *one* value of the shearing force.

Example 1. A beam 20 ft. long rests on supports at each end and carries a load of $\frac{1}{2}$ ton per foot run, and an additional load of $1\frac{1}{2}$ ton per foot run for 12 ft. from the left-hand end. Find the position

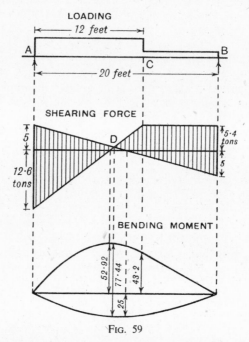

Fig. 59

and magnitude of the maximum bending moment, and draw the diagrams of shearing force and bending moment.

The loading is indicated at the top of Fig. 59 at ACB.

The reactions due to the $\frac{1}{2}$ ton per foot are 5 tons at A and B. For the $1\frac{1}{2}$ ton per foot load, the centre of gravity of which is 6 ft. from A

$$\text{(reaction at B)} \times 20 = 18 \times 6$$

$$\left. \begin{array}{l} \text{reaction at B} = 5\cdot4 \text{ tons} \\ \text{hence reaction at A} = 18 - 5\cdot4 = 12\cdot6 \text{ tons} \end{array} \right\} \text{due to second load}$$

The shearing-force diagrams for the two loads have been set off separately on opposite sides of a horizontal line, and the resultant diagram is shown shaded.

The bending moment is a maximum where the shear force is zero, as shown at D. The distance from the left support is perhaps most easily found from the fact that the shearing force at the left support is 17·6 tons, and falls off at the rate of 2 tons per foot run, and therefore reaches zero at a distance

$$\frac{17·6}{2} \text{ or } 8·8 \text{ ft. from the left-hand support}$$

The bending moment at 8·8 ft. is

$$17·6 \times 8·8 - 8·8 \times 2 \times \frac{8·8}{2} = 77·44 \text{ tons-ft.}$$

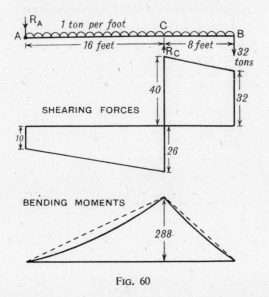

SHEARING FORCES

BENDING MOMENTS

Fig. 60

The bending-moment diagrams for the two loads have been drawn on opposite sides of the same base-line in Fig. 59, giving a combined diagram for the two, by vertical measurements between the boundaries.

For the ½ ton per foot load alone the maximum bending moment is at the middle of the span, and is

$$5 \times 10 - \tfrac{1}{2} \times 10 \times 5 = 25 \text{ tons-ft.}$$

For the 1½ ton per foot load alone the maximum occurs where the shearing force due to that load would be zero, a distance from A which is given by

$$12·6 \div 1·5 = 8·4 \text{ ft.}$$

The maximum ordinate of this curve is then

$$12{\cdot}6 \times 8{\cdot}4 - 8{\cdot}4 \times 1\tfrac{1}{2} \times \frac{8{\cdot}4}{2} = 52{\cdot}92 \text{ ton-ft.}$$

At C the ordinate of this curve is

$$5{\cdot}4 \times 8 = 43{\cdot}2 \text{ ton-ft.}$$

and to the right of C it varies directly as the distance from B—the curve being a straight line.

Example 2.   A horizontal beam, AB, 24 ft. long, is hinged at A, and rests on a support at C, 16 ft. from A, and carries a distributed load of 1 ton per foot run, and an additional load of 32 tons at B. Find the reactions, shearing forces, and bending moments.   If the load at B is reduced to 8 tons, what difference will it make?

Let R_C be the upward reaction at support C.

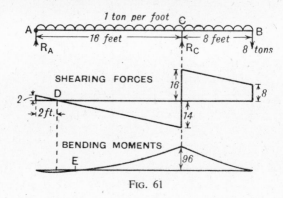

FIG. 61

Taking moments about A (Fig. 60)

$$16 \, . \, R_C = (32 \times 24) + (24 \times 12) = 1056$$
$$R_C = 66 \text{ tons}$$

If the upward reaction at $A = R_A$

$$R_A = 24 + 32 - 66 = -10 \text{ tons}$$

or 10 tons *downward*.

The shearing-force diagram is shown in Fig. 60.   From B, where the shearing force is 32 tons, it increases uniformly by 8 to C, where it is reduced by 66 tons to 26 of opposite sign.   From C to A the total change at a uniform rate is 16 tons, giving a value 10 at A.

The bending moment at C is $(32 \times 8) + (8 \times 4) = 288$ ton-ft.

This falls to zero at A and B, and does not reach a maximum value, in the mathematical sense, in either range.   The bending moment 4 ft. from B is

$$(32 \times 4) + (4 \times 2) = 136 \text{ ton-ft.}$$

Midway between A and C it is $(10 \times 8) + (8 \times 4) = 112$ ton-ft.
The full diagram is shown in Fig. 60.
Treating the problem with only 8 tons load at B

$$16R_C = (24 \times 8) + (12 \times 24) = 192 + 288 = 480$$
$$R_C = 30 \text{ tons}$$
$$\text{Total load} = 24 + 8 = 32 \text{ tons}$$
$$R_A = 2 \text{ tons } \textit{upward}$$

The diagrams of shearing force and bending moment are shown in Fig. 61. The shearing force at B is 8 tons, and increases by a further 8 tons to 16 at C, where it decreases by 30 tons to 14 of opposite sign. From C to A it changes by 16 to 2 tons at A, changing sign and passing through zero between C and A.

The section which has a (mathematical) maximum bending moment between A and C is that for which the shearing force is zero, and since the shear is 2 tons at A and falls off at 1 ton per foot run, the zero value will be, at a section D, 2 ft. from A.

The bending moment at C is $(8 \times 8) + (8 \times 4) = 96$ ton-ft.

At 4 ft. from B it is $(8 \times 4) + (4 \times 2) = 40$ ton-ft.

Between A and C, at a distance x from A, it is

$$x \times \tfrac{1}{2}x - 2x \text{ or } x(\tfrac{1}{2}x - 2)$$

which is zero, for $x = 4$ ft., *i.e.* 4 ft. from A, where a point of contraflexure E occurs. This distance might have been inferred otherwise, for it is evidently twice that of the point D from A.

Finally, $M_D = 2 \times 1 - 2 \times 2 = -2$ ton-ft.

Example 3.   A beam simply supported at each end has a span of 20 ft. The load is distributed and is at the rate of 1 ton per foot run at the left support, and 4 tons per foot run at the right-hand support, and varies uniformly from one rate to the other along the span. Find the position and amount of the maximum bending moment.

The load may conveniently be divided into a uniformly spread load of 1 ton per foot run, and a second varying from zero at the left to 3 tons per foot run at the right. The first will evidently cause a reaction of 10 tons at each support. The second load has an average intensity of 1·5 ton per foot run, or is 30 tons in all; its centre of gravity will be $\tfrac{2}{3}$ of the span from the left end, so that the right-hand reaction due to this load will be $\tfrac{2}{3}$ of 30 tons, or 20 tons, and the left-hand one will be 10 tons.

The total reactions are therefore 20 tons and 30 tons at the left- and right-hand ends respectively.

The load per foot at a distance x ft. from the left support is

$$1 + \tfrac{3}{20}x \text{ tons per ft.}$$

since it increases $\tfrac{3}{20}$ ton per ft. per foot.

The average over the length x ft. is

$$\tfrac{1}{2}(1+1+\tfrac{3}{20}x) \text{ or } 1+\tfrac{3}{40}x \text{ tons per ft.}$$

and the total load on x ft. is $x(1+\tfrac{3}{40}x)$.

The bending moment is a maximum when the shearing force is zero, *i.e.* at the section where the load carried to the left of it is equal to the left-hand reaction of 20 tons. For this point the shearing force

$$F=20-x(1+3x/40)=0$$
$$3x^2+40x-800=0$$
$$x=10.96 \text{ ft.}=10 \text{ ft. } 11.5 \text{ in.}$$

The bending moment at a distance x ft. from the support is

$$20x-x\times\frac{x}{2}-\frac{3x^2}{40}\times\tfrac{1}{3}x$$

and when $x=10.96$ ft., $M=219-60-33=126$ ton-ft.

The shearing-force and bending-moment curves may be plotted from the two above expressions for F and M.

Examples IV

1. A cantilever 12 ft. long carries loads of 3, 7, 4, and 6 tons at distances 0, 2, 5, and 8 ft. respectively from the free end. Find the bending moment and shearing force at the fixed end and at the middle section of the beam.

2. A cantilever 10 ft. long weighs 25 lb. per foot run, and carries a load of 200 lb. 3 ft. from the free end. Find the bending moment at the support, and draw the diagrams of shearing force and bending moment.

3. A beam rests on supports 16 ft. apart, and carries, including its own weight, a load of 2 tons (total) uniformly distributed over its whole length and concentrated loads of $1\frac{1}{2}$ ton and $\frac{1}{2}$ ton, 5 ft. and 9 ft. respectively from the left support. Find the bending moment 4 ft. from the left-hand support, and the position and magnitude of the maximum bending moment.

4. Where does the maximum bending moment occur in a beam of 24 ft. span carrying a load of 10 tons uniformly spread over its whole length, and a further load of 12 tons uniformly spread over 8 ft. to the right from a point 6 ft. from the left support? What is the amount of the maximum bending moment, and what is the bending moment at mid-span?

5. A beam of span l ft. carries a distributed load, which increases uniformly from zero at the left-hand support to a maximum w tons per ft. at the right-hand support. Find the distance from the left-hand support of the section which has a maximum bending moment and the amount of that bending moment. Obtain numerical values when $l=18$ ft. and $w=2$ tons per foot run.

6. A horizontal beam AB 30 ft. long is supported at A and at C 20 ft. from A, and carries a load of 7 tons at B and one of 10 tons midway between A and C. Draw the diagrams of bending moment and find the point of contraflexure.

7. Find the point of contraflexure in the previous example if there is an additional distributed load of $\frac{1}{4}$ ton per foot run from A to C.

8. A girder 40 ft. long is supported at 8 ft. from each end, and carries a load of 1 ton per foot run throughout its length. Find the bending moment

at the supports and at mid-span. Where are the points of contraflexure? Sketch the curve of bending moments.

9. A beam of length l carries an evenly distributed load and rests on two supports. How far from the ends must the supports be placed if the greatest bending moment to which the beam is subjected is to be as small as possible? Where are the points of contraflexure?

10. A beam 18 ft. long rests on two supports 10 ft. apart, overhanging the left-hand one by 5 ft. It carries a load of 5 tons at the left-hand end, 7 tons midway between the supports, and 3 tons at the right-hand end. Find the bending moment at the middle section of the beam and at mid-span, and find the points of contraflexure.

11. If the beam in the previous example carries an additional load of 1 ton per foot run between the supports, find the bending moment at mid-span and the positions of the points of contraflexure.

12. A horizontal beam 24 ft. long rests on supports 14 ft. apart overhanging the left one by 6 ft. It carries a load of 7 tons at the left-hand end and loads of 5, 4, 12, 9, and 4 tons at 4, 9, 13, 17, and 24 ft. respectively from the left-hand end. Draw the diagrams of shearing force and bending moment and measure from the latter the bending moments midway between the supports and at each support. State also the distances of the points of contraflexure from the nearest support.

13. A girder of span l is simply supported at its ends and is loaded at $n-1$ points spaced l/n apart, starting at distances l/n from either end. Each load is W/n (half this amount being transferred directly to each end support so as to cause no bending). Find the bending moment at the centre of the span (*a*) if n is even, (*b*) if n is odd, and sketch the bending moment diagrams.

14. Solve Problem No. 13 if there are n loads each W/n, spaced l/n apart, starting at distances $\frac{1}{2}l/n$ from either end.

CHAPTER V

STRESSES IN BEAMS

43. Theory of Elastic Bending. The relations existing between the straining action, the dimensions, the stresses, strains, elasticity, and curvature of a beam are, under certain simple assumptions, very easily established for the case of *simple bending*, *i.e.* flexure by pure couples applied to a beam without shearing force.

Most of the same simple relations may generally be used as close approximations in cases of flexure which are not " simple," but which are of far more common occurrence, the strains involved from the shearing force being negligible. In such cases, the justification of the " simple theory of bending " must be the agreement of its conclusions with direct bending experiments, and with those of more complex but more exact theory of elastic bending.

44. Simple Bending. A straight bar of homogeneous material subjected only to equal and opposite couples at its ends has a uniform bending moment throughout its length, and if there is no shearing force, is said to suffer simple bending. Such a straining action is illustrated in Fig. 51 for the beam between its two points of support. The beam will be supposed to be of the same cross-section throughout its length, and symmetrical about a central longitudinal plane, in and parallel to which the opposite straining couples act, and parallel to which bending takes place; the intersections of such a plane with transverse section of the beam will be principal axes (see Arts. 36 and 37) of the sections. In Fig. 62, central longitudinal sections before and after bending and a transverse section are shown, the cross-section being symmetrical about an axis YY.

It will be assumed that transverse plane sections of the beam remain plane and normal to longitudinal fibres after bending, which seems reasonable, since the straining action is the same on every section. The assumption is called Bernoulli's.

Consider any two transverse sections AB and CD very close together. After bending, as shown at A'B' and C'D', they will not be parallel, the layer of material at AC being extended to A'C', and that at BD being pressed to B'D'. The line EF represents the layer of material which is neither stretched nor shortened during bending. This surface EF suffers no longitudinal strain, and is called the *neutral surface*. Its line of intersection ZZ with a transverse section is called the *neutral axis* of that section.

Suppose the section A'B' and C'D' produced to intersect, at an angle θ (radians), in a line perpendicular to the figure and represented by O, and that the radius of curvature OE' of the neutral surface E'F' about O is R.   Let y be the height (E'G') of any layer (H'G') of material originally parallel to the neutral surface FE. Then

$$\frac{H'G'}{E'F'} = \frac{(R+y)\theta}{R\theta} = \frac{R+y}{R}$$

and the strain at the layer H'G' is

$$e = \frac{H'G' - HG}{HG} = \frac{H'G' - E'F'}{E'F'} = \frac{(R+y)\theta - R\theta}{R\theta} = \frac{y}{R}$$

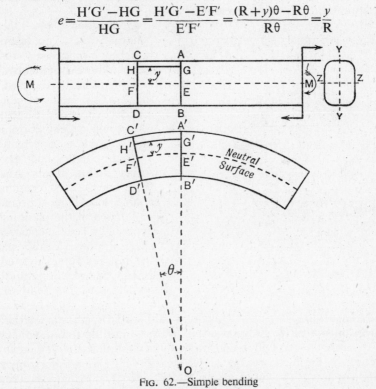

FIG. 62.—Simple bending

The longitudinal tensile-stress intensity p at a height y from the neutral surface, provided the limit of elasticity has not been exceeded, is therefore

$$p = E . e = E . y/R \quad . \quad . \quad . \quad . \quad . \quad (1)$$

where E is Young's Modulus, provided that the layers of material behave under longitudinal stress as if free and are not hindered by the surrounding material, which has not the same intensity of stress. The intensity of compressive stress will be the same at an equal distance y on the opposite side of the neutral surface, provided E is the same in compression as in tension.

The intensity of direct longitudinal stress p at every point in the cross-section is then proportional to its distance from the neutral axis; its value at unit distance (*i.e.* at $y=1$) is E/R, and it reaches a maximum value at the boundary furthest from the neutral surface. The variation in intensity of longitudinal stress is as shown in Fig. 63, where the arrow-heads denote the direction of the force exerted by the portion R on the portion L at the section AB. Since the stresses on opposite sides of the neutral surface are of opposite sign or kind, they may be represented as at *aeb*.

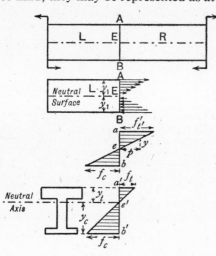

FIG. 63

45. Position of the Neutral Axis. The beam has been supposed subjected to pure couples only, and therefore the portion, say, to the left of the section AB (Figs. 62 and 63), being in equilibrium under one externally applied couple and the forces acting across AB, these forces must exert a couple balancing the external one in the plane of bending. The (vertical) shearing force being *nil*, the internal forces exerted across AB are wholly horizontal (or longitudinal), and since they form a couple the total tensile forces must balance the compressive ones, *i.e.* the algebraic sum of the horizontal internal forces must, like the external ones, be zero. Putting this statement in symbols, we can find the position of the neutral axis. The cross-section of the beam in Fig. 62 is symmetrical about a horizontal axis, but this is not necessary to the argument. Taking any other forms of cross-sections symmetrical about the plane of bending YY, as in Fig. 64, let δa or z . δy be an elementary strip of its area parallel to the neutral axis ZZ, z being the (variable) width of the section. Then, the total horizontal force being zero

$$\Sigma(p . \delta a) = 0 \text{ or } \Sigma(p . z . \delta y) = 0$$

and since by (1), Art. 44

$$p = Ey/R$$

$$E \Sigma(y \delta a)/R = 0 \text{ or } E \Sigma(yz \delta y)/R \quad . \quad . \quad . \quad (2)$$

the quantity $\Sigma(y \cdot \delta a)$ or $\Sigma(y \cdot z \cdot \delta y)$ represents the total moment of the area of section about the neutral axis, and this can only be zero if the axis passes through the centre of gravity or centroid of the section.

The use of the value Ey/R for p in all parts of the cross-section involves the assumption that the value of E is the same in compression as in tension, an assumption justified by experiment within the limits of elasticity.

Assumptions made in the Theory of Simple Bending. It may be well to recall the assumptions made in the above theory of " simple bending " under the conditions stated:

(1) That plane transverse sections remain plane and normal after bending.

(2) That the material is homogeneous, isotropic, and obeys Hooke's Law, and the limits of elasticity are not exceeded.

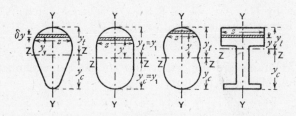

FIG. 64

(3) That every layer of material is free to expand or contract longitudinally and laterally under stress, as if separate from other layers. Otherwise, E in the relation (1), Art. 44 would not be Young's Modulus, but some modified elastic constant; but the relation would otherwise remain unaltered.

(4) That the modulus of direct elasticity has the same value in compression as for tensile strains.

46. Value of the Moment of Resistance. Having found the intensity of longitudinal stress Ey/R at any distance y from the neutral axis, and knowing that these longitudinal internal forces form a couple equal to the bending moment at every section, it remains to express the value of the couple, which is called the moment of resistance (see Art. 39), in terms of the dimensions of the cross-section, and the intensity of stress produced.

Using Fig. 64, as in the previous article, the elementary area of cross-section, at a distance y from the neutral axis, is δa, or $z \cdot \delta y$, the total stress on the elementary area is $p \cdot \delta a$ or $p \cdot z \cdot \delta y$, and the moment of this stress is $p \cdot y\delta a$ or $p \cdot z \cdot y \cdot \delta y$, and the total moment throughout the section is

$$M = \Sigma(p \cdot y \cdot \delta a) \text{ or } M = \Sigma(p \cdot z \cdot y \cdot \delta y) \quad . \quad . \quad (1)$$

and putting $p = Ey/R$ (Art. 44)   . . . .   (2)

$$M = E\,\Sigma(y^2\delta a)/R \text{ or } E\,\Sigma(zy^2\delta y)/R \quad . \ . \ . \ .\quad (3)$$

The sum $\Sigma(y^2\delta a)$, or $\Sigma(zy^2\delta y)$, represents the limiting value of the sum of the products of elements of area, multiplied by the squares of their distances from the axis, when the elements of area are diminished indefinitely, and is usually called the Moment of Inertia of the area of the section about the axis.   The values of the moments of inertia for various sections were dealt with in Arts. 34, 35, and 36.   If we denote the moment of inertia of the area of the section by I, so that

$$\Sigma(y^2\delta a) = \Sigma(zy^2\delta y) = I$$

the formula (3) becomes

$$M = EI/R \text{ or } M/I = E/R \quad . \ . \ . \ . \ .\quad (4)$$

and since by (1), Art. 44, $E/R = p/y$ (the stress intensity at unit distance from the neutral axis), we have

$$p/y = M/I = E/R \ . \ . \ . \ . \ . \ .\quad (5)$$

These relations are important and should be remembered.   If we put this relation in the form

$$p = My/I \text{ or } Ey/R$$

we have the intensity of longitudinal stress at a distance y from the neutral axis, in terms of the bending moment and dimensions (I) of cross-section, or in terms of the radius of curvature and an elastic constant for the material.   The extreme values of p, tensile and compressive, occur at the layers of material most remote from the neutral axis.   Thus, in Figs. 63 and 64, if the extreme layers on the tension and compression sides are denoted by y_t and y_c respectively, f and f_c being the extreme intensities of tensile and compressive stress respectively

$$\frac{p}{y} = \frac{f_t}{y_t} = \frac{f_c}{y_c} = \frac{M}{I} = \frac{E}{R}$$

or $f_t = M\,.\,\dfrac{y_t}{I} \qquad f_c = M\,.\,\dfrac{y_c}{I}$

or $M = f_t\,.\,\dfrac{I}{y_t} = f_c\,.\,\dfrac{I}{y_c} \qquad . \ . \ . \ . \ .\quad (6)$

The variation of intensity of stress for an unsymmetrical section is shown in Fig. 63 at $a'e'b'$.

For sections which are symmetrical about the neutral axis, the distances y and y_c will be equal, being each half the depth of the section. If we denote the half depth by y_1, and the equal intensities of extreme or skin stress by f_1, so that

$$M = f_1 I/y_1$$

the quantity I/y_1 is called the modulus of section (see Art. 49), and is usually denoted by the letter Z, so that

$$M = fZ \text{ or } f = \frac{M}{Z} \quad . . . . . . (7)$$

the moment of resistance (M) being proportional to the greatest intensity of stress reached and to the modulus of section.

In the less usual case of unsymmetrical sections, the modulus of section would have the two values

$$\frac{I}{y_t} \text{ and } \frac{I}{y_c}$$

which may be denoted by Z_t and Z_c, so that the relation (6) becomes

$$M = f_t Z_t = f_c Z_c \quad . . . . . . (8)$$

47. Ordinary Bending. The case of *simple bending*, dealt with in the previous articles, refers only to bending where shearing force is absent, but such instances are not usual, and generally bending action is accompanied by shearing force, which produces a (vertical) shear stress across transverse sections of the beam (see Figs. 43 to 50, etc.). In such cases the forces across any section at which the shearing force is not zero have not only to balance a couple, but also the shearing force at the section, and, therefore, at points in the cross-section there will be tangential as well as normal longitudinal stresses. The approximate distribution of this tangential stress is dealt with in Art. 53, and the deflection due to shearing in Art. 97. When the shearing stresses are not zero, the longitudinal stress at any point in the cross-section is evidently not the principal stress (Arts. 14 and 54) at that point, and the strain is not quite of the simple character assumed in Art. 44 and Fig. 62, and there is then no reason to assume that plane sections remain plane.

But for most practical cases the theory of " Simple Bending " (Arts. 44, 45, and 46) is quite sufficient, and gives results which enable the engineer to design beams and structures, and calculate their stresses and strains with a considerable degree of approximation. It may be noticed that in many cases of continuous loading the *greatest* bending moment occurs as a mathematical maximum at the sections for which the shearing force is zero (Art. 33, and Figs. 47 to 54), and for which the conditions correspond with those for *simple* flexure; in numerous cases where the section of the beam is uniform throughout its length, the maximum longitudinal stress occurs at the section of maximum bending moment; the usefulness of the *simple* theory in such a case is evident.   Further, it often happens that where the shearing force is considerable the bending moment is small, and in such cases the intensity of shear stress can be calculated sufficiently nearly by the method of Art. 53.

In this book the usual engineer's practice of using the simple beam theory will be followed, a few modifications in the strains and stresses in certain cases will be mentioned.

48. Summary of the Simple Theory of Bending.   At any transverse section of a horizontal beam carrying vertical loads, from the three usual conditions of equilibrium, we have:

(1) The total vertical components of stresses across a vertical section are together equal to the algebraic sum of the external forces to either side of the section, *i.e.* to the shearing force F.

(2) The algebraic total horizontal force is zero.

(3) The total moment of resistance of the horizontal forces across the section is equal to the algebraic sum of the moments of the external forces to either side of the section, *i.e.* to the bending moment M.

If plane sections remain plane, longitudinal strain is proportional to the distance from the neutral axis, e being equal to y/R; hence, longitudinal stress intensity at any point in a cross-section is proportional to the same distance, or

$$p \propto y \text{ and } p = Ey/R$$

Summing the moments of longitudinal stress

$$M = EI/R = pI/y$$

or

$$p/y = M/I = E/R = f_1/y_1$$

where f_1 and y_1 are the intensity of skin stress, and the vertical distance from the neutral axis to the outer boundary of the section respectively.

In applying these relations to numerical examples, it should be remembered that the units must be consistent; as cross-sections are usually stated in inches, and stresses in pounds or tons per square inch, it is well to take the bending moment, or moment of resistance, in lb.-inches or ton-inches and the radius of curvature R in *inches*.

Example 1.   To what radius of curvature may a steel beam of symmetrical section, 12 in. deep, be bent without the skin stress exceeding 5 tons per sq. in.?   (E = 13,500 tons per sq. in.)

Since $E/R = f_1/y_1$ $\therefore$ $R = Ey_1/f_1$

y_1 being the half-depth, which is 6 in.

Hence $R = \dfrac{13,500 \times 6}{5} = 16,200$ in., or 1,350 ft.

Example 2.   If the elastic limit is not exceeded, find the stress induced in a strip of spring steel, $\frac{1}{20}$ in. thick, by bending it round a drum 2·5 ft. diameter?   (E = 13,500 tons per sq. in.)

$$f_1 = Ey_1/R$$

The greatest value of y is $\frac{1}{2} \times \frac{1}{20} = \frac{1}{40}$ in.   The radius being 15 in.

$$f_1 = \frac{13,500 \times \frac{1}{40}}{15} = 22\cdot5 \text{ tons per sq. in.}$$

Example 3.   The moment of inertia of a symmetrical section (see B.S.B. 30, Table I in Appendix) being 2,654 (in.)[4] and its depth 24 in., find the longest span over which, when simply supported, a beam could carry a uniformly distributed load of 1·2 ton per foot run, without the stress exceeding 7·5 tons per sq. in.

If l = span in inches, the load per inch run being 1·2/12, or 0·1 ton, the maximum bending moment which occurs at mid-span is

$$M = \tfrac{1}{8} \times 0\cdot1 \times l^2 \text{ (see Fig. 49)}$$

And since $M = f_1 \cdot I/y_1$, and y_1 the half depth is 12 in.

$$\tfrac{1}{8} \times \tfrac{1}{10} \times l^2 = 7\cdot5 \times \tfrac{2654}{12}$$

$$l^2 = \frac{80 \times 7\cdot5 \times 2654}{12} = 132,700$$

$$l = 364 \text{ in., or 30 ft. 4 in.}$$

49. Modulus of Section.   The value of the moment of resistance of a beam is found (Art. 46) by multiplying the extreme value of the intensity of stress by the *modulus of section* (Z) which is the moment of inertia I of the section about the neutral axis divided by the distance to the furthest point in the section from the neutral axis. In the case of sections which are not symmetrical about the neutral axis there will generally be two moduli of section, and two unequal extreme values of stress intensity (tensile and compressive) corresponding to two unequal distances from the neutral axis to the extreme points of the section perimeter.   The numerical value of the modulus of section will normally be expressed in (in.)[3], the dimensions of sections being in inches.

The Table on pp. 94–95 gives the values of the modulus of section, etc., for sections frequently employed in beams of various kinds.

The I, T, angle, channel, and Z sections are actually rolled with rounded corners, as shown in Fig. 36 and elsewhere, and the values in the table are those for square-cornered, parallel-limbed sections; they may be applied to give approximate results if mean values of thicknesses are taken.   Such sections have been standardised by the British Standards Institution, and tabulated values of their properties with standard dimensions are given in the Appendix.   The methods applicable to making calculations of the properties of such sections have been dealt with in Arts. 34 and 35.

Section	Distance of centroid from outer edge	Moment of Inertia I	Modulus of section Z
	$\dfrac{d}{2}$ $\dfrac{b}{2}$	$I_{XX} = \frac{1}{12}bd^3$ $I_{YY} = \frac{1}{12}db^3$	$\frac{1}{6}bd^2$ $\frac{1}{6}db^2$
	$\dfrac{D}{2}$ $\dfrac{B}{2}$	$I_{XX} = \frac{1}{12}(BD^3 - bd^3)$ $I_{YY} = \frac{1}{12}(DB^3 - db^3)$	$\frac{1}{6D}(BD^3 - bd^3)$ $\frac{1}{6B}(DB^3 - db^3)$
	$\dfrac{D}{2}$	$I_{XX} = I_{YY} = \frac{\pi}{64}D^4$	$\frac{\pi}{32}D^3$
	$\dfrac{D}{2}$	$I_{XX} = I_{YY} = \frac{\pi}{64}(D^4 - d^4)$	$\frac{\pi}{32} \cdot \frac{D^4 - d^4}{D}$
	$\dfrac{D}{2}$ $\dfrac{B}{2}$	$I_{XX} = \frac{1}{12}(BD^3 - bd^3)$ $I_{YY} = \frac{1}{12}(2TB^2 - dt^3)$	$\frac{1}{6D}(BD^3 - bd^3)$ $\frac{1}{6B}(2TB^3 + dt^3)$

Section	Distances to extreme fibres	Moments of inertia	Section moduli
	$y_1=\dfrac{tD^2+(B-t)T^2}{2\{tD+(B-t)T\}}$ $\dfrac{B}{2}$	$I_{xx}=\tfrac{1}{3}\{By_1^3+ty_2^3-(B-t)(y_1-T)^3\}$ $I_{YY}=\tfrac{1}{12}\{TB^3+(D-T)t^3\}$	$\dfrac{I_{xx}}{y_1}$ and $\dfrac{I_{xx}}{y_2}$ $\dfrac{2I_{YY}}{B}$
	$y_2=\dfrac{D^2+(B-t)t}{2(D+B-t)}$ $y_1=D-y_2$	$I_{xx}=\tfrac{1}{3}\{ty_1^3+By_2^3-(B-t)(y_2-t)^3\}$	Unsymmetrical bending. See Art. 52.
	$y_2=\dfrac{2D^2T+bt^2}{2(2DT+bt)}$ $y_1=D-y_2$ $\dfrac{B}{2}$	$I_{xx}=\tfrac{1}{3}\{2Ty_1^3+By_2^3-b(y_2-t)^3\}$ $I_{YY}=\tfrac{1}{12}\{DB^3-(D-t)b^3\}$	$\dfrac{I_{xx}}{y_1}$ and $\dfrac{I_{xx}}{y_2}$ $\dfrac{1}{6B}\{DB^3-(D-t)b^3\}$
	$\dfrac{D}{2}$ $B-\dfrac{t}{2}$	$I_{xx}=\tfrac{1}{12}\{BD^3-(B-t)d^3\}$ $I_{YY}=\tfrac{1}{12}\{T(2B-t)^3+dt^3\}$	$\dfrac{1}{6D}\{BD^3-(B-t)d^3\}$ $\dfrac{2I_{YY}}{2B-t}$

A caution is required in applying the tabulated values to such a section as an angle if used *alone*; the principal axes (Art. 36) are not those shown in the table, and XX is not the neutral axis for loading in the plane YY, nor are the distances y_1 and y_2 shown in the table the extreme distances from the neutral axis. The bending is unsymmetrical and the subject is treated in Art. 52.

In choosing a section suitable for carrying a given load from such tables as are given in the Appendix, it is necessary to select one which shall restrict the bending stress to a safe limit, but it is also often necessary to limit the deflection. This point is dealt with in Chapter VII.

Modulus Figures. The first derived area, obtained as in Fig. 38 when drawn for the neutral axis instead of for an external line XX, is sometimes called a modulus figure, for the modulus of section is equal to the sum of the products of these areas on either side of the neutral axis and the distance of their respective centroids from the neutral axis GG, or to either area multiplied by the distance apart of their centroids. The modulus of section is of course equal to the product of the total second derived areas and the extreme distance, $d/2$, of the perimeter of the section from the neutral axis GG.

The " centres " of the parallel longitudinal stresses on either side of the neutral axis will evidently be at the centre of area or centroid (or centre of gravity) of the modulus figure. The longitudinal forces across a transverse section are statically equivalent to uniformly distributed stresses of the actual extreme intensity acting on the whole of the modulus figure or to the total of the tensile forces acting at the centroid of the modulus figure on the tension side, together with the (equal) total thrust at the centroid of the modulus figure (which is the centre of pressure) on the compression side.

In comparing algebraic and graphical methods, it is useful to remember that the expression $\int yzdy/y_1$ represents the area of the modulus figure between the lines corresponding to the limits of integration and parallel to the neutral axis, y_1 or $d/2$ being the half depth.

Example 1. A timber beam of rectangular section is to be simply supported at the ends and carry a load of $1\frac{1}{2}$ ton at the middle of a 16-ft. span. If the maximum stress is not to exceed $\frac{3}{4}$ ton per sq. in. and the depth is to be twice the breadth, determine suitable dimensions.

The reactions at the ends are each $\frac{3}{4}$ ton, and the bending moment at the centre is

$$\tfrac{3}{4} \times 8 \times 12 = 72 \text{ ton-in.}$$

The modulus of section (Z) is given by

$$\tfrac{3}{4} \times Z = 72 \text{ ton-in.} \quad Z = 96 \text{ (in.)}^3$$

and if
$$b = \tfrac{1}{2}d$$
$$\tfrac{1}{6}bd^2 = \tfrac{1}{12}d^3 = 96 \text{ (in.)}^3$$
$$d = 3\sqrt[3]{1152} = 10\cdot5 \text{ in. nearly}$$
$$b = 5\cdot25 \text{ in.}$$

Example 2. Compare the weights of two beams of the same material and of equal strength, one being of circular section and solid and the other being of hollow circular section, the internal diameter being $\frac{3}{4}$ of the external.

The resistance to bending being proportional to the modulus of section, if D is the diameter of the hollow beam and d that of the solid one

$$\frac{\pi}{32}\left\{ \frac{D^4 - (\tfrac{3}{4}D)^4}{D} \right\} = \frac{\pi}{32}d^3$$

$$(1 - \tfrac{81}{256})D^3 = d^3$$

$$\frac{D}{d} = 3\sqrt[3]{\tfrac{256}{175}} = 1\cdot135$$

The weights are

$$\frac{\text{solid}}{\text{hollow}} = \frac{d^2}{D^2 - (\tfrac{3}{4}D)^2} = \frac{16}{7} \times \left(\frac{d}{D}\right)^2 = \frac{16}{7} \times \frac{1}{(1\cdot135)^2} = 1\cdot77$$

50. Common Steel Beam Sections. Such geometrical figures as rectangles and circles, although they often represent the cross-section of parts of machines and structures subjected to bending action, do not form the sections for the resistance of flexure with the greatest economy of material, for there is a considerable body of material situated about the neutral surface which carries a very small portion of the stress. The most economical section for a constant straining action will evidently be one in which practically the whole of the material reaches the maximum intensity of stress. For example, to resist economically a bending moment which produces a longitudinal direct stress the intensity of which at any point of a cross-section is proportional to the distance from the neutral axis, much of the area of cross-section should be placed at a maximum distance from the neutral axis. This suggests the **I** section, which is the commonest form of steel beam, whether rolled in a single piece (see Fig. 36) or built up by riveting together component parts. In such a section most of the area is situated at nearly the full half depth, so that, neglecting the thin vertical web, the moment of inertia $\Sigma(y^2\delta A)$, approximates to

$$\text{(area of two flanges)} \times (d/2)^2$$

or the radius of gyration approximates to $d/2$, and the modulus of

E

section, Z, which is the moment of inertia divided by $d/2$, approximates to

$$\text{(area of two flanges)} \times d/2$$

or $\qquad Z = 2bt \times d/2 = b \cdot t \cdot d$ approximately

where t is the mean thickness of the flange, generally measured in a rolled section at $\frac{1}{4}$ the breadth from either end. These approximations are often very close to the true values, for they exaggerate by taking the flange area wholly at $d/2$ from the neutral axis XX and under-estimate by neglecting the vertical web.

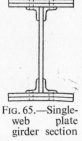

FIG. 65.—Single-web plate girder section

Plate Girder Sections. The plate girder consisting of horizontal plate flanges united to a vertical plate web by angles (see Fig. 65) is of such great importance in structural steel work that it is now considered more fully. Either the depth or the flange area is often varied so that the moment of inertia of every cross-section is roughly proportional to the greatest bending moment to which it is subjected as explained in Chapter XVIII, Arts. 176 and 177. Various approximations are in use for estimating the modulus of section and moment of resistance of such a section. For a fairly deep girder perhaps the best approximation is

$$\text{Modulus of section } Z = A \times d$$

where $A =$ net area of one flange, including plates and angles, but no part of web, and $d =$ depth to outside of angles. Sometimes d is taken between the centroids of the flanges and sometimes A includes $\frac{1}{6}$ or $\frac{1}{8}$ of the web. It is usual in calculating A to subtract from the plate and angle sectional areas the area of rivet holes which may lie even approximately in the same plane of cross-section, and a hole $\frac{1}{16}$ in. or $\frac{1}{8}$ in. larger than the nominal rivet diameter is so deducted. It is frequently desirable for purposes of design to work from a simple approximation and then to check, and if necessary adjust the resulting dimensions by a more exact calculation.

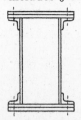

FIG. 66.— Double - web or box plate girder section

Box Plate Girder. This form possesses considerable lateral flexural stiffness, and is in considerable use (see Fig. 66).

Compound Girder Section. Built-up sections consisting of plate flanges added to rolled **I** and channel sections are shown in Figs. 67, 68, and 69. The moment of inertia of the (net) plate area about the neutral axis (see theorem I, Art. 34) is added to the known moment of inertia of the rolled sections, and the sum divided by the half-depth gives the modulus of section.   An approximate correction for rivet holes in the rolled sections may easily be made (see Example 3, page 101).

Example 1.   A box plate girder has a span of 36 feet, and its depth over the angles is 42 in.   It has to carry a load equivalent to 3·5 tons per foot run, with a maximum bending stress of 6 tons per sq. in.   The two $\frac{3}{8}$-in. webs are connected to the flanges by angles $4 \times 4 \times \frac{1}{2}$ in. (see B.S.E.A. 11, Table V, Appendix).   Calculate

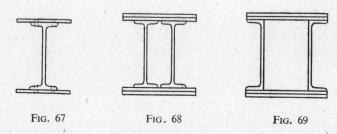

FIG. 67   FIG. 68   FIG. 69

the total flange area required at the centre of the span, allowing for two $\frac{7}{8}$-in. rivets in each flange; and if the total thickness is $1\frac{1}{8}$ in., what width of plate will be required?

Central bending moment $=\frac{1}{8}Wl=\dfrac{3\cdot5\times36\times36\times12}{8}=6{,}804$ ton-in.

Modulus of section (Z) required $=\frac{6804}{6}=1{,}134$ (in.)^3
 Let B=width required.
Gross area of two angles $=2\times3\cdot749=7\cdot5$ sq. in.
Net area of two angles, allowing, say, two holes $1\times\frac{1}{2}$ in. each$=$
  $7\cdot5-2=5\cdot5$ sq. in.
Then taking 1-in. holes, net area of flange $(A)=(B-2)1\frac{1}{8}+5\cdot5=$
  $1\cdot125B+3\cdot25$ sq. in.
 Approximately

$$Z=(1\cdot125B+3\cdot25)\times42=1{,}134 \text{ (in.)}^3$$
$$B=21\cdot1 \text{ in.}$$

Checking this approximation by the more exact method, we find
$$I=\tfrac{1}{12}\{(B-2)(44\cdot25^3-42^3)+6\cdot75(42^3-41^3)+1\cdot75(41^3-34^3)$$
$$+\tfrac{3}{4}\times34^3\}-1\cdot75\times2\times19^2$$

the last term being an approximation for the horizontal holes through the angles and web.   This gives $I=1046(B-2)+8430$ (in.)^4.
 Now, the required value of I is $22\frac{1}{8}\times Z=1134\times22\frac{1}{8}=25{,}090$

hence $B-2=\frac{16660}{1046}=15\cdot9$
$$B=17\cdot9 \text{ in.}$$

which shows the approximation to be somewhat far on the safe side in this case.   If $\frac{1}{8}$ of the web area were included in the flange area A, we should have had

$$1{\cdot}125B + 3{\cdot}25 + \tfrac{1}{8} \times 42 \times \tfrac{3}{4} = \tfrac{1134}{42} = 27$$
$$1{\cdot}125B = 19{\cdot}8 \qquad\qquad B = 17{\cdot}6 \text{ in.}$$

which more nearly agrees with the more exact calculation.

   Example 2.   A single web plate girder has a span of 40 ft., and its depth over the angle is 42 in.   It has to carry a uniformly distributed load of 89 tons with a maximum bending stress of 6 tons per sq. in.   What thickness of plate 14 in. wide is required in the flanges if the angles are $6 \times 6 \times \frac{1}{2}$ in. and the web $\frac{1}{2}$ in. thick? (Allow for 2 rivet holes say 1 in. diameter in each flange and angle.)

$$\text{Central bending moment} = \frac{89 \times 40 \times 12}{8} = 5{,}340 \text{ ton-in.}$$

$$\text{Modulus of section required} = \tfrac{5340}{6} = 890 \text{ (in.)}^3$$

$$\text{Approximate flange area required} = \tfrac{890}{42} = 21{\cdot}2 \text{ sq. in.}$$

and if $t =$ thickness of flats, allowing say two 1-in. holes and four in the angles

$$12t + 2(11{\cdot}5 - 2)\tfrac{1}{2} = 12t + 9{\cdot}5 = 21{\cdot}2$$

hence $12t = 11{\cdot}7 \qquad\qquad t = 0{\cdot}975,$ say 1 in.

Checking by the more exact method, neglecting horizontal holes through angles and web

$$I = \tfrac{1}{12}\{12(44^3 - 42^3) + 10{\cdot}5(42^3 - 41^3) + 1{\cdot}5(41^3 - 30^3) + \tfrac{1}{2} \times 30^3\}$$
$$= 21{,}982 \text{ (in.)}^4$$

Allow for neglected rivet holes, say $2 \times 1{\cdot}5 \times 1 \times 17{\cdot}5^2 = 919.$

$$\text{Net value of } I = 21{,}063 \text{ (in.)}^4$$
$$\text{Value of } Z = \tfrac{21063}{22} = 957 \text{ (in.)}^3$$
$$\text{Excess} = 957 - 890 = 67 \text{ (in.)}^3$$

corresponding to an area $\tfrac{67}{42} = 1{\cdot}5$ sq. in. say, or on flats of 12 in. net width $\frac{1}{8}$ in. thickness.   Hence $\frac{7}{8}$ in. thickness would be sufficient.

   This example illustrates the use of the approximate formula, for to have to find t directly by the more exact rule would have involved the unknown quantity in the third power, *i.e.* a cubic equation in t.

   The limitations of an empirical rule for different proportions may also be noted, for had $\frac{1}{8}$ of the web area been added to the flange area the simple rule would have given too thin a plate to the flange. This would also have been so, but in a smaller degree, if the effective depth had been taken as that between the centres of gravity of the flanges, which in this case is less than the 42-in. depth over the angles. The simpler rules cannot be correct for all cases including large and small angles and varying proportions of depth to flange area, but are nevertheless useful, and may easily be framed so as always to err on the side of safety.

Example 3. A compound girder (as in Fig. 68) is to be made by riveting six $\frac{1}{2}$-in. flats on to the flanges of two 15×6 in. **I** beams (B.S.B. 26, Table I, Appendix). What width of plate will be necessary if the girder has to carry a total uniformly distributed load of 74 tons over a span of 20 ft. with a maximum stress of 5 tons per sq. in.? ($\frac{7}{8}$-in. rivets.)

Referring to column 9, Table I, for the given sections, $I=628 \cdot 9$.

$$\text{Central bending moment} = \frac{74 \times 20 \times 12}{8} = 2,220 \text{ ton-in.}$$

$$Z \text{ required} = \tfrac{2220}{5} = 444 \text{ (in.)}^3$$
$$I \text{ required} = 444 \times \tfrac{18}{2} = 3,996 \text{ (in.)}^4$$
$$I \text{ for two rolled sections} = 2 \times 628 \cdot 9 = 1,258$$

$$\text{difference} = 2,738 \text{ (in.)}^4$$

Add for holes in **I** beam flanges, say $4 \times 0 \cdot 8 \times 7 \cdot 5^2 = 180$
$$I \text{ required for flats} = 2,918 \text{ (in.)}^4$$

If B=required width

$$\frac{B-2}{12}(18^3 - 15^3) = 204 \cdot 75(B-2) = 2,918$$

$$B = 2 + \frac{2,918}{204 \cdot 75} = 16 \cdot 2 \text{ in.}$$

Example 4. A girder is made up of two channels (as in Fig. 69) and two flats. The channels are 15×4 in. (see B.S.C. 27, Table II, Appendix). The flats are 14×$\frac{1}{2}$ in. What load may the girder carry at its centre over a 14-ft. span (neglecting its own weight) without the extreme bending stress exceeding 5 tons per sq. in.? Allow for two $\frac{7}{8}$-in. rivets in each flange section. Referring to line 1, column 10 of Table II, Appendix, $I=377$ per channel = 754 (in.)^4 for the two.

$$I = 754 + \tfrac{12}{12}(16^3 - 15^3) - 4 \times 1 \times 0 \cdot 63 \times 7 \cdot 5^2$$
$$= 754 + 721 - 142 = 1,333 \text{ (in.)}^4$$
$$Z = \tfrac{1333}{8} = 167 \text{ (in.)}^3$$

Moment of resistance $= 167 \times 5 = 835$ ton-in.

If W=central load in tons
$$\tfrac{1}{4} \times W \times 14 \times 12 = 835 \qquad \text{or, } W = 19 \cdot 9 \text{ tons.}$$

Example 5. The girder in Example 2, Art. 40, is to carry a live load of 52·5 tons uniformly distributed, and a dead load of 23·17 tons similarly applied at cross-girders. If the depth of girder over the angles is 4 ft., width of flanges 21 in., and angles $4 \times 4 \times \frac{1}{2}$ in., find the necessary flange plates at the central section, using the dynamic method (Art. 31) with a dead-load stress of 6·5 tons per sq. in.

Using the result of Example 2, Art. 40, in direct proportion, bending moment due to live load at centre (and at all points between b and b') is

$$271 \cdot 2 \times \frac{52 \cdot 5}{56 \cdot 5} = 252 \text{ ton-ft.}$$

and due to dead load

$$271 \cdot 2 \times \frac{23 \cdot 17}{56 \cdot 5} = 111 \text{ ton-ft.}$$

From Art. 31 (7) we may find the working stress for the total bending moment $252 + 111$, or from (1) we may use 6·5 tons per sq. in. with a bending moment $111 + (2 \times 252) = 615$ ton-ft. Selecting the latter method, we have

$$\text{Modulus of section (Z) required} = \frac{615 \times 12}{6 \cdot 5} = 1,135 \text{ (in.)}^3$$

Net area of flange required $= \frac{1135}{48} = 23 \cdot 64$ sq. in.

The two angles (B.S.E.A. 11, Table V, Appendix), less four rivet holes $\frac{15}{16}$ in. diameter, give

$$7 \cdot 498 - 1 \cdot 875 = 5 \cdot 623 \text{ sq. in.}$$

The plates therefore require $23 \cdot 64 - 5 \cdot 62 = 18 \cdot 02$ sq. in.
Net width of flange allowing four rivets $\frac{7}{8}$ in. $= 21 - 4 \times \frac{15}{16} = 17 \cdot 25$ in.

$$\text{Thickness required} = \frac{18 \cdot 02}{17 \cdot 25} = 1 \cdot 05, \text{ say } 1\frac{1}{16} \text{ in.}$$

which may be made up by $\frac{9}{16}$-in. main plates (next to angles) and $\frac{1}{2}$ in. outer plates.

51. Cast Iron Girders. Cast iron is generally five or six times as strong in compression as in tension, but a symmetrical section would in bending get approximately equal extreme intensities of tension and compression so long as the material does not greatly deviate from proportionality between stress and strain (see Art. 46). Cast iron has no considerable plastic yield, so that the distribution of stress beyond the elastic limit will not be greatly different from that within it. Hence a cast-iron beam of symmetrical section would fail by tension due to bending, and it would appear reasonable to so proportion the section that the greatest intensity of compressive stress would be about five times that of the tensile stress. This could be done by making the section of such a form that the distance of its centroid from the extreme compression layers is five times that from the extreme tension layers. This, in a flanged or irregular **I** section, would involve a large tension flange, and a much smaller compression flange: so great a difference as that indicated above involves serious initial stresses due to the quicker cooling of the small compression flange compared to that of the larger tension flange, and experience shows that distances of the compression and tension edges to the centroid in the ratio of about 2 or 3 to 1 (see Fig. 70) give the most economical results, the tension flange being made wide in order to avoid great thickness, which would involve relatively slow cooling. The moment of inertia of such a section as that shown in Fig. 70 may be estimated by division into rectangles (see Art. 34), or as in Art. 35.

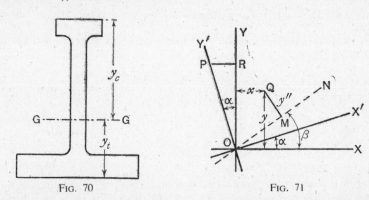

FIG. 70   FIG. 71

52. Unsymmetrical Bending. In considering simple bending (Art. 44) it was assumed that the beam had a cross-section symmetrical about the axis through its centroid and in the plane of bending. The planes of bending and that of the external bending couple will be parallel if the axis of cross-section in the plane of the external moment is a principal axis (Art. 36). If this condition is not fulfilled, let OY', Fig. 71, be the plane of the external bending moment (shown by its trace on the section which is in the plane of the figure) inclined at an angle α to the principal axis OY, or let the bending couple M be in a plane perpendicular to OX'. If the couple M, represented by OP, say, be resolved into components represented by OR and RP about the principal axes OX and OY, these components will be

$$M \cos \alpha \text{ and } -M \sin \alpha \text{ respectively.}$$

The intensity of bending stress and the strain everywhere on the section can then be found by taking the algebraic sum of the effects produced by the component bending moments about the two principal axes. Thus, the unit stress at any point Q the co-ordinates of which referred to the principal axes OX and OY are x, y will be from (5), Art. 46

$$p = \frac{y \cdot M \cos \alpha}{I_x} - \frac{xM \sin \alpha}{I_y} \quad \ldots \quad \ldots \quad (1)$$

where I_x and I_y are the principal moments of inertia of the beam section about OX and OY respectively. For a point the co-ordinates of which are $-x$, y:

$$p = \frac{y \cdot M \cos \alpha}{I_x} + \frac{xM \sin \alpha}{I_y} \quad \ldots \quad \ldots \quad (2)$$

For points on the neutral axis, putting $p=0$ in (1)

$$y = x \frac{I_x}{I_y} \tan \alpha \quad \ldots \quad \ldots \quad (3)$$

which is a straight line ON through the centroid of the section inclined to OX at an angle β, so that

$$y = x \tan \beta \quad \ldots \quad \ldots \quad (4)$$

and

$$\tan \beta = \frac{I_x}{I_y} \tan \alpha \quad \ldots \quad \ldots \quad (5)$$

It may be noted that the relation (5), which may be written

$$\tan \beta = \frac{k_x^2}{k_y^2} \tan \alpha \quad \ldots \quad \ldots \quad (6)$$

is that between the slopes of conjugate axes of the momental ellipse (Art. 36), the principal semi-axes of which are the radii of gyration k_y about OY in the direction OX and k_x about OX in the direction OY. Consequently, if the momental ellipse is drawn the direction of the neutral axis ON (Fig. 71) may be found by drawing the diameter conjugate to OY′, which is easily accomplished by joining O to the point of bisection of a chord parallel to OY′.

To find the maximum stress in a given section resulting from a given bending moment in any given plane we first calculate the direction of the principal axes and values of the principal moments of inertia as described in Art. 36. Then calculate the direction of the neutral axis from (5) and draw it on the given section and find by inspection the point in the section furthest from the neutral axis and apply equation (1). The intensity of stress might also be stated in terms of y'', the distance from the neutral axis (Fig. 71) for

$$QM = y'' = y \cos \beta - x \sin \beta \quad \ldots \quad (7)$$

and from (5)

$$y \frac{\cos \alpha}{I_x} \div x \frac{\sin \alpha}{I_y} = \frac{y \cos \beta}{x \sin \beta} \quad \ldots \quad \ldots \quad (8)$$

hence

$$\left(\frac{y \cos \alpha}{I_x} - \frac{x \sin \alpha}{I_y} \right) = y'' \cdot \frac{\sin \alpha}{\sin \beta} \cdot \frac{1}{I_y} \quad \ldots \quad (9)$$

and substituting this in (1) and then for $\sin \alpha$ from (8)

$$p = \frac{M \cdot y''}{I_y} \cdot \frac{\sin \alpha}{\sin \beta} = \frac{M \cdot y''}{\sqrt{(I_x{}^2 \cos^2 \beta + I_y{}^2 \beta \sin^2 \beta)}} \quad . \quad (10)$$

The maximum value f_1, tensile or compressive of p, can be found by writing the maximum value of y'' on the tensile or compressive side of the neutral axis.

Another form of the result. The value of p might also be stated directly in terms of the moment of inertia of the section about the neutral axis ON from the general formula (5) Art. 46, for the component bending moment about ON resulting from the bending moment M about OX' is M $\cos (\beta - \alpha)$, hence

$$p = \frac{y'' \cdot M \cos (\beta - \alpha)}{I_N} \quad . \quad . \quad . \quad . \quad (11)$$

where I_N is the moment of inertia about the neutral axes ON, which may be found graphically as described in Art. 36 from the momental ellipse or from (2) Art. 36, writing β for α, which gives from (11) above

$$p = \frac{y'' M \cos (\beta - \alpha)}{I_x \cos^2 \beta + I_y \sin^2 \beta} \quad . \quad . \quad . \quad . \quad (12)$$

a formula easily reduced to the form (10) by the relation (5) between β and α.

The choice of one or other method of dealing with a case of unsymmetrical bending will depend partly on the type of section. Thus in rectangular sections a corner will always be a point of maximum stress, and formula (2) may be applied directly. In other sections it may be more convenient to draw the neutral axis to determine for which point in the section the unit stress is a maximum.

Example 1. Calculate the allowable bending moment on a British Standard unequal angle $6 \times 3\frac{1}{2} \times \frac{3}{8}$ in., carrying a load on the short edge with the long edge vertically downwards, if the stress is limited to 6 tons per sq. in. and the area, principal moments of inertia, and position of the centroid of the section are given.

The particulars from the standard tables are given in Fig. 72, and as follows. Tan XOX'$=\tan \alpha = 0.344$, hence $\alpha = 19°$; $I_x = 13.908$ (in.)^4; $I_y = 1.963$ (in.)^4; area $= 3.424$ sq. in., hence $k_x = 2.015$ in., $k_y = 0.757$ in.

These may be obtained approximately from Table IV (B.S.U.A. 20) in the Appendix. I_x and I_y are obtained by substituting the values given in columns 9 and 10 in equations (9) and (10) of Art. 36.

E*

The position of the neutral axis may be found by (5)

$$\tan \beta = \frac{13 \cdot 908}{1 \cdot 963} \times 0 \cdot 344 = 2 \cdot 437 = \tan 67 \cdot 7°$$

The neutral axis ON is set off on the left of Fig. 72, and by inspection it is evident that P is the furthest point in the section from ON; its distance from OX is 3·84 in. $= -y$, and its distance from OY is 0·83 in. $= +x$, hence from (1) putting $p = 6$ tons per sq. in.

$$6 = -\frac{3 \cdot 84 M \cos 19°}{13 \cdot 908} - \frac{0 \cdot 83 M \sin 19°}{1 \cdot 963} = -M(0 \cdot 261 + 0 \cdot 1375)$$

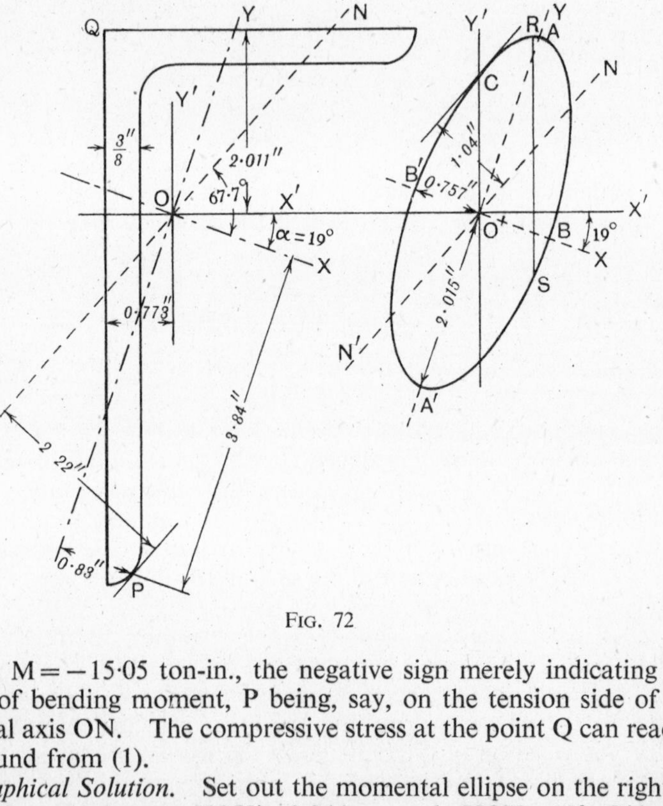

FIG. 72

hence $M = -15 \cdot 05$ ton-in., the negative sign merely indicating the kind of bending moment, P being, say, on the tension side of the neutral axis ON. The compressive stress at the point Q can readily be found from (1).

Graphical Solution. Set out the momental ellipse on the right of Fig. 72, such that $\tan XOX' = 0 \cdot 344$ or angle $XOX = 19°$, $O'A = k_x = 2 \cdot 015$ in., $O'B = 0 \cdot 757$ in. (on any scale). Draw any chord RS parallel to OY', and bisect it in V; draw NO'N' the neutral axis through O' and V. Set out this neutral axis ON on the section, as shown to the left of the figure, and look out the distance from it of the most remote point P which measures 2·22 in. Through C draw the tangent to the ellipse parallel to ON, and measure its perpendicular distance from NO'N' which is 1·04 in.   Then the moment of inertia of the section about ON is

$$(1·04)^2 \times 3·424 = 3·70 \text{ (in.)}^4$$

Then measuring the angle NOX' as 48·7° and applying (11)

$$6 = 2·22 \times M \times \cos 48·7° \div 3·70 = 0·396M$$

and M = 15·15 ton-in., confirming approximately the previous result.

Example 2.   A British Standard equal angle section measures $4\frac{1}{2} \times 4\frac{1}{2} \times \frac{3}{8}$ in. and is rounded to a radius of 0·275 in. at its outer ends or toes.   Its area of section is 3·236 sq. in., and the distance of its centroid from either outside edge is 1·244 in.   Its principal moments of inertia are 9·768 (in.)^4 and 2·514 (in.)^4, the former being about an axis through the intersection of the outer edges.   A beam of this section, and simply supported at its ends, has one side of the angle horizontal and carries on it a vertical load of $\frac{1}{2}$ ton midway between the supports, which are 5 ft. 4 in. apart.   Find the greatest tensile and compressive stresses in the material.

In this case from the symmetry α = 45°, and the given values may be obtained from Table V (B.S.E.A. 12) in the Appendix.   One principal moment of inertia is found from columns numbered 3 and 10, and the other then follows from equation (1), Art. 36.

If β is the angle which the neutral axis makes with the principal axis passing through the intersection of the edges, from (5)

$$\tan \beta = \frac{9·768}{2·514} = 3·885$$

Hence from tables   β = 75·6°

The neutral axis is inclined to the loaded edge at an angle

$$75·6° - 45° = 30·6°$$

The most distant point in tension may be measured from a drawing to scale or calculated; it occurs on the curved toe, as in Fig. 72. The co-ordinates of the centre of the curve referred to axes parallel to the angle edges are known, and hence the distance from the neutral axis is easily calculated about an oblique neutral axis; the distance to the curved toe exceeds the distance to the centre by the radius 0·275 in.   Either method gives $y'' = 2·26$ in.

About the neutral axis

$$I_N = 9·768 \cos^2 75·6° + 2·514 \sin^2 75·6 = 2·96 \text{ (in.)}^4$$

which may be checked by drawing the momental ellipse.   The bending moment M midway between the supports is

$$\tfrac{1}{4} \times \tfrac{1}{2} \times 64 = 8 \text{ ton-in.}$$

Hence from (11)

$$\text{Maximum tensile stress} = \frac{2\cdot26 \times 8 \times \cos 30\cdot6°}{29\cdot6} = 5\cdot26 \text{ tons per sq. in.}$$

Also from the neutral axis to the intersection of the outer edges where the compressive stress is greatest measured 1·70 in. (viz. $1\cdot244 \times \sqrt{2} \times \sin 75\cdot6°$). Hence, similarly, the maximum compressive stress is

$$\frac{1\cdot70 \times 8 \times \sin 75\cdot6°}{2\cdot96} = 3\cdot97 \text{ tons per sq. in.}$$

53. Distribution of Shear Stress in Beams. In considering the equilibrium of a portion of a horizontal beam in Art. 39 it was found convenient to resolve the forces across a vertical plane of

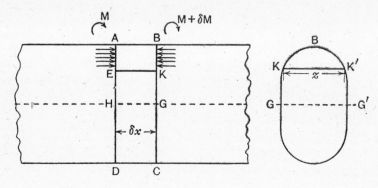

Fig. 73

section into horizontal and vertical components. The variation in intensity of the horizontal or longitudinal components of stress has been investigated in Arts. 44, 45, and 46, and we now proceed to examine the distribution of the tangential or shearing stress over the vertical cross-section. The vertical shear stress at any point in the cross-section is accompanied by a horizontal shear stress of equal intensity (see Art. 8), the tendency of the former being to produce a vertical relative sliding on either side of the section, and the tendency of the latter being to produce relative horizontal sliding on either side of a horizontal or longitudinal section. The mean intensity of shear stress at a height y from the neutral axis for a beam may be found approximately as follows:

In Fig. 73 let AD and BC be two cross-sections of the beam distant EK or δx apart measured along the neutral surface GH; let the variable breadth at any height y from GH be denoted by z; let the bending moment at the section AD be M, and at BC be $M + \delta M$.

Then, at any height y from the neutral surface, the longitudinal or horizontal direct stress intensity on the section AD is

$$p = \frac{My}{I} \text{ (Art. 44)}$$

where I is the moment of inertia of the cross-section.   Consider the equilibrium of a portion ABKE between the two sections.   On any element of cross-section, of area zdy, the longitudinal thrust at AE is

$$p \cdot z \cdot dy \text{ or } \frac{My}{I} \cdot z \cdot dy$$

But at BK, on the element at the same height, the thrust is

$$\frac{(M + \delta M)y}{I} \cdot z \cdot dy$$

The thrusts on any element at BK being in excess of those at AE by the difference in the above quantities, viz.

$$\frac{\delta M}{I} \cdot y \cdot z \cdot dy$$

the total excess thrust on the area BK over that at AE will be

$$\int_y^{y_1} \frac{\delta M}{I} \cdot y \cdot z \cdot dy \text{ or } \frac{\delta M}{I} \int_y^{y_1} y \cdot z \cdot dy$$

where y_1 is the extreme value of y, *i.e.* HA, and z represents the variable breadth of section between EK and AB.   Since the net horizontal force on the portion ABKE is zero, the excess thrust at BK must be balanced by the horizontal shearing force on the surface EK; hence, if q represents the mean intensity of shear stress at a height y (neglecting any change in q in the length δx), the shearing stress on EK is $q \cdot z \cdot dx$, and

$$q \cdot z \cdot \delta x = \frac{\delta M}{I} \int_y^{y_1} y \cdot z \cdot dy$$

hence

$$q = \frac{\delta M}{\delta x} \cdot \frac{1}{I \cdot z} \int_y^{y_1} y \cdot z \cdot dy = \frac{F}{I \cdot z} \int_v^{y_1} y \cdot z \cdot dy \quad . \quad (1)^{[1]}$$

---

[1] If the beam is of varying cross-section, instead of the relation $\delta p = \frac{y}{I}\delta x$ we get from $p = \frac{M \cdot y}{I}$ the relation $\frac{dp}{dx} = \left(I \cdot y\frac{dM}{dx} - My\frac{dI}{dx}\right) \div I^2$, and hence (I) becomes $q = \frac{FI - M\frac{dI}{dx}}{zI^2}\int_y^{y_1} yzdy$, which may easily be found if I is a simple function of x and z of y.

where $F = dM/(dx)$ (Art. 42 (2)) = total shearing force on the cross-section of the beam. Actually the intensity of shear stress at a height y varies somewhat laterally, being greatest at the inside.[1]

In the expression $\dfrac{F}{Iz} \displaystyle\int_y^{y_1} y \cdot z \cdot dy$, the symbol z outside the sign of integration, and the symbol y, which is the lower limit of integration, refer to a particular pair of values corresponding to the height above HG for which q is stated, while in the product $y \cdot z$ within the sign of integration each letter refers to a variable over the range y_1 to y, or A to E (Fig. 73). It may be noted that the quantity

$$\int_y^{y_1} y \cdot z \cdot dy$$

is the moment of the area KBK' about the neutral axis GG', which is equal to the area multiplied by the distance of its centre of gravity or centroid from GG', or the area of so much of a modulus figure (see Art. 49) as lies above KK', multiplied by the height HA or y_i so that

$$q = \frac{F}{I \times KK} \times (\text{area KBK}') \times (\text{distance of its centroid from GG}') \quad (2)$$

or

$$q = \frac{F \times y_1}{I \times KK} \times (\text{area of modulus figure between B and KK}') \quad . \quad (3)$$

which give graphical methods of calculating the intensity of shear stress at any part of the cross-section.

It is obvious from the above expressions (1) or (3) that q is a maximum when the lower range of integration is zero (*i.e.* at the neutral surface), and that it is zero at either edge ($y = y_1$ or $y = -y_1$). If the graphical method with modulus figures be used, the areas on opposite sides of the neutral axis should be reckoned of opposite signs.

Rectangular Section (Fig. 74). Width b, depth d. At any height y from the neutral axis, since z is constant and equal to b

$$q = \frac{F}{Iz} \int_y^{\frac{d}{2}} y \cdot z \cdot dy = \frac{F}{I} \int_y^{\frac{d}{2}} y \cdot dy = \frac{12F}{bd^3} \left(\tfrac{1}{2} y^2\right)_y^{\frac{d}{2}} = \frac{6F}{bd^3} \left\{ \left(\frac{d}{2}\right)^2 - y^2 \right\} \quad . \quad (4)$$

---

[1] For a simple idea of the errors involved in (1), see a paper on " Faults in the Theory of Flexure," by H. S. Prichard, in *Trans. Am. Soc. Civil Engineers*, vol. lxxv, pp. 905–908. This also gives a good idea of the distortion of initially plane cross-sections and simple approximate estimates of the corresponding deviation of stresses from those obtained by the theory of *simple* bending.

If the various values of q are shown by ordinates on d as a base-line as in Fig. 74, the curve is a parabola, and when $y=0$

$$q=\tfrac{3}{2}\frac{F}{bd} \qquad \ldots \quad \ldots \quad \ldots \quad (5)$$

The mean intensity of shear stress is $F\div bd$; the greatest intensity is thus 50 per cent. greater than the mean.

Rectangular **I** *Section with Sharp Corners* (Fig. 75). In the flange, at a height y from the neutral axis

$$q=\frac{F}{IB}\int_{y}^{\frac{D}{2}}y\,.\,B\,.\,dy=\frac{F}{2I}\left(\frac{D^2}{4}-y^2\right)$$

and when $y=\dfrac{d}{2}$ at the inner edge of the flange

$$q=\frac{F}{I}\,.\,\frac{D^2-d^2}{8}$$

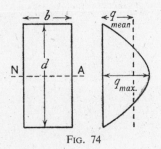

Fig. 74

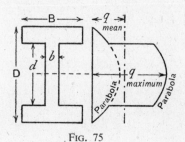

Fig. 75

In the web $q=\dfrac{F}{Ib}\displaystyle\int_{y}^{\frac{D}{2}}y\,.\,z\,.\,dy$, where $z=B$ over part of the range

and $z=b$ over the remainder (the web). The integral may conveniently be split up thus

$$q=\frac{F}{Ib}\left(B\int_{\frac{d}{2}}^{\frac{D}{2}}y\,dy+b\int_{y}^{\frac{d}{2}}y\,dy\right)=\frac{F}{I}\left(\frac{B}{b}\,.\,\frac{D^2-d^2}{8}+\frac{d^2}{8}-\frac{y^2}{2}\right)$$

When $y=\dfrac{d}{2}$, just inside the web

$$q=\frac{F}{I}\,.\,\frac{D^2-d^2}{8}\times\frac{B}{b}\quad\text{or}\quad\frac{B}{b}\text{ times that just inside the flange.}$$

And when $y=0$

$$q=\frac{F}{I}\left\{\left(\frac{B}{b}\,.\,\frac{D^2-d^2}{8}\right)+\frac{d^2}{8}\right\}$$

The curves in Fig. 75 show the variation in intensity at different heights, both parts being parabolic.

The mean shear-stress intensity anywhere might conveniently be stated from (2) above; thus, in the web at level y

$q = \dfrac{F}{Ib} \times$ (moment of section area above level y about neutral axis)

e.g. the maximum stress, when $y=0$ is (taking moments of parts)

$$q = \frac{F}{Ib}\left\{ B\left(\frac{D}{2}-\frac{d}{2}\right)\left(\frac{D}{2}+\frac{d}{2}\right)\tfrac{1}{2} + b \cdot \frac{d}{2} \cdot \frac{d}{4} \right\}$$

which agrees with the previous result.

Built-up Girder Section. Fig. 76 shows the intensity of shear

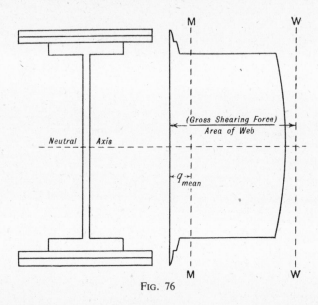

FIG. 76

stress at different parts of the section of a built-up girder. The stress intensities have been calculated, as in Fig. 75, for the **I** section, but the integration requires splitting into three parts, as there are three different widths of section.

Approximation. The usual approximation in calculating the intensity of shear stress in the web is to assume that the web carries the whole vertical shearing force with uniform distribution. Fig. 76 shows that the intensity in the web does not change greatly. The intensity of shear stress according to the above approximation is shown by the dotted line WW, which represents the quotient when the whole shearing force on the section is divided by the area of the section of the web. Judging by Fig. 76, this simple approximation to the mean shear stress in the web for such a section is a good one. The line MM shows the mean intensity of shearing stress, *i.e.* the whole shearing force divided by the whole area of section; this is evidently no guide to the intensity of shear stress in the web, which everywhere greatly exceeds it.

Example 1.   A beam of **I** section, 20 in. deep and $7\frac{1}{2}$ in. wide, has flanges 1 in. thick and web 0·6 in. thick, and carries a shearing force of 40 tons. Find what proportion of the total shearing force is carried by the web and the maximum intensity of stress in it, given $I = 1,647$ inch units. ˙

At any height y from the neutral axis of the section the mean intensity of shearing stress in the web section is

$$q = \frac{40}{1,647 \times 0.6}\left(7.5\int_9^{10} y\,dy + 0.6\int_y^9 y\,dy\right)$$

$$= \frac{40}{1,647 \times 0.6 \times 2}\{(7.5 \times 19) + 0.6(81 - y^2)\}$$

$$= 3.87 - 0.01213 y^2 \qquad .$$

The stress on a strip of web of depth dy situated at a height y from the neutral axis is

$$q \times 0.6 \times dy$$

and the whole shearing force carried by the web section is

$$0.6\int_{-9}^9 q\,dy = 0.6\int_{-9}^9 (3.87 - 0.01213 y^2)dy$$

$$= 1.2(34.83 - 0.00404 \times 729) = 38.26 \text{ tons}$$

or 95·6 per cent. of the whole.

The maximum value of q (when $y = 0$) is evidently 3·87 tons per sq. in.

Testing the usual approximation of taking all the shearing stress as spread uniformly over the web section

$$\frac{40}{0.6 \times 18} = 3.70 \text{ tons per sq. in.}$$

which is intermediate between the mean value of q in the web, viz.

$$\frac{38.26}{0.6 \times 18} \text{ or } 3.54 \text{ tons per sq. in.}$$

and the maximum intensity 3·87 tons per sq. in.

54. Principal Stresses in Beams.   The intensity of direct stress due to bending, as found in Arts. 44 to 48, and the intensity of horizontal and vertical shear stress, as found in Art. 53, are only, as indicated in Arts. 39, 47, and 48, component stresses in conveniently chosen directions. Within the limitations for which the simple theory of bending is approximately correct (Art. 47), the methods of Arts. 18 and 19 may be applied to find the direction and magnitude of the principal stresses, the greater of which, at any point, has the same sign as the longitudinal direct component there, and makes the smaller (acute) angle with it. Fig. 77 shows the directions of the principal stresses at numerous points in a simply supported beam of rectangular cross-section carrying a uniformly distributed load, as well as the intensities of the component horizontal direct and vertical shear stresses on certain vertical sections, and the intensities of the two opposite principal stresses on one section. The distribution of horizontal direct component stress over a given section is as shown in Fig. 63, and the values of its

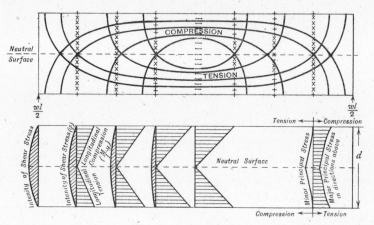

Fig. 77.—Curves of principal stress and magnitudes of principal and component stresses

intensity for a given height vary along the length of the beam, as shown in the bending-moment diagram, Fig. 49. The distribution of tangential or shear stress across vertical sections is as in Fig. 74, and the intensities at a given height vary along the length of the beam, as in the shearing-force diagram in Fig. 49. For the purpose of illustration, the intensity of vertical shearing stress has been made excessive for a rectangular section by taking a span, *l*, only four times the depth of the beam. The maximum intensity of vertical (and horizontal) shear stress, which occurs at the middle of the end section, is, by Fig. 49 and Art. 53,

$$q = \tfrac{3}{2} \cdot \tfrac{1}{2}wl/bd = \tfrac{3}{4}wl/bd$$

where *w* is the load per inch run on the span *l*.

The maximum intensity of horizontal direct stress, which occurs at the top and bottom of the middle section, is, by Fig. 49 and Art. 46 (7)

$$f = \tfrac{1}{8}wl^2 \div \tfrac{1}{6}bd^2 = \tfrac{3}{4}\frac{wl^2}{bd^2}$$

hence

$$\frac{\text{maximum } q}{\text{maximum } f} = \frac{d}{l} = \tfrac{1}{4}$$

The *magnitudes* of the principal stresses for all points in the one cross-section $\tfrac{1}{8}l$ from the right-hand support have been calculated from the formula (5A) in Art. 18 and are shown in Fig. 77. The two principal stresses are of opposite sign, and the larger one has the same sign as the direct horizontal stress, *i.e.* it is compressive above the neutral axis and tensile below it. The diagram does not represent the direction of the principal stresses at every point in this section.

For such a large ratio of depth to span as $\tfrac{1}{4}$, the simple theory of bending could not be expected to give exact results, but with larger spans the shearing stresses would evidently become more insignificant for a rectangular section. The magnitudes shown in Fig. 77 must be looked upon as giving an idea of the variation in intensity rather than an exact measure of it.

Curves of Principal Stress.   Lines of principal stress are shown in Fig. 77 on a longitudinal section of the beam. They are such that the tangent and normal at any point give the direction of the two principal stresses at that point. There are two systems of curves which cut one another at right angles: both cross the centre line at 45° (see Arts. 8 and 15). The intensity of stress along each curve is greatest when it is parallel to the length of the beam and diminishes along the curve to zero, where it cuts a face of the beam at right angles. For larger and more usual ratios of length to depth, for rectangular beams the curves would be much flatter, the vertical shearing stress being smaller in proportion about mid-span.

Maximum Shearing Stress.   At any point in the beam the intensity of shear stress is a maximum on two planes at right angles, inclined at 45° to the principal planes, and of the amount shown in Art. 18 (6A), viz. half the algebraic difference of the principal stress intensities, which is, in the case shown in Fig. 77, half the arithmetic sum of the magnitudes of the principal stress intensities taken with like sign.

Principal Stress in **I** *Sections.*   In **I** sections, whether rolled in one piece or built up of plates and angles, it has been shown (Art. 50) that the web area is of little importance in resisting the longitudinal direct stresses due to bending, or, in other words, it contributes little to the modulus of section; and in Art. 53 (Fig. 76) it was shown that the flanges carry little of the shear stress. It should be noticed, however, that in the web near the flange the *intensity* of longitudinal direct stress is not far below the maximum on the section at the outer layers while the intensity of vertical shear stress is not much lower than the maximum, which occurs at the neutral plane. The principal stress in such a position may consequently be of higher intensity than either of the maximum component stresses (see example below). Only low shear-stress intensities are allowed in cross-sections of the webs of **I** section girders; it should be remembered that the shear stresses involve tensile and compressive principal stresses, which may place the thin web in somewhat the condition of a long strut. See also remarks in Art. 24 on the strength of material acted on by principal stresses of opposite kinds, which is always the case in the webs of **I** sections, where, in the notation of Art. 18,

$$p = \frac{p_1}{2} \pm \sqrt{\left\{ \left(\frac{p_1}{2} \right)^2 + q^2 \right\}}$$

The stresses in and design of plate girder webs is further dealt with in Art. 178.

Example. A beam of **I** section, 20 in. deep and $7\frac{1}{2}$ in. wide, has flanges 1 in. thick, and web 0·6 in. thick. It is exposed at a particular section to a shearing force of 40 tons, and a bending moment of 800 ton-in. Find the principal stresses (*a*) at the outside edges; (*b*) at the middle of the cross-section; (*c*) $1\frac{1}{2}$ in. from the outer edges.

The moment of inertia about the neutral axis is

$$\tfrac{1}{12}(7 \cdot 5 \times 20^3 - 6 \cdot 9 \times 18^3) = 1,647 \text{ (in.)}^4$$

(*a*) At the outside edges $f = \dfrac{800 \times 10}{1,647} = 4 \cdot 86$ tons per sq. in. pure

tension or compression, the other principal stress being zero.

(*b*) At the middle of the cross-section the intensity of vertical and horizontal sheer stress is

$$q = \frac{40}{1,647 \times 0 \cdot 6} \left(7 \cdot 5 \int_9^{10} y\,dy + 0 \cdot 6 \int_0^9 y\,dy \right) = 3 \cdot 87 \text{ tons per sq. in.}$$

as in example at end of Art. 53.

This being a pure shear, the equal principal stresses of tension and compression are each inclined 45° to the section, and are of intensity 3·87 tons per sq. in.

(*c*) Intensity of direct stress perpendicular to the section is

$$p_1 = \frac{800 \times 8 \cdot 5}{1,647} = 4 \cdot 13 \text{ tons per sq. in.}$$

The intensity of vertical shear stress on the section is

$$q = \frac{40}{1,647 \times 0.6}\left(7.5\int_{9}^{10} y\,dy + 0.6\int_{8.5}^{9} y\,dy\right)$$

$$= \frac{40}{1,647 \times 2 \times 0.6}\{(7.5 \times 19) + 0.6(81 - 72.25)\}$$

$$q = 2.99 \text{ tons per sq. in.}$$

Hence, the principal stresses are, by Art. 18

$$p = \frac{p_1}{2} \pm \sqrt{\left[\left\{\left(\frac{p_1}{2}\right)^2 + q^2\right\}\right]} = 2.065 \pm 3.63$$

which are 5·695 and −1·565 tons per sq. in., and the major principal stress is inclined at an angle

$$\tan^{-1}\frac{2.99}{5.695} \text{ or } 27° \; 40' \text{ (see Art. 18 (2A))}$$

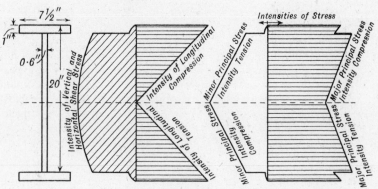

FIG. 78.—Magnitudes of component and principal stress intensities in I-section beam

to the corresponding direct stress along the flange, or 62° 20′ to the cross-section.

This illustrates the fact that just within the flange of an **I** section, carrying a considerable bending moment and shearing force, the intensity of the principal stress (5·695) may exceed that at the extreme outside layers of the section.

The intensities of principal stress in the web, calculated as above, are shown in Fig. 78, which shows that the material bears principal stresses the greater of which is nowhere greatly less than the maximum. In accepting such conclusions as to principal stresses, the limitations of the simple theory of bending should be borne in mind: these results can only be looked upon as approximations giving a useful idea of the magnitude of the stresses.

55. Flitched Beam.   An example of a composite form of construction now of interest rather than importance is a wooden beam reinforced by a steel plate.   A symmetrical form is shown in section in Fig. 79 and consists of two wooden joists with a steel plate between them, the three parts being fastened together by bolts so that the composite member deforms as if it were a single piece.   In the flexure of a straight beam the measure of deformation is the degree of curvature (1/R), which must be the same for the wood and the steel plate.   Unit curvature (that of 1-in. radius) is very large, but since, in the symbols of Art. 46, $M = EI/R$, the bending moment per unit of curvature is EI, or in terms of (4) Art. 46, we may say

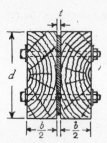

Flitched Beam
FIG. 79

that the elastic resistance (moment) developed per unit of deformation (curvature) in either the wood or the steel is EI.   Thus from (5) of Art. 21, if the bending moment sustained by the beam is μ, the moment of resistance exerted by the steel will be

$$M_S = \mu \cdot E_S I_S / (E_S I_S + E_W I_W) . \quad . \quad . \quad (1)$$

where E_S = Young's Modulus for steel, E_W that for wood and I_S = second moment of area of steel section = $td^3/12$, and I_W = second moment of area of timber section = $bd^3/12$.

Similarly the moment of resistance exerted by the wood will be

$$M_W = \mu \cdot E_W I_W / (E_S I_S + E_W I_W) \quad . \quad . \quad . \quad (2)$$

Or to put the matter fundamentally, since the curvature of all three components of the beam is 1/R by Art. 46

$$1/R = M_S / (E_S I_S) = M_W / (E_W I_W) \quad . \quad . \quad . \quad (3)$$

and

$$M_S + M_W = \mu \quad . \quad . \quad . \quad . \quad . \quad (4)$$

From (3) and (4) equations (1) and (2) follow by simple algebra. The maximum intensity of bending stress from (6) and (7) of Art. 46 are

In the steel $f_1 = M_S d / 2I = 6 M_S / (td^2) \quad . \quad . \quad . \quad . \quad (5)$

In the wood $f_1 = M_W d / 2I_W = 6 M_W / (bd^2) \quad . \quad . \quad . \quad (6)$

And if the depth of section is not the same for the wood and steel portions the appropriate value of d can be inserted.

56. Reinforced Concrete Beams.   Cement and concrete are well adapted to stand high compressive stress, but little or no tension. They can be used to withstand bending by *reinforcement* with metal to take the tension involved, the metal being by various means held fast in the concrete.   Often it is held only by the adhesion which is available when the concrete sets from the fluid to the solid state and grips the fairly smooth metal surface. The usual assumption is that the metal carries the whole of the tension, and the concrete the whole of the compression. In the case of a compound beam of this kind, the neutral axis will not generally pass through the centroid of the area of cross-section because of the unequal values of the direct modulus of elasticity (E) of the two materials (see Art. 45). It may be found approximately by equating the total compressive force or thrust in the cement to the total pull in the metal. As the cross-section of metal usually occupies a very little of the depth, it is usual to take the area of metal as concentrated at the depth of its centre and subject to a uniform intensity of stress equal to that at its centre.

The following simple theory of flexure of ferro-concrete beams must be looked upon as conventional and approximate only, since the tension in the concrete is neglected; and further, in a heterogeneous substance like concrete, the proportionality between stress and strain will not hold accurately with usual working loads. More elaborate and less simple empirical rules have been devised and tested by experiment, but the following methods of calculation are the most widely recognised.

Suppose a ferro-concrete beam has the sectional dimensions shown at (*a*) in Fig. 80; assume that, as in Arts. 44 and 48, the strain due to bending is proportional to the distance from the neutral axis and to the direct modulus of elasticity of the material. Let *n* be the depth of the neutral axis from the compression edge of the section, f_c the (maximum) intensity of compressive stress at that edge, and f_t the intensity of tensile stress in the metal reinforcement, this being practically uniform. Let E_c be the direct modulus of elasticity of the concrete in compression, and E_s that of the steel in tension.

Then f_c/E_c is the proportional strain in the concrete at the compression edge (see Art. 44), and f_t/E_s is the proportional strain in the metal.

The distances from the neutral axis at which these strains occur are *n* and $(d-n)$ respectively, and since the strains are to be assumed proportional to the distance from the neutral axis (Arts. 44 and 48)

$$\frac{f_c}{E_c} \div \frac{f_t}{E_s} = \frac{n}{d-n}$$

or

$$\frac{f_c}{f_t} = \frac{n}{d-n} \cdot \frac{E_c}{E_s} \quad \cdot \quad \cdot \quad \cdot \quad \cdot \quad (1)$$

Modular Ratio. The ratios of E_s to E_c for given materials are known; for steel and concrete the ratio is usually from 12 to 15; it is called the *modular ratio* and is given the symbol *m*. The variation in *m* as used in calculations arises from the variations in E_c.

This modulus has been the subject of much research and discussion. It varies with the mixture in the concrete which in no case follows a proportional law of strain to stress. Thus the value of m is more or less conventional.

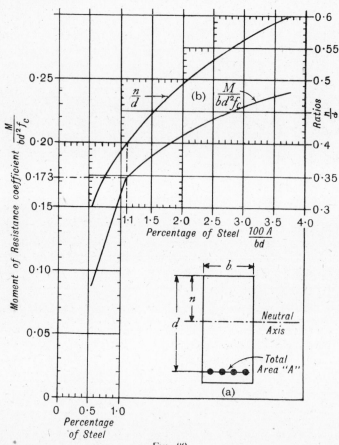

FIG. 80

The total thrust is

(mean intensity of compressive stress) × (compression area)

$$= \tfrac{1}{2}f_c \cdot nb \quad . \quad . \quad . \quad . \quad . \quad . \quad (2)$$

The total tension, neglecting any in the concrete, is

$$f_t \times (\text{area of section of reinforcement}) = f_t \cdot A \quad . \quad (3)$$

And since the total thrust equals the total pull (the two together forming the couple which is the moment of resistance)

$$\tfrac{1}{2}f_c \cdot nb = f_t \cdot A \text{ or } f_c/f_t = 2A/nb \quad . \quad . \quad . \quad (4)$$

and therefore from (1)

$$\frac{nb}{2A} = \frac{d-n}{n} \cdot \frac{E_s}{E_c} = \frac{d-n}{n} \cdot m \quad . \quad . \quad . \quad . \quad (5)$$

which gives a quadratic equation for n in terms of the quantities b, A, d, and m, which suffice to fix the value of n and therefore the (conventional) position of the neutral axis.

The solution of the quadratic equation is $n/d = \sqrt{(m^2r^2 + 2mr)} - mr$, where $r = A/bd$.

The designer with many calculations to make, instead of solving numerous quadratic equations assigns a number of values to n/d and finds the corresponding values of A/bd from (5) and plots a graph from which he can read off the value of n (or n/d) for various values of A/bd (or $100A/bd$ the percentage area of steel in the cross-section).

Moment of Resistance. The moment of resistance M of the beam is the value of the couple formed by the equal pull or thrust exerted across the section multiplied by the arm a of the couple. Since the centre of the compression area nb is $\frac{2}{3}n$ from the neutral axis or $n/3$ from the outer edge

$$a = d - n/3 \quad . \quad . \quad . \quad . \quad . \quad (6)$$

and

$$M = f_t \cdot A(d - n/3) = \tfrac{1}{2}f_c \cdot nb(d - n/3) . \quad . \quad . \quad . \quad (7)$$

The bending moment on the beam must not of course exceed either of the two moments of resistance obtained by writing for f_t and f_c the allowable limits of these stress intensities. Such limits for various grades of concrete and steel are given in the codes which govern the design of reinforced concrete construction.

Economic Proportions. The value of A from (4), viz. $\tfrac{1}{2}nbf_c/f_t$, corresponding to the allowable limits of f_t and f_c, gives the most economic proportion of steel. And 100 times the ratio A/bd is then called the economic percentage of reinforcement (see Example 2 following). With these proportions of steel and concrete both materials will be stressed to their allowed limits.

Strength Graphs. Two graphs may be drawn for the safe moment of resistance M from the two values given in equation (7) when A has a series of assigned values and when f_t and f_c are the allowable limits of intensity of stress for tension in the steel and compression in the concrete respectively. The two curves intersect at the critical point giving the equal values of M at the economic value of the percentage of steel. Instead of using values of A as the horizontal ordinates we may take the percentage of steel, viz. $100A/bd$ and instead of M as the vertical ordinate we may take $M/(bd^2)$ which would be of the dimensions of a stress intensity or

$M/(bd^2 . f_c)$ which is a ratio or purely numerical quantity. By so choosing the ordinates we have a graph of wider use applicable to any beam having the same value for m and the same ratio of ultimate values f_t/f_c. By giving n/d any values we can find the corresponding percentages of steel, viz. from (5)

$$100A/bd = \frac{100}{2m} \frac{n^2}{(d-n)d} \quad \cdots \quad (8)$$

And from (7)

$$M/bd^2 = f_t A(1 - \tfrac{1}{3}n/d)/bd \text{ or } f_c n(1 - \tfrac{1}{3}n/d)/2d$$

or $\qquad M/bd^2 f_c = \dfrac{f_t}{f_c} \cdot \dfrac{A}{bd}(1 - \tfrac{1}{3}n/d) \text{ or } \tfrac{1}{2}(n/d)(1 - \tfrac{1}{3}n/d) \quad \cdots \quad (9)$

where from (8), A/bd is equal to $\dfrac{(n/d)^2}{2m(1-n/d)}$

A sample graph is shown at (b) of Fig. 80, where $m = 12$ and at the allowable limits of stress $f_t/f_c = 18$ and the value of n/d equal to 0·3, 0·4, 0·5, 0·54, and 0·57 have been used to plot the curve. The economic proportion is for the value of A given by (4) for which

$$A = \tfrac{1}{2}nb \times f_c/f_t = \tfrac{1}{2}nb/18 = nb/36.$$

And from (5)

$$nb/2A = 18 = 12(d-n)/n;$$

hence $n = 0·4d$ and $A/bd = 1/90$ or $100A/bd = 100/90 = 1·111$, the economic percentage.

The designer with many beams to design from such a graph to a larger scale can quickly read off the percentage of steel necessary for any given moment of resistance so long as m and f_t/f_c remain the same. For higher values of m the graphs would be similar but the vertical ordinates greater. The values of n/d for any percentage of steel are shown in the broken-line graph.

Ferro-concrete beam sections are generally rectangular, but in case of the compression part of the section having any other shape, we should proceed as follows to state the total thrust in terms of the maximum intensity f_c at the extreme edge at the (unknown) distance n from the neutral axis.

Let z be the width of section parallel to the neutral axis at a height y from it, varying in a known manner with, say, the distance $(n-y)$ from the compression edge, and let p be the intensity of stress at any height y from the neutral axis; then

$$p/y = f_c/n, p = f_c y/n \quad \cdots \quad (10)$$

$$\text{Total thrust} = \int_0^n p \cdot z \cdot dy = \frac{f_c}{n} \int_0^n y \cdot z \cdot dy . \quad (11)$$

which can be found when the width z is expressed in terms of, say, $n-y$.   This might also be written

Total thrust $= f_c \times$ (area of compression modulus figure)

(see end of Art. 49).   In the rectangular section of Fig. 80, $z = b =$ constant, this being the simplest possible case.

Frequently the compression area of ferro-concrete is **T**-shaped, consisting partly of a concrete slab or flooring and partly of the upper part of the rectangular supporting rib, the lower part of which is reinforced for tension, the floor and beam being in one piece, or "monolithic" (see Example 3, page 126, and note following it).   The breadth is then constant over two ranges, into which the above integrations can conveniently be divided.   The thrust, if any, in the upper part of the vertical leg of the   is often negligible compared to that in the cross-piece or slab.

The resisting moment, about the neutral axis, of the total thrust would be

$$\frac{f_c}{n} \int_0^h y^2 \cdot z\, dy \text{ or } f_c \cdot \frac{I}{n}$$

where I is the moment of inertia of the compression area about the neutral axis.   The graphical equivalent of this would be

$f_c \times$ (area of compression modulus figure) $\times$ (distance of its centroid
    from the neutral axis)

the centroid of the modulus figure being the centre of pressure or thrust, or, using the second derived area as in Art. 49

resisting moment of the thrust $= f_c \times n \times$ second derived area of
                        compression section

The resisting moment, about the neutral axis, of the total tension is evidently $f_t \times A \times (d-n)$ and the total moment of resistance is

total thrust (or pull) $\times$ distance of centre of thrust from
    reinforcement.

Example 1.   A reinforced concrete beam 20 in. deep and 10 in. wide has four bars of steel 1 in. diameter placed with their axes 2 in. from the tension face of the beam.   Find the position of the neutral axis and the moment of resistance exerted by the section when the greatest intensity of compressive stress is 1,000 lb. per sq. in.   What is then the intensity of tensile stress in the steel? Take the value of E for steel 12 times that for concrete.

Using the symbols of Fig. 80 and those above

$$d = 20 - 2 = 18 \text{ in.}$$

$$\frac{f_c}{E_c} \div \frac{f_t}{E_t} = \frac{\text{maximum compressive strain}}{\text{tensile strain in metal}} = \frac{n}{18-n}$$

$$\frac{f_c}{f_t} = \frac{E_c}{E_t} \cdot \frac{n}{18-n} = \frac{n}{12(18-n)}$$

and equating the total pull in the steel of sectional area π to the thrust in the concrete

$$\pi f_t = \tfrac{1}{2} f_c . n . 10$$

Therefore $\qquad \dfrac{f_c}{f_t} = \dfrac{\pi}{n . \frac{1}{2} . 10} = \dfrac{\pi}{5n} = \dfrac{n}{(18-n)12}$

hence $\qquad 5n^2 + 12\pi n - 216\pi = 0$

and solving this $\qquad n = 8\cdot 475$ in.

The distance from the neutral axis to the centre of the steel rods $= 18 - 8\cdot 475 = 9\cdot 525$ in.   The total thrust is

$$\frac{1,000}{2} \times 10 \times 8\cdot 475 = 42,375 \text{ lb.}$$

and the total tension in the metal is equal to this.

The distance of the centre of pressure from the neutral axis is $\frac{2}{3}$ of $8\cdot 475$ in., and that of the tension is $9\cdot 525$ in.

The arm of the couple formed by the total thrust and total pull is therefore $9\cdot 525 + 2 \times 8\cdot 475/3 = 15\cdot 175$ in.   Or from (6) $18 - 8\cdot 475/3 = 15\cdot 175$ in.   The moment of resistance is therefore $M = 15\cdot 175$ in. $\times 42,375$ lb. $= 643,000$ lb.-in.

The intensity of tensile stress in the steel of area π sq. in. is

$$f_t = \frac{42,375}{\pi} = 13,490 \text{ lb. per sq. in.}$$

or thus $\qquad \dfrac{f_t}{1,000} = 12 \times \dfrac{9\cdot 525}{8\cdot 475} = 13,490$

which checks the above result.

The moment of resistance could of course be found from a graph such as in Fig. 80.   Even on this small-scale diagram it can be found approximately.   The percentage of steel is $100\pi/(18 \times 10) = 1\cdot 745$ (per cent.) and for this the value of $M/(bd^2 f_c)$ is nearly $0\cdot 20$.   If $b = 10$ in., $d = 18$ in., and $f_c = 1,000$ lb. per sq. in.

$$M = 0\cdot 2 \times bd^2 \times f_c = 0\cdot 2 \times 3,240,000 = 648,000 \text{ lb.-in. (approx.)}$$

It is also evident from the dotted graph of n/d that for this proportion of steel $n/d = 0\cdot 47$ (approx.) or $n = 0\cdot 47 \times 18 = 8\cdot 46$ in. (approx.), from which M could be calculated.

Example 2.   A reinforced concrete floor, simply supported, is to carry a uniformly spread load, the span being 12 ft. and the floor 10 in. thick.   Determine what reinforcement is necessary and what load per square foot may be carried, the centres of the steel bars being placed $1\frac{1}{2}$ in. from the lower side of the floor, the allowable stress in the concrete being 600 lb. per sq. in., and in the steel 12,000 lb. per sq. in., and the modulus of direct elasticity for steel being 15 times that for concrete.   If the load per square foot of floor is 300 lb., estimate the extreme stresses in the materials, assuming bending in one direction only.

Let $n=$ distance of the neutral axis from the compression edge.

Then the distance from the centres of the steel rods is $10 - 1 \cdot 5 - n = 8 \cdot 5 - n$ in.

The ratio of stress intensities is

$$\frac{\text{intensity of tensile stress}}{\text{maximum intensity of pressure}} = \frac{12{,}000}{600} = \frac{8 \cdot 5 - n}{n} \times 15$$

hence

$$8 \cdot 5 - n = 4n/3$$

$$n = 3 \cdot 643 \text{ in.}$$

Taking a strip of floor 1 in. wide

$$\text{thrust of concrete} = \tfrac{600}{2} \times 3 \cdot 643 \times 1 = 1{,}093 \text{ lb.}$$

The total tension in the steel must also be 1,093 lb., and the area of section required is therefore

$$\frac{1{,}093}{12{,}000} = 0 \cdot 0911 \text{ sq. in.}$$

per inch width of floor. If round bars 1 in. diameter are used, they might be spaced at a distance apart of centre lines of

$$\frac{0 \cdot 7854}{0 \cdot 0911} = 8 \cdot 63 \text{ in.}$$

This gives a beam of economic proportions. The economic percentage is $100 \times 0 \cdot 0911/8 \cdot 5 = 1 \cdot 07$ per cent. *under the given conditions*.

The total moment of resistance is (per inch width)

$$1{,}093\{(\tfrac{2}{3} \times 3 \cdot 643) + (8 \cdot 5 - 3 \cdot 643)\} = 7{,}962 \text{ lb.-in.}$$

which is the product of the total thrust (or tension), and the distance between the centre of pressure and the centres of the rods.

If $w=$ load per inch run, which is also the load per square inch of the floor, equating the moment of resistance to the bending moment

$$\tfrac{1}{8}w \times 144 \times 144 = 7{,}962$$

$$144w = \frac{8 \times 7962}{144} = 442 \text{ lb.}$$

which is the load per square foot (including about 120 lb. per sq. ft. weight of the slab itself).

If the load were only 300 lb. per sq. ft., the stresses would be proportionally reduced, and

$$\text{maximum intensity of pressure} = 600 \times \tfrac{300}{442}$$

$$= 408 \text{ lb. per sq. in.}$$

$$\text{intensity of tensile stress} = 12{,}000 \times \tfrac{300}{442}$$

$$= 8{,}145 \text{ lb. per sq. in.}$$

Example 3.   A reinforced beam is of **T** section, the cross-piece or compression flange being 20 in. wide and 4 in. deep, and the vertical leg 14 in. deep by 8 in. wide.   The reinforcement consists of two round bars of steel $1\frac{1}{2}$ in. diameter placed with their axes 2 in. from the lower face.   Making the usual assumptions, calculate the intensity of stress in the steel, and the total amount of resistance exerted by a section of the beam when the compressive-stress in the concrete reaches 500 lb. per sq. in.   Take the modulus of direct elasticity in steel 12 times that for concrete in compression.

Let f=intensity of stress in the steel

n=distance of the neutral axis from the compression edge (see Fig. 81).

The ratio of the stress intensities is then

$$\frac{f_t}{500}=\frac{16-n}{n}\times 12$$

whence $$f_t=\frac{16-n}{n}\times 6{,}000 \quad . \quad . \quad . \quad . \quad . \quad (1)$$

The total thrust $=\dfrac{500}{n}\displaystyle\int_{n-4}^{n} 20y\,dy+\dfrac{500}{n}\displaystyle\int_{0}^{n-4} 8y\,dy$

$$=\frac{10{,}000}{n\times 2}\{n^2-(n-4)^2\}+\frac{4{,}000}{2n}(n-4)^2$$

$$=\frac{40{,}000}{n}(n-2)+\frac{2{,}000}{n}(n-4)^2$$

the first term representing the thrust in the cross-piece, and the second that in the vertical leg above the neutral axis.   The total tension is

$$2 \cdot \frac{\pi}{4} \cdot \frac{9}{4}f_t=\frac{9\pi}{8}f_t$$

and substituting for f_t from (1) and equating to the total thrust

$$\frac{9\pi}{8} \cdot \frac{16-n}{n} \cdot 6{,}000=\frac{40{,}000}{n}(n-2)+\frac{2{,}000}{n}(n-4)^2$$

from which $n=6 \cdot 6$ in. and

$$f_t=6{,}000 \cdot \frac{16-6 \cdot 6}{6 \cdot 6}=8{,}550 \text{ lb. per sq. in.}$$

The moment of the thrust about the neutral axis is

$$\frac{500}{6 \cdot 6}\int_{2 \cdot 6}^{6 \cdot 6} 20 \cdot y^2 \cdot dy+\frac{500}{6 \cdot 6}\int_{0}^{2 \cdot 6} 8 \cdot y^2 \cdot dy=\frac{500\times 20}{6 \cdot 6\times 3}\{(6 \cdot 6)^3-(2 \cdot 6)^3\}$$

$$+\frac{500\times 8}{6 \cdot 6\times 3}(2 \cdot 6)^3=140{,}000 \text{ lb. in.}$$

The moment of the tension is

$$8,550 \times \frac{9\pi}{8} \times 9 \cdot 4 = 284,000 \text{ lb.-in.}$$

and the total moment of resistance is

$$140,000 + 284,000 = 424,000 \text{ lb.-in.}$$

The values found for total thrust and the moment of resistance would not be greatly altered by the omission of the second term in the respective integrals, *i.e.* by neglecting the small thrust in the vertical leg of the section above the neutral axis. The moment of resistance might be estimated graphically by drawing the modulus

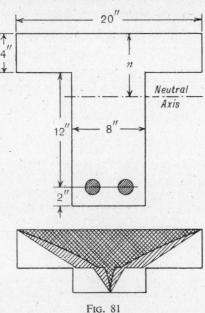

FIG. 81

figure for the compression area with a pole on the neutral axis (see Fig. 81); the moment of resistance for compression would then be

500 × (area of compression modulus figure) × (distance of its centroid from the axis)

or if a second derived figure be drawn, the moment would be

500 × 6·6 × (area second derived figure).

The total tension moment would be

500 × (area of first compression modulus figure) × 9·4

Note.—A very common example of a **T** section occurs in ferro-concrete floors with monolithic cross-beams, the floor forming the cross-piece of the **T**. The cross-piece is then often very wide in proportion to the remainder of the **T** section, and with a moderately high intensity of stress in the reinforcement the neutral axis would fall within the cross-piece instead of below it. This would involve tension in the lower side of the floor slab, which is not always reinforced for tension in that direction, and might start cracks. This undesirable result can be avoided by employing more reinforcement at a consequently lower intensity of stress in the cross-beam or vertical leg of the **T** section.

57. Doubly Reinforced Beam. While reinforcement on the tension side of the neutral plane of a concrete beam is primarily desirable, reinforcement on the compression side is common. Steel being stronger than concrete in compression such reinforcement reduces the size of a beam and relatively slender compression bars

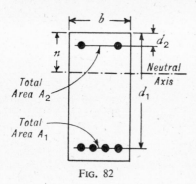

FIG. 82

can be used because, being imbedded in concrete they are thereby supported laterally against buckling, provided they are adequately bound in with stirrups. It may also happen that such a beam, supported at several points has opposite forms of bending action at different parts of its length. Thus what is compression reinforcement at one cross-section may be necessary as tensile reinforcement at another.

Fig. 82 represents the cross-section of such a doubly reinforced beam, A_1 being the area of section of the tensile reinforcement and A_2 that of the compression reinforcement, d_1 and d_2 the respective distances of their centres from the compression outer edge. Let f_2 be the intensity of compressive stress in steel and the other symbols be as in Art. 56 and Fig. 80.

As in Arts. 56 and 44, if plane cross-sections remain plane after flexure the strains at any points of the section are proportional to the distances from the neutral axis or

$$f_c/E_c : f_t/E_s : f_2/E_s = n : d_1 - n : n - d_2 \quad . \quad . \quad . \quad (1)$$

The intensity of compressive stress in the steel reinforcement is m times that in the concrete which it replaces in the rectangular compression area $b \times n$, *i.e.* from (1)

$$f_2 = \frac{E_s}{E_c} . f_c . \frac{n - d_2}{n} = m . f_c . (n - d_2)/n \quad . \quad . \quad (2)$$

and the total thrust in the compression reinforcement is

$$A_2 f_2 (n - d_2)/n \quad . \quad . \quad . \quad . \quad . \quad (3)$$

Hence the *excess* thrust across the area A_2 due to the greater modulus of elasticity of the steel is

$$A_2(m-1)f_c(n-d_2)/n \quad . \quad . \quad . \quad . \quad (4)$$

(It is convenient to consider the area bn as continuous concrete, thus including the area A_2, leaving $(m-1)A_2$ as the equivalent excess area in terms of concrete under the stress intensity $f_c(n-d_2/n)$.)

The total thrust across the section equals the total pull or

$$f_c\{\tfrac{1}{2}bn+(m-1)A_2(n-d_2)/n\}=f_t . A_1 \quad . \quad . \quad (5)$$

and equating f_t/f_c from this to f_t/f_c from (1), *i.e.* to $m(d_1-n)/n$, we get a quadratic equation for n in terms of A_1, A_2, d_1, d_2, b, and m, all of which for a given beam have known numerical values. (See Example below.)

We can very simply calculate the moment of resistance by adding the moments about the neutral axis of : (1) the pull in the tensile reinforcement $f_t . A_1$; (2) the thrust in the concrete if the compression reinforcement were replaced in the area A_2 by concrete, viz. $\tfrac{1}{2}f_c . bn$; and (3) the *excess* thrust due to the presence of the steel as given at (4). The moment of resistance, using (4), is

$$M=f_t A_1(d_1-n)+\tfrac{1}{2}f_c(bn \times \tfrac{2}{3}n)+(m-1)A_2 f_c(n-d_2)^2/n . \quad (6)$$

from which

$$M=f_t A_1(d_1-n)+f_c\{bn^2/3+A_2(m-1)(n-d_2)^2/n\} \quad . \quad (7)$$

If we wish, for comparison with (6) of Art. 56, to state the arm a of the couple formed by the total thrust and total pull across the section we could divide M as given by (7) by the total pull $T=f_t . A_1$ or the (equal) thrust P made up of the sum of $\tfrac{1}{2}f_c bn$ and the expression (4). The result, though a little unwieldy in symbols, is quite simple numerically.

Example 1. If the beam in Example 1 of Art. 56 has two steel bars each 1 in. diameter with axes 2 in. from the compression edge. Find the (conventional) position of the neutral axis, the stress intensities in the steel reinforcements, and the moment of resistance when the stress in the concrete reaches 800 lb. per sq. in. (Take $m=12$.)

As in Example 1, Art. 56, $b=10$, $A_1=\pi$ sq. in., $d_1=20-2=18$ in. In addition we have $A_2=\pi/2$ sq. in., and $d_2=2$ in.

From equation (1)

$$f_t/800=m(18-n)/n \quad . \quad . \quad . \quad . \quad . \quad (8)$$

and from equation (5)

$$800\{0\cdot5 \times 10 \times n+(m-1)(n-2)\pi/2n\}=f_t . \pi \quad . \quad . \quad (9)$$

or $\qquad f_t/800=\{5n+11(n-2)\pi/2n\}/\pi \quad . \quad . \quad . \quad (10)$

F

Hence equating the right-hand sides of (8) and (10)

$$5n/\pi + 11(n-2)/2n = 12(18-n)/n$$
$$n^2 + 11n - 142\cdot7 = 0$$
$$n = -5\cdot5 + 13\cdot14 = 7\cdot64 \text{ in.}$$

The stress intensity in the tensile reinforcement is

$$f_t = f_c \times m(18-7\cdot64)/7\cdot64 = 800 \times 12 \times 10\cdot36/7\cdot64 = 13,020 \text{ lb. per sq. in.}$$

And from (2) the stress intensity in the compression reinforcing bars is

$$f_2 = 12 \times 800 \times (7\cdot64-2)/7\cdot64 = 7,087 \text{ lb. per sq. in.}$$

And the moment of resistance is

$$M = 13,020 \times \pi \times (18-7\cdot64) + 800 \times 10 \times 7\cdot64^2/3 + (11/12)7,087 \times 5\cdot64 \times 1\cdot571$$
$$= 423,800 + 155,700 + 57,550 = 637,050 \text{ lb.-in.}$$

Example 2. If the beam in Example 1 is to be brought to economic proportions by increasing the tensile stress in the steel to 18,000 lb. per sq. in., find to what cross-sectional area the tensile reinforcement may be reduced. What will then be the maximum moment of resistance.

From (1) of Art. 56

$$\frac{f_c}{f_t} = \frac{800}{18,000} = \frac{n}{18-n} \times \frac{1}{12}$$

Hence $n = 144/23 = 6\cdot26$ in.

From (5) the total thrust will be

$$P = 800(0\cdot5 \times 10 \times 6\cdot26 + 11 \times 1\cdot571 \times 4\cdot26/6\cdot26) = 800(31\cdot30 + 11\cdot77) = 34,456 \text{ lb.}$$
$$A_1 = 34,456 \text{ lb}/18,000 \text{ lb. per sq. in.} = 1\cdot914 \text{ sq. in.}$$

an area which could be provided by three $\frac{3}{4}$-in. bars and one $\frac{7}{8}$-in. bar. The moment of resistances calculated from moments about the neutral axis would be

$$M = 34,456 \times 11\cdot74 + 800\{10 \times (6\cdot26)^2/3 + 1\cdot571 \times 11 \times (4\cdot26)^2/6\cdot26\}$$
$$= 404,500 + 144,600 = 549,100 \text{ lb.-in.}$$

58. Bond Stress. There is at the junction between the concrete and the steel reinforcement a superficial shear stress where the two materials hold together and resist any relative sliding of the steel through the concrete. When the bending moment and moment of resistance change along the length of the beam, the tension in the reinforcement varies proportionally and this change of tension has to be transmitted from one material to the other by superficial longitudinal tangential stress, in the case of plain bars, which is called the bond stress. Fig. 83 represents diagrammatically a short length and a cross-section of a singly reinforced beam. Here we do not need to consider any convention of signs for M, the bending moment or the moment of resistance or for the shearing force F.   From the conditions of equilibrium of a short length δx of the beam, shown at ABCD, where the total thrust P in the concrete is equal to the total tension T in the reinforcement, it is evident that, to the first order of small quantities

$$\delta M = F.\delta x \text{ or } F = \delta M/\delta x \quad . \quad . \quad . \quad . \quad (1)$$

Also $\qquad\qquad M = aT \text{ (or } aP) \quad . \quad . \quad . \quad . \quad . \quad (2)$

where a is the arm of the resisting moment or distance apart of the parallel forces T and P.   Hence $\delta M = \delta(aT) = a\delta T$ since a is constant. (It is equal to $d - n/3$.)   Thus (1) may be written

$$F = a\delta T/\delta x \text{ or } \delta T = F . \delta x/a \quad . \quad . \quad . \quad (3)$$

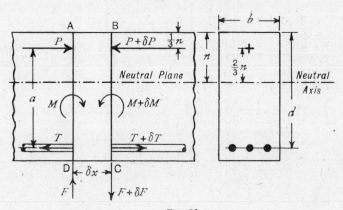

FIG. 83

But δT, the change in tension, has to be transmitted tangentially through the surface between the steel and concrete in the length δx, the area of this surface being

$\delta x \times$ total perimeter of the section of the bars.

Then if f_b is the (tangential) bond stress

$$\delta T = f_b \times \delta x \times \text{total perimeter of bar sections} \quad . \quad . \quad (4)$$

and from (3)

$$f_b = F \div (a \times \text{total perimeter of bar sections}) \quad . \quad . \quad (5)$$

A numerical example is given at the end of Art. 59.

59. Shear Reinforcement.   If a beam is simply supported at its ends, then about the portion which is subjected to the maximum bending moment the principal stresses are nearly parallel to the longitudinal axis of the beam as will be realised from Fig. 77, which relates to a solid beam of homogeneous material and not reinforced but will serve to illustrate the general direction of the principal stresses. Near the ends of such a beam the shearing force is greatest.

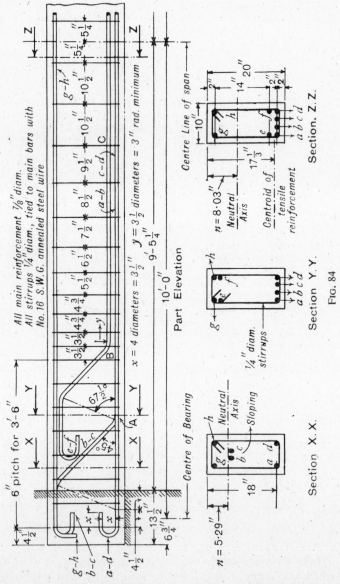

FIG. 84

And the shear stresses involve principal stresses (see Art. 8), one of which is tensile. A reinforced beam is therefore given shear reinforcement near the ends and Fig. 77 will sufficiently indicate the direction in which reinforcement is required to relieve the concrete of tension. The general character of one form of such reinforcement is diagrammatically shown in Fig. 84. Some of the reinforcing bars are bent at 45 degrees to the longitudinal axis of the beam and then terminate in a hook which gives an increased grip in the compression region of the concrete. These resist the tensile principal stress. There are many kinds of shear reinforcement some taking the form of stirrups attached to the tension reinforcement and anchored by hooks in the compression region or attached to the compression reinforcement, if there is any. The stirrups may be vertical, as in Fig. 84, or inclined like the shear reinforcement bars in Fig. 84.

The distribution of shear stress over a vertical section probably cannot be calculated with the same degree of accuracy as for say a steel girder. It is to be remembered that the calculations of longitudinal bending stress necessary for practical design are definitely conventional. They ignore the tension which in fact exists, in the concrete, and assume exact proportionality of stress to strain in concrete. Some idea of the intensity of shear stress might be obtained from (2) of Art. 53 or of the maximum value from (5) of Art. 53. This value, $3F/(2bd)$, where d is overall depth, differs little from $F/(ab)$, where a is used as in Art. 56. It is equivalent to taking a as equal to $\frac{2}{3}$ of the overall depth of the beam. Too great a refinement of calculation here on a slender foundation of ascertained fact is to be deprecated.

Example. The full moment of resistance of the beam shown in Fig. 84 is exerted in supporting a uniformly distributed load on a span of 20 ft., subject to the condition that the compressive stress in the concrete does not exceed 1,000 lb. per sq. in.[1] Find the bond stress on the reinforcing bars at the supports. Take $m=12$.

There are six $\frac{7}{8}$-in. round tension bars and two $\frac{7}{8}$-in. round compression bars. Take their sections as 0·6 sq. in. each.

$$A_1=6\times0·6=3·6 \text{ sq. in.}; \quad A_2=2\times0·6=1·2 \text{ sq. in.}$$

The centroid of the tension bar cross-sections is $\frac{1}{3}$ of 2 in. $=0·6$ in. above the centre line of the lower four bars, or distance of centroid from the compression edge $=18-0·6=17·3$ in. If f_c=maximum compressive stress intensity in concrete

Stress intensity in compression steel $=f_2=mf_c(n-2)/n$.

Stress intensity in tension steel $=f_t=mf_c(17·3-n)/n$.

Total tension $=f_c\times12\times3·6\times(17·3-n)/n$.

Total thrust $=f_c\{\frac{1}{2}bn+11\times1·2(n-2)/n\}$.

---

[1] The ratio of length to width is slightly high for the use of the full permissible 1,000 lb. per sq. in. compressive stress. Design regulations might require that the beam be secured laterally or the maximum compressive stress reduced by about 6·5 per cent.

Equating these, dividing by f_c, multiplying by n, and putting $b=10$

$$3 \cdot 6 \times 12(17 \cdot 3 - n) = 5n^2 + 13 \cdot 2(n-2)$$
$$n^2 + 11 \cdot 28n - 155 = 0$$
$$n = 8 \cdot 03, \text{ say, 8 in.}$$

Total thrust $= \frac{1}{2}f_c \times 8 \cdot 03 \times 10 + f_c \times 11 \times 1 \cdot 2 \times 6 \cdot 03/8 \cdot 03$
$$= f_c(40 \cdot 15 + 9 \cdot 91) = 50 \cdot 06 f_c \text{ lb.}$$

Total tension $= f_c \times 3 \cdot 6 \times 12 \times 9 \cdot 3/8 \cdot 03 = 50 \cdot 03 f_c$ lb.

Moment of resistance (about neutral axis)

Of thrust $= 40 \cdot 15 f_c \times \frac{2}{3} \times 8 \cdot 03 + 9 \cdot 91 \times 6 \cdot 03 f_c$
$$= (214 \cdot 9 + 59 \cdot 8) f_c = 274 \cdot 7 f_c \text{ lb.-in.}$$

Of tension $= 50 \cdot 03 f_c \times 9 \cdot 3 \quad = 465 \cdot 3 f_c$

Total $740 \cdot 0 f_c$ lb.-in.

or 740,000 lb.-in. if $f_c = 1,000$ lb. per sq. in.
$$f_t = f_c \times 12 \times 9 \cdot 3/8 \cdot 03 = 13 \cdot 9 f_c = 13,900 \text{ lb. per sq. in.}$$

Extreme stress in steel $= 1,000 \times 12 \times 10/8$
$$= 15,000 \text{ lb. per sq. in. (approx.)}$$

If W is the uniformly distributed load on a 20-ft. span.

Maximum B.M. $= \frac{1}{8}W \times 240$ (in.) $= 740,000$ lb.-in.
$$W = 24,667 \text{ lb.}$$

Shearing force at supports $= \frac{1}{2}W = 12,333$ lb.

Since four of the tension bars are bent up, two remain (in the bottom row), *i.e.* for section at supports $A_2 = 1 \cdot 2$ sq. in.   At this section $f_t = 12 f_c \times (18-n)/n$

Total thrust $= f_c\{\frac{1}{2} \, . \, 10n + 11 \times 1 \cdot 2 \times (n-2)/n\}$
Total tension $= f_c \times 12 \times 1 \cdot 2 \times (18-n)/n$

Equating these

$$5n^2 + 27 \cdot 6n - 285 \cdot 6 = 0$$
$$n = 5 \cdot 286 \text{ in.}$$

Total thrust $= f_c(\frac{1}{2} \times 10 \times 5 \cdot 286 + 11 \times 1 \cdot 2 \times 3 \cdot 286/5 \cdot 286)$
$$= f_c(26 \cdot 43 + 8 \cdot 21) = 34 \cdot 63 f_c$$

Moment of resistance $= f_c\{ 34 \cdot 63(18 - 5 \cdot 286) + 26 \cdot 43 \times \frac{2}{3} \times 5 \cdot 286 + 8 \cdot 21(5 \cdot 286 - 2)\}$
$$= 560 \cdot 4 f_c$$

Lever arm $a = 560 \cdot 4/34 \cdot 64 = 16 \cdot 18$ in.

The total perimeter of two $\frac{7}{8}$-in. bars is $2 \times 2 \cdot 75 = 5 \cdot 5$ in.
Equating the moments on a length δx

$$f_b \times 5 \cdot 5 \times \delta x \times 16 \cdot 18 = 12,333 \times \delta x$$

Bond stress, $f_b = \dfrac{12,333}{88 \cdot 99} = 139$ lb. per sq. in.

which falls within an allowable limit.

The horizontal and sloping parts of the bars *b* and *c* are in tension and in a direction bisecting the angle between them there is a compressive force in the concrete the vertical component of which increases the bond resistance of the bars *a* and *d* thereby making permissible a bond stress double that for a bar in simple tension.

The bars *e* and *f* must not be turned upward within such a distance of the middle of the beam as would leave the moment of resistance of the section with the bars *a, b, c, d, g, and h* insufficient to balance the bending moment. The point B where they may be turned up is readily seen from a (parabolic) bending moment diagram for the beam (as in Fig. 255 for a built-up girder with the number of plates in the flanges diminishing towards the ends). Similarly the bars *b* and *c* are only turned up at a point A at such a distance from mid-span that the safe moment of resistance of the remaining section would suffice for the bending moment at that section of the beam.

The shearing force varies uniformly from zero at mid-span to the supports (as in Fig. 49). From mid-span to B the stirrups alone suffice to resist the relatively low shearing forces. From B to A they suffice to take the excess over the shearing force carried by the sloping parts of bars *e* and *f* (which is limited by their bond lengths) and from A to the end supports of the beam the stirrups suffice to take the shear force in excess of that safely carried by the bent-up bars *b* and *c*. At the middle of the beam the pitch of the stirrups is limited to $10 \cdot 5$ in. to prevent buckling of the compression reinforcement bar.

EXAMPLES V

1. Find the greatest intensity of direct stress arising from a bending moment of 90 ton-in. on a symmetrical section 8 in. deep, the moment of inertia being 75 (in.)[4].

2. Calculate the moment of resistance of a beam section 10 in. deep, the moment of inertia of which is 145 in. units when the skin stress reaches $7 \cdot 5$ tons per sq. in.

3. What total distributed load may be carried by a simply supported beam over a span of 20 ft., the depth of section being 12 in., the moment of inertia being 375 (in.)[4], and the allowable intensity of stress $7 \cdot 5$ tons per sq. in.? What load at the centre might be carried with the same maximum stress?

4. To what radius may a beam of symmetrical section 10 in. deep be bent without producing a skin stress greater than 6 tons per sq. in., if $E = 13,500$ tons per sq. in.? What would be the moment of resistance, if the moment of inertia of the section is 211 (in.)[4]?

5. A wooden beam of rectangular section 12 in. deep and 8 in. wide has a span of 14 ft., and carries a load of 3 tons at the middle of the span. Find the greatest stress in the material and the radius of curvature at mid-span. $E = 800$ tons per sq. in.

6. What should be the width of a joist 9 in. deep if it has to carry a uniformly spread load of 250 lb. per foot run over a span of 12 ft., with a stress not exceeding 1,200 lb. per sq. in.

7. A floor has to carry a load of 3 cwt. per sq. ft. The joists are 12 in. deep

by $4\frac{1}{2}$ in. wide, and have a span of 14 ft.   How far apart may the centre lines be placed if the bending stress is not to exceed 1,000 lb. per sq. in.?

8. Compare the moments of resistance for a given maximum intensity of bending stress of a beam of square section placed (*a*) with two sides vertical, (*b*) with a diagonal vertical, the bending being in each case parallel to a vertical plane.

9. Over what length of span may a rectangular beam 9 in. deep and 4 in. wide support a load of 250 lb. per foot run without the intensity of bending stress exceeding 1,000 lb. per sq. in.?

10. A beam of I section 12 in. deep has flanges 6 in. wide and 1 in. thick, and web $\frac{7}{8}$ in. thick.   Compare its flexural strength with that of a beam of rectangular section of the same weight, the depth being twice the breadth.

11. A rolled steel joist 10 in. deep has flanges 6 in. wide by $\frac{3}{4}$ in. thick. Find approximately the stress produced in it by a load of 15 tons uniformly spread over a span of 14 ft.

12. Find the bending moment which may be resisted by a cast-iron pipe 6 in. external and $4\frac{1}{2}$ in. internal diameter when the greatest intensity of stress due to bending is 1,500 lb. per sq. in.

13. Find in inch units the moment of inertia of a T section, about an axis through the centroid or centre of gravity of the section and parallel to the cross-piece.   The height over all is 4 in., and the width of cross-piece 5 in., the thickness of each piece being $\frac{1}{2}$ in.

14. The compression flange of a cast-iron girder is 4 in. wide and $1\frac{1}{2}$ in. deep; the tension flange 12 in. wide by 2 in. deep, and the web 10 in. by $1\frac{1}{2}$ in. Find (1) the distance of the centroid from the tension edge; (2) the moment of inertia about the neutral axis; (3) the load per foot run which may be carried over a 10-ft. span by a beam simply supported at its ends without the skin tension exceeding 1 ton per sq. in.   What is then the maximum intensity of compressive stress?

15. A compound girder consists of two rolled I sections 18 × 7 in. (BSB 28, Table I in Appendix) and four $\frac{5}{8}$-in. flats, 18 in. wide forming the flanges (2 on each).   For what maximum span may this girder be used to support a load of 3 tons per foot run including its own weight if the maximum bending stress is not to exceed 7·5 tons per sq. in., neglecting the weight of the girder? Allow two $\frac{7}{8}$-in. rivet holes in each flange.

16. Find the maximum stress in a compound girder consisting of three I beams 14 × 6 in. (BSB 23) having four $\frac{1}{2}$-in. flats 20 in. wide on the flanges (2 on each), when carrying a load of 50 tons at the centre of a span of 18 ft. in addition to its own weight, which is 280 lb. per foot.   Allow for three $\frac{7}{8}$-in. rivets in each flange section.

17. A box plate girder is to be 30 in. deep over the angles for a span of 30 ft. and is to carry a load of 43 tons at its centre with a working stress of 5 tons per sq. in.   The two webs are each $\frac{3}{8}$ in. thick and the four angles are each 4 × 4 × $\frac{1}{2}$ in. (BSEA 11, Table V Appendix).   The flanges are each to be made of three plates, the outer one $\frac{3}{8}$ in., the next $\frac{3}{8}$ in., and the inner one $\frac{1}{2}$ in.   Find the necessary width of flanges.

18. A single-web plate girder has a span of 34 ft. and a depth over angles of 36 in., the web being $\frac{1}{2}$ in. thick.   It is required to carry a load of 72 tons evenly distributed along its length.   If the angles are 6 × 6 × $\frac{1}{2}$ in., what thickness of flats 14 in. wide will be required in order that the working stress shall be about 5 tons per sq. in.?

19. Find the greatest intensity of vertical shear stress on an I section 10 in. deep and 8 in. wide, flanges 0·97 in. thick, and web 0·6 in. thick, when the total vertical sheer stress on the section is 30 tons.   What is the ratio of the maximum to the mean intensity of vertical shear stress?

20. The section of a plate girder has flanges 16 in. wide by 2 in. thick; the web, which is 36 in. deep and $\frac{3}{4}$ in. thick, is attached to the flanges by angles $4 \times 4 \times \frac{5}{8}$ in., and the section carries a vertical shearing force of 100 tons. Find approximately the intensity of vertical shear stress over all parts of the section and plot a curve showing its variation. (Neglect the rivet holes and rounded corners of the angle plate.)

21. If the above section in No. 20 is also subjected to a bending moment of 5,000 ton-in., find the principal stresses in the web 7 in. from the outer edge of the tension flange.

22. A flitched timber beam consists of two timber joists each 4 in. wide and 12 in. deep, with a $\frac{1}{2}$-in. steel plate 9 in. deep placed symmetrically between and firmly attached to them. What is the total moment of resistance of a section when the bending stress in the timber reaches 1,200 lb. per sq. in., and what is the greatest intensity of stress in the steel? (E for steel may be taken 20 times that for the timber.)

In Problems Nos. 23 to 28 inclusive the tension in the concrete is to be neglected, and the modulus of direct elasticity of steel in tension taken as fifteen times that of concrete in compression. The concrete is to be taken as perfectly elastic within the working stresses.

23. A reinforced concrete beam 10 in. wide and 22 in. deep has four $1\frac{1}{4}$-in. bars of round steel placed 2 in. from the lower edge. If simply supported at the ends, what load per foot run would this beam support over a 16-ft. span if the compressive stress in the beam reaches 600 lb. per sq. in.? What would be the intensity of tensile stress in the reinforcement?

24. A reinforced concrete floor is 9 in. thick, and the reinforcement is placed 2 in. from the lower face. What area of section of steel reinforcement is necessary per foot width if the stress in the concrete is to reach 600 lb. per sq. in., when that in the steel is 15,000 lb. per sq. in., and what load per square foot could be borne with these stresses over a span of 10 ft.?

25. A concrete beam is 18 in. deep and 9 in. wide, and has to support a uniformly distributed load of 1,000 lb. per foot run over a span of 15 ft. What area of section of steel reinforcement is necessary, the bars being placed with their centres 2 in. above the lower face of the beam, if the intensity of pressure in the concrete is not to exceed 600 lb. per sq. in.?

26. A ferro-concrete floor is 8 in. thick, and carries a load of 200 lb. per sq. ft. over a span of 12 ft. What sectional area of steel reinforcement 2 in. from the lower surface is necessary per foot width of floor if the pressure in the concrete is to be limited to 600 lb. per sq. in.? What would then be the working stress in the steel?

27. Part of a concrete floor forms with a supporting beam a **T** section, of which the cross-piece is 30 in. wide by 6 in. deep, and the vertical leg is 8 in. wide, and is to be reinforced by bars placed with their centres 12 in. below the under side of the floor. What area of cross-section of steel will bring the neutral axis of the section in the plane of the under side of the floor? What would then be the intensity of tension in the steel when the maximum compression reaches 600 lb. per sq. in.?

28. A reinforced concrete beam of **T** section has a cross-piece 24 in. wide and 5 in. deep, the remainder being 10 in. wide by 18 in. deep. The reinforcement consists of two 2-in. round bars placed with their centres 3 in. from the lower face of the beam. Find the intensity of tension in the steel and moment of resistance of the section when the extreme compressive stress in the concrete reaches 600 lb. per sq. in.

F*

CHAPTER VI

MOVING LOADS

60. Maximum Straining Actions. The bending moment and shearing force diagrams found in Chapter IV give the straining actions at all sections of beams subjected only to a stationary load. In designing a bridge girder, it is necessary to know the greatest bending moment and shearing force which every section has to resist for all possible dispositions of the movable load, and in this chapter various cases of moving loads will be examined to find

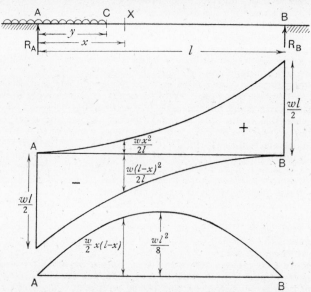

Fig. 85.—Uniformly distributed load longer than the span

these maximum straining actions at every section of a beam simply supported at its ends.

Signs. It may be well to recall the convention of signs adopted in Art. 42, viz. Positive shearing force at any section of a horizontal beam is numerically equal to the upward external force to the right of the section, and positive bending moment is that which tends to produce upward convexity, and is equal to the clockwise moment of the external forces to the right of the section, or to the contra-clockwise moment of the external forces to the left of the section.

61. Uniformly Distributed Load longer than the Span. *Shearing Force.* Suppose the load w per foot approaches a section X of a span AB of length l, from the left support A (Fig. 85). When the load covers a length AC=y from A, the positive shearing force at X, to the right of C will be

$$\text{positive } F_X = R_B = \tfrac{1}{2}wy^2/l \quad \ldots \ldots \quad (1)$$

which is the moment of the load about A divided by l. As the load advances this value increases until when the load reaches X, $y=x$, and

$$\text{positive } F_X = R_B = \tfrac{1}{2}wx^2/l \quad \ldots \ldots \quad (2)$$

As soon as the load passes the section X the shearing force at X decreases, for the increase in upward force at B is obviously less than the downward force to the right of X. Hence the positive shear is a maximum at the section X when the load extends from A to X, and its amount is

$$\text{maximum positive } F_X = \tfrac{1}{2}wx^2/l \quad \ldots \ldots \quad (3)$$

The curve of maximum positive shear is thus a parabola with vertex at A and reaching an ordinate $\tfrac{1}{2}wl$ at B. Similarly the maximum negative shear at X occurs when in approaching from the right or receding towards the right the load covers the portion BX of the span, when

$$\text{maximum negative } F_X = -R_A = -\tfrac{1}{2}w(l-x)^2/l \quad . \quad (4)$$

The curve of maximum negative shear being a parabola with vertex at B and reaching an ordinate $\tfrac{1}{2}wl$ at A.

Bending Moment. As the load approaches X from A the bending moment at X (which is always negative), taking contra-clockwise moments of extreme forces to the right of X, is

$$M_X = -R_B(l-x) = -\tfrac{1}{2}wy^2(l-x)/l \quad . \quad . \quad . \quad (5)$$

and increases in magnitude as C approaches X. After C passes X the bending moment at X, taking clockwise moments to the left, is

$$M_X = -R_A x + \tfrac{1}{2}wx^2 \quad \ldots \ldots \quad (6)$$

of which only R_A varies with the position of C, and the greatest magnitude is reached when R_A is greatest, viz. when the load covers the whole span, and then

$$\text{maximum } M_X = \tfrac{1}{2}wlx + \tfrac{1}{2}wx^2 = -\tfrac{1}{2}wx(l-x) \quad . \quad . \quad (7)$$

The curve of maximum bending moments (Fig. 85) is a parabola having a maximum ordinate $-wl^2/8$ at $x=\tfrac{1}{2}l$. It is evidently the same curve as for a fixed load w per foot covering the whole span (Art. 40 and Fig. 49).

62. Single Concentrated Load. *Shearing Force.* As the load distant y from A approaches the section X (Fig. 86) from A

$$\text{positive } F_X = R_B = Wy/l \quad \ldots \ldots \quad (1)$$

which increases as W approaches X and reaches the value

$$\text{maximum positive } F_X = Wx/l \quad . \quad . \quad . \quad (2)$$

when W reaches X $(y = x)$. When W passes to the right of X the shearing force at X is evidently negative. Taking the upward force to the left of X

$$\text{negative } F_X = -R_A = -W(l - y)/l \quad . \quad . \quad (3)$$

which has its greatest magnitude when $y = x$, when

$$\text{maximum negative } F_X = -W(l - x)/l \quad . \quad . \quad (4)$$

The curve of positive and negative shearing force are straight lines shown in Fig. 86.

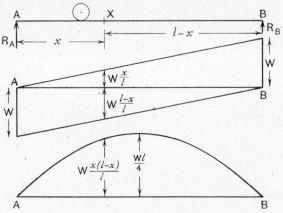

FIG. 86.—Single concentrated load

Bending Moment. As W approaches X from A the bending moment (negative) at X from contra-clockwise moments to the right of X is

$$M_X = -R_B(l - x) = -Wy(l - x)/l \quad . \quad . \quad (5)$$

which increases in magnitude until $y = x$. As soon as W has passed X the bending moment from clockwise moments to the left of X is

$$M_X = -R_A x = -Wx(l - y)/l \quad . \quad . \quad . \quad (6)$$

which is greatest when $y = x$. Thus both (5) and (6) give the same maximum bending moment

$$\text{maximum } M_X = -Wx(l - x)/l \quad . \quad . \quad . \quad (7)$$

The curve of maximum bending moments is a parabola having a maximum ordinate $-\frac{1}{4}Wl$ at $x = \frac{1}{2}l$.

63. Uniformly distributed Load shorter than the Span. *Shearing Force.* Let c be the length covered by a uniformly distributed load w per foot approaching from the left-hand support A (Fig. 87).

Before the leading point b reaches the section X, provided the whole load is on the span, the positive shear at X is

$$\text{positive } F_X = R_B = wcy/l \quad \ldots \ldots \quad (1)$$

where y is the distance of the centre of gravity G of the load from A. This evidently increases with y until b reaches X. After this the value of F_X diminishes, for the downward load to the right of X evidently more than balances any increase in R_B upward; hence the maximum shearing force occurs when b reaches X, and then $y = x - \frac{1}{2}c$ and

$$\text{maximum positive } F_X = wc\frac{x - \frac{1}{2}c}{l} \quad \ldots \quad (2)$$

The curve of maximum positive shearing force for this part of the

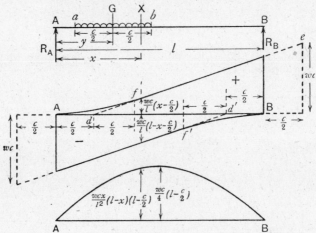

FIG. 87.—Uniformly distributed load shorter than the span

span (where the shearing force is equal to the reaction due to the whole load wc) is from (2), a straight line reaching $\frac{1}{2}wc(2l-c)/l$ at $B(x=l)$, and which would reach; 0 at $x=\frac{1}{2}c$ and wc at $x=l+\frac{1}{2}c$ if it applied to these points (see Fig. 87). But the whole load wc only gets on a length c, and the straight line (2) only applies from $x=c$ to $x=l$; it is easily drawn by joining the points de. For points between $x=0$ and $x=c$ the maximum positive shearing force is evidently as for a load longer than the span, viz. when b reaches the section considered as in (2), Art. 61

$$\text{maximum positive } F_X = R_B = \frac{1}{2}wx^2/l \quad \ldots \quad (3)$$

and curve Af (Fig. 87) being a parabola as in Fig. 85, and the ordinate being the same as for the straight line (2) when $x=c$, viz. $\frac{1}{2}wc^2/l$.

The maximum negative shearing force is evidently found in a similar manner; writing $l-x$ for x in (2), from $x=0$ to $x=l-c$

$$\text{maximum negative } F_X = -wc \cdot \frac{l-x-\frac{1}{2}c}{l} \quad . \quad . \quad (4)$$

and corresponding to (3) from $x=l-c$ to $x=l$

$$\text{maximum negative } F_X = -\tfrac{1}{2}w(l-x)^2/l \quad . \quad . \quad (5)$$

Bending Moment. As b approaches the section X the (negative) bending moment

$$M_X = -R_B(l-x)$$

increases. After b has passed the section X as in Fig. 87

$$M_X = -R_B(l-x) + \frac{w}{2}(y+\tfrac{1}{2}c-x)^2$$

$$= wc\frac{y}{l}(l-x) + \frac{w}{2}(y-\tfrac{1}{2}c-x)^2 \quad . \quad . \quad . \quad (6)$$

Differentiating to find the value of y for a maximum (negative) bending moment

$$\frac{dM_X}{dy} = -wc(l-x)/l + \tfrac{1}{2}w(2y+c-2x)$$

which is zero when

$$y+\tfrac{1}{2}c-x = c(l-x)/l \quad . \quad . \quad . \quad . \quad (7)$$

or the length

$$bX = \frac{BX}{AB} \cdot c \quad . \quad . \quad . \quad . \quad . \quad (8)$$

that is, the section X divides the loaded length c in the same ratio $\left(\dfrac{BX}{AX}\right)$ as it divides the span AB.

Inserting the value of y from (7) in (6)

$$\text{maximum (negative) } M_X = -wc \cdot \frac{l-x}{l}\left(c \cdot \frac{l-x}{l} - \frac{c}{2} + x\right) + \frac{w}{2}\left(c \cdot \frac{l-x}{l}\right)^2$$

$$= -\frac{wcx(l-x)}{l}\left(1 - \frac{c}{2l}\right) \quad . \quad . \quad . \quad . \quad (9)$$

The curve of maximum M_x is a parabola, Fig. 87 having a maximum ordinate found by putting $x=\tfrac{1}{2}l$ in (9) to be

$$-\tfrac{1}{4}wc(l-\tfrac{1}{2}c) . \quad . \quad . \quad . \quad . \quad . \quad (10)$$

64. Two Concentrated Loads. Let W_1 and W_2 (Fig. 88) be the loads (W_1 being the greater) at a fixed distance d apart, d being less than $W_2/(W_1+W_2)$ times the span l.

Shearing Force. As the loads approach any section X from the left support A

$$\text{positive } F_X = R_B = \{W_1 y + W_2(y+d)\}/l$$

which increases until W_2 reaches X, after which it suddenly decreases.[1]

If x is greater than d both loads are on the span when W_2 reaches X, $(y=x-d)$, and the maximum shearing force which then occurs is (from moments about A)

$$\text{maximum positive } F_X = \{W_2 x + W_1(x-d)\}/l \quad . \quad . \quad (1)$$

the curve being a straight line *ce* rising from $W_2 d/l$ at c (when $x=d$) to $W_2 + W_1(l-d)/l$ at B. From A to c the curve is a straight line

$$\text{maximum positive } F_X = W_2 x/l \quad . \quad . \quad . \quad (2)$$

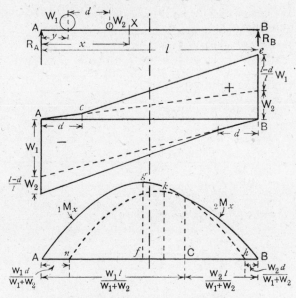

FIG. 88.—Two concentrated loads

Similarly, when the load W_1 is over any section X,

$$\text{maximum negative } F_X = -\{W_1(l-x) + W_2(l-x-d)\}/l \quad . \quad (3)$$

if x is less than $l-d$, and for values of x greater than $l-d$, the maximum negative shear occurs when the load W_2 is off the span, and

$$\text{maximum negative } F_X = -W_1(l-x)/l \quad . \quad . \quad . \quad (4)$$

Bending Moment. As W_2 approaches X, the bending moment is

$$M_X = -R_B(l-x) = -\{W_1 y + W_2(y+d)\}(l-x)/l \quad . \quad (5)$$

---

[1] F_X then increases again until W_1 passes X. As W_1 reaches X, F_X has risen to $R_B - W_2 = \{W_2(x+d) + W_1 x\}/l - W_2$ or $\{W_2(x+d-l) + W_1 x\}/l$. This would exceed the value (1) if $W_2(d-l)$ exceeds $-W_1 d$, *i.e.* if d exceeds $\dfrac{W_2}{W_1 + W_2} l$. It has been assumed that d is less than $\dfrac{W_2}{W_1 + W_2} l$. The other case presents no special difficulty.

which evidently increases in negative magnitude as W_2 approaches X, reaching the value

$$_2M_X = -\{W_1(x-d)+W_2x\}(l-x)/l$$

or

$$= -\{(W_1+W_2)x-W_1d\}(l-x)/l \quad . \quad . \quad . \quad (6)$$

when W_2 is at X (or $y+d=x$), provided W_1 is then on the span. The curve is a parabola which has evidently zero values for $x=l$

and $x = \dfrac{W_1}{W_1+W_2} \cdot d$; it is shown at nkB (Fig. 88).

When W_2 has passed the section X and W_1 has not reached it, the bending moment at X

$$_0M_X = -R_B(l-x)+W_2(y+d-x)$$
$$= -\{W_1y+W_2(y+d)\}(l-x)/l+W_2(y+d-x) \quad . \quad . \quad (7)$$

and differentiating with respect to y

$$\frac{d_0M_X}{dy} = -(W_1+W_2)(l-x)/l+W_2 \quad . \quad . \quad . \quad (8)$$

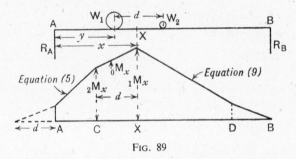

FIG. 89

which does not vary or vanish for any value of y (except for the section $x=W_1l/(W_1+W_2)$ when it is zero for all possible values of y), hence the greatest and least values of $_0M_X$ occur at the limits of , the range of equation (7), viz. $x=y$ and $x=y+d$. This will be clear from Fig. 89, which represents the bending moments at a given section X for various values of y (the distance of W_1 from A). The values of y are shown horizontally from A along the base AB. If the section X is at a distance $W_1l/(W_1+W_2)$ from A, the curve above CX would be horizontal. If such curves as Fig. 89 were drawn for every section of the beam, the maximum ordinates of each would be ordinates of the curve of maximum bending moment shown in Fig. 88.

When W_1 has passed the section X, the bending moment

$$M_X = -R_A \cdot x = -\{W_1(l-y)+W_2(l-y-d)\}x/l \quad (9).$$

which decreases in negative magnitude as W_1 recedes to the right from X, its maximum value being

$$_1M_X = -x\{W_1(l-x) + W_2(l-x-d)\}/l$$

or $\qquad -x\{(W_1+W_2)(l-x) - W_2d\}/l$ . . . . (10)

when W_1 is at X (and $y=x$), provided W_2 is still on the span, *i.e.* not to the right of B. The curve is a parabola which has evidently zero values for $x=0$ and $x=l-W_2d/(W_1+W_2)$; it is shown by A*gh* (Fig. 88).

The value $_1M_X$ from (10) is of greater (negative) magnitude than $_2M_X$ from (6), if

$$-W_2xd \text{ exceeds } -W_1(l-x)d$$

i.e. if $l-x$ exceeds W_2x/W_1, or x is less than $W_1(l-x)/W_2$

Hence if a point C (Fig. 88) divides the span AB so that

$$AC/CB = W_1/W_2 \text{ or } AC = W_1l/W_1 + W_2$$

then in the range AC, $_1M_X$ gives the maximum bending moment; and in the range CB, $_2M_X$ gives the maximum bending moment. If W_1 is greater than W_2, the greatest bending moment anywhere in the span evidently occurs where $_1M_X$ is a maximum. This occurs at a value of x midway between the values which give $_1M_X=0$, or, differentiating (10) with respect to x.

$$\frac{d_1M_X}{dx} = -\{W_1(l-x) + W_2(l-x-d) - W_1x - W_2x\}/l . \quad (11)$$

which is zero for $\qquad x = \tfrac{1}{2}l - \tfrac{1}{2}dW_2/(W_1+W_2)$ . . . . (12)

i.e. the greatest bending moment on the beam occurs at a section under W_1 when the centre of the span AB is midway between W_1 and the centre of gravity of the two loads W_1 and W_2, the centre of gravity being a distance $\tfrac{1}{2}dW_2/(W_1+W_2)$ to the right of mid-span, and W_1 an equal distance to the left. This is a particular case of the general theorem given in the next article.

The greatest bending moment anywhere is found by substituting the value (12) of x in (10) which gives

$$-\frac{W_1+W_2}{4l}\left(l - \frac{W_2}{W_1+W_2}d\right)^2 \quad . \quad . \quad . \quad (13)$$

which is the ordinate *gf* (Fig. 88); the distance $dW_2/(W_1+W_2)$ is the distance of the centre of gravity of W_1 and W_2 from the greater load W_1. The value (10) for $_1M_X$ only holds good so long as W_2 is on the span, *i.e.* to the left of B. This condition is complied with from A to C, where $_1M_X$ gives the maximum bending moment, for we have supposed that d is less than the length CB, or $lW_2/(W_1+W_2)$. Similarly the value (6) for $_2M_X$ holds good over the portion CB, for since d is less than $lW_1/(W_1+W_2)$ the load W_1 is always on the span when W_2 is between C and B.   If d should exceed $lW_2/(W_1+W_2)$, the maximum bending-moment curve is made up of parts of *three* parabolas, viz. the curves from (10) and (6), and the curve of maximum bending moment for W_1 alone as in Fig. 86, Art. 62.

The intersection of this curve with the other two may easily be found by equating $-W_1x(l-x)/l$ from (7) (Art. 62) to (10) and (6) of the present article.   If the distance d between the two loads is sufficiently great compared to l, the greatest maximum bending moment anywhere may occur when W_1 only is on the span, viz. when d exceeds the value obtained by equating $-\frac{1}{4}W_1l$ (see Art. 62) to the value (13).

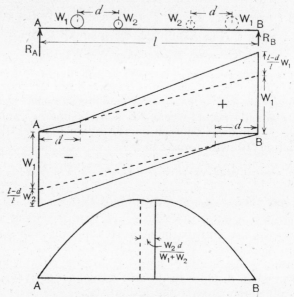

FIG. 90.—Two loads in reversible order

Reversed Order.   If the pair of loads W_1 and W_2 may cross the span AB with either W_1 or W_2 to the left (as in the case of a traction engine crossing a bridge in either direction), the diagrams of maximum shearing force may be found from Fig. 88 by taking the greater of the two ordinates, positive or negative, at a given distance from the centre or ends, and using this in both positive and negative shearing-force diagrams as shown in Fig. 90.   Similarly the diagram of maximum bending moment may be drawn by setting up on either side of the centre of the span ordinates equal to the greatest of the two ordinates at the same distance from the centre in Fig. 88; this is also shown in Fig. 90.

65. Several Loads. The methods of the previous article become complex with more than two loads, and a graphical method which will give results as nearly correct as may be desired is usually adopted.[1]

Theorem. When a series of wheel loads pass over a beam simply supported at its ends, the maximum bending moment under any given wheel occurs when its axis and the centre of gravity of the whole load on the span are equidistant from the centre of the span (or from opposite ends of the span).

Let AB (Fig. 91) be the span, and let W be the total load. Let the given wheel have reached a position P distant y from A. Let W_1 be the load on the length AP, and let d and d' be the distances of W and W_1 respectively from P. Taking moments about B

$$R_A = W(l - y + d)/l$$

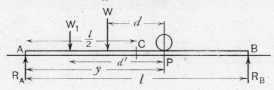

FIG. 91

The bending moment under the wheel is

$$M_P = W_1 d' - R_A \cdot y = W_1 d' - W(l - y + d)y/l$$

differentiating with respect to y

$$\frac{dM_P}{dy} = -W(l - 2y + d)/l$$

The maximum value of M_P occurs when $\dfrac{dM_P}{dy} = 0$, *i.e.* for $y = \frac{1}{2}l + \frac{1}{2}d$, when the wheel P and the centre of gravity of W are each $\frac{1}{2}d$ on opposite sides of C the centre of the span AB.

General Method.[2]

Bending Moment. Let AB, BC, CD, and DE (Fig. 92) be four loads which cross a span equal in length to X_1Y_1. Set off the force line *abcde* to represent the magnitudes of the four loads; choose a pole *o*, and draw the rays *ao*, *bo*, *co*, *do*, and *eo*, and the open funicular polygon *ut*, *uv*, vx_1, x_1w, and wy_1; the extreme sides meet at *t* in the vertical line through the centre of gravity of the whole load.

---

[1] An interesting exact graphical construction of maximum bending-moment diagrams for several loads is given in the *Proc. Inst. C.E.*, vol. cxli (1900), p. 93.

[2] This method, with examples, will be found explained in articles on " Moving Loads on Railway Under-bridges," by Mr. H. Bamford, in *Engineering*, Sept. 7th, 1906; also published separately.

This polygon will serve as bending-moment diagram for various positions of the loads on the span if we consider the span as moving to the left instead of the loads moving to the right.   Divide the span into, say, five equal parts (ten would give greater accuracy, but five are used to avoid complication in the figure and explanation). Take the first position of the span between verticals through X_1Y_1, so that the large load CB nearest the c.g. of the whole load is over the left abutment (X_1).   Draw vertical lines through the abutments

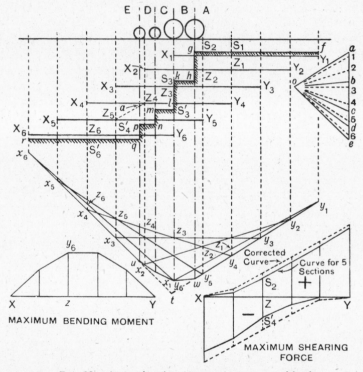

FIG. 92.—Approximation or several concentrated loads

to meet the funicular polygon in x_1 and y_1.   Joining x_1y_1 then x_1y_1w is the bending-moment diagram, and the bending moment anywhere may be scaled off from the vertical distance between x_1y_1 and the lines x_1w and wy_1, e.g. the bending moment $\frac{2}{5}$ of the span from the left abutment is z_1y_4.

Now if the span moves $\frac{1}{5}$ of its length to the left, the base line of the bending-moment diagram $x_2vx_1wy_2$ is the closing side x_2y_2 vertically under the span X_2Y_2; e. g. the bending moment $\frac{2}{5}$ of the span from the left support (X_2) is z_2y_5.   Similarly moving the span successive fifths of its length to the left gives the base lines x_3y_3, x_4y_4, x_5y_5, and x_6y_6, under the span positions X_3Y_3, X_4Y_4, X_5Y_5, and X_6Y_6 respectively. The approximate greatest bending moment at each $\frac{1}{5}$ of the span may now be measured and set off on a base line XY equal to the span, *e.g.* for the six positions taken the bending moments $\frac{2}{5}$ of the span from the left support are z_1y_4, z_2y_5, z_3y_6 (or z_3x_1), z_4x_2, z_5x_3, and z_6x_4, and the greatest of these is z_3y_6, which is then set off at zy_6 in the diagram of maximum bending moments on the base XY. The maximum bending moment under the load CB occurs when the centre of the span is midway between the vertical through t and the line CB; the base line of bending moments for this position is not shown, but would join a point nearly midway between x_3 and x_4 to a point nearly midway between y_3 and y_4, and could easily be drawn. The greatest bending moment anywhere under load CB would occur at a short distance (half the distance of t from the vertical line CB) from the centre of the span XY. It is evident that this too would be greater than any occurring under any other of the loads, which have their maxima values further from mid-span. A curve through the maximum bending moments at each $\frac{1}{5}$ of the span gives an approximate diagram of maximum bending moments at all points of the span, which, like Fig. 88, would be really made up of a number of parabolic arcs; further subdivision of the span would give a result more closely approximating to the true curve.

Maximum Shearing Force. Through the pole o draw lines $o1$, $o2$, $o3$, $o4$, $o5$, and $o6$, parallel respectively to x_1y_1, x_2y_2, x_3y_3, x_4y_4, x_5y_5, and x_6y_6, meeting *abcde*, in 1, 2, 3, 4, 5, and 6 respectively. Draw horizontal lines through a, b, c, d, and e, crossing the spaces A, B, C, D, and E respectively; these lines joined by the verticals *gh*, *kl*, *mn*, and *pq*, are shown cross-hatched and form the shearing-force diagrams. The bases are the lines X_1Y_1, X_2Y_2, X_3Y_3, etc., corresponding to the position of the span. Taking, for example, the position X_3Y_3, the line $o3$ parallel to x_3y_3, divides the load line *ae* into reactions $e3$, and $3a$ at the left and right supports respectively, and the shear diagram *qpnmlkhg* on the base X_3Y_3 follows as in Art. 41. The maximum positive and negative shearing forces at each $\frac{1}{5}$ of the span are scaled from the various base lines, and plotted on the line XY of the maximum shearing-force diagram, *e.g.* at $\frac{2}{5}$ of the span from the left support the positive shearing forces in the first three positions are Z_1S_1, Z_2S_2, and Z_3S_3, after which there is no positive shear at this section. The maximum positive ordinate for this section is Z_2S_2, which is set up at ZS_2. The negative shearing forces for this section in the last four positions of the span are $Z_3S'_3$, $Z_4S'_4$, $Z_5S'_5$, and $Z_6S'_6$, and the greatest is $Z_4S'_4$, which is set downwards at ZS'_4.

Some inaccuracy of the maximum shear diagram results from the fewness of the parts (five) into which the span has been divided, *e.g.* the maximum negative shearing force $\frac{2}{5}$ of the span from the left-hand support is measured from the line X_3Y_3 under the load BC. If a base line intermediate to X_5Y_5 and X_4Y_4 were drawn, the value of negative shear obtained for this section occurs just as the load ED passes over it, and the amount is readily found by joining the points Z_4, Z_5, meeting the vertical line ED in α; then αq is the maximum negative shearing force for this section. The same method may be applied sometimes as an exact, and sometimes as an approximate one to other points, for over a moderate range the ends X and Y and consecutive positions of other selected points on the span are collinear; for as long as the whole load is on the span the changes in the end reactions (and therefore shears between axles) are proportional to the travel. Corrected in this way the method yields a much closer approximation, and for a short load on a long span, exact values in the parts of the diagram which are important, *i.e.* where the ordinates are greatest. It will be noticed in drawing out the figure (which the reader should actually do to appreciate the method) that the greatest ordinates are determined by the outer loads, *i.e.* the positive and negative maximum shears at most sections occur when AB and ED respectively are passing over them. But the five divisions of the span were given positions with respect to the load CB which dominates the greatest ordinates of the maximum bending-moment diagram; consequently this diagram gave a closer approximation to the true values. Increased accuracy in the bending-moment diagram may be obtained by marking vertical reaction lines through X and Y, and a vertical line midway between them on a piece of tracing paper, and picking out maximum bending moments under dominating loads such as BC for other points on the span. The result of Art. 81 may be employed in conjunction with the graphical method to obtain increased accuracy if desired.

Sometimes a diagram such as Fig. 92 is set off from a horizontal base line either by taking the pole *o* on the level of *a* say, or by calculating the moments of the loads about some point, and setting these off in succession as intercepts on a vertical line through the chosen point, and thus drawing in a polygonal bending-moment diagram without the use of the force diagram *oabcde*, the inverse of the process in Art. 33 and Fig. 30.

These methods are particularly convenient for a series of spans, for the diagrams of bending moment and shearing force for say a 300-ft. span will serve with movable base lines for picking out maximum values for all smaller spans. A sheet of tracing-paper with parallel lines ruled on it forms a convenient movable base line.

Reversed Order. If, as is usual, the order of loads is reversible, the maximum bending-moment diagram will reach equal ordinates at equal distances from the centre of the span, and the shearing forces of opposite signs will also be of equal magnitude at equal distances on opposite sides from the centre of the span; the larger values in Fig. 92 will give those required on either side of the centre.

66. Position of Load for Maximum Bending Moment at any Section of a Beam. For a series of concentrated loads the position to give a maximum bending-moment to any given section C (Fig. 93) in passing over a beam AB may be found as follows. Let W_1 be the load to the left of C, W the total load on AB, and x the distance of its centre of gravity from A; let the (constant) distance of the centre of gravity of W_1 to the left of W be d. Then the bending moment at C,

$$M_C = -R_A a + W_1(d+a-x) = -Wa(l-x)/l + W_1(d+a-x) \quad . \quad (1)$$

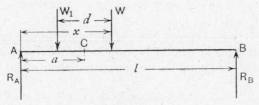

FIG. 93

For a small movement to the right

$$dM_C/dx = Wa/l = -W_1$$

which is also equal to

$$a\{W - W_2 - W_1(l-a)/a\}/l \quad . \quad . \quad . \quad . \quad (2)$$

For a maximum value of (negative) M_C this must change from negative to positive. (For a distributed load it will attain a zero value, but for concentrated loads it will pass discontinuously through zero as a load passes over C). This can only take place as a load passes C moving to the right. (A load passing B decreases W, and cannot change (2) from negative to positive; a load passing A increases W_1 more than it does Wa/l, and therefore cannot change (2) from negative to positive.) Regarding the load just passing C as partly on either side, and equating (2) to zero

$$dM_C/dx = 0 = Wa/l - W_1 \text{ or } Wa/l = W_1 \text{ or } W/l = W_1/a \quad . \quad (3)$$

i.e. the average load per foot between A and C is equal to the average load per foot for the whole span; hence also the average load $(W-W_1)/(l-a)$ between B and C has also the same value. It may perhaps most conveniently be remembered that the passage of the load over the section C changes

$$(W - W_1) - W_1(l-a)/a$$

from negative to positive, *i.e.* changes the quantity

load to right of $C-(l-a)/a \times$ load to left of C

from negative to positive. This defines the position of the load to give a maximum bending moment at any section C. In the passage of a given set of wheel loads two or more maximum values may occur each satisfying condition (3). The value M_C for each position must be calculated, and the greatest of these values is the maximum required.

At the centre of a span $a = \frac{1}{2}l$, and (3) becomes

$$W = 2W_1 \text{ or } W - W_1 = W_1 \quad . \quad . \quad . \quad (3\text{A})$$

i.e. the load on either side of the centre is equal, which condition is satisfied when a load is passing over the centre of the span changing $(W-W_1)-W_1$ from negative to positive; that is, changing

load on right − load on left of centre

from negative to positive.

Case for a Braced Girder. If the beam is a jointed frame or truss carrying the loads on say the bottom joints, the foregoing investigation will only hold good for maximum moments about those joints. For any other, such as C in Fig. 94, let W_1 be the load on panels from A to E, W_2 the load on the panel ED in which C lies, and W the total load on the span AB, the positions of the centres of gravity being as shown in Fig. 94, the horizontal distance of C from E being h and the length of the panel ED being k. The portion of the load W_2 carried at E will be

$$W_2 \times FD/ED = W_2 . (AD - x - d')/k \quad . \quad . \quad . \quad (4)$$

and the bending moment at C is

$$M_C = -R_A a + W_1(a-x) + W_2(AD - x - d)h/k$$
$$= -Wa(l-x-d)/l + W_1(a-x) + W_2(AD - x - d')h/k \quad (5)$$

$$dM_C/dx = Wa/l - W_1 - W_2 h/k \quad . \quad . \quad . \quad . \quad . \quad . \quad . \quad . \quad . \quad (6)$$

For a maximum (negative) value of M_C this changes from negative to positive;

$$dM_C/dx = 0 = Wa/l - W_1 - W_2 h/k$$

or $$\frac{W}{l} = \frac{W_1 + W_2 h/k}{a} \quad . \quad . \quad . \quad . \quad . \quad . \quad (7)$$

This only differs from the result (3) for a solid beam or over one of the loaded bottom joints in that the term $W_2 h/k$ appears instead of that part of W_2 which lies on the length h to the left of C. The difference would generally be very small.

67. Load Position for Maximum Shearing Force at any Section of a Beam. In the case of a solid beam with concentrated moving loads directly carried there will be at any given section a continuous and uniform change of shearing force as any load approaches the section, and a sudden or discontinuous change as each load passes it; hence there will be a succession of maximum shearing-force values (positive and negative) for that section. The greatest of these values may easily be found by trial as in Art. 65.

Case of a Truss. Using Fig. 94 and the notation given in Art. 66,

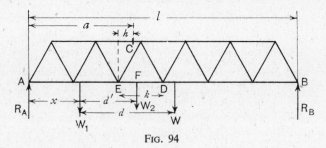

FIG. 94

for any section C, the negative shearing force at C

Negative $F_C = -R_A + W_1 + W_2 FD/ED$

$$= -W(l-x-d)/l + W_1 + W_2(AD-x-d')/k \quad . \quad (1)$$

For a maximum value

$$dF_C/dx = 0 = W/l - W_2/k \quad . \quad . \quad . \quad . \quad (2)$$

or $\qquad W/l = W_2/k \qquad W_2 = Wk/l \quad . \quad . \quad . \quad (3)$

or if there are n equal panels of length k in span l

Load on panel $(W_2) =$ load on span $(W)/l$ . . (4)

For a maximum shearing force at C there would generally be no load to the right of D, and for a maximum negative shearing force no load to the left of E, condition (4) giving the load on ED.

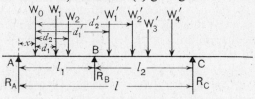

FIG. 95

68. Load Position for Maximum Pressure on Supports.

When a number of axle loads at fixed distances apart traverse a series of longitudinal beams, called rail bearers or stringers, supported on cross-girders which convey the load to the main girders of a bridge, it is important to consider the maximum load carried on any support or cross-girder. Let AB and BC, Fig. 95, be two consecutive spans supported at A, B, and C, the beams being discontinuous at each support. In the position of loads shown in Fig. 95, let the variable distance of the first load W_0 from A be x. Then by moments about A and C the total reaction at B

$$R_B\{W_0x+W_1(x+d_1)+W_2(x+d_2)+ \text{ etc. }\}/l_1$$
$$+[W_1'\{l-(x+d_1')\}+W_2'\{l-(x+d_2')\}+ \text{ etc.}]/l_2 \quad . \quad . \quad (1)$$

and for a small change in x

$$dR_B/dx=(W_0+W_1+W_2+\text{etc.})/l_1-(W_1'+W_2'+W_3'+\text{etc.})/l_2$$
$$= \Sigma(W)/l_1- \Sigma(W')/l_2 \quad . \quad . \quad . \quad . \quad . \quad . \quad . \quad . \quad (2)$$

For maximum values of R_B, dR_B/dx must change from positive to negative. As in Art. 66, this can only occur when a load is passing from one span to the next, crossing B. When this load is partly on each span $dR_B/dx=0$, and for this condition

$$\frac{dR_B}{dx}=0=\frac{\Sigma(W)}{l_1}-\frac{\Sigma(W')}{l_2} \text{ or } \frac{\Sigma(W)}{l_1}=\frac{\Sigma(W')}{l_2} \quad . \quad . \quad (3)$$

i.e. the average load on each span of the rail bearer or stringer is the same, and the same as the average on the two spans. Taking the loads as moving to the right, this condition (3) occurs as one load is crossing the support B, and so bringing the average load per foot on BC up to or beyond that on AB. During the passage of a given set of loads there may be two or more minima for positions satisfying (3); if so the pressure for each must be calculated and the greatest value found. The pressure on B when the maximum value occurs is easily calculated as in (1), which must include the weight directly over B.

If $l_1=l_2$ condition (3) becomes

$$\Sigma(W)= \Sigma(W') \quad . \quad . \quad . \quad . \quad . \quad . \quad (4)$$

i.e. the load on the two adjacent spans must be equal.

It will be noticed that the condition (3) for a maximum reaction at the intermediate support in the length AC (Fig. 95) is the same as for maximum bending moment at any intermediate section in the length AB (Fig. 93) given at (3), Art. 66.

Further, if M_C is the bending moment at C (Fig. 93), and R_C is the reaction at C, if there were a support at C, AC and BC being discontinuous, by taking moments it is easy to show that

$$R_C=-M_C\times\{1/a+1/(l-a)\} \text{ or } -M_C\times l/\{a(l-a)\}. \quad (5)$$

And in particular if the spans a and $l-a$ are equal ($\frac{1}{2}l$)

$$R_C=-M_C\times4/l \text{ or } -M_C\times2/a \quad . \quad . \quad . \quad (6)$$

i.e. the maximum pressure on cross-girders pitched a distance a apart is $2/a$ times the greatest bending moment on a span $2a$ for the same moving load.

69. Equivalent Uniformly Distributed Load. For designing the flanges and other parts of a girder to suit the varying bending moment, it is usual in British railway practice to find the uniformly distributed load which would give a bending moment everywhere at least equal to that caused by the actual greatest rolling load. The bending-moment diagram for such an equivalent load would be a symmetrical parabola completely enveloping the diagram of maximum bending moments for rolling loads. In the single rolling load (Art. 62), or a uniformly distributed moving load shorter than the span (Art. 63), the diagrams of maximum bending moment (Figs. 86 and 87) are parabolic, and the same parabolas will be the diagrams for the equivalent distributed load on the whole span. The load per foot w' equivalent to the concentrated load W is found by equating the moments

$$\tfrac{1}{2}w'x(l-x)=\mathrm{W}(l-x)x/l$$

as in (7) Art. 61, and (7) Art. 62, which gives

$$w'=2\mathrm{W}/l$$

And the value of w' equivalent to a distributed load w per ft. on a length c (see (9) Art. 63) is found from

$$\tfrac{1}{2}w'x(l-x)=wcx(l-x)(2l-c)/(2l^2)$$

which gives

$$w'=2wc(2l-c)/2l^2$$

In more general cases the maximum (central) ordinate of an enveloping parabola is often much greater than the neighbouring maximum ordinate of the diagram of maximum bending moments for the actual rolling load, and this arises partly from the fact that the enveloping parabola includes all ordinates, including small ones close to the end supports. But this is not generally necessary, for the flanges areas, modulus of section, and resistance to bending of a girder will near the supports for practical reasons be more than ample for resisting the small bending moments. A more reasonable plan for determining the modulus of the central section of a girder is to determine the parabola (and corresponding load) through the ends of the span, and enveloping the maximum bending-moment diagram for that part of the length of the beam over which the bending moment may exceed the minimum safe moment of resistance of the girder, viz. its safe moment of resistance at its ends. Experience shows about what fraction of the maximum modulus of section the minimum modulus will be for given length of span; such a fraction will decrease with increased length of span. A numerical example will make this point clear.

Example. Two loads of 10 tons each 12 ft. apart cross a span of 24 ft. Find the equivalent uniformly distributed load if the minimum modulus of section or product of depth and flange area is at least 40 per cent. of the maximum modulus of section on a 24-ft. span.

From (10), Art. 64, the maximum bending moment at a distance x from one end is

$$M_x = -x\{20(24-x)-120\}/24 = -5x(18-x)/6 \text{ ton-ft.}$$

which reaches zero for $x=0$ and $x=18$ ft., and a maximum negative magnitude for $x=9$ ft. When its value is

$$-7.5 \times 9 = -67.5 \text{ tons-ft. 3 ft. from the centre of the span.}$$

The diagram of maximum bending moment is shown at ADCGB, Fig. 96. The safe moment of resistance of all parts of the girder will exceed

$$\tfrac{40}{100} \times 67.5 = 27 \text{ ton-ft.}$$

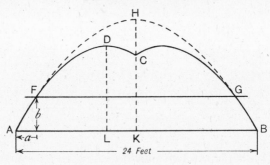

FIG. 96

So we may neglect all points on the diagram below the level (27 ton-ft.) of the horizontal line FG, and circumscribe the remainder of the diagram by a parabola AFHGB. This may be accomplished by drawing a parabola through A and F, having the centre line KC as axis. Let a and b be the co-ordinates of the intersection F of the line FG and the parabola AFC. The length a may be measured from the diagram or calculated thus: $b=27$ ton-ft., and from the above equation for M_x

$$\tfrac{5}{6}x(18-x)=27 \quad \text{hence } x \text{ or } a=9-\sqrt{(48.6)}=2.03 \text{ ft.}$$

The central height h or HK of the parabola is then

$$h=b\frac{(l/2)^2}{a(l-a)}=27 \times \frac{144}{44.60}=87.2 \text{ ton-ft.,}$$

giving the vertex H from which the parabola AFHGB can easily be drawn. If w is the equivalent load per foot

$$wl^2/8 \text{ or } 72w=87.2 \qquad w=1.21 \text{ ton per foot run.}$$

The parabola circumscribing the *whole* figure from A to B would have the same tangent at A as the parabola AFDC; its slope at $x=0$ is found by differentiating M_X to be $\frac{5}{6} \times 18 = 15$ ton-ft. per foot. For a central ordinate h' the slope at $A = 4h'/l = 4h'/24 = 15$. Hence $h' = 90$ ton-ft. The vertex might also easily be found graphically from the fact that the vertex D bisects the projection of the tangent at A on the axis DL, and the vertex of the circumscribing parabola bisects the projection of the same tangent (produced) on the axis KC.

Other Cases. The formula

$$h = b \frac{(l/2)^2}{a(l-a)}$$

will hold good when the co-ordinates such as a and b of various points are determined graphically by such a method as is given in Art. 65, trial being necessary with various points to find the greatest value of h, *i.e.* the height of the parabola which will envelop all the points.

The equivalent uniform load is also sometimes taken as that which would give the same maximum, and in some cases as that which would give the same average ordinate of the maximum bending-moment diagram; such an equivalent will generally give maximum bending-moment values for some sections which are less than the actual values, and for other sections values greater than the actual ones. In other words, the parabolic diagram will in some places fall within and in others outside the actual diagram of maximum bending moments. The errors will decrease with increase of span when the actual diagram of maximum bending moments will become more nearly a symmetrical parabola. Equality of average ordinate is the safer rule, and gives generally a greater central value. It may be approximately found by making the parabola agree with the actua' diagram at $\frac{1}{4}$-span from the supports, so that if w' is the unifo... load per foot from (7) Art. 61

$$(w'/2)(l/4)(3l/4) = \text{moment at } \tfrac{1}{4}\text{-span}$$
$$w' = 32/3 \times (\text{M at } \tfrac{1}{4}\text{-span})/l^2$$

There is no definite and general convention as to the precise significance of the term " equivalent " uniform load.

Equivalent uniformly distributed rolling loads for shear may also be found giving the same maximum ordinate as the actual diagram, but lower ordinates near the middle of the span; these loads will be greater than the equivalent uniform load for bending moments, particularly in short spans. No uniformly distributed load will give a maximum shear diagram completely enveloping that for the actual loads, for it cannot give, say, the same maximum positive shearing force very near to the left support, as occurs there under a concentrated wheel load; an inspection of Figs. 85 and 86 will show this, since the parabola with vertical axis has a horizontal tangent at its vertex. But near the middle of the span the shearing resistance of a girder will usually be greater than is necessary, and where the positive shears are low near a support the girder has a resistance sufficient for high negative shears.

Other Equivalent Loads. The actual maximum bending moments and shearing forces produced by a given train load may very nearly be reproduced by a uniformly distributed load, together with a concentrated load. Thus, Lea[1] finds that for a large number of locomotive loads on British railways for spans from 100 to 200 ft. (single track) for all sections the maximum shearing force may be represented by the effect of loads of 2 tons per ft., together with a load of 18 tons in the most influential position (see Arts. 73 and 74). The same loading gives close results for the maximum bending

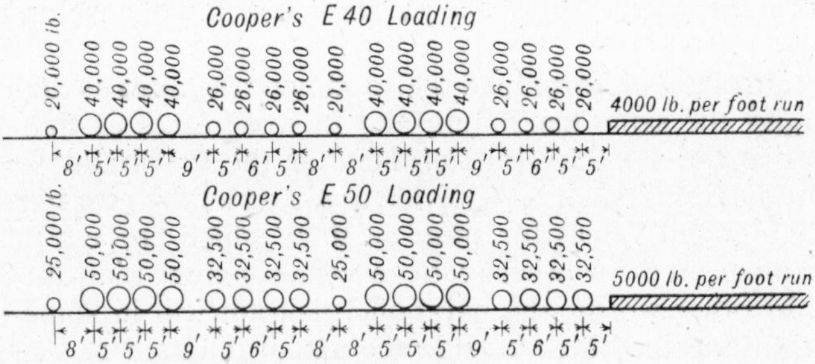

FIG. 97

moments, but may, of course, be replaced by a uniform load of $2+36/l$ tons per ft.

70. Conventional Train Loads. Instead of using equivalent uniformly distributed loads for the purpose of bridge design, a common practice in America and elsewhere is to use a conventional train load, consisting of axle loads representing something like railway loads, but simplified in distances apart and load per axle. In Cooper's system the spacing of the locomotive axles is in whole numbers of feet, and is kept constant for trains of different weights. Consequently, for every section in a given span the maximum bending moments and shearing forces are proportional, and if calculated for one train loading can be found for any other by multiplying by a constant factor. Fig. 97 represents Cooper's E 40 and E 50 loadings for a single line of railway. Thus class E 40 consists of two locomotives (each weighing about 127 English tons) with the axle loads shown, followed by a train load uniformly distributed of

[1] *Proc. Inst. C.E.*, vol. clxi, p. 284.

4,000 lb. per ft.   Class E 50 is derived from it by multiplying all loads by $\frac{5}{4}$. For bridge design loading on this basis is chosen of such weight as to be at least equivalent to any train load used on the railway.   One advantage of this method over tables of equivalent uniformly distributed loading for bending moment is that the same loading may be applied to find the maximum shearing force.

Standard Loading for British Railways.   The system of " unit " loading recommended by the Ministry of Transport is that devised and published by the British Standards Institution.[1]   As shown in Fig. 98, the distances between the axles are stated and a ratio is specified between the loads on driving axles and tender axles of locomotives, and the proportion of wagon load is similarly specified as a fraction of a unit of load per lineal foot.   An alternative two-axle load is provided for short spans, where the effect is to put more weight in longitudinal girder under 10-ft. span and to put more on cross-girders than would result from a four-axle distribution.   In

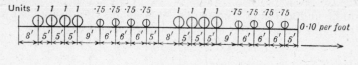

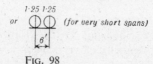

FIG. 98

the British Standard Specification No. 153, tables will be found giving the maximum bending moments produced by a one-unit loading for spans up to 300 ft. and the corresponding uniformly distributed load.   The figures given in the table only need to be multiplied by the prescribed number of units for any class of line and traffic to give the corresponding bending moments or equivalent loads.   A usual conventional load for main lines is 18 units (which corresponds to 18 tons on each driving axle, 13·5 tons on each tender axle and a train load of 1·8 tons per lineal ft).

The tables drawn up by the Bridge Stress Committee (see Art. 31) add to these values an allowance for hammer blow, *i.e.* for an impact effect.

Example 1.   Find the maximum bending moment at the centre of a 40-ft. span when it is crossed by the load E_{40}, Art. 70.   Marking on the edge of a strip of paper a length of 40 ft., and its middle point to scale and sliding it under load E_{40}, Fig. 97, it is evident that the

---

[1] B.S.S. No. 153, Appendix to Parts 3, 4, and 5 (1925).   Also Addendum (1930). These include unit loadings for highway bridges.

condition (3A), Art. 66, is satisfied when the fourth load from the left
is passing over the middle of the span.   For then the load in 1,000-lb.
units is $20+40+40+40=140$ to the left of the middle, and $40+26+26=92$ to the right of the centre, and the load 40 passing to the right
increases the 92 to 132 as it reduces 140 to 100, the loads on either
side passing through equal values.   The bending moment for this
position is easily calculated; taking moments about the right-hand
support for a 40-ft. span in 1,000-lb. units.

Left-hand reaction $\times 40=20\times 38+40(30+25+20+15)+26(6+1)$
$=4,542$.

Left-hand reaction $=\frac{4542}{40}=113 \cdot 5$ thousand pounds.

Bending moment at centre $=-113\cdot 5\times 20+(20\times 18)+40(10+5)=$
$-1,311$ units, a bending moment of 1,311,000 lb.-ft.

Example 2.   Find the maximum reaction on one of a series of
cross-girders spaced 20 ft. apart when they are traversed by a load
E_{50}, Art. 70.

By (6), Art. 68, this would be $\frac{2}{20}$ or $\frac{1}{10}$ times the maximum
bending moment at the centre of a 40-ft. span.   But using the result
of Example 1 above, this bending moment would be

$$1,311,000\times\tfrac{5}{4}=1,638,750 \text{ lb.-ft.,}$$

hence the maximum reaction is

$$\frac{1638750}{10}=163,875 \text{ lb.}$$

71. Combined Shearing Force Diagrams.   The shearing force
exerted by the dead loads on a beam is at any section always the
same, being positive at some section and negative at others.   At any
given section the extreme values of the resultant shearing force are
found by adding algebraically the constant shear due to the dead
load to the maximum positive and negative shears respectively caused
by the line load.   The resultants will form a diagram showing the
limits of the shearing force at every cross-section and whether or not
at any given section any change of sign in the shearing force takes
place.

At (3) of Fig. 99 the ordinates from $A'B'$ to $e'f'$ are equal to those
from AB to ef at (2), and the ordinates vertically upwards from $e'f'$
to $A'gc'$ give the maximum positive shear due to the combined
loads; the ordinate at g is zero, the negative shear due to the dead
load being at this section just sufficient to neutralise the maximum
positive shearing force due to the live load.   To the left of g the
negative shearing forces of the dead load exceed the maximum
shear forces due to the live load; the shear to the left of g is always
negative, the ordinates from gf' to gA' giving the minimum magnitudes of the negative shears, and the ordinates from gf' to $B'd'$
giving the maximum magnitudes.   Similarly to the right of h the
shearing force is always positive, the vertical ordinates from he'

to A'*gc*' giving the maximum magnitudes and those to *h*B' the minimum magnitudes.

Sections between *g* and *h* are subject to a change from positive to negative shearing force of the magnitudes given by the vertical ordinates from the line *e'f'* or *gh* to A*gc*' and to B'*hd*' respectively.

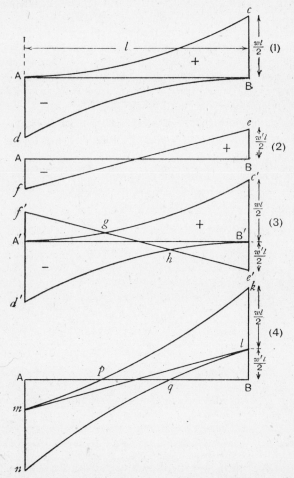

Fig. 99.—Combined shearing-force diagrams for moving and dead loads

The diagram of the extreme values of the shearing force on the span AB is again shown at (4), Fig. 99, the ordinates being measured from the horizontal base line AB, and being the algebraic sum of the ordinates in (1) and (2). The form (3) is rather easier to construct, but (4) is perhaps clearer. The length *pq* over which the shearing

G

force changes sign is sometimes called the *focal length* of the span. The position of the point *p* may be found graphically from the diagram, or algebraically if general expressions for shearing force due to each kind of load separately can be written and equated.

Example. Span 50 ft., live load 2 tons per foot run, dead load $\frac{3}{4}$ ton per ft. Find the length over which the shearing force changes sign.

At a distance *x* from the left end—

Maximum positive shear due to live load $= wx^2/2l = 2x^2/100 = x^2/50$ tons.

Magnitude of negative shear due to dead load $= w(\frac{1}{2}l - x) = \frac{3}{4}(25 - x)$.

These magnitudes are equal when

$$x^2/50 = \tfrac{3}{4}(25 - x) \text{ or } x^2 + 37 \cdot 5x - 937 \cdot 5 = 0$$

and neglecting the negative value of *x* (which is not on the span)

$$x = 17 \cdot 15 \text{ ft.}$$

Distance over which shear changes sign is

$$50 - 2 \times 17 \cdot 15 = 15 \cdot 7 \text{ ft.}$$

72. Influence Lines. An influence line is a curve showing for *one* section of a beam the shearing force, bending moment, stress, deflection or similar function for all positions of a moving load. It

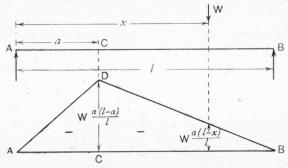

FIG. 100.—Influence line for bending moment

is important to distinguish between influence lines for bending moment or for shear and the diagrams previously dealt with in this chapter showing the *maximum* bending moment and shearing force at *all* sections of the beam.[1]

73. Influence Line for Bending Moment. *Single Load.* Consider the influence line for a point C, Fig. 100, on a span AB $= l$, distant *a*

[1] For supplementary work on influence lines see W. Abbot's *Practical Geometry and Engineering Graphics*, 3rd edition (Blackie), pp. 110–120. For application to continuous beams see "Moving Loads on Continuous Beams," by J. J. O'Dovovan iu *Engineering*, Nov. 21st and 28th, 1947.

from the support A and $l-a$ from the support B, for a single load W crossing the beam AB. When the load is distant x (greater than a) from A, the reaction at A is $W(l-x)/l$, and the bending moment at C, neglecting the negative sign, is

$$W(l-x)a/l$$

which varies from $Wa(l-a)/l$ to zero as x increases from a to l, *i.e.* as the load moves from C to B. The vertical ordinates of the line DB represent this varying bending moment at the fixed point C. Similarly the line AD by its ordinates gives the bending moment at C for all positions of the load between A and C, and ADB is the complete influence line in this case. It is quite evident that the

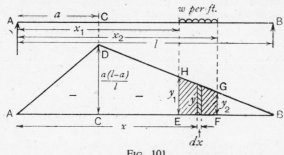

FIG. 101

bending moment at C is a maximum for $x=a$, *i.e.* when the load is at C, as already mentioned in Art. 62; the maximum bending moment for two concentrated loads has been shown in Art. 64, Fig. 89, which is a modified influence line for two loads.

Uniformly Distributed Load. Let the influence line ADB, Fig. 101, be drawn as in Fig. 100 for the point C for unit load (say 1 ton). Then any ordinate y distant x (greater than a, say) from A represents a bending moment at C

$$-a(l-x)/l$$

and if the moving load is w per foot run, a length dx distant x from A would exert a bending moment

$$-wdx \times a(l-x)/l$$

at C, represented by w times the strip of area ydx. Similarly every strip of area above a load between E and F represents a bending moment, and the total bending moment at C resulting from a uniformly distributed load from E to F would be represented by area

$$w \times \text{EFGH} \quad \text{or} \quad w\int_{x_1}^{x_2} ydx$$

and for all positions the bending moment at C is represented by the area over the loaded portion.

For a load longer than the span it is evident that the maximum bending moment at C occurs when the bending moment is represented by the whole triangle ADB, *i.e.* when the load covers the whole span. For loads shorter than the span it is easy to show here that condition (8), Art. 63, must be satisfied for the bending moment at C to be a maximum, and if d is the length of the load the distance of the loaded portion from A is $a-ad/l$.

The scale on which the area under the line ADB represents the bending moment is wqq' ton-ft. to 1 sq. in. if the linear horizontal scale is q ft. to 1 in. and the scale of bending moment vertically for the unit load is q' ton-ft. to 1 in., *i.e.* $DC=a(l-a)/lq'$ in.

74. Influence Lines for Shearing Force. *Single Load.* Consider the influence line for shear at the point C (Fig. 102), distant a from

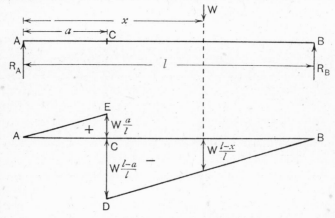

FIG. 102.—Influence line for shearing force

the support and $l-a$ from the support B on a beam of span l crossed by a single load W. When the load is distant x greater than a from the end A, the (negative) shear at C is equal to the upward reaction at A, which is found by taking moments about B

$$R_A l = W(l-x)$$

Shearing force at $C = -R_A = -W(l-x)/l$ . . . (1)

This value varies as the ordinates of a straight line DB, from 0 at B, where $x=l$, to a maximum negative value $DC = -W(l-a)/l$ at C, where $x=a$. When the load is between A and C, x is less than a, and the positive shear at C is equal to the reaction at B, viz.

$$\text{Shearing force at } C = +Wx/l$$

which varies as shown by the straight line AE from 0 at A, where

$x=0$, to a maximum $EC=Wa/l$ at C, where $x=a$. The complete influence line for shearing force at C is AEDB. The maximum shears obviously occur when the load is just reaching C.

Uniformly Distributed Load. Let ADEB (Fig. 103) represent the influence line for shear at C for a unit load, say 1 ton, moving over the span AB. Then the ordinate y, at a distance x from A, represents

$$-1 \times (l-x)/l \quad \text{or} \quad +1 \times x/l$$

according as x is greater or less than a. If a distributed load w per foot is on the span, an element wdx, distant x from A, exerts at C a shearing force wdx times that represented by the ordinate y, and is

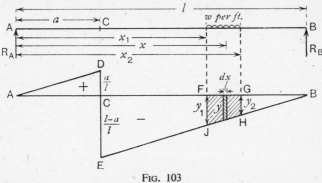

FIG. 103

represented by the area $y \cdot dx$ in the figure. A similar conclusion holds for every vertical strip of area between, say, F and G, and the total shearing force at C resulting from a distributed load between F and G is represented by the area

$$w \times \text{FGHJ}, \quad \text{or} \quad w\int_{x_1}^{x_2} ydx$$

and for all positions the shearing force at C is represented by the area enclosed over the loaded portion by the line ADEB. The shearing force (positive or negative) at C evidently has its greatest value when the load just reaches C; if the load extends on each side of C the areas must be added with proper algebraic sign.

The scale on which the area under the line ADEB represents the shearing force is wqq' tons per sq. in. if the linear or horizontal scale is q ft. to 1 in., and the scale of shearing force for the unit load is q' tons to 1 in., *i.e.* $DC=a/(lq')$ in. and $EC=(l-a)/(lq')$ in.

75. Influence Lines for Frame or Truss. (1) *For Shearing Force.* When the rolling load is transferred to the beam at joints as in an articulated frame or truss, or any bridge floor supported on cross-girders, the shearing force at all sections in any one panel (or

space between two consecutive joints) is the same.   Thus in Fig. 104,
if the load is carried by the lower joints, between D and C, the shearing force is the same for all points.   Consider the influence line for
shearing force in this panel when unit load (say 1 ton) crosses the
span AB, which is divided into n equal panels each l/n long.   Let
there be m panels to the left of D, and therefore $n-1-m$ panels to
the right of C.   When the load is between A and D, distant x from
A, the shearing force in the panel DC is equal to the reaction at B,
viz.

$$1 \times x/l$$

and the influence line is AE varying from 0 at A to m/n at D.

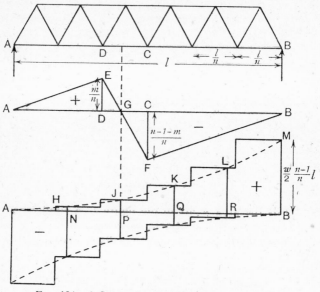

FIG. 104.—Influence line for shear in braced girder

Similarly when the load is between C and B the shearing force in
the panel DC is equal to minus the reaction at A, and the influence
line is FB varying from $(n-1-m)/n$ at C to zero at B.   As the load
moves from D to C, the shearing force between D and C diminishes
from the (variable) reaction at B by the amount of the load carried
at the joint C, which, like the reaction at B, varies uniformly with
increase of x: hence, the shearing force in the panel varies uniformly
with x, that is, as the ordinates of a straight line.   Hence the straight
line EF is the influence line.   In symbols the shearing force in the
panel DC, which is the reaction at B minus the load carried at C
(found by moments about D), is

$$x/l - (x - ml/n) \div l/n = (x - nx + ml)/l \quad . \quad . \quad . \quad (1)$$

which varies as a straight line from m/n when $x=ml/n$ at D to $-(n-1-m)/n$ at C when $x=(m+1)l/n$.

The line AEFB is then the whole influence line for shearing force in the panel DC. The maximum positive and negative shearing forces occur when the load is just to the left of D and right of C respectively.

Exactly as for the solid beam the area under the line AEFB and above any uniformly distributed load w per unit length, represents the shearing force in DC due to the distributed load. Evidently if the load is longer than BG the maximum shearing forces in the panel DC occur when the load reaches from an abutment to a point G which divides DC in the ratio m to $n-1-m$ so that

$$\text{DG}=\frac{m}{n-1}\cdot\text{DC}=\frac{m}{n-1}\cdot\frac{l}{n}, \quad \text{CG}=\frac{n-1-m}{n-1}\cdot\text{DC}=\frac{n-1-m}{n-1}\cdot\frac{l}{n} \quad (2)$$

$$\text{AG}=ml/(n-1) \quad \text{BG}=(n-1-m)l/(n-1) \quad . \quad . \quad (3)$$

It may be noted that $w\times\text{DG}=w\cdot\text{AG}/n$ in accordance with (4), Art. 67.

The maximum positive shearing force on the panel DC is

$$w\times\text{area AEG}=\frac{w}{2}\times\text{ED}\cdot\text{AG}=\frac{w}{2}\cdot\frac{m}{n}\left(m\frac{l}{n}+\frac{m}{n-1}\cdot\frac{l}{n}\right)$$

$$=\tfrac{1}{2}wm^2l/n(n-1) \quad . \quad . \quad . \quad . \quad . \quad . \quad (4)$$

And in the last panel on the right $m=n-1$, and the maximum shearing force is $\frac{w}{2}\cdot\frac{n-1}{n}\cdot l$, which would be the maximum shearing force at the abutment of a solid beam of length equal to $n-1$ panels.

The maximum negative shearing force in the panel DC is

$$w\times\text{area BGF}=\frac{w}{2}\times\text{CF}\cdot\text{GB}=\frac{w}{2}\cdot\frac{n-1-m}{n}\left(\frac{n-1-m}{n}\cdot l\right.$$

$$\left.+\frac{n-1-m}{n-1}\cdot\frac{l}{n}\right)=\frac{w}{2}\cdot\frac{(n-1-m)^2}{n(n-1)}\cdot l \quad . \quad . \quad (5)$$

And on the first panel on the left $m=0$, and the maximum negative shearing force is $\tfrac{1}{2}w(n-1)l/n$ as for the positive value at the other end of the span.

The maximum shears in the 1st, 2nd, 3rd, 4th, etc., up to the nth panel are respectively

$$0, 1^2, 2^2, 3^2, \text{etc.} \quad . \quad . \quad . \quad (n-1)^2 \text{ times } \tfrac{1}{2}wl/n(n-1) \quad . \quad (6)$$

or

$$0, \left(\frac{1}{n-1}\right)^2, \left(\frac{2}{n-1}\right)^2, \left(\frac{3}{n-1}\right)^2 \cdots \left(\frac{n-3}{n-1}\right)^2, \left(\frac{n-2}{n-1}\right)^2 \cdots 1$$

$$\text{times } \frac{w}{2}\cdot\frac{l}{n}\cdot(n-1).$$

which is the value in the end panels. Thus a parabola AHJKLM, the ordinate BM being $\frac{1}{2}w(n-1)l/n$, shows the maximum shearing force in each panel if the span is divided at ANPQRB into $n-1$ equal parts, and ordinates erected to cut the parabola. The points of division N, P. Q, R, B also indicate the load positions for maximum shearing forces, for in (3) above AG=$ml/(n-1)$, the points of division for the successive panels being 0, $l/(n-1)$, $2l/(n-1)$ . . . $(n-2)l/(n-1)$ and l from A.

For application of this influence line see Art. 133, and for extensions to the case of trusses with a curved chord see Art. 134.

(2) *For Bending Moments.* For a vertical section which cuts *a joint* of the *loaded* chord, say AB, Fig. 105, the influence line will be as in Fig. 100, Art. 73. For other sections such as C, Fig. 105 (including joints of the top chord), when loads are carried from

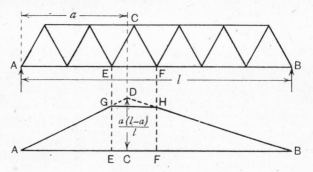

FIG. 105.—Influence line for bending moment in braced girder

joints of the lower chord the influence line will be the same for say unit load crossing the span AB as for a solid beam when the load is between A and E or between F and B. Hence it is AG and HB (Fig. 105) over these respective ranges where ADB would be the influence line for a solid beam. When the load is between E and F, *i.e.* in the panel in which the vertical section through C falls, the influence line will no longer be as for a solid beam, since the load is carried by the beam at the joints E and F. But it is evident that the bending moment at C will vary uniformly with the distance advanced by the load between E and F, *i.e.* the influence line will be a straight line joining G to H, and hence AGHB is the complete influence line for C when unit load traverses the span AB. For uniformly distributed loads we proceed as in Art. 73, *i.e.* the bending moment at C is represented by areas under the line AGHB and above the loaded portion, which clearly shows that the bending moment at C is a maximum when the span is fully loaded.

EXAMPLES VI

1. A load of 1 ton per ft. and over 60 ft. long crosses a span of 60 ft. Draw diagrams of maximum shearing force and bending moment. State the maximum positive and negative shearing force and maximum bending moment at 15 and 30 ft. from the left-hand support.

2. A single rolling load of 2 tons crosses a girder of 30-ft. span. Draw the diagrams of maximum shearing force and maximum bending moment, and state the maximum positive and negative shearing forces and the maximum bending moment at sections 5, 10, and 15 ft. from one end.

3. Draw the diagrams of maximum positive and negative shearing force and maximum bending moment for a load of $\frac{1}{2}$ ton per ft. and 30 ft. long crossing a span of 100 ft. What is the maximum positive shearing force at 15, 40, and 50 ft. from the left-hand support? State the maximum bending moment at the same sections. What load per foot extending over the whole span would produce the same maximum bending moment at every section as the above load?

4. The axle loads of a traction engine arc 16 and 8 tons at a distance of 15 ft. apart, and the engine crosses a girder of 50-ft. span, the smaller load leading from left to right. Draw the diagram of maximum bending moments. State the greatest ordinate and its distance from the centre of the span; also the maximum bending moment midway between the supports.

5. Work Problem No. 4 for a span of 25 ft. Below what span will the greatest bending moment anywhere occur when the smaller load is off the span?

6. Five loads A, B, C, D, and E, in the order given, cross a span of 60 ft. The loads at A=12 tons, B=20 tons, C=20 tons, D=8 tons, E=8 tons. The distance between the loads in the same order are 7, $7\frac{1}{2}$, 7, and 6 ft. Draw the diagrams of maximum shearing force and maximum bending moment. Where does the maximum bending moment occur and what is its amount?

7. Calculate the maximum bending moment at the centre of a span of 80 ft. when crossed by a train load class E_{30} (Art. 70). Also for a span of 30 ft.

8. Estimate the maximum pressure on cross-girders 15 ft. apart when a load of class E_{50} crosses a bridge.

9. Estimate the uniformly distributed load which would give the same maximum bending moment at 20 ft. from one support as the load E_{40} (Art. 70), on an 80-ft. span. Find the greatest maximum bending moment anywhere on the span for the uniform and for the actual load.

10. With the data of Problem No. 1, find the length over which the shear changes sign if the dead load is $\frac{3}{4}$ ton per foot run.

11. By means of the influence lines find maximum bending moments and positive and negative shearing forces at a point 40 ft. from the left abutment when a girder of 100-ft. span is traversed by a rolling load of 1 ton per ft., extending over a length of 30 ft.

DEFLECTION OF BEAMS

76. Stiffness and Strength. It is usually necessary that a beam should be *stiff* as well as strong, *i.e.* that it should not, due to loading, deflect much from its original position. The greatest part of the deflection is generally due to bending, which produces curvature related to the intensity of stress in the manner shown in Art. 44. A knowledge of the relation between the loading and deflection of a beam is often the first step in finding the bending moments to which a beam is subjected by given loadings and methods of fixing; also in finding the stresses in other parts of a structure of which the beam forms a part. Structures in which the distribution of force due to given loads cannot be determined by the ordinary methods applicable to rigid bodies, but depends upon the relative stiffness of the various parts, are called *Statically Indeterminate*. We now proceed to find the deflection of various parts of beams under a variety of different loadings and supported in various ways. The symbol y, a variable, will be used for deflections for different points along the neutral plane, from their original positions. This symbol is not to be confused with the variable y already used for the distances of points in a cross-section from the neutral axis of that section, although it is estimated in the same direction, usually vertically. It will be assumed that all deflections take place within the elastic limit, and are very small compared to the length of the beam.

77. Deflection in Simple Bending : Uniform Curvature. When a beam of constant section is subjected throughout its length to a uniform bending moment M it bends (see Arts. 44 and 46) to a circular arc of radius R, such that

$$\frac{E}{R} = \frac{M}{I} \text{ or } \frac{1}{R} = \frac{M}{EI}$$

where E is the modulus of direct elasticity, and I is the moment of inertia of the area of cross-section about the neutral axis. If a beam AB (Fig. 106) of length l, originally straight, bends to a circular arc AP'B, the deflection PP' or y, at the middle, can easily be found from the geometry of Fig. 106.

For
$$PP' \cdot PC = PB^2 = (\tfrac{1}{2}l)^2$$
$$PP'(2R - PP') = l^2/4$$
$$2PP' \cdot R - (PP')^2 = l^2/4$$

and for small deflections, neglecting $(PP')^2$, the square of a small quantity

$$2PP' \cdot R = l^2/4$$

$$y_1 \text{ or } PP' = \frac{l^2}{8R} = \frac{1}{8}\frac{Ml^2}{EI} \quad \cdots \cdots \quad (1)$$

since
$$R = \frac{EI}{M} \text{ (Art. 46)}$$

In this case the whole length is subject to the maximum bending moment M as between the supports in Fig. 51.   In other cases where parts of the beam are subject to less than the maximum bending

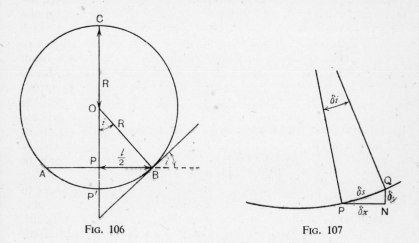

FIG. 106   FIG. 107

moment, the factor in the above expression for maximum deflection will be less than $\frac{1}{8}$.

If i is the angle of slope which the ends of the beam make with the original position AB, taking $i = \sin i$ for small deflections (in radians)

$$i = \frac{PB}{OB} = \frac{l}{2R} = \frac{Ml}{2EI} \quad \cdots \cdots \quad (2)$$

Uniform curvature is also treated in Art. 80, section (*d*).

78. Relations between Curvature, Slope, Deflections, etc.   Measuring distances x, along the (horizontal) span from any convenient origin, y (vertical), deflections perpendicular to x, i angles of slope (in radians) of the beam to some fixed direction, usually horizontal, and s lengths of arc of the profile of the neutral surface of the beam when bent (Fig. 107)

$$dy/dx = \tan i = i \text{ (very nearly if } i \text{ is always very small)}$$

The curvature of a line is usually defined as the change of i per unit length of arc, or

$$di/ds$$

and since (Fig. 107) δi is very small, δx is sensibly equal to δs, or $ds/dx = 1$, hence the curvature

$$\frac{1}{R} = \frac{di}{ds} = \frac{di}{dx} = \frac{d}{dx}\left(\frac{dy}{dx}\right) = \frac{d^2y}{dx^2} \quad \cdots \cdots \quad (1)^1$$

and

$$\frac{M}{EI} = \frac{1}{R} = \frac{d^2y}{dx^2} \quad \cdots \cdots \cdots \quad (2)$$

for any point x along the beam, for this relation, established for uniform curvature $\dfrac{1}{R}$, will also hold for every elementary length ds in cases where the curvature $\dfrac{1}{R}$ is variable.

Hence the slope

$$i \text{ or } \frac{dy}{dx} = \int \frac{d^2y}{dx^2}dx = \int \frac{M}{EI}dx \quad \cdots \cdots \quad (3)$$

the integration being between suitable limits.

And the deflection

$$y = \int \frac{dy}{dx}dx = \int i\,dx \text{ or } \iint \frac{M}{EI}dxdx \quad \cdots \quad (4)$$

between proper limits.

Combining the above relations with those in Art. 42 viz.

$$dM/dx = F \text{ and } dF/dx = w = d^2M/dx^2$$

where F is the shearing force and w is the load per unit length of span at a distance x from the origin, we have

$$F = \frac{d}{dx}\left(EI\frac{d^2y}{dx^2}\right) = EI\frac{d^3y}{dx^3} \quad \cdots \cdots \quad (5)$$

when E and I are constant, and

$$w = EI\frac{d^4y}{dx^4} \text{ or } \frac{d^4y}{dx^4} = \frac{w}{EI} \quad \cdots \cdots \quad (6)$$

If w is constant or a known integrable function of x, general expressions for F, M, i, and y at any point of the beam may be

---

[1] The approximation may be stated in another way.. The curvature

$$\frac{1}{R} = \frac{d^2y/dx^2}{\{1+(dy/dx)^2\}^{\frac{3}{2}}}$$

and if dy/dx is very small, higher powers than the first may be neglected, and $1/R$ reduces to d^2y/dx^2.

found by one, two, three, or four integrations respectively of the equation

$$EI\frac{d^4y}{dx^4}=w$$

a constant of integration being added at each integration. If sufficient conditions of the fixing or supporting of the beam are given, the values of the constants may be determined. If the general expression for the bending moment at any point can be written as an integrable function of x, as in Art. 40, general expressions for i and y may be found by twice integrating the equation

$$\frac{d^2y}{dx^2}=\frac{M}{EI}$$

Examples of both the above methods are given in the next article.

Signs. For y positive vertically downwards slopes i or dy/dx will be positive downwards in the direction of x positive (generally to the right); and convexity upwards corresponds to increase of dy/dx with increase of x, *i.e.* to positive values of d^2y/dx^2. In Art. 42, the sign of the bending moment was so chosen that a clockwise

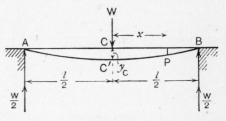

Fig. 108

moment of the external forces to the right was positive. Hence, if the clockwise moment of the external forces to the right of a section is written for M in equation (2) (whether positive or negative) positive curvature, *i.e.* $+d^2y/dx^2$, must be written on the other side of the equation. The same, of course, applies for the contraclockwise moments to the left of a section. If the moments are estimated in the opposite senses to those stated $-d^2y/dx^2$ must be used in equation (2). A violation of the rule of signs will lead to an error in the signs of i and y resulting from integrations of (2). It may be noted that a positive clockwise moment of external forces to the right of a section gives a positive value to d^2y/dx^2, *i.e.* the beam will be convex upward at that section.

79. Uniform Beam simply supported at its Ends with Simple Loads. The two following examples are worked out in considerable detail to illustrate the method of finding the constants of integration.

(a) Let there be a central load W (Fig. 108), and take C as origin. Then at P, distant x horizontally along the half-span CB from the origin C

$$\frac{d^2y}{dx^2}=\frac{M}{EI}=-\frac{1}{EI}\cdot\frac{W}{2}\left(\frac{l}{2}-x\right) \text{ (see Fig. 47)}$$

and integrating this

$$i \text{ or } \frac{dy}{dx} = \int \frac{d^2y}{dx^2} dx = -\frac{W}{2EI}\left(\frac{l}{2}x - \frac{x^2}{2}\right) + A$$

where A is a constant.

Since $i=0$ when $x=0$, substituting these values, $0=0+A$, therefore $A=0$; and with this choice of origin (C) A disappears, and

$$i \text{ or } \frac{dy}{dx} = -\frac{W}{2EI}\left(\frac{l}{2}x - \frac{x^2}{2}\right) \quad \dots \quad (1)$$

Integrating again

$$y = \int \frac{dy}{dx} dx = -\frac{W}{2EI}\left(\frac{l}{4}x^2 - \frac{x^3}{6}\right) + B \quad \dots \quad (2)$$

the constant of integration, B, being $+Wl^3/(48EI)$ since $y=0$ when $x=\frac{1}{2}l$. The equations (1) and (2) give the slope and deflection anywhere on the half-span, *e.g.* at the end, or $x=\frac{1}{2}l$,

$$i_B = -\frac{W}{2EI}\left(\frac{l^2}{4} - \frac{l^2}{8}\right) = -\frac{Wl^2}{16EI} \quad \dots \quad (3)$$

and at the centre, $y_C = \frac{Wl^3}{48EI}$ $\dots \dots \dots \dots$ (4)

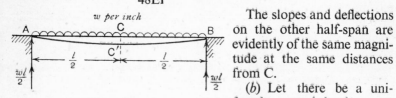

FIG. 109

The slopes and deflections on the other half-span are evidently of the same magnitude at the same distances from C.

(*b*) Let there be a uniformly spread load *w* per unit length. Take the origin at A (Fig. 109), and use the equation $EId^4y/dx^4 = w$. The four integrations require four known conditions to evaluate the four added constants. The four conditions in this case are

$$EId^2y/dx^2 = M = 0 \text{ for } x=0$$
$$d^2y/dx^2 = 0 \text{ for } x=l$$
$$y=0 \text{ for } x=0, \text{ and } y=0 \text{ for } x=l$$
$$EId^4y/dx^4 = w \quad \dots \dots \dots \dots (5)$$

Integrating $\qquad EId^3y/dx^3 = wx + A \dots \dots \dots$ (6)

Integrating again $\quad EId^2y/dx^2 = \frac{1}{2}wx^2 + Ax + 0$

the added constant being zero, since both sides must reduce to 0 for $x=0$.

Putting $\qquad d^2y/dx^2 = 0 \text{ when } x=l$
$$0 = \frac{1}{2}wl^2 + Al$$

hence $\qquad A = -\frac{1}{2}wl$

(a result which might also be obtained from (6), since the shearing force is zero for $x = \frac{1}{2}l$).

Then substituting for A

$$EI\, d^2y/dx^2 = \tfrac{1}{2}wx^2 - \tfrac{1}{2}wlx \quad \ldots \ldots \quad (7)$$

Integrating this

$$i = dy/dx = (\tfrac{1}{6}wx^3 - \tfrac{1}{4}wlx^2 + B)/EI \quad \ldots \quad (8)$$

Integrating again

$$y = (\tfrac{1}{24}wx^4 - \tfrac{1}{12}wlx^3 + Bx + 0)/EI$$

the constant being zero, since $y = 0$ for $x = 0$.

Putting
$$y = 0 \text{ for } x = l$$
$$0 = \tfrac{1}{24}wl^4 - \tfrac{1}{12}wl^4 + Bl$$

therefore
$$B = \tfrac{1}{24}wl^3$$

which might also be found from (8), since by symmetry $i = 0$ for $x = \frac{1}{2}l$,

and
or
$$\left.\begin{array}{l} y = (\tfrac{1}{24}wx^4 - \tfrac{1}{12}wlx^3 + \tfrac{1}{24}wl^3x)/EI \\ y = wx(l-x)(l^2 + lx - x^2)/(24EI) \end{array}\right\} \quad . \quad (9)$$

(6), (7), (8), and (9) give F, M, i, and y respectively for any point distant x along the beam from the end A. For example, i is a maximum when $di/dx = 0$ or $M = 0$, *i.e.* at the ends; thus, writing $x = 0$ in (8)

$$i_A = \frac{B}{EI} = \frac{wl^3}{24EI} \quad \ldots \ldots \quad (10)$$

y is a maximum when dy/dx or $i = 0$, *i.e.* when $x = \frac{1}{2}l$,

and then
$$y_C = \frac{wl^4}{24EI}(\tfrac{1}{16} - \tfrac{1}{4} + \tfrac{1}{2}) = \frac{5}{384}\frac{wl^4}{EI} \quad \ldots \quad (11)$$

or, if the whole load $wl = W$

$$y_C = \frac{5}{384} \cdot \frac{Wl^3}{EI} \quad \ldots \ldots \quad (12)$$

The signs here all agree with and illustrate the convention given at the end of Arts. 42 and 78.

Overhanging Ends. For points between two supports a distance l apart the work would be just as before, except that $EI\, d^2y/dx^2$ at each support would be equal to the bending moment due to the overhanging end instead of zero.

Propped Beam. If this beam were propped by a central support to the same level as the ends, the central deflection becomes zero, or, in other words, the upward deflection caused by the reaction of the prop (and proportional to it) is equal to the downward deflection as used by the load at the middle of the span.

Let P be the upward reaction of the prop; then from (4) and (11)

$$\frac{Pl^3}{48EI} = \frac{5}{384}\frac{wl^4}{EI} \qquad \ldots \ldots \quad (13)$$

and $P = \frac{5}{8}wl$, *i.e.* the central prop carries $\frac{5}{8}$ of the whole load, while the end supports each carry $\frac{3}{16}$ of the load.

Sinking of Prop. If the prop is not level with the end supports, but removes $1/n$ of the deflection due to the downward load, the reaction of the prop will be $1/n$ of the above amount.

Elastic Prop. If the central prop and end supports were originally at the same level, but were elastic and such that the pressure required to depress each unit distance is e, the compression of the prop is P/e, and of each end support $\dfrac{wl-P}{2e}$. Then equating the difference of levels to the downward deflection due to the load, minus the upward deflection due to P

$$\frac{P}{e} - \frac{wl-P}{2e} = \frac{5}{384}\frac{wl^4}{EI} - \frac{Pl^3}{48EI}$$

$$P\left(\frac{3}{2e} + \frac{l^3}{48EI}\right) = wi\left(\frac{5}{384}\frac{l^3}{EI} + \frac{1}{2e}\right)$$

$$P = wl\frac{\frac{5}{8} + \dfrac{24EI}{el^3}}{1 + \dfrac{72EI}{el^3}} \qquad \ldots \quad (14)$$

which evidently reduces to the previous result for perfectly rigid supports for which e is infinite, and approaches $\frac{1}{3}wl$ for very elastic supports. If the elasticities of the end supports and central prop are different, the modification in the above would be simple.

Relation between Bending Stress and Deflection. For a beam simply supported at each end and carrying a uniformly distributed load, if δ = central deflection, f = maximum bending stress in tons per sq. in., and d = depth of symmetrical section in inches, from (12)

$$\delta = \frac{5}{384}\frac{Wl^3}{EI} \qquad \ldots \ldots \quad (15)$$

And from Art. 46

$$\tfrac{1}{8}Wl = f \cdot \frac{2I}{d} \quad \text{or} \quad \frac{Wl}{I} = \frac{16f}{d}$$

hence substituting in (15)

$$l^2 = \tfrac{24}{5}d\delta E/f \qquad \ldots \ldots \quad (16)$$

The deflection δ for steel beams is commonly limited to $\frac{1}{400}$ of the span l, then taking $E=12,500$ tons per sq. in. (16) becomes

$$l=150d/f \text{ in.} \quad . \quad . \quad . \quad . \quad . \quad . \quad (17)$$

which gives the limit of span for uniform loading: if $f=7\cdot5$ tons per sq. in., $l/d=20$. Any degree of concentration of the load with the same limitations of stress and deflection will allow a greater ratio of span to depth, *e.g.* for a central load the equation corresponding to (17) would be $l=187\cdot5d/f$ in.

Example 1.   A beam of 10-ft. span is supported at each end and carries a distributed load which varies uniformly from nothing at one support to 4 tons per foot run at the other. The moment of inertia of the cross-section being 375 (in.)^4, and E 13,000 tons per sq. in., find the slopes at each end and the magnitude and position of the maximum deflection.

The conditions of the ends are as before.   Take the origin at the light end; then at a distance x in. along the span the load per inch run is

$$\frac{x}{120}\times\frac{4}{12}=\frac{x}{360} \text{ tons}$$

$$d^4y/dx^4=x/(360\text{EI})$$

$$d^3y/dx^3=(\tfrac{1}{2}x^2+\text{A})/(360\text{EI})$$

$$d^2y/dx^2=(\tfrac{1}{6}x^2+\text{A}x+0)/(360\text{EI})$$

$$d^2y/dx^2=0 \text{ for } x=l; \text{ hence } \text{A}=-l^2/6 \text{ and}$$

$$d^2y/dx^2=(x^3-l^2x)/(2160\text{EI})$$

$$dy/dx=(\tfrac{1}{4}x^4-\tfrac{1}{2}l^2x^2+\text{B})/(2160\text{EI})$$

$$y=(\tfrac{1}{20}x^5-\tfrac{1}{6}l^2x^3+\text{B}x+0)/(2160\text{EI})$$

$y=0$ for $x=l$; hence

$$\text{B}=\frac{l^4}{6}-\frac{l^4}{20}=\frac{7l^4}{60}$$

$$dy/dx=(\tfrac{1}{4}x^4-\tfrac{1}{2}l^2x^2+7l^4/60)/(2160\text{EI})$$

and $\qquad y=(\tfrac{1}{20}x^5-\tfrac{1}{6}l^2x^2+7l^4/60)/(2160\text{EI})$

At the light end $x=0$

$$\frac{dy}{dx}=\frac{7\times120^4}{60}\times\frac{1}{2160\times13,000\times375} \text{ radians}=0\cdot131°$$

At the heavy end $x=120$ in., $dy/dx=0\cdot150°$.

At the point of maximum deflection $dy/dx=0$; therefore

$$\frac{x^4}{4}-\frac{l^2x^2}{2}+\frac{7}{60}l^4=0$$

hence, solving $\qquad\qquad x=0\cdot52l=62\cdot4$ in.

and substituting this value, $\qquad y=0\cdot0925$ in.

Example 2. A wooden plank 12 in. wide, 4 in. deep, and 10 ft. long, is suspended from a rigid support by three wires, each of which is $\frac{1}{8}$ sq. in. in section and 15 ft. long, one being at each end, and one midway between them. All the wires being just drawn up tight, a uniform load of 400 lb. per foot run is placed on the plank. Neglecting the weight of the wood, find the tension in the central and end wires, and the greatest intensity of bending stress in the plank, the direct modulus of elasticity (E) for the wires being 20 times that for the wood.

Let E_s be the modulus for the wires, and E_w that for the wood $= \frac{1}{20}E_s$. The force per inch stretch of the wires $(e) = \dfrac{E_s}{8 \times 180}$, the strain being $\frac{1}{800}$. For the wooden beam supported at the centre

$$I = \tfrac{1}{20} \times 12 \times 64 = 64 \text{ (in.)}^4$$

The load on the central wire may be found from (14) above; the term

$$\frac{24E_w I}{el^3} = \frac{24E_w \times 64 \times 8 \times 180}{E_s \times 120 \times 120 \times 120} = 0.064$$

hence, by (14) the total tension in the middle wire is

$$P = 4,000 \times \frac{0.625 + 0.064}{1 + (3 \times 0.064)} = 4,000 \times 0.578 = 2,312 \text{ lb.}$$

In each end wire, total pull $\quad = \dfrac{4,000 - 2,312}{2} = 844 \text{ lb.}$

The greatest bending moment may occur at the middle support, where the diagram is discontinuous, or as a mathematical maximum between the end and the middle of the beam.

At x in. from one end

$$M = 844x - \tfrac{1}{2} \cdot \tfrac{400}{12} x^2$$

$$\frac{dM}{dx} = 844 - 1\tfrac{100}{3} x$$

which is zero for $x = 25.32$ in.

Substituting this for x

$$M = 21,370 - 10,685 = 10,685 \text{ lb.-in.}$$

At the middle of the span

$$M = (844 \times 60) - (2,000 \times 30) = -9,360 \text{ lb.-in.}$$

this being less than that at $x = 25.32$ in.

The greatest intensity of bending stress is

$$\frac{M y_1}{I} = \frac{10,685 \times 2}{64} = 334 \text{ lb. per sq. in.}$$

80. Uniform Cantilever simply loaded. (*a*) A concentrated load W at the free end. Take the origin O (Fig. 110) at the fixed end. Then for $x=0$, $dy/dx=0$, and $y=0$.

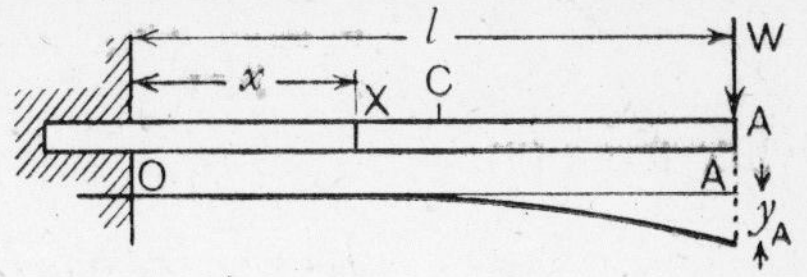

At any point x the bending moment

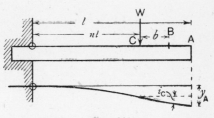

FIG. 110

$$EI \cdot d^2y/dx^2 = W(l-x)$$
$$EI\,dy/dx = W(lx - \tfrac{1}{2}x^2) + 0$$
$$EI \cdot y = W(\tfrac{1}{2}lx^2 - \tfrac{1}{6}x^3) + 0$$

At the end A

$$\left(\frac{dy}{dx}\right)_A \quad \text{or} \quad i_A = \frac{W}{EI}(l^2 - \tfrac{1}{2}l^2) = \frac{Wl^2}{2EI} \quad \ldots \ldots \quad (1)$$

and
$$y_A = \frac{Wl^3}{EI}(\tfrac{1}{2} - \tfrac{1}{6}) = \frac{Wl^3}{3EI} \quad \ldots \ldots \quad (2)$$

Note that the upward deflection of the support relative to the centre of the beam in Fig. 108 might be found from the formula (2), viz.

$$\frac{\dfrac{W}{2} \cdot \left(\dfrac{l}{2}\right)^3}{3EI} = \frac{Wl^3}{48EI} \text{ (as in (4), Art. 79)}$$

(*b*) A concentrated load distant nl from the fixed end. Origin at O (Fig. 111) at the fixed end, all conditions as above.

FIG. 111

From O to C
$$EI\,d^2y/dx^2 = W(nl - x)$$
$$EI\,dy/dx = W(nlx - \tfrac{1}{2}x^2) + 0$$
$$EI \cdot y = W(\tfrac{1}{2}nlx^2 - \tfrac{1}{6}x^3)$$

At C
$$\left(\frac{dy}{dx}\right)_C \quad \text{or} \quad i_C = \frac{W(nl)^2}{2EI} \text{ (as before)} \quad \ldots \quad (3)$$

and
$$y_C = \frac{W(nl)^3}{3EI} \quad \ldots \ldots \quad (4)$$

At any point B beyond C the slope remains the same as at C, and the deflection at B exceeds that at C by

$$b \times \text{(slope from C to B)} = b \cdot \frac{W(nl)^2}{2EI}$$

In particular
$$y_A = \frac{W(nl)^3}{3EI} + \frac{Wn^2l^3(1-n)}{2EI} = \frac{Wl^3n^2}{6EI}(3-n) \quad \ldots \quad (5)$$

The same formula would be applicable to any number of loads and for a number of different values of W and n may be written

$$y_A = \frac{l^3}{6EI}\{3\,\Sigma(Wn^2) - \Sigma(Wn^3)\} \quad . \quad . \quad (5A)$$

while from (3)

$$i_A = \frac{l^2}{2EI}\Sigma(Wn^2) \quad . \quad . \quad . \quad . \quad . \quad . \quad (3A)$$

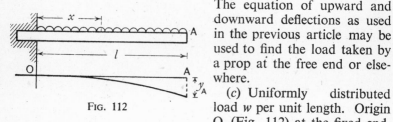

The equation of upward and downward deflections as used in the previous article may be used to find the load taken by a prop at the free end or elsewhere.

(*c*) Uniformly distributed load *w* per unit length. Origin O (Fig. 112) at the fixed end.

FIG. 112

A start may be made from relation (2) or (6) of Art. 78. Selecting the former

$$M = EI\,d^2y/dx^2 = \tfrac{1}{2}w(l-x)^2 = \tfrac{1}{2}w(l^2 - 2lx + x^2)$$

$$EI\,dy/dx = \tfrac{1}{2}w(l^2x - lx^2 + \tfrac{1}{3}x^3) + 0$$

$$EI\,.\,y = \tfrac{1}{2}w(\tfrac{1}{2}l^2x^2 - \tfrac{1}{3}lx^3 + \tfrac{1}{12}x^4) + 0$$

For $x = l -$

$$i_A \text{ or } \left(\frac{dy}{dx}\right)_A = \frac{wl^3}{2EI}(1 - 1 + \tfrac{1}{3}) = \tfrac{1}{6}\frac{wl^3}{EI} \text{ or } \tfrac{1}{6}\frac{Wl^2}{EI} \quad . \quad (6)$$

where $W = wl$.

$$y_A = \frac{wl^4}{2EI}(\tfrac{1}{2} - \tfrac{1}{3} \times \tfrac{1}{12}) = \tfrac{1}{8}\frac{wl^4}{EI} \text{ or } \tfrac{1}{8} \cdot \frac{Wl^3}{EI} \quad . \quad . \quad (7)$$

The result (12), Art. 79, might be deduced from the above, for the upward deflection of the support relative to the centre of the beam is

$$\frac{\frac{wl}{2} \cdot \left(\frac{l}{2}\right)^3}{3EI} - \frac{w\left(\frac{l}{2}\right)^4}{8EI} = \frac{5}{384} \cdot \frac{wl^4}{EI}$$

Partial Uniformly Distributed Load. If the load only extended a distance *nl* from the fixed end, the deflection at the free end would be, by the method employed in (5) above

$$y = \tfrac{1}{8}\frac{w(nl)^4}{EI} + (1-n)\frac{l}{6} \cdot \frac{w(nl)^3}{EI} = \frac{wl^4n^3}{24EI}(4-n) \quad . \quad . \quad (7A)$$

If the load extended from the free end to a distance nl from the fixed end, the deflection of the free end would be found by subtracting (7A) from (7).

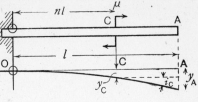

(d) Bending couple μ at a distance nl from the fixed end where n is a fraction. Origin at the fixed end O (Fig. 113).

FIG. 113

From O to C
$$EId^2y/dx^2 = \mu$$
$$EIdy/dx = \mu x + 0$$
$$EIy = \tfrac{1}{2}\mu x^2$$

At C and beyond
$$dy/dx = i_C = \mu nl/EI \qquad . \quad . \quad . \quad . \quad . \quad . \quad . \quad (8)$$
$$y_C = \tfrac{1}{2}\mu(nl)^2/(EI) \qquad . \quad . \quad . \quad . \quad . \quad . \quad (9)$$
$$y_A = y_C + l(1-n)i_C = \mu nl^2(1 - \tfrac{1}{2}n)/EI \quad . \quad . \quad (10)$$

And if $n = l$
$$i_C = \mu l/EI \qquad y_C = \mu l^2/2EI \quad . \quad . \quad . \quad . \quad . \quad (11)$$

Which agree with (2) and (1), Art. 77, if we write M for μ and $\tfrac{1}{2}l$ for l. If the couple μ consists of two opposite vertical forces at a distance a apart each will be equal to μ/a, and if the downward force is distant nl from the fixed end the downward deflection at the free end due to it from (5) is

$$\frac{\mu}{a}\left\{\frac{(nl)^3}{3EI} + l(1-n)\frac{(nl)^2}{2EI}\right\} \quad . \quad . \quad . \quad . \quad (12)$$

while the resultant deflection of the free end due to the two forces is found by subtracting from (12) the corresponding expression with $(nl - a)$ substituted for nl throughout. The result will approach the value (9) as a approaches zero. From (3) the slope between $x = nl$ and $x = l$ is

$$\frac{\mu}{a} \cdot \frac{1}{2EI}\{(nl)^2 - (nl-a)^2\} = \frac{\mu}{2EI}(2nl - a) \quad . \quad . \quad . \quad (13)$$

which approaches (8) as a approaches zero.

Propped Cantilever. From (2) and (7) it is evident, by equating upward and downward deflections, that a prop at the free end, level with the fixed end, when loaded, would carry $\tfrac{3}{8}$ of the whole distributed load. The bending-moment diagram may be drawn by superposing diagrams such as Fig. 43 and Fig. 45, making $W = \tfrac{3}{8}wl$, and taking the difference of the ordinates as representing the resulting bending moments. The curve of shearing force is a straight line similar to that of Fig. 45, but raised throughout by an amount $\tfrac{3}{8}wl$ relative to the base-line. Other types of loading of propped cantilevers may be dealt with on similar principles. For example, if P is the pressure on an end prop for a beam loaded as in Fig. 113 from (2) and (10)

$$\frac{Pl^3}{3EI} = \frac{\mu n l^2}{EI}\left(1 - \frac{n}{2}\right) \quad . \quad . \quad . \quad . \quad (14)$$

hence

$$P = 3\mu n(1 - \tfrac{1}{2}n)/l \quad . \quad . \quad . \quad . \quad (15)$$

It may be noted for future reference (Art. 89) that if $n=1$, $P=3\mu/2l$ and at the fixed end O of the beam, the bending moment

$$M_O = \mu - Pl = \mu - 3\mu/2 = -\tfrac{1}{2}\mu \quad . \quad . \quad . \quad (16)$$

which is half the bending moment at the propped end and of opposite sign, implying opposite curvature.

The reader should work out some simple cases fully as an exercise, noting the points of maximum deflection, contraflexure, etc., by integration of the equation $EId^4y/dx^4 = w$, the conditions being $y=0$ at both ends, slope $=0$ at the fixed end, and $d^2y/dx^2=0$ at the free end.

Sinking Prop. If the prop is below the level of the fixed end, the load carried by it would be proportionately reduced. If it is above that level, the load on it would be proportionately increased.

Elastic Prop. If the fixed end is rigid and the support at the free end is elastic, requiring a force e per unit of depression and being before loading at the same level as the fixed end, for the above simple case of distributed load, equating the depression of the prop to the difference of deflections due to the load and the prop

$$\frac{P}{e} = \tfrac{1}{8}\frac{wl^4}{EI} - \frac{Pl^3}{3EI}$$

whence

$$P = wl\left(\frac{\frac{3}{8}}{1 + \dfrac{3EI}{el^3}}\right)$$

For other types of loading or positions of prop, similar principles would hold good.

Example 1. A cantilever carries a concentrated load W at $\frac{3}{4}$ of its length from the fixed end, and is propped at the free end to the level of the fixed end. Find what proportion of the load is carried on the prop.

Let W be the load, and P the pressure on the prop. Then

$$\frac{Pl^3}{EI} = \tfrac{1}{3}\frac{W(\tfrac{3}{4}l)^3}{EI} + \tfrac{1}{4}l \cdot \frac{W(\tfrac{3}{4}l)^2}{2EI}$$

$$\tfrac{1}{3}P = W(\tfrac{9}{64} + \tfrac{91}{128}) = \tfrac{27}{128}W$$

$$P = \tfrac{81}{128}W$$

Example 2. A cantilever 100 ft. long carries a uniformly spread load over 5 ft. of its length, running from a point 3 ft. from the fixed end to a point 2 ft. from the free end, which is propped to the same level as the fixed end. Find what proportion of the load is carried by the prop.

Let w=load per foot run, and P=pressure on the prop. The total load is $\frac{1}{2}wl$. Deflection of the free end if unpropped would be

$$\frac{1}{8}\frac{w(0\cdot8l)^4}{EI}+0\cdot2l\,.\,\frac{1}{6}\frac{w(0\cdot8l)^3}{EI}-\left\{\frac{1}{8}\frac{w(0\cdot3l)^4}{EI}+0\cdot7l\,.\,\frac{1}{6}\frac{w(0\cdot3l)^3}{EI}\right\}$$

$$=\frac{wl^4}{EI}\left\{\frac{0\cdot4096}{8}+\frac{0\cdot1024}{6}-\frac{0\cdot0081}{8}-\frac{0\cdot0189}{6}\right\}=0\cdot0641\frac{wl^4}{EI}$$

Therefore $\qquad\qquad \frac{1}{3}\frac{Pl^3}{EI}=0\cdot0641\frac{wl^4}{EI}$

$$P=0\cdot1923wl \text{ or } 0\cdot385 \text{ of the total load.}$$

Note that this is less than half the load, although the centre of gravity of the load is nearer to the propped end.

Example 3. A vertical stanchion 15 ft. long is fixed at the lower end and hinged at the top end so as to form a cantilever propped at the free end. It is acted upon by two equal and opposite horizontal forces which form a couple of 10 ton-ft., the more distant being 10 ft. and the nearer one 7·5 ft. from the fixed end. Find the reaction at the hinged end and the bending moments at the loads and fixed end (Fig. 114). Using expression (12) where $\frac{\mu}{a}=\frac{10}{2\cdot5}=4$ tons, or equation (5), the deflection of the hinged end A, if free, would be

$$\frac{4\times15^3}{EI}\left\{\frac{8}{27\times3}+\frac{4}{27\times2}\right\}-\frac{4\times15^3}{EI}\left\{\frac{1}{8\times3}+\frac{1}{2}\,.\,\frac{1}{4}\,.\,\frac{1}{2}\right\}=\frac{4\times15^3}{EI}\times\frac{89}{16\times81}$$

And if R=horizontal reaction at the hinge from (2), the opposite deflection counteracting that of the couple is

$$\frac{R\times15^3}{3EI}$$

hence $\qquad R=\dfrac{12\times89}{16\times81}=0\cdot824$ tons.

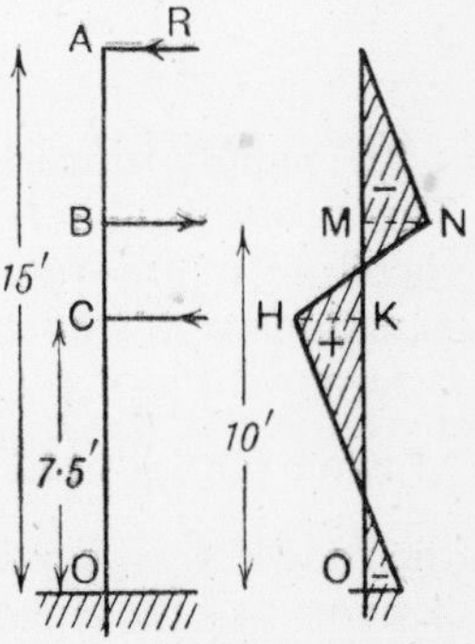

Bending moment at B (Fig. 114)=
$-5\times0\cdot824=-4\cdot12$ ton-ft.
Bending moment at C=
$-7\cdot5\times0\cdot824+10=+3\cdot82$ ton-ft.
Bending moment at O=
$-15\times0\cdot824+10=-2\cdot36$ ton-ft.

FIG. 114

The bending-moment diagram is shown to the right of Fig. 114, the positive sign corresponding to convexity towards the left. The points of inflexion could easily be calculated. The ordinate MN exceeds the ordinate HK. The position of application of the couple to produce least bending moment might be found by equating expressions for MN and HK in terms of a variable corresponding to OB or OC.

Example 4. A bar of steel 2 in. square is bent at right angles 3 ft. from one end; the other and longer arm is firmly fixed vertically in the ground, the short (3-ft.) arm being horizontal and 10 ft. above the ground. A weight of $\frac{1}{4}$ ton is hung from the end of the horizontal arm. Find the horizontal and vertical deflection of the free end. E = 13,000 tons per sq. in.

The bending moment throughout the long arm is sensibly the same as that at the bend, viz. $\frac{1}{4} \times 36 = 9$ ton-in.

It therefore bends to a circular arc, the lower end remaining vertical. A line joining the two ends of the long arm would therefore make with the vertical an angle

$$\frac{Ml}{2EI} \text{ (Art. 77 (2) or (11) Art. 80)} = \frac{9 \times 120}{2EI}$$

$$= \frac{9 \times 120 \times 12}{2 \times 13,000 \times 16} = \frac{81}{2,600} \text{ radians}$$

and the horizontal deflection of the whole of the short arm will be

$$\tfrac{81}{2600} \times \tfrac{120}{1} = \tfrac{243}{65} = 3\cdot74 \text{ in.}$$

The inclination of the upper end of the long arm to the vertical is evidently twice the amount $\frac{81}{2600}$, which is the average inclination. The downward slope of the short cantilever arm is therefore $\frac{81}{1300}$ at the bend. The total vertical deflection at the free end is

$$36 \times \tfrac{81}{1300} + \frac{\frac{1}{4} \times 36 \times 36 \times 36 \times 12}{3 \times 13,000 \times 16} = 2\cdot243 + 0\cdot224 = 2\cdot467 \text{ in.}$$

81. Simply supported Beam with Concentrated Load or Couple. This problem involves a discontinuity in the bending moment and therefore in the rate of change of slope of the beam. Different equations apply to the two parts of the span thus involving the determination of four constants of integration for two integration of two equations $\left(EI\dfrac{d^2y}{dx^2} = M \right)$. The constants may be found from the four known conditions, viz. zero deflections ($y = 0$) at each end support and the equal values of y and of dy/dx at the junction of the two parts of the span of the load. The work can, however, be much simplified by a device due to R. Macaulay.[1]

---

[1] "Note on the Deflection of Beams," *Messenger of Mathematics*, Vol. 48 (1919).

Single Load. Let W be a load concentrated at a distance *a* from one support A (Fig. 115 (*a*)) and *b* (or *l*−*a*) from the other support B, the span (AB) being *l*.

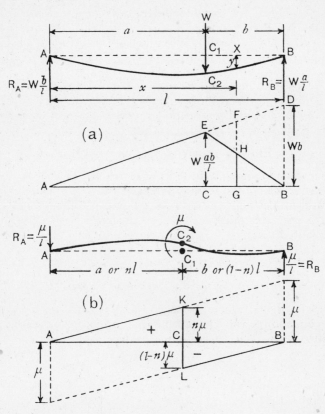

(a)

(b)

FIG. 115

Then the reactions at A and B are

$$R_A = Wb/l \text{ and } R_B = Wa/l$$

Taking A as origin, for values of x from A to C_1, the bending moment is

$$M = -Wbx/l \quad . \quad . \quad . \quad . \quad (1)$$

and from C_1 to B, the bending moment HG is

$$M = -Wbx/l + W(x-a) \quad . \quad . \quad . \quad (2)$$

and since $EId^2y/dx^2 = M$, from C_1 to B

$$EId^2y/dx^2 = Wbx/l + W(x-a) \quad . \quad . \quad . \quad (3)$$

The equations (1) and (2) indicate the discontinuity of M and therefore of the rate of change of slope of the beam at the load. The bending-moment diagram is AEB. But referring to equation (3) the first term on the right-hand side; $-Wbx/l$ represents EI times the rate of increase of slope due to R_A (which being negative shows a *decrease* of slope) and the second term $W(a-x)$ represents EI times the rate of increase of slope due to W, which is only valid when $x > a$. The slope at any section X distant x from A will be equal to the initial slope i_A at A plus the algebraic increase from A to X, which is to be found by integrating the rate of change from A to X making proper allowance for the discontinuity in the rate at C_1, *i.e.* for the addition of the term $W(x-a)$ from C_1 to X if X is to the right of C_1 and ignoring it when $x < a$. Thus integrating (3)

$$EIi_x = EIdy/dx = -\tfrac{1}{2}Wbx^2/l + \tfrac{1}{2}W(x-a)^2 + EIi_A \quad . \quad . \quad (4)$$

on the understanding that the term involving $(x-a)^2$ is to be ignored when $x < a$. (Note the form of integration of $x-a$ which is legitimate with proper adjustment of the constant of integration. Also that i_A is the value of dy/dx for $x=0$ where the term $\tfrac{1}{2}W(x-a)^2$ is to be ignored.)

Integrating equation (4) and again ignoring the second term $\tfrac{1}{2}W(x-a)^2$ when $x < a$

$$EIy = -\tfrac{1}{6}Wbx^3/l + \tfrac{1}{6}W(x-a)^3 + EIi_Ax + 0 \quad . \quad . \quad (5)$$

since $y=0$ for $x=0$ where the second term is ignored.

This equation is valid for all the span provided the second term is omitted when $x < a$. And since $y=0$ when $x=l$

$$0 = -(-Wbl^2 + Wb^3)/6EI + i_Al$$

hence $i_A = Wb(l^2 - b^2)/(6EIl)$

Substituting this in (5)

$$y = \frac{W}{6EI} \cdot \left\{ \frac{bx(l^2 - b^2 - x^2)}{l} + (x-a)^3 \right\} \quad . \quad . \quad (6)$$

where the term $(x-a)^3$ is to be ignored when $x < a$. This may also be stated in a form convenient for application to several loads by writing nl for a where n is the fraction a/l,

$$y = \frac{W}{6EI} \left[\frac{(1-n)\{n(2-n)l^2 - x^2\}x}{l} + (x-nl)^3 \right] \quad . \quad . \quad (7)$$

where the last term $(x-nl)^3$ is only to be used for $x > nl$.

From (6) or (7) the deflection C_1C_2 at the load is

$$y_C = \frac{Wa^2b^2}{3EIl} \quad \text{or} \quad \frac{Wl^3n^2(1-n)^2}{3EI} \quad . \quad . \quad . \quad (8)$$

But this is not the maximum deflection unless $n=\frac{1}{2}$. The maximum and zero slope can be found where $dy/dx=0$. From (6) or from (4) and the value of i_A, for $x<a$

$$\frac{dy}{dx}=\frac{Wb}{6EIl}(-3x^2+l^2-b^2)$$

which is zero if $x^2=(l^2-b^2)/3$ or $x=\sqrt{\{(l^2-b^2)/3\}}$, and substituting this is (6) (ignoring the term $(x-a)^3$)

$$v_{max}=\frac{Wb(l^2-b^2)^{\frac{3}{2}}}{9\sqrt{3}EIl}=\frac{Wl^3(1-n)(2n-n^2)^{\frac{3}{2}}}{9\sqrt{3}EI} \quad . \quad . \quad (9)$$

Several Loads. The general formula (6) or (7) will serve to calculate the deflection at any point if there are several loads (*i.e.* several values of a or n and W) provided that the last term is ignored for values of $x<a$. A simpler method is given in Art. 82.

Distributed Loads. The same method is applicable to say a load uniformly distributed over a length b from B to C_1 ignoring term in $(x-a)$ when $x<a$.

And distributed loads from C to a point short of B may be dealt with by superposing a neutralising upward load and adding its effects to those of the downward load for any unloaded length to the left of B.

Couple. Let μ be a clockwise couple applied at C_2, Fig. 115 (*b*). The reactions are μ/l, downward at A and upward at B to produce a contra-clockwise balancing couple of magnitude μ.

The bending moment is

$$EI d^2y/dx^2=\mu x/l-\mu \quad . \quad . \quad . \quad . \quad . \quad (10)$$

where $-\mu$ is to be ignored for values of $x<a$.

Integrating this in the same way as before.

$$\frac{dy}{dx}=i_A+\frac{\mu x^2}{3EIl}-\frac{\mu(x-a)}{EI} \quad . \quad . \quad . \quad . \quad (11)$$

where the last term $M(x-a)/EI$ is to be ignored for $x<a$.

Integrating again

$$v=i_A x+\frac{\mu x^3}{6EIl}-\frac{\mu(x-a)^2}{2EI}+0 \quad . \quad . \quad (12)$$

and putting $\quad\quad\quad v=0$ for $x=l$

$$i_A=-\frac{\mu l}{6EI}+\frac{\mu(l-a)^2}{2EIl} \quad . \quad . \quad . \quad (13)$$

and substituting this in (12)

$$v=\frac{\mu}{6EIl}\{x^3+x(2l^2-6al+3a^2)-3(x-a)^2l\} \quad . \quad . \quad (14)$$

the last term $-3(x-a)^2l$ being ignored when $x<a$.

Otherwise

$$y = \mu\{x^3 + xl^2(2 - 6n + 3n^2) - 3(x - nl)^2l\}/(6EIl) \quad . \quad (15)$$

At $x = a = nl$

$$y_C = \frac{\mu a}{3EIl}(l - 2a)(l - a) = \frac{\mu l^2 n(n - 1)(2n - 1)}{3EI} \quad . \quad . \quad (16)$$

Differentiating (14)

$$i = dy/dx = \mu\{3x^2 + l^2(2 - 6n + 3n^2) - 6(x - nl)l\}/(6EIl) . \quad (17)$$

Zero slope and maximum deflection occur for $x = l\sqrt{(2n - n^2 - \frac{2}{3})}$. For values of n which are 0.5 ± 0.077 there are two zero slopes and one zero value of y (as shown in Fig. 115 (*b*)). For values of n outside this range the beam is bent in such a way as not to cross its original or unstrained axis. The value of the maximum deflection may be found by substituting the foregoing value of x in (14) for the larger of the two segments a and b.

At C, where $x = nl$, from (17)

$$i_C = \mu l(3n^2 - 3n + 1)/(3EI) \quad . \quad . \quad . \quad (18)$$

And if $n = 1$ or $n = 0$

$$i_C = \mu l/(3EI) \quad . \quad . \quad . \quad . \quad (19)$$

while if $x = 0$ and $n = 1$

$$i_A = -\mu l/(6EI) . \quad . \quad . \quad . \quad (20)$$

Distribution of Moment (μ). It will be observed from (10) or from Fig. 115 (*b*) that the bending moment at C on the left-hand portion AC, which can conveniently be denoted by M_{CA}, is $n\mu$ and on the right-hand portion CB, denoted by M_{CB} is $(1 - n)\mu$, the two moments being proportional respectively to the lengths AC and CB. But if C is constrained to remain in the straight line AB the conditions are vitally altered. The necessary supporting force R_C is readily found by equations (8) and (16), substituting for W the downward force R_C which gives a deflection at C equal and opposite to that produced by μ. From such an equation

$$R_C = (\mu/l)(2n - 1)/n(1 - n) \quad . \quad . \quad . \quad (21)$$

This downward force will be balanced by vertically upward forces $(1 - n)R_C$ at A and nR_C at B. If these be added to the supporting forces μ/l (downward at A and upward at B), shown in Fig. 115 (*b*), then for the modified arrangement

$$M_{CA} = \mu(1 - n) \text{ and } M_{CB} = \mu n \quad . \quad . \quad . \quad (22)$$

Thus the moment μ is divided *inversely* as lengths a and b (or inversely as n and $1 - n$). This is in accordance with the general rule (4), (5), and (6) of Art. 21, for with C remaining in AB the common distortion of the elements AC and CB is solely the rotation i_C at C. Hence the moment μ is divided between AC and CB in the ratio BC to AC. It will be noticed from (19) that the distortion (angular) i_C is proportional to l/I, or the elastic resistance is proportional to I/l. Hence if AC and CB were of different sections, having second moments of cross-section of I_A and I_B respectively, the distribution of μ would be inversely as n/I_A and $(1-n)/I_B$ or directly proportional to I_A/n and $I_B/(1-n)$ respectively as in (22). Thus $M_{CA}/M_{CB}=(I_A/n)\div\{I_B/(1-n)\}$. We shall find the same distribution when the ends A and B are both fixed in the direction AB (Art. 89). (When C is not constrained to remain in the line AB the common elastic distortion at C is partly angular and partly linear and not simply proportional to l/I.

Example. A beam of 20-ft. span is freely supported at the ends, and is propped 9 ft. from the left-hand end to the same level as the supports, thus forming two spans of 9 and 11 ft. The beam carries a load of 3 tons 5 ft. from the left-hand support, and one of 7 tons 4 ft. from the right-hand end. Find the reactions at the prop and at the end supports.

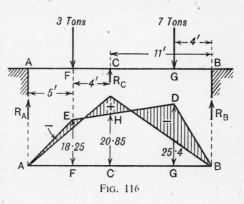

FIG. 116

If the beam were not propped, the deflection at C (Fig. 116), 9 ft. from A, would be, for the 3-ton load, taking $a=5$, $b=15$, $W=3$ and $x=9$ in (6),

$$y_C = \frac{3}{6EI}\left\{\frac{15\times9(400-225-81)}{20}+64\right\}=\frac{349.25}{EI}$$

And for the 7-ton load, taking $a=16$, $b=4$, $W=7$, $x=9$ in (6)

$$y_C = \frac{7}{6EI}\left\{\frac{4\times9(400-16-81)}{20}\right\}=\frac{636.3}{EI}$$

Adding these, the downward deflection of the beam would be, if it were not propped

$$\frac{985.55}{EI}$$

If R; is the reaction of the prop at C, the upward deflection is, by (8) above

$$y_C = \frac{R_C\times81\times121}{3EI\times20}=\frac{163.35R_C}{EI}$$

Equating this to the above deflection at C

$$R_C = \frac{985 \cdot 5}{163 \cdot 35} = 6 \cdot 031 \text{ tons}$$

The reactions at A and B follow by taking moments about the free ends.

$$R_B = \frac{(3 \times 5) + (7 \times 16) - (6 \cdot 03 \times 9)}{20} = 3 \cdot 636 \text{ tons}$$

$$R_A = 10 - 6 \cdot 031 - 3 \cdot 635 = 0 \cdot 334 \text{ ton.}$$

82. Deflection and Slope from Bending-moment Diagrams.

Slopes. The change of slope between any two points on a beam may be found from the relation shown in (3), Art. 78

$$i \text{ or } \frac{dy}{dx} = \int \frac{d^2y}{dx^2} \cdot dx = \int \frac{M}{EI} dx = \frac{1}{EI} \int M dx$$

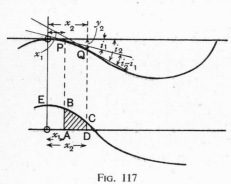

if E and I are constant.

Between two points P and Q (Fig. 117, in which the slopes and deflections are greatly exaggerated), on a beam of constant cross-section, the change of inclination $i_2 - i_1$, which is the angle between the two tangents at P and Q, may be represented by

$$i_2 - i_1 = \frac{1}{EI} \int_{x_1}^{x_2} M dx. \quad (1)$$

FIG. 117

The quantity $\int_{x_1}^{x_2} M dx$ represents the area ABCD of the bending-moment diagram between P and Q. If the lower limit x_1 be zero, from O, where the beam is horizontal, to Q, where the slope is i_2, the actual slope is equal to the change of inclination, viz.

$$i_2 = \frac{1}{EI} \int_0^{x_2} M dx \text{ (which is proportional to OECD)} \quad . \quad (2)$$

Thus the change of slope between two points on a beam is proportional to the area of the bending-moment diagram between them, and *from a point of zero slope* to any other point the area under the bending-moment curve is proportional to the actual slope at the second point. Changes of sign in the bending-moment diagram must be taken into account if the curve passes through zero. One algebraic sign, generally positive, is attached to bending, which produces convexity upwards, and the opposite sign to a bending moment, producing convexity downwards (see Art. 78), but the choice is of little importance in the present chapter.

Scales. If in the bending-moment diagram 1 in. (horizontally) represents q in., and 1 in. (vertically) represents s lb.-in., 1 sq. in. of bending-moment diagram area represents $q \cdot s$ lb.(in.)^2 and also represents $\dfrac{q \cdot s}{EI}$ radians slope if E is in pounds per square inch and I in (inch)^4 units.

Deflection. From the equation

$$d^2y/dx^2 = M/EI \quad ((2), \text{Art. 78})$$
$$x\,d^2y/dx^2 = Mx/EI$$

Integrating between $x = x_2$ and $x = x_1$, using the method of integration by parts for the left-hand side

$$\left(x\frac{dy}{dx} - y\right)_{x=x_1}^{x=x_2} = \int_{x_1}^{x_2} \frac{Mx}{EI}\,dx = \frac{1}{EI}\int_{x_1}^{x_2} Mx\,dx \text{ (if EI is constant)} \quad . \quad (3)$$

or

$$(x_2 i_2 - y_2) - (x_1 i_1 - y_1) = \frac{1}{EI}\int_{x}^{x_2} Mx\,dx \quad . \quad . \quad . \quad (4)$$

If the limits of integration between which the deflection is required are such that $x\,dy/dx$ is zero (from either of the factors x or dy/dx being zero) at each limit, the expression

$$\left(x\frac{dy}{dx} - y\right)_{x=x_1}^{x=x_2} \text{ becomes } -(y_2 - y_1) \quad . \quad . \quad . \quad (5)$$

and $\dfrac{1}{EI}\displaystyle\int_{x_1}^{x_2} Mx\,dx$ gives the change in level of the beam between the two points.

The quantity

$$\int_{x_1}^{x_2} Mx\,dx$$

represents the moment *about the origin* of the area of the bending-moment diagram between x_2 and x_1. If A is this area and $\bar{x}$ is the distance of its centre of gravity or centroid from the origin, $\displaystyle\int_{x_1}^{x_2} Mx\,dx$ may be represented by A $. \bar{x}$.

This quantity only represents the change in level when $x\,dy/dx$ vanishes at *both limits*. The product $x\,dy/dx$ or $x \cdot i_x$ denotes the vertical projection of the tangent at x, the horizontal projection of which is x. If the lower limit is zero, and y is zero at the origin, the quantity

$$\left(x \cdot \frac{dy}{dx} - y\right)_{0}^{x}$$

represents the difference between the vertical projection of the tangent at x, over a horizontal length x, and the deflection at x; in other words, the vertical deflection of the beam from its tangent. Hence, in this case, the deflection at a distance x from the origin is equal to the difference between $x \cdot i_x$ and $\dfrac{1}{EI} \times$ (moment of bending-moment diagram area), or

$$x \cdot i_x - \frac{1}{EI}\int_0^x Mxdx \quad . \quad . \quad . \quad . \quad (4\text{A})$$

where $\displaystyle\int_0^x Mxdx$ may be either positive or negative.

Scales. If in the bending-moment diagram 1 in. (horizontally) represents q in., and 1 in. (vertically) represents s lb.-in., A being measured in square inches and $\bar{x}$ in inches, the product $A \cdot \bar{x}$ represents the deflection on a scale $\dfrac{q^2 s}{EI}$ in. to 1 in.

Applications: (a) *Cantilever with Load* W *at the Free End* (see Fig. 43). If the origin be taken at the free end before or after deflection

$$\text{for } x = 0 \quad xdy/dx = 0$$

and at the fixed end $x = l$ and $dy/dx = 0$, hence

$$(x \cdot dy/dx - y)_0^l$$

gives the difference of level of the two ends $y_0 - y_l$, which is equal to

$$\frac{A \cdot \bar{x}}{EI}$$

where $A = \frac{1}{2} \cdot Wl \cdot l$ and $\bar{x} = \frac{2}{3}l$.

So that the deflection is

$$\tfrac{1}{2}Wl^2 \times \tfrac{2}{3}l \div EI = Wl^3/(3EI)$$

which agrees with (2), Art. 80.

Similarly, if the load is at a distance nl from the fixed end. $A = \frac{1}{2}W(nl)^2$, $\bar{x} = l - \dfrac{n}{3}l$, and the deflection of the free end is

$$\frac{W(nl)^2}{2EI}l\left(1 - \frac{n}{3}\right) = \frac{Wn^2l^3}{6EI}(3 - n)$$

which agrees with (5), Art. 80, and might be applied to the case of any number of isolated loads.

The deflection of a cantilever carrying a uniformly distributed load might similarly be found from the diagram of bending moment (Fig. 45) if the distance of the centroid of the parabolic spandril of Fig. 45 from the free end is known. Otherwise the moment of that area may be found by integration. Taking the origin at A (Fig. 45)

$$\frac{1}{\text{EI}}\int_0^l \text{M}xdx = \frac{w}{2\text{EI}}\int_0^l x^3dx = \tfrac{1}{8}\frac{wl}{\text{EI}}$$

which agrees with (7), Art. 80.

(*b*) *Irregularly Loaded Cantilever.* For any irregular loading of a cantilever the same method can be applied after the bending-moment diagram ABFEDA has been drawn (Fig. 118). The deflection of the free end is given by $\dfrac{\text{A}\,.\,\bar{x}}{\text{EI}}$ as before, the scales being suitably chosen. The method in such a case is a purely graphical one, consisting in drawing the bending-moment diagram to scale, measuring A and finding $\bar{x}$ by any of the various graphical methods, or finding the product A$\bar{x}$ by a derived area, as in Art. 35; the derived area corresponding to the pole B would represent the area under a curve M . x with origin at B.

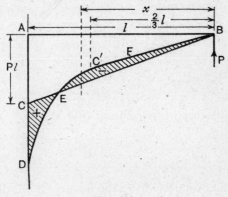

FIG. 118

If the irregular loading consists of a number of concentrated loads, the whole area A may be looked upon as the sum of the areas of a number of triangles, and the product A . $\bar{x}$ as the sum of the products of the areas of the several triangles and the distances of their centroids from the free end.

Propped Cantilever. Irregular Load. If the cantilever is propped at the end, let P be the upward reaction of the prop at B (Fig. 118). The bending-moment diagram for the irregular loading is ABFED, and that for the prop is the triangle ABC, the ordinates being of opposite sign.   The moments of these two areas about B are together zero, for the quantity $(xdy/dx - y)$ between limits 0 and *l* is zero, every term being zero, hence

$$\text{A}\,.\,\bar{x} = \tfrac{1}{2}\,.\,\text{P}l \times l \times \tfrac{2}{3}l$$
$$\text{P} = 3\text{A}\,.\,\bar{x}/l^3$$

a general formula applicable to regular or irregular loads, the latter problem being worked graphically.

The resultant bending-moment diagram is shown shaded in

H

Fig. 118, E giving the point of inflection. The parts DCE and EFB are of opposite sign. The reader should apply this method to the various cases given in Art. 80.

The deflection of any point X between A and B may be found by taking the moment about X of so much of this diagram as lies between verticals through X and A, taking account of the signs of the areas. Since the areas reckoned from A represent the slopes, the slope is zero, and the deflection a maximum at some point to the right of E where the area to the right of E is equal to DCE.

If the cantilever is propped somewhere between A and B the above formula holds good, provided the area A and the length $\bar{x}$ refer to the portion of the diagram ABFED between A and the prop, $\bar{x}$ being measured from the prop, and l refers to the distance of the prop from A.

(c) *Beam supported at two Points on the same Level.* Taking the origin at one end A (Figs. 115 and 119)

$$\left(x\frac{dy}{dx}-y\right)_0^l=l\,.\,i_B=\frac{1}{EI}\int_0^l Mxdx=\frac{A\bar{x}}{EI}$$

where A is the area of the bending-moment diagram, and $\bar{x}$ is the distance of its centroid from A, or A . $\bar{x}$ represents the moment of the area about the origin A, hence

$$i_B=\frac{A\,.\,\bar{x}}{EI\,.\,l} \qquad\qquad (6)$$

and similarly from the moment about B

$$i_A=-\frac{A(l-\bar{x})}{EI\,.\,l} \qquad\qquad (7)$$

and is of opposite sign to i_B. With the convention of signs given in Art. 78, A is negative for a beam carrying downward loads which produce convexity downwards; hence i_A is positive and i_B is negative.

Thus (in magnitude) the slopes at the supports are proportional to the area of the bending-moment diagram between them, and the ratio of one to the other is inversely proportional to the ratio of the distances of the supports from the centroid of that area—just the same kind of relation, it may be noted, that the reactions at the supports have to the total load.

If the area of the bending-moment diagram from A to a point X, distance x to the right of A, be A_x, which is negative for convexity downwards, and the slope at x is

$$i_x=i_A+\frac{1}{EI}\int_0^x Mdx \text{ or } i_A+\frac{A_x}{EI} \qquad\qquad (8)$$

which is zero at the section where maximum deflection occurs, A^x being negative.

Again, since
$$\left(x\frac{dy}{dx}-y\right)_0^x = xi_x - y_x = \frac{1}{EI}\int_0^x Mxdx$$

$$y_x = x \cdot i_x - \frac{1}{EI}\int_0^x Mxdx \quad . \quad . \quad . \quad (8A)$$

and substituting for i_x from (8)

$$y_x = x \cdot i_A + \frac{x}{EI}\int_0^x Mdx - \frac{1}{EI}\int_0^x Mxdx$$

$$= xi_A + \frac{xA_x}{EI} - \frac{1}{EI}\text{ (moment of } A_x \text{ about A)} \quad . \quad (9)$$

or the deflection at X is

$$y_x = (x \times \text{slope at A}) + (\text{moment of } A_x \text{ about X})/EI \quad . \quad (10)$$

which gives the deflection anywhere along the beam, the second term being negative. And from (8A) we may write

$$y_x = (x \times \text{slope at X}) - (\text{moment of } A_x \text{ about A})/EI \quad . \quad (11)$$

remembering that A_x is a negative quantity.

Probably the form (10) is more convenient than (11), i_A being a constant. As indicated by (8), the slope at X will be negative if X is beyond the point of maximum deflection. Note that the second term in (10) is negative, and represents the vertical displacement of the beam at X from the tangent at A, and the second term in (11) represents the vertical displacement of the beam at A from the tangent at X. In the case of convexity upwards the signs of these second terms would be changed. The reader should illustrate the geometrical meaning of the various terms on sketches of beams under various conditions.

Overhanging Ends. The deflection at any point on an overhanging end, such as in Figs. 51, 52, 60, or 61, may be determined as for a cantilever, provided the deflection due to the slope at the support be added (algebraically). For points between the supports of an overhanging beam the above relations hold, provided that the signs of the areas and moments of areas, etc., be taken into account. For irregular loading these processes may be carried out graphically, and the moments of areas $(A \cdot \bar{x})$ may be found by a " derived area," as in Art. 35 without finding the centres of gravity of the areas.

When the above expressions for slopes and deflections, which are applicable to any kind of loading, are written down symbolically in terms of dimensions of the bending-moment diagram, they give algebraic expressions, such as have already been obtained in other ways for various cases of loading, *e.g.* the deflection and slope anywhere for a beam carrying a single concentrated load may be found in this way as an alternative to the methods in Art. 81.

Non-central Load. The bending-moment diagram is shown in Fig. 115 (*a*). It is perhaps simplest to consider the ordinates and areas and moments of areas as those of the triangle ADB, minus those of the triangle EDB. And this will illustrate the principles of Macaulay's method adopted in Art. 81. Thus the bending moment is the algebraic sum of the moments of R_A and W about X, *viz.* $-FG+FH$ or $-Wbx/\iota+W(x-a)$ the term $W(x-a)$ only appearing when x is greater than a, *i.e.* to the right of C. From (7)

$$i_A = \frac{1}{EIl} \text{ (moment of ADB about B} - \text{moment of EDB about B)}$$

$$= \frac{1}{EIl} (\tfrac{1}{2}Wbl \times \tfrac{1}{3}l - \tfrac{1}{2}Wb \times b \times \tfrac{1}{3}b)$$

or $$i_A = \frac{Wb(l^2-b^2)}{6EIl} \text{ or } \frac{Wl^2n(1-n)(2-n)}{6EI} \quad . \quad . \quad (12)$$

(as in Art. 81). And from (8) within the range C to B.

$$i_x = i_A - \frac{1}{EI} \text{ (area AFG} - \text{area EFH)}$$

$$= \frac{Wb}{6EIl}(l^2-b^2) - \frac{1}{EI}\left\{\frac{Wbx}{l}\times\frac{x}{2} - \frac{Wb}{2}\times\frac{(x-a)^2}{b}\right\}$$

$$i_x = \frac{W}{6EI}\left\{\frac{b(l^2-b^2-3x^2)}{l}+3(x-a)^2\right\} \quad . \quad . \quad (13)$$

which agrees with the value of dy/dx from (7) of Art. 81. And evidently from Fig. 115 (*a*), when $x<a$, *i.e.* for the range A to C, the area EFH and consequently the term $3(x-a)^2$ in (13) will be omitted.

In this range A to C

$$i_x = 0 \text{ when } x^2 = (l^2-b^2)/3 = n(2-n)l^2/3$$

or $$x = \sqrt{\{(l^2-b^2)/3\}} \text{ or } l\sqrt{\{n(2-n)/3\}}$$

From (10)

$$y = i_A x - \frac{1}{EI}\{\text{moment of AFG about } x - \text{moment of EFH about X}\}$$

$$y = i_A x - \frac{1}{EI}\left\{\frac{Wbx}{l}\times\frac{x}{2}\times\frac{x}{3} - W(x-a)\tfrac{1}{2}(x-a)\tfrac{1}{3}(x-a)\right\}$$

$$y = \frac{W}{6EI}\left\{\frac{(l^2-b^2-x^2)bx}{l}+(x-a)^3\right\} \quad . \quad . \quad . \quad . \quad . \quad (14)$$

and in the range A to C the term $(x-a)^3$ will disappear. This agrees with (6) of Art. 81.

At C, under the load, $x=a$ and

$$y_C = \frac{Wab(l^2-b^2-a^2)}{6EIl} = \frac{Wa^2b^2}{3EIl} \text{ or } \frac{Wl^3n^2(1-n)^2}{3EI} . \quad (15)$$

And the maximum deflection may be found by substituting the foregoing value of x for $i_x - 0$ in (14).

Several Loads. If there are several vertical loads W_1, W_2, W_3, and W_4, at P_1, P_2, P_3, and P_4 (Fig. 119), distant a_1, a_2, a_3, and a_4 from A, the bending-moment diagram may be drawn as in Art. 41, or calculated as in Art. 39. Let the bending moments at P_1, P_2, P_3, etc., be M_1, M_2, M_3, etc., respectively. Let the total area of the bending-moment diagram be A, and let it be divided by verti-

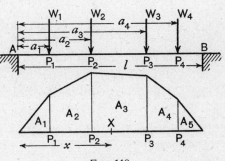

FIG. 119

cals through P_1, P_2, P_3, and P_4 (Fig. 119), into five parts, A_1, A_2, A_3, A_4, and A_5, as shown, so that

$$A_1 = \frac{a_1 M_1}{2} \quad A_2 = \frac{M_1+M_2}{2}(a_2-a_1) \quad A_3 = \frac{M_2+M_3}{2}(a_3-a_2)$$

and so on, all the areas being negative for downward loads.

Then

$$i_A = -\frac{1}{EI} \cdot \frac{A(l-\bar{x})}{l}$$

where $\bar{x}$ is the distance of the centroid of the area A from the origin A, and $l-\bar{x}$ is its distance from B.

The quantity $A(l-\bar{x})$, or the moment of the area A about B, may be found by the sum of the moments of the triangular areas of the bending-moment diagrams, which might be drawn for the several weights separately, *i.e.* the quantity i_A is the sum of four such terms as (12) above.

The slopes at P_1, P_2, P_3, etc., are then

$$i_1 = i_A + \frac{A_1}{EI} \quad i_2 = i_A + \frac{A_1+A_2}{EI} \quad i_3 = i_A + \frac{A_1+A_2+A_3}{EI}$$

and so on, the second term in each case being negative.

The segment in which the slope passes through zero is easily found from the slope, or total area from point A to successive loads.

If the zero slope occurs between, say, P_2 and P_3, the slopes at P_2 and P_3 are of opposite sign

$$-(A_1+A_2) \text{ is less than } -\frac{A(l-\bar{x})}{l}$$

$$-(A_1+A_2+A_3) \text{ is greater than } -\frac{A(l-\bar{x})}{l}$$

If the zero slope is at X, distant x from A, the bending moment there is $M_2+\dfrac{x-a^2}{a_3-a_2}(M_3-M_2)$, and the slope being zero, the area from point A to the point X of zero slope is equal to $A \cdot \dfrac{l-\bar{x}}{l}$, or

$$A_1+A_2+\tfrac{1}{2}\left\{M_2+\frac{x-a_2}{a_3-a_2} \cdot (M_3-M_2)\right\}(x-a_2)=A \cdot \frac{l-\bar{x}}{l}$$

from which quadratic equation x may be found.

The magnitude of the maximum deflection is then easily found from (11) above, viz.

$$-\frac{1}{EI} \text{ (moment about point A of the bending-moment diagram}$$

over AX)

an expression which may conveniently be written down after dividing the area over AX into triangles, say, by diagonals from P_2. The deflection elsewhere may be found from equation (10). With numerical data this method will appear much shorter than in the above symbolic form. Other purely graphical methods for the same problem are given in the next article.

Other Cases. Beams carrying uniformly distributed loads over part of the span might conveniently be dealt with by these methods, the summation of moments of the bending-moment diagram area being split up into separate parts with proper limits of integration at sudden changes or discontinuities in the rate of loading.

Example 1. The example at the end of Art. 81 may be solved from the bending-moment diagram as follows:

Let the bending-moment diagram be drawn by the funicular polygon (see Art. 41), or by calculation (see Art. 40). It is shown in Fig. 116, AEDB being the diagram for the two loads on the unsupported span AB. Then from (7)

$$i_A -\frac{1}{EI} \text{ (moment of area AEDB about B)} \div AB$$

Divide the negative area AEDB into four triangles by joining DF for convenience in calculating the above moment. Using ton and feet units

$$i_A = \frac{1}{20EI}\left[\left(\frac{25\cdot4\times4}{2}\cdot\tfrac{2}{3}\cdot4\right)+\left\{\frac{25\cdot4\times11}{2}\times(4+\tfrac{11}{3})\right\}+\left\{\left(\frac{18\cdot25\times11}{2}\right)\right.\right.$$

$$\left.\left.\times(4+\tfrac{22}{3})\right\}+\left\{\left(\frac{18\cdot25\times5}{2}\right)(15+\tfrac{5}{3})\right\}\right]$$

$$i_A = \frac{155\cdot2}{EI}$$

And from (10), dividing EHCF by a diagonal FH

$$y_C = \frac{155\cdot2}{EI}\times9-\frac{1}{EI}\left[\left(\frac{20\cdot85\times4}{2}\cdot\tfrac{4}{3}\right)+\left(\frac{18\cdot25\times4}{2}\cdot\tfrac{8}{3}\right)\right.$$

$$\left.+\left\{\left(\frac{18\cdot25\times5}{2}\right)(4+\tfrac{5}{3})\right\}\right]$$

$$y_C = \frac{1,397-411\cdot5}{EI} = \frac{985\cdot5}{EI} \text{ (downward)}$$

For an upward load R_C at C, by (15)

$$y_C = \frac{R_C\times81\times121}{3EI\times20} = \frac{163\cdot35R_C}{EI} \text{ (upward)}$$

Equating this to the downward deflection at C

$$R_C = \frac{985\cdot5}{163\cdot35} = 6\cdot03 \text{ tons}$$

$$R_A = \frac{(7\times4)+(15\times3)-(6\cdot03\times11)}{20} = 0\cdot334 \text{ ton}$$

$$R_B = 10-0\cdot334-6\cdot03 = 6\cdot636 \text{ tons}$$

The above methods might now be applied to the resultant bending-moment diagram, shown shaded in Fig. 116, to determine the deflection anywhere between A and C, or between C and B, and the position of the maximum deflection, etc.

Example 2.   Find the deflection of the free ends of the beam in Fig. 52. From (6) and (7) above, slopes downward towards the right

$$i_A = -i_B = -\frac{1}{EI}\cdot\frac{l_2}{2}\cdot\frac{1}{l_2}\int_0^{l^2}\left\{\frac{wl_1{}^2}{2}-\frac{w}{2}(l_2x-x^2)\right\}dx$$

or

$$-\frac{1}{2EI}\left(\frac{wl_1{}^2l_2}{2}-\frac{wl_2{}^2}{8}\times\tfrac{2}{3}\times l_2\right) = -\frac{wl_2}{24EI}(6l_1{}^2-l^2{}_2)$$

which is negative if l_2 is less than $l_1\sqrt{6}$.

Downward deflection at the free end is

$$-i_Al_1+\frac{wl_1{}^4}{8EI} = \frac{wl_1}{24EI}(6l_1{}^2l_2-l_2{}^3+3l_1{}^3)$$

Upward deflection at the centre consists of

(upward deflection due to end loads)—(downward deflection due to
load between supports)

which, using (11) for the first term, is

$$\frac{1}{EI}\left(0+\frac{wl_1{}^2}{2}\cdot\frac{l_2}{2}\cdot\frac{l_2}{4}\right)-\tfrac{5}{384}\frac{wl_2{}^4}{EI}=\frac{wl_2{}^2}{16EI}(l_1{}^2-\tfrac{5}{24}l_2{}^2)$$

which is positive if l_2 is less than $\sqrt{(4\cdot8l)}$.

Example 3.   Find the deflection at B and midway between A and
C in Example 2 of Art. 42 (see Fig. 60).

Taking the origin at A, R_A being 10 tons, by (6), downwards
towards B

$$i_C=\frac{1}{16EI}\int_0^{16}\left(10x+\frac{x^2}{2}\right)xdx=\frac{1}{16EI}\left(\tfrac{10}{3}x^3+\frac{x^4}{8}\right)_0^{16}=\frac{21,845\cdot3}{16EI}$$

E being in tons per square foot, and I in (feet)[4]

$$\text{Deflection at B}=\left(8\times\frac{21,845}{16EI}\right)+\frac{32\times8\times8\times8}{3EI}+\frac{8\times8\times8\times8}{8EI}$$

$$=\frac{16,896}{EI}\text{ ft.}$$

(If E and I are in inch units, deflection at B$=1,728\times\dfrac{16,896}{EI}$ in.).

Taking an origin midway between A and C and x positive towards C

$$M=10(8+x)+\tfrac{1}{2}(8+x)^2=\frac{x^2}{2}+18x+112\text{ tons-ft.}$$

and using (4A) over the range from the origin to C, the deflection
upward at the origin (or downward at C relative to the origin) is

$$8\times\frac{21,845\cdot3}{16EI}-\frac{1}{EI}\int_0^8\left(\frac{x^3}{2}+18x^2+112x\right)dx$$

$$=\frac{1}{EI}(10,922-7,168)=\frac{3,754}{EI}\text{ ft.}$$

or, $1,728\times\dfrac{3,754}{EI}$ in. if E is in tons per square inch and I in (inches)[4].

83. Other Graphical Methods.

First Method.   The five equations of Art. 78 immediately suggest
a possible graphical method of finding deflections, slopes, etc., from
the curve showing the distribution of load on the beam.   If the five
quantities w, F, M, i, and y (see Art. 78) be plotted successively on
the length of the beam as a base-line, each curve will represent the
integral of the one preceding it, *i.e.* the difference between any two
ordinates of any curve will be proportional to the area included

between the two corresponding ordinates of the preceding curve. Hence, if the first be given, the others can be deduced by measuring areas, *i.e.* by graphical integration. Five such curves for a beam simply supported at each end are shown in Fig. 120. At the ends the shearing forces and slopes are not zero, but the methods of finding their values have already been explained, and are shown in Fig. 120, G and G′ being the centroids of the loading- and bending-

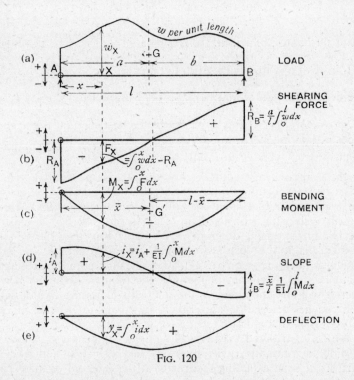

Fig. 120

moment diagrams respectively. The reader should study the exact analogies between the various curves. In carrying into practice this graphical method the various scales are of primary importance; the calculation of these is indicated below.

In the case of a cantilever, the F and M curves corresponding to (*b*) and (*c*), Fig. 120, must start from zero at the free end (unless there is a concentrated end load), and the *i* and *y* curves corresponding to (*d*) and (*e*), Fig. 120, must start from zero at the fixed end.

Scales for Fig. 120. Linear scale along the span, *q* in. to 1 in., E in pounds per square inch; I in (inches)[4].

(*a*) Ordinates, *p* lb. per inch run = 1 in.

Therefore 1 sq. in. area represents *p* . *q* lb. load.

(b) Ordinates, n sq. in. from $(a) = 1$ in. $= n \cdot p \cdot q$ lb.
   Areas 1 sq. in. represent $n \cdot p \cdot q^2$ lb.-in.

(c) Ordinates, m sq. in. from $(b) = 1$ in. $= mnpq^2$ lb.-in.
   Areas 1 sq. in. represent $mnpq^3$ lb.-(in.)^2.

(d) Ordinates, n' sq. in. from $(c) = 1$ in. $= \dfrac{n' mnpq^3}{EI}$ radians.

   Areas 1 sq. in. represent $\dfrac{n' mnpq^4}{EI}$ in.

(e) Ordinates, m' sq. in. from $(d) = 1$ in. $= \dfrac{m' n' mnpq^4}{EI}$ in.

If instead of p lb. per inch run to 1 in. the force scale is p lb. to 1 in., the deflection scale would be $\dfrac{m' n' mnpq^3}{EI}$ in. to 1 in.

Second Method.   This is probably the best method for irregular types of loading.   The equations

$$d^2y/dx^2 = M/EI \quad \text{and} \quad d^2M/dx^2 = w$$

or the diagrams in Fig. 120 show that the same kind of relation exists between bending moment (M) and deflection (y) as between the load per unit of span (w) and the bending moment.   Hence, the curve showing y on the span as a base-line can be derived from the bending-moment diagram in the same way that the bending-moment diagram is derived from the diagram of loading, viz. by the funicular polygon (see Art. 41).   If the bending-moment diagram be treated as a diagram of loading, the funicular polygon derived from it will give the polygon, the sides of which the curve of deflection touches internally, and which approximates to the curve of deflection with any desired degree of nearness.

With a distributed load it was necessary (Art. 41) to divide the loading diagram into parts (preferably vertical strips), and take each part of the load as acting separately at the centroid of these parts. Similarly, the bending-moment diagram, whether derived from a distributed load or from concentrated loads, must be divided into parts (see Fig. 121), and each part of the area treated as a force at its centre of gravity or centroid.   A second pole O' is chosen, and the distances ab, bc, cd, de, etc., set off proportional to the areas of bending-moment diagram, having their centroids on the lines AB, BC, CD, DE, etc.   The second funicular polygon, with sides parallel to lines radiating from O', gives approximately the curve of deflection; the true curve is that inscribed within this polygon, for the tangents to the deflection curve at any two cross-sections must intersect vertically below the centroid of that part of the bending-moment diagram lying between those two sections.

To show the form of the beam when deflected the deflection curve must be drawn on a base parallel to the beam, *i.e.* horizontal. This can be done by drawing the second vector polygon again with a pole on the same level as r', and drawing another funicular polygon corresponding to it, or by setting off the ordinates of the second funicular polygon from a horizontal base-line.

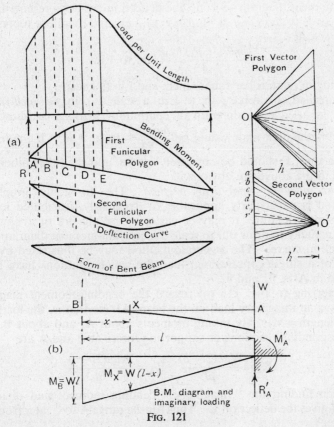

Fig. 121

This method is applicable to other cases than that of the simply supported beam here illustrated, provided the bending-moment diagram has been determined. When different parts of a beam have opposite curvature, *i.e.* when the curvature changes sign, *e.g.* in a overhanging or in a built-in beam (see Chapter VIII), the proper sign must be attached to the vertical vectors in the vector polygon. If bending-moment diagram areas of one kind are represented by downward vectors, those of opposite kind (or sign) must be represented by upward vectors.

Scales. If the linear horizontal scale is q in. to 1 in. and the force scale is p lb. to 1 in., the horizontal polar distance of the first vector polygon being h in., the scale of the bending-moment diagram ordinates is $p \cdot q \cdot h$ lb.-in. to 1 in., as in Art. 41. One sq. in. area of the bending-moment diagram represents $p \cdot q^2 \cdot h$ lb.-(in.)^2; and if the (horizontal) polar distance of the second vector polygon is h' in., and the vector scale used for it is m sq. in. of bending-moment diagram to 1 in., the deflection curve represents EI $\cdot y$ on a scale $m \cdot p \cdot q^3 \cdot h \cdot h'$ lb.-(in.)^3 to 1 in., and therefore represents y on a scale

$$\frac{m \cdot p \cdot q^3 \cdot h \cdot h'}{\text{EI}} \text{ in. to 1 in.}$$

E being in pounds per square inch, and I in (inches)^4.

If instead of a force p lb. to 1 in. a scale of p lb. *per inch run* to 1 in. be used on a diagram of continuous loading, as shown in Fig. 91, the final scale would be $\dfrac{mpq^4hh'}{\text{EI}}$ in. to 1 in. If the forces are in tons, E should be expressed in tons, and the other modifications in the above are obvious.

Corresponding Analytical Method. The foregoing graphical method is particularly applicable to irregularly distributed loads. For simple loadings it may be easier to use algebra or arithmetic than actually to draw out to scale the bending-moment diagram and deflection curve. The algebraic method may be illustrated by the case of a single concentrated load for which solutions have been found in Arts. 81 and 82.

Referring to Fig. 115 (*a*) regard the bending-moment diagram AEB as an imaginary load on the beam AB (so that w, the load per unit length = M). By taking moments about A, and about B, the corresponding reactions or supporting forces at B and A are

$$R'_B = \frac{Wab(2l-b)}{6l} \qquad R'_A = \frac{Wab(2l-a)}{6l}$$

Then finding the " imaginary " bending moment and dividing by EI gives the deflection y. Thus for the range A to C, at x from A.

$$y = \frac{1}{\text{EI}}\left(R'_A x - Wb\frac{x}{l} \times \frac{x}{2} \times \frac{x}{3}\right)$$

$$= \frac{Wb}{6\text{EI}l}\{ax(2l-a)-x^3\} = Wbx(l^2-b^2-x^2)/(6\text{EI}l)$$

which agrees with (6), Art. 81, and (14), Art. 82.

(We have here ignored the negative sign of the first and second (or imaginary) bending moments, as the repetition of the process produces a positive deflection.)

This and the corresponding graphical method are particularly suitable for the beam simply supported at its two ends. The conditions of support of the imaginary load by simple reactions R'_A and R'_B are only justified by the fact that the deflections at the ends (corresponding to the second or imaginary bending moment) are zero. In other cases the form of support or constraint of the imaginary loading must be determined by the known statical conditions of equilibrium. Thus points of zero deflection in the actual beam must be points of zero, B.M. for the second or imaginary loading. And points of zero slope must be points of zero shearing force for the second or imaginary loading. This may be illustrated by the case of a cantilever with a concentrated load at the free end. Thus with the notation of Fig. 121 (*b*), at the free end A the B.M. is zero but neither the slope nor the deflection is zero, hence, for the second loading given by the bending-moment diagram M'_A and R'_A neither the B.M. nor the reaction at A is zero. And at B, $M'_B=0$ and $F'_B=0$. By moments about A for the imaginary loading

$$M_A = \frac{Wl \times l}{2} \times \tfrac{2}{3}l = \tfrac{1}{3}Wl^3$$

And since $F'_B=0$, $R_B=0$, and $R'_A=\tfrac{1}{2}Wl \times l=\tfrac{1}{2}Wl^2$.

And by taking the moment about X of the B.M. diagram to the left of X

$$EIy=M'_x=\tfrac{1}{2}Wlx \times \tfrac{2}{3}x+\tfrac{1}{2}W(l-x) \times x \times \tfrac{1}{3}x=Wx^2(\tfrac{1}{2}l-\tfrac{1}{6}x)$$

in agreement with Art. 80, and for $x=l$, $y_A=Wl^3/(3EI)$.

84. Beams of Variable Cross-Section. The slopes and deflections so far investigated have been those for beams of constant section, so that the relation (3) of Art. 78

$$i=\int \frac{M}{EI}dx \text{ has become } \frac{1}{EI}\int Mdx$$

If, however, I is not constant, but E is constant, this becomes

$$i=\frac{1}{E}\int \frac{M}{I}dx$$

and the equation (1), Art. 82, becomes

$$i_2-i_1=\frac{1}{E}\int_{x_1}^{x_2} \left(\frac{M}{I}\right)dx$$

and the equation (3), Art. 82, becomes

$$\left(x\frac{dy}{dx}-y\right)_{x=x_1}^{x=x_2}=\frac{1}{E}\int_{x_1}^{x_2} \frac{Mx}{I}dx$$

The methods of finding the slopes and deflections employed in Arts. 79, 80, 82, and 83 may therefore be applied to beams of variable section, provided that the quantity $\dfrac{M}{I}$ is used instead of M throughout.

Where I and M are both expressed as simple algebraic functions of x (distance along the beam), analytical methods can usually be employed (see Example 1 below), but when either or both vary in an irregular manner, the graphical methods should be used. Thus equation (3) of Art. 82 may be written

$$\left(x\frac{dy}{dx}-y\right)^{x_2}_{x_1}=\frac{A\bar{x}}{E}$$

where A or $\displaystyle\int^{x_2}_{x_1}\frac{M}{I}dx=$ area under the curve $\dfrac{M}{I}$ and $\bar{x}$ is the distance

of its centroid from the origin. The moment A . $\bar{x}$ may of course be found conveniently by a derived area (see Art. 35). When the quantity I varies suddenly at some section of the beam, but is a simply expressed quantity over two or more ranges, neglecting the effects of a discontinuity in the cross-section, ordinary integration may be employed if the integrals are split up into ranges with suitable limits (see Example 2 below). The solution of problems on propped beams of all kinds by equating the upward deflection at the prop caused by the reaction of the prop to the downward deflection of an unpropped beam caused by the load, is still valid, the deflections being calculated for the varying section as above. For example, the equation giving the load carried by a prop at the end of a cantilever, with any loading, as in Fig. 118, may be stated as follows. If M is the bending moment in terms of the distance from the free end B

$$\int^l_0\frac{M}{I}x\,dx=\int^l_0\frac{Px}{I}x\,dx=P\int^l_0\frac{x^2}{I}dx$$

and

$$P=\int^l_0\frac{Mx}{I}dx\div\int^l_0\frac{x^2}{I}dx$$

For a graphical solution, let A be the area enclosed by the curve $\dfrac{M}{I}$, and $\bar{x}$ the distance of its centroid from B. Assume any load p on the prop, and let $P=\alpha p$. Draw the bending-moment diagram (a straight line) for the end load p; divide each ordinate $(p\,.\,x)$ by I, giving a curve $\dfrac{p\,.\,x}{I}$. Let A′ be the area enclosed by this curve, and

$\bar{x}'$ the distance of its centroid from B.   Then the above equation in graphical form becomes

$$A \cdot \bar{x} = \alpha \cdot A' \cdot \bar{x}'$$

$$\alpha = A\bar{x} \div A'\bar{x}' \text{ and } P = \alpha p$$

The moments $A \cdot \bar{x}$ and $A' \cdot \bar{x}'$ may be most conveniently found graphically by the derived area method of Art. 35, with B as pole; the bases (l) being the same for each diagram, the equation $A \cdot \bar{x} = \alpha A'\bar{x}'$ becomes

first derived area of $A = \alpha$ (first derived area of A')

The scales are not important, α being a mere ratio; it is only necessary to set off the ordinate pl in the bending-moment diagram for the assumed reaction p, on the same scale as the bending-moment diagram for the loading.   A more general application of these methods to other cases is referred to in Arts. 88 and 93.

Example 1.   A cantilever of circular section tapers in diameter uniformly with the length from the fixed end to the free end, where the diameter is half that at the fixed end.   Find the slope and deflection of the free end due to a weight W hung there.

Let D be the diameter at the fixed end at O, which is taken as origin (Fig. 110).   Then diameter at a distance x from O is

$$D(1 - x/2l) \text{ or } \tfrac{1}{2}D(2l - x)/l$$

At O about the neutral axis, $I_0 = \pi D^4/64$ (see Arts. 34 and 49); hence at a distance x from O

$$I = \frac{\pi}{64} D^4 \left(1 - \frac{x}{2l}\right)^4 \text{ or } \frac{I_0}{16l^4}(2l - x)^4$$

and $M = W(l - x)$ (see Fig. 43).

Then $\quad \dfrac{dy}{dx}$ or $i = \dfrac{1}{E} \displaystyle\int_0^x \dfrac{M}{I} dx = \dfrac{16Wl^4}{EI_0} \displaystyle\int_0^x \dfrac{l - x}{(2l - x)^4} dx$

or in partial fractions

$$i = \frac{16Wl^4}{EI_0} \int_0^x \left\{ \frac{-l}{(2l - x)^4} + \frac{1}{(2l - x)^3} \right\} dx$$

$$= \frac{16Wl^4}{EI_0} \left\{ -\tfrac{1}{3} \cdot \frac{l}{(2l - x)^3} + \tfrac{1}{2} \frac{1}{(2l - x)^2} - \frac{1}{12l^2} \right\}$$

the constant term $-1/(12l^2)$ being such that $i = 0$ for $x = 0$.

Then, for $x = l$

$$i_A = \tfrac{4}{3} \cdot \frac{Wl^2}{EI_0}$$

Also

$$y=\int_0^x idx=\frac{16Wl^4}{EI_0}\left\{-\frac{1}{6}\frac{l}{(2l-x)^2}+\frac{1}{2(2l-x)}-\frac{x}{12l^2}-\frac{5}{24l}\right\}$$

and for $x=l$ $$y_A=\tfrac{2}{3}\cdot\frac{Wl^3}{EI_0}$$

If the deflection only were required, it might be obtained by a single integration by modifying (3), Art. 82, taking the origin at the free end A, Fig. 110

$$\left(x\frac{dy}{dx}-y\right)_0^l=y_A=\frac{1}{E}\int_0^l\frac{Mx}{I}dx$$

$$y_A=\frac{16Wl^4}{EI_0}\int_0^l\frac{x^2}{(l+x)^4}dx=\frac{16Wl^4}{EI_0}\int_0^l\left\{\frac{l^2}{(l+x)^4}-\frac{2l}{(l+x)^3}+\frac{1}{(l+x)^2}\right\}dx$$

$$=\frac{16Wl^4}{EI_0}\left\{-\tfrac{1}{3}\frac{l^2}{(l+x)^3}+\frac{l}{(l+x)^2}-\frac{1}{(l+x)}\right\}_0^l=\frac{2}{3}\frac{Wl^3}{EI_0}\text{ (as before)}$$

Example 2. A cantilever of circular section is of constant diameter from the fixed end to the middle, and of half that diameter from the middle to the free end. Estimate the deflection at the free end due to a weight W there.

If I_0=moment of inertia of the thick end (fixed)
$\frac{1}{16}I_0=$,,   ,,   ,,   thin ,, (free).

As in Art. 80, taking the origin at the fixed end O (Fig. 110), from O to C (the middle point)

$$\frac{d^2y}{dx^2}=W(l-x)/EI_0$$

$$i\text{ or }\frac{dy}{dx}=W(lx-\tfrac{1}{2}x^2)/EI_0+0$$

and at $x=\tfrac{1}{2}l$ $$i_C=\tfrac{3}{8}Wl^2/EI_0$$

$$y=\int idx=W(lx^2-\tfrac{1}{3}x^3)/(2EI_0)+0$$

and at $x=\tfrac{1}{2}l$ $$y_C=5Wl^3/(48EI_0)$$

From C to A (free end)

$$i=16W(lx-\tfrac{1}{2}x^2)/EI_0+A$$

at $x=\tfrac{1}{2}l$ $i=\tfrac{3}{8}Wl^2/EI_0$ (above)   hence $A=-\tfrac{45}{8}Wl^2/EI_0$

$$y=\int idx=W\{\ldots\}/EI_0\{8(lx^2-\tfrac{1}{3}x^3)-\tfrac{45}{8}l^2x+B\}/EI$$

at $x=\tfrac{1}{2}l$ $y=\tfrac{5}{48}Wl/EI_0$ (above)   hence $B=\tfrac{5}{4}l^3$

$$y=W\{8(lx^2-\tfrac{1}{3}x^3)-\tfrac{45}{8}l^2x+\tfrac{5}{4}l^3\}/EI_0$$

and at $x=l$ $$y_A=\tfrac{23}{24}Wl^3/EI_0$$

To find the deflection only, the method of Art. 82 might be used, taking the origin at A, the free end (Fig. 110). Then $M = Wx$, and splitting the integration into two ranges, over which I is I_0 and $\frac{1}{16}I_0$

$$y = \frac{1}{E} \int_0^l \frac{Mx}{I} dx = \frac{1}{EI_0} \int_{\frac{1}{2}l}^l Wx^2 dx + \frac{16}{EI_0} \int_0^{\frac{1}{2}l} Wx^2 dx$$

$$= \frac{W}{EI_0} \left[\frac{1}{3} \left\{ l^3 - \left(\frac{l}{2} \right)^3 \right\} + \frac{16}{3} \left(\frac{l}{2} \right)^3 \right] = \frac{23}{24} \frac{Wl^3}{EI_0}$$

EXAMPLES VII

1. A beam of **I** section, 14 in. deep, is simply supported at the ends of a 20-ft. span. If the moment of inertia of the area of cross-section is 440 (in.)^4, what load may be hung midway between the supports without producing a deflection of more than $\frac{1}{4}$ in., and what is the intensity of bending stress produced? What total uniformly distributed load would produce the same deflection, and what would then be the maximum intensity of bending stress? ($E = 13,000$ tons per sq. in.)

2. A beam is simply supported at its ends and carries a uniformly distributed load W. At what distance below the level of the end supports must a rigid central prop be placed if it is to carry half the total load? If the prop so placed is elastic and requires a pressure e to depress it unit distance, what load would it carry, the end supports remaining rigid?

3. A beam rests on supports 20 ft. apart and carries a distributed load which varies uniformly from 1 ton per ft. at one support to 4 tons per ft. at the other. Find the position and magnitude of the maximum deflection if the moment of inertia of the area of cross-section is 2,654 (in.)^4, and E is 13,000 tons per sq. in.

4. A cantilever carries a load W at the free end and is supported in the middle to the level of the fixed end. Find the load on the prop and the deflection of the free end.

5. A cantilever carries a load W at half its length from the fixed end. The free end is supported to the level of the fixed end. Find the load carried by this support, the bending moment under the load and at the fixed end, and the position and amount of the maximum deflection.

If this cantilever is of steel, the moment of inertia of cross-section being 20 (in.)^4, and the length 30 in., find what proportion of the load would be carried by an end support consisting of a vertical steel tie-rod 10 ft. long and $\frac{1}{2}$ sq. in. in section, if the free end is just at the level of the fixed end *before* the load is placed on the beam.

6. A cantilever carries a uniformly spread load W, and is propped to the level of the fixed end at a point three-quarters of its length from the fixed end. What proportion of the whole load is carried on the prop?

7. A cantilever carries a distributed load which varies uniformly from w per unit length at the fixed end to zero at the free end. Find the deflection at the free end.

8. A girder of **I** section rests on two supports 16 ft. apart and carries a load of 6 tons, 5 ft. from one support. If the moment of inertia of the area of cross-section is 375 (in.)^4, find the deflection under the load and at the middle of the span, and the position and amount of the maximum deflection. ($E = 13,000$ tons per sq. in.)

9. If the beam in the previous problem carries an additional load of 8 tons, 8 ft. from the first one, and is propped at the centre to the level of the ends, find the load on the prop. By how much will it be lessened if the prop sinks 0·1 in.?

10. A girder of 16-ft. span carries loads of 7 and 6 tons, 4 and 6 ft. respectively from one end. Find the position of the maximum deflection and its amount if the moment of inertia of the cross-section is 345 (in.)^4 and E= 13,000 tons per sq. in.

11. A steel beam 20 ft. long is suspended horizontally from a rigid support by three vertical rods each 10 ft. long, one at each end and one midway between the other two. The end rods have a cross-section of 1 sq. in. and the middle one has a section of 2 sq. in., and the moment of inertia of cross-section of the beam is 480 (in.)^4. If a uniform load of 1 ton per foot run is placed on the beam, find the pull in each rod.

12. A cantilever carries a uniformly distributed load throughout its length and is propped at the free end. What fraction of the load should the prop carry if the intensity of bending stress in the cantilever is to be the least possible, and what proportion does this intensity of stress bear to that in a beam propped at the free end exactly to the level of the fixed end?

13. At what fraction of its length from the free end should a uniformly loaded cantilever be propped to the level of the fixed end in order that the intensity of bending stress shall be as small as possible, and what proportion does this intensity of stress bear to that in a beam propped at the end to the same level? What proportion of the whole load is carried by the prop?

14. A cast-iron girder is simply supported at its ends and carries a uniformly distributed load. What proportion of the deflection at mid-span may be removed by a central prop without causing tension in the compression flange? What proportion of the deflection at ¼ span may be removed by a prop there under a similar restriction?

15. A beam, AB, carries a uniform load of 1 ton per foot run and rests on two supports, C and D, so that AC=3 ft., CD=10 ft., and DB=7 ft. Find the deflections at A, B, and F from the level of the supports, F being midway between C and D. I=375 (in.)^4. E=13,000 tons per sq. in. How far from A is the section at which maximum upward deflection occurs?

16. If the beam in the previous problem carries loads of 5, 3, and 4 tons at A, F, and B respectively, and no other loads, find the deflections at A, F, and B, and the section at which maximum deflection occurs.

17. A cantilever is rectangular in cross-section, being of constant breadth and depth, varying uniformly from d at the wall to $\frac{1}{2}d$ at the free end. Find the deflection of the free end of the cantilever due to a load W placed there, the moment of inertia of section at the fixed end being I_0.

18. A vertical steel post is of hollow circular section, the lower half of the length being 4 in. external and $3\frac{1}{2}$ in. internal diameter, and the upper half 3 in. external and $2\frac{1}{2}$ in. internal diameter. The total length of the post is 20 ft., the lower end being firmly fixed. Find the deflection of the top of the post due to a horizontal pull of 125 lb., 4 ft. from the top. (E=30,000,000 lb. per sq. in.)

19. A beam rests on supports at its ends and carries a load W midway between them. The moment of inertia of its cross-sectional area is I_0 at mid-span, and varies uniformly along the beam to $\frac{1}{2}I_0$ at each end. Find an expression for the deflection midway between the supports.

20. Find the deflection midway between the supports of the beam in the previous problem if the load W is uniformly spread over the span.

CHAPTER VIII

CONSTRAINED BEAMS

85. Encastré or Built-in Beams. By this term is understood a beam firmly fixed at each end so that the supports completely constrain the inclination of the beam at the ends, as in the case of the " fixed " end of a cantilever. The two ends are usually at the same level, and the slope of the beam is then usually zero at each end if the constraint is effectual. The effect of this kind of fastening on a beam of uniform section is to make it stronger and stiffer, *i.e.* to reduce the maximum intensity of stress and to reduce the deflection everywhere. When the beam is loaded the bending moment is not zero at the ends as in the case of a simply supported beam, the end fastening imposing such " fixing moments " as make the beam convex *upwards* at the ends, while it is convex downwards about the middle portion, the bending moment passing through zero and changing sign at two points of contraflexure.

If the slope is zero at the ends, the necessary fixing couples at the ends are, for distributed loads, the greatest bending moments anywhere on the beam. Up to a certain degree, relaxation of this clamping, which always takes place in practice when a steel girder is built into masonry, tends to reduce the greatest bending moment by decreasing the fixing moments and increasing the moment of opposite sign about the middle of the span. In a condition between perfect fixture and perfect freedom of the ends, the beam may be subject to smaller bending stresses than in the usual ideal form of a built-in beam with rigidly fixed ends. The conditions of greatest strength will be realized when the two greatest convexities are each equal to the greatest concavity, the greatest bending moments of opposite sign being equal in magnitude.

Simple cases of continuous loading of built-in beams where the rate of loading can be easily expressed algebraically may be solved by integration of the fundamental equation

$$EId^4y/dx^4 = w \text{ (Art. 78)}$$

Taking one end of the beam as origin, the conditions will usually be $dy/dx = 0$ for $x = 0$ and for $x = l$, and $y = 0$ for $x = 0$ and for $x = l$.

For example, suppose that the load is uniformly distributed, being w per unit length of span (Fig. 122), integrating the above equation

$$EId^3y/dx^3 = wx + A \qquad . \quad . \quad . \quad . \quad . \quad . \quad . \quad (1)$$

$$EId^2y/dx^2=\tfrac{1}{2}wx^2+Ax+B \quad\quad\quad (2)$$

$$EIdy/dx=\tfrac{1}{6}wx^3+\tfrac{1}{2}Ax^2+Bx+0 \quad\quad (3)$$

since $dy/dx=0$ for $x=0$, and putting $dy/dx=0$ for $x=l$

$$0=\tfrac{1}{6}wl^2+\tfrac{1}{2}Al+B \quad\text{and}\quad B=-\tfrac{1}{6}wl^2-\tfrac{1}{2}Al$$

$$EIdy/dx=\tfrac{1}{6}wx^3+\tfrac{1}{2}Ax^2-\tfrac{1}{6}wl^2x-\tfrac{1}{2}Alx \quad\quad (4)$$

$$EI \cdot y=\tfrac{1}{24}wx^4+\tfrac{1}{6}Ax^3-\tfrac{1}{12}wl^2x^2-\tfrac{1}{4}Alx^2+0 \quad (5)$$

since $y=0$ for $x=0$, and putting $y=0$ for $x=l$, and dividing by l^3

$$0=\tfrac{1}{24}wl-\tfrac{1}{12}wl+\tfrac{1}{6}A-\tfrac{1}{4}A$$

hence $\quad\quad\quad A=-\tfrac{1}{2}wl \quad\text{and}\quad B=\tfrac{1}{12}wl^2$

Substituting these values in the above equations, the values of the shearing force, bending moment, slope, and deflection everywhere are found, viz.

$$F=EId^3y/dx^3=w(x-\tfrac{1}{2}l) \quad\quad\quad (6)$$

$$M=EId^2y/dx^2=\tfrac{1}{12}w(6x^2-6lx+l^2) \quad\quad (7)$$

which reaches a zero value for $x=l(\tfrac{1}{2}\pm0\cdot289)$, *i.e.* $0\cdot289l$, on either side of mid-span. Also for $x=0$, or $x=l$, $M=\tfrac{1}{12}wl^2$, and for $x=\tfrac{1}{2}l$, $M=-\tfrac{1}{24}wl^2$

$$i=dy/dx=w(2x^3-3lx^2+l^2x)/(12EI) \quad\quad (8)$$

which reaches zero for $x=0$, $x=l$, $x=\tfrac{1}{2}l$

$$y=wx^2(l-x)^2/(24EI). \quad\quad\quad (9)$$

and at the centre, where $x=\tfrac{1}{2}l$, the deflection is

$$\tfrac{1}{24}\frac{w}{EI}\cdot\left(\frac{l}{2}\right)^2\cdot\left(\frac{l}{2}\right)^2=\tfrac{1}{384}\frac{wl^4}{EI} \quad\quad\quad (10)$$

or $\tfrac{1}{5}$ of that for a freely supported beam (see (12), Art. 79).

The bending-moment diagram is shown in Fig. 122; it should be noticed that the bending moment varies in the same way as if the ends were free, varying from $+\tfrac{1}{12}wl^2$ to $-\tfrac{1}{24}wl^2$, a change of $\tfrac{1}{8}wl^2$, as in the freely supported beam (see Fig. 49), but the greatest bending moment to which the beam is subjected is only $\tfrac{1}{12}wl^2$ instead of $\tfrac{1}{8}wl^2$, so that with the same cross-section the greatest intensity of direct bending stress will be reduced in the ratio 3 to 2. The greatest bending moment and greatest shearing force ($\tfrac{1}{2}wl$) here occur at the

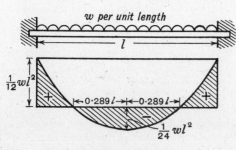

FIG. 122

same section. Evidently, to attain the greatest flexural strength the bending moment at the centre should be equal to that at the ends, each being half of $\frac{1}{8}wl^2$. In this case the equation to the bending-moment curve would be, from (7), Art. 79

$$M = EId^2y/dx^2 = \tfrac{1}{2}wx^2 - \tfrac{1}{2}wlx + \tfrac{1}{16}wl^2 \quad . \quad . \quad . \quad (11)$$

the last or constant term alone differing from the equation used above. Integrating this twice and putting $y=0$ for $x=0$ and for $x=l$, or integrating once and putting $dy/dx=0$ for $x=\frac{1}{2}l$ because of the symmetry, the necessary slope at the ends is found to be $wl^2/(96EI)$ or $\frac{1}{4}$ of that in a beam freely supported at its ends (see (10), Art. 79).

Other types of loading where w is a simple function of x may be easily solved by this method.

As another example, suppose that $w=0$, but one end support sinks a distance δ, both ends remaining fixed horizontally. Taking the origin at the end A, say, which does not sink

$$EId^4y/dx^4 = 0 \quad . \quad . \quad . \quad . \quad . \quad (12)$$

$$EId^3y/dx^3 = F \quad . \quad . \quad . \quad . \quad . \quad (13)$$

where F is the (constant) shearing force throughout the span,

$$EId^2y/dx^2 = Fx + m \quad . \quad . \quad . \quad . \quad (14)$$

where m is the bending moment for $x=0$

$$EIdy/dx = \tfrac{1}{2}Fx^2 + mx + 0 \quad . \quad . \quad . \quad (15)$$

and putting $dy/dx=0$ for $x=l$ $m = -\tfrac{1}{2}Fl$ . . . . (16)

and $$EIdy/dx = \tfrac{1}{2}F(x^2 - lx) \quad . \quad . \quad . \quad . \quad (17)$$

$$EIy = \tfrac{1}{2}F(\tfrac{1}{3}x^3 - \tfrac{1}{2}lx^2 + 0) \quad . \quad . \quad (18)$$

and putting $y=\delta$ for $x=l$

$$EI\delta = -\tfrac{1}{12}Fl^3 \quad . \quad . \quad . \quad . \quad . \quad (19)$$

$$F = 12EI\delta/l^3 \quad m = 6EI\delta/l^2 \quad . \quad . \quad (20)$$

and the bending moment anywhere is

$$\frac{6EI \cdot \delta}{l^2} - \frac{12EI \cdot x \cdot \delta}{l^3} \quad . \quad . \quad . \quad . \quad (21)$$

a straight line reaching the value

$$-6EI\delta/l^2 \text{ at } x=l$$

and $6EI\delta/l^2$ at $x=0$ . . . . . . (22)

The equal and opposite vertical reactions at the supports are each of magnitude F.

Consistent units must be used and it is best to employ inches, giving a moment in lb.-inches or ton-inches.

86. Effect of Fixed Ends on the Bending-Moment Diagram. In a built-in beam the effect of the fixing moments applied at the walls or piers when a load is applied, if acting alone, would be to make the beam convex upwards throughout. Suppose only these " fixing couples " act on the beam, the bending moment due to them at any point of the span may easily be found by looking on the beam as one simply supported, but overhanging the supports at each end and carrying such loads on the overhanging ends as would produce at the supports the actual fixing moments of the built-in beam. If these fixing moments are equal they produce a bending moment of the same magnitude throughout the span (see Fig. 51). If the fixing moments at the two ends are unequal, being say M_A at one end A (Fig. 123) and M_B at the other end B, the bending moment throughout the span varies from M_A to M_B as a straight-line diagram, *i.e.* at a constant rate along the span, as the reader will find by sketching the diagram of bending moments for a beam over-hanging

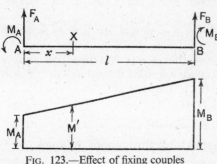

FIG. 123.—Effect of fixing couples

its two supports and carrying end loads. At a distance x from A the bending moment due to fixing couples will be

$$M' = M_A + (M_B - M_A)x/l \text{ (see Fig. 123)}$$

The actual bending moment at any section of a built-in beam will be the algebraic sum of the bending moment which would be produced by the load on a freely supported beam, and the above quantity M'.

Without any supposition of the case of an overhanging beam, we may put the result as follows for any span of a beam not " free " at the ends.

Let F_A (Fig. 123) be the shearing force just to the right of A, and F_B the shearing force just to the left of B, M_A and M_B being the moments imposed by the constraints at A and B respectively. Let w be the load per unit length of span whether constant or variable. Then, as in Art. 78, with A as origin

$$d^2M/dx^2 = w \quad . \quad . \quad . \quad . \quad . \quad . \quad (1)$$

$$F \text{ or } dM/dx = \int_0^x w\,dx + F_A \quad . \quad . \quad . \quad . \quad (2)$$

F_A being the value of F for $x=0$.

Then $$M = \int_0^x \int_0^x w\,dx\,dx + F_A \cdot x + M_A \quad . \quad . \quad . \quad . \quad (3)$$

M_A being the value of $EI d^2y/dx^2$ for $x=0$.   Putting $x=l$

$$M_B = \int_0^l \int_0^l w\,dx\,dx + F_A l + M_A$$

hence

$$F_A = \frac{M_B - M_A}{l} - \frac{1}{l}\int_0^l \int_0^l w\,dx\,dx \quad \ldots \quad (4)$$

Note that the term $\dfrac{1}{l}\displaystyle\int_0^l \int_0^l w\,dx\,dx$ is the value of the reaction at A

if $M_B = M_A$, or if both are zero as in the freely supported beam. Substituting the value of F_A in (3)

$$EI\frac{d^2y}{dx^2} \text{ or } M = \int_0^x \int_0^x w\,dx\,dx + (M_B - M_A)\frac{x}{l} + M_A - \frac{x}{l}\int_0^l \int_0^l w\,dx\,dx \quad (5)$$

or re-arranging

$$M = M_A + (M_B - M_A)x/l + \int_0^x \int_0^x w\,dx\,dx - (x/l)\int_0^l \int_0^l w\,dx\,dx \quad . \quad (6)$$

With free ends $M_A = M_B = 0$, and

$$M = \int_0^x \int_0^x w\,dx\,dx - x/l \int_0^l \int_0^l w\,dx\,dx$$

and if the ends are not free there is the additional bending moment, which may be written

$$M' = M_A + (M_B - M_A)x/l. \quad \ldots \quad \ldots \quad (7)$$

or $$M' = M_A(l-x)/l + M_B \cdot x/l \quad \ldots \quad . \quad (7\text{A})$$

a form which will be used in Arts. 88 and 91.

With this notation (5) may be written

$$M = EI d^2y/dx^2 = \mu + M' = \mu + M_A + (M_B - M_A)x/l \quad . \quad (8)$$

where μ is the bending moment at any section for a freely supported beam similarly loaded, and M' is the bending moment (Fig. 123) at
that section due to the fixing
moments M_A and M_B at the
ends.   Usually μ and M' will
be of opposite sign; if the
magnitudes of μ and M' are
then plotted on the same side
of the same base-line, the
actual bending moment M at
any section is represented by
the   ordinates   giving   the

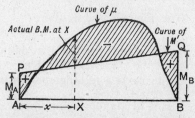

FIG. 124

difference between the two curves (see Fig. 124).   The conventional algebraic signs used in the above integrations (see Art. 78) make M negative for concavity upwards.   The reactions R_A ($= -F_A$) and R_B may be found from equation (4). If $M_B - M_A$ is positive, the reaction at A is less (in magnitude) than it would be for a simply supported beam by $(M_B - M_A)/l$ and the reaction at B is greater than for a simply supported beam by the same moment.

87. Built-in Beam with any Symmetrical Loading. For a symmetrically loaded beam of constant cross-section the fixing couples at the supports are evidently equal, and Fig. 51 shows that equal couples at the ends of a span cause a bending moment of the same amount throughout. Or, from (7), Art. 86, if $M_B = M_A$, $M' = M_A = M_B$ at every section. Hence, the resulting ordinates of the bending-moment diagram (see Art. 86) will consist of the difference in ordinates of a rectangle (the trapezoid APQB, Fig. 124, being a rectangle when $M_A = M_B$) and those of the curve of bending moments for the same span and loading with freely supported ends. And since between limits

$$dy/dx \text{ or } i = \int (M/EI)dx \text{ (see (3), Art. 78)}$$

if E and I are constant, the change of slope $\int_0^l Mdx/EI$ between the two ends of the beam is

$$\frac{1}{EI} \int_0^l (\mu + M')dx$$

with the notation of the previous article, where l is the length of span and the origin is at one support. Now in a built-in beam, if both ends are fixed horizontally, the change of slope is zero, hence

$$\left. \begin{array}{c} \int_0^l (\mu + M')dx = 0 \\ \\ \text{or} \qquad -\int_0^l M'dx = \int_0^l \mu dx \\ \\ \text{or} \qquad -M' = \frac{1}{l} \int_0^l \mu dx \end{array} \right\} \quad . \quad . \quad . \quad . \quad (1)$$

This may also be written

$$A + A' = 0 \quad . \quad . \quad . \quad . \quad . \quad (2)$$

where A stands for the area of the μ curve, and A' stands for the area of the trapezoid APQB or M' curve (Fig. 124), which in this special case is a rectangle, AA'BB' (Fig. 125).

$\int_0^l (\mu + M')dx$ represents the area of the bending-moment diagram for the whole length of span, and equation (1) shows that the total area is zero. Hence the rectangle of height M_A (or M'), and the bending-moment diagram μ for the simply supported beam have the same area $-A$, and the constant value (M_A) of M' is $-\frac{1}{l} \int_0^l \mu dx$;

the ordinate representing it is —A/*l*, A and μ being generally negative.

Hence, to find the bending-moment diagram for a symmetrically loaded beam, first draw the bending-moment diagram as if the beam were simply supported (ACDC′B, Fig. 125), and then reduce all ordinates by the amount of the average ordinate, or, in other words, raise the base-line AB by an amount M_A, which is represented by the mean ordinate of the diagram ACDC′B, or (area ACDC′B)÷(length AB). The points N and N′ vertically under C and C′ are points of contraflexure or zero bending moment,

and the areas AA′C and BB′C′ are together equal to the area CDC′ and of opposite sign. With downward load, the downward slope from A to N increases and is at N proportional to the area AA′C. From N towards mid-span the slope decreases, becoming zero at

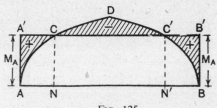

FIG. 125

mid-span when the net area of the bending-moment diagram from A is zero, *i.e.* as much area is positive as negative.

The slopes and deflections may be obtained from the resulting bending-moment diagram by the methods of Art. 82, taking account of the sign of the areas. Or the methods of Art. 83 may be employed, remembering the opposite signs of the different parts of the bending-moment diagram area, and that the slope and deflection are zero at the ends. Another possible method is to treat the portion NN′ between the points of contraflexure (or virtual hinges) as a separate beam supported at its ends on the ends of two cantilevers, AN and BN′.

If the slopes at the ends A and B are not zero, but are fixed at equal magnitudes *i* and of opposite sign, both being downwards towards the centre, slopes being reckoned positive downwards to the right, equation (1) becomes

$$\int_0^l (\mu + M')dx = -2i \cdot EI$$

and $\int_0^l M'dx = -\int_0^l \mu dx - 2i \cdot EI$ or $M' = -\frac{1}{l}\int_0^l \mu dx - \frac{2i \cdot EI}{l}$

μ being usually negative, and for minimum intensity of bending stress this value of M′ should be equal in magnitude to half the maximum value of μ.

Example 1. Uniformly distributed load *w* per unit span on a built-in beam.   The area of the parabolic bending-moment diagram for a simply supported beam (see Fig. 49) is

$$\tfrac{2}{3} \times \tfrac{1}{8}wl^2 \times l = \tfrac{1}{12}wl^3$$

The mean bending moment is therefore $\tfrac{1}{12}wl^2$.   By reducing all ordinates of Fig. 49 by the amount $\tfrac{1}{12}wl^2$, we get exactly the same diagram as shown in Fig. 122.

Example 2.   Central load W on a built-in beam.

The bending-moment diagram for the simply supported beam is shown in Fig. 47.   Its mean height is proportional to $\tfrac{1}{2} \cdot \dfrac{Wl}{4}$ or $\dfrac{Wl}{8}$.

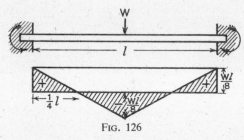

FIG. 126

Hence, for the built-in beam the bending-moment diagram is as shown in Fig. 126.   The points of contraflexure are evidently $\tfrac{1}{4}l$ from each end, and the bending moments at the ends and centre are $\tfrac{1}{8}Wl$.

Taking the origin at the centre or either end, using the method of Art. 82 (3) and taking account of the signs, dy/dx vanishes at both limits and y at one limit, and the central deflection under the load is

$$\frac{1}{EI}\left\{\left(\tfrac{1}{2} \cdot \frac{Wl}{8} \times \frac{l}{4}\right)\left(\frac{l}{2} - \tfrac{1}{3}\frac{l}{4}\right) - \left(\tfrac{1}{2} \cdot \frac{Wl}{8} \cdot \frac{l}{4}\right)\left(\tfrac{1}{3} \cdot \frac{l}{4}\right)\right\} = \frac{Wl^3}{192EI}$$

88. Built-in Beams with any Loading.

As in the previous article, and with the same notation, if I and E are constant

$$\left.\begin{aligned}\int_0^l (\mu + M')dx = 0\\ A + A' = 0\end{aligned}\right\} \quad \ldots \quad \ldots \quad (1)$$

or

or substituting for M' its value from (7), Art. 87

$$\int_0^l \left\{\mu + M_A + (M_B - M_A)\frac{x}{l}\right\}dx = 0 \quad \ldots \quad (2)$$

The loading being not symmetrical, M_B is not necessarily equal to M_A, and the area A' is not a rectangle but a trapezoid (Fig. 127), and the equation of areas A and A' is insufficient to determine the *two* fixing couples M_A and M_B.   We may, however, very conveniently proceed by the method used in Art. 82 to establish a second relation.   Thus, taking one end of the span, say A, Fig. 127, as origin

$$\frac{d^2y}{dx^2} = \frac{\mu + M'}{EI}$$

and multiplying by x and integrating (by parts), with limits l and 0

$$\left(x\frac{dy}{dx}-y\right)_0^l=\frac{1}{EI}\int_0^l(\mu+M')x\,dx=\frac{1}{EI}\left(\int_0^l\mu x\,dx+\int_0^l M'x\,dx\right)$$

or

$$EI\left(x\frac{dy}{dx}-y\right)_0^l=A\bar{x}+A\bar{x}'$$

where $\bar{x}$ and $\bar{x}'$ are the respective distances of the centres of gravity or centroids of the areas A and A' from the origin. Further, the term

$$\left(x\,dy/dx-y\right)_0^l$$

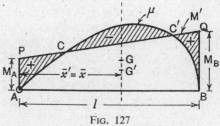

FIG. 127

is obviously zero, since each part of it vanishes at both limits $x=l$ and $x=0$; hence

$$Ax+A'\bar{x}'=0=\int_0^l\mu x\,dx+\int_0^l M'x\,dx \quad . \quad . \quad . \quad (3)$$

or the moments about either support of the areas A and A' are equal in magnitude, in addition to the areas themselves being equal, or, in other words, their centroids are in the same vertical line (see Fig. 127).

Evidently, from Fig. 127, the area APQB or $A'=\frac{1}{2}(M_A+M_B)l$, hence from (1)

$$\tfrac{1}{2}(M_A+M_B)l=-A \quad . \quad . \quad . \quad . \quad . \quad (4)$$

and, taking moments about the point A (Fig. 127), dividing the trapezoid into triangles by a diagonal PB

$$A'\bar{x}'=(\tfrac{1}{2}M_A\, . \,l\, . \,\tfrac{1}{3}l)+(\tfrac{1}{2}M_B\, . \,l\, . \,\tfrac{2}{3}l)=\tfrac{1}{6}l^2(M_A+2M_B) \quad . \quad (4\text{A})$$

or from (3)

$$\tfrac{1}{6}l^2(M_A+2M_B)=-A\bar{x} \quad . \quad . \quad . \quad (5)$$

or

$$M_A+2M_B=-6A\bar{x}/l^2$$

and from (4)

$$M_A+M_B=-2A/l$$

from which

$$M_B=\frac{2A}{l}-\frac{6A\bar{x}}{l^2} \quad\text{or}\quad \frac{2A}{l}\left(1-\frac{3\bar{x}}{l}\right) \quad . \quad . \quad (6)$$

$$M_A=6\frac{A\bar{x}}{l^2}-4\frac{A}{l} \quad\text{or}\quad 2\frac{A}{l}\left(\frac{3\bar{x}}{l}-2\right) \quad . \quad . \quad (7)$$

Thus the fixing moments are determined in terms of the area of the bending-moment diagram (A) and its moment ($A\bar{x}$) about one support, or the distance of its centroid from one support. The trapezoid APQB (Fig. 127) can then be drawn, and the difference of ordinates between it and the bending-moment diagram for the simply supported beam gives the bending moments for the built-in beam. The resultant diagram is shown shaded in Fig. 127. With the convention as to signs used in Art. 78, the area A must be reckoned negative for values of M producing concavity upwards. With loading which gives a bending moment the area of which and its moment are easily calculated, M_B and M_A may be found algebraically or arithmetically from (6) and (7), and then the bending moment elsewhere found from the equation (8) of Art. 86. With irregular loading the process may be carried out graphically; the quantity A . $\bar{x}$ may then conveniently be found by a " derived area," as in Art. 35, Fig. 38, using the origin A as a pole, without finding $\bar{x}$.

When the resultant bending-moment diagram has been determined, either of the graphical methods of Art. 83 may be used to find the deflections or slopes at any point of the beam, taking proper account of the difference of sign of the areas and starting both slope and deflection curves from zero at the ends. Or the methods of Art. 82, (b) and (c), may be employed, taking account of the different signs in calculating slopes from the areas of the bending-moment diagram or deflections from the moments of such areas. When the bending moment has been determined, the problem of finding slopes, deflections, etc., for the built-in beam is generally simpler than for the merely supported beam, because the end slopes are generally zero. The shearing-force diagram for the built-in beam with an unsymmetrical load changes from point to point just as for the corresponding simply supported beam (since $dF/dx = w$), but the reactions at the ends are different, as shown by (4), Art. 86, one (R_B) being greater in magnitude, and the other (R_A) being less by the amount $(M_B - M_A)/l$, which may be positive or negative.

If the ends of the beam are built in so that the end slopes are not zero, equation (1) becomes

$$A + A' = EI(i_B - i_A) \quad \ldots \quad \ldots \quad (8)$$

where i_B and i_A are the fixed slopes at the ends B and A, and are reckoned positive if downward to the right (usually they will have opposite signs). Equation (3) then becomes

$$A\bar{x} + A'\bar{x}' = EI . l . i_B \quad \ldots \quad \ldots \quad (9)$$

and the values of M_B and M_A are

$$M_B = \frac{2A}{l} - \frac{6A\bar{x}}{l^2} + \frac{2(2i_B + i_A)EI}{l} \quad \ldots \ldots \quad (10)$$

$$M_A = \frac{6A\bar{x}}{l^2} - \frac{4A}{l} - 2\frac{(i_B + 2i_A)EI}{l} \quad \ldots \ldots \quad (11)$$

quantities which will be less in magnitude (the area A being negative) than (6) and (7) when both ends slope downwards towards the centre, unless i_B and i_A are very unequal in magnitude. To secure the greatest possible flexural strength from a given section it would be necessary to make the two fixing moments M_B and M_A equal, and opposite to half the maximum bending moment for the freely supported beam. The necessary end slopes could more easily be calculated than secured in practice. And in the case where $A=0$

$$i_A = -\frac{l}{6EI}(2M_A + M_B), \quad i_B = +\frac{l}{6EI}(M_A + 2M_B) \quad . \quad (12)$$

while if A is not zero

$$i_A = -\frac{l-\bar{x}}{l}\cdot\frac{A}{EI} - \frac{l}{6EI}(2M_A + M_B), \quad i_B = \frac{A\bar{x}}{lEI} + \frac{l}{6EI}(M_A + 2M_B) \quad (13)$$

which reduces to (7) and (6), Art. 82, when $M_A = 0 = M_B$. Also

$$i_A - i_B = -\frac{A}{EI} - \frac{l}{2EI}(M_A + M_B) \quad . \quad . \quad . \quad (13\text{A})$$

another form of equation (8).

Sinking of Support. If the end B sinks a distance δ relative to A but remains fixed in direction a term $6EI\delta/l^3$ is added to the right-hand side of (11) and $-6EI\delta/l^3$ to the right-hand side of (10), as shown by (21) of Art. 85.

An Alternative Method

A very simple method of dealing with a beam *encastré* at its ends is to look upon it as a cantilever fixed at one end, A, say (Fig. 128),

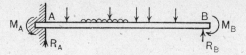

Fig. 128

the otherwise free end, B, being propped by a force R_B (the reaction at B) and subject to a couple, M_B, that of the wall. Then principles, similar to those used in Art. 80, readily give R_B and M_B. Thus let the slope and deflection produced at B if free by the loads be i and δ respectively. Then using (1) and (11), Art. 80, and equating the resultant upward slope to the right at B to zero, say

$$\frac{R_B l^2}{2EI} - \frac{M_B l}{EI} - i = 0, \quad \text{or} \quad \tfrac{1}{2}R_B \cdot l^2 - M_B \cdot l - EI \cdot i = 0 \quad . \quad (14)$$

And using (2) and (11), Art. 80, and equating the resultant deflection to zero

$$\frac{R_B l^3}{3EI} - \frac{M_B \cdot l^2}{2EI} - \delta = 0, \quad \text{or} \quad \tfrac{1}{3}R_B l^3 - \tfrac{1}{2}M_B l^2 - EI \cdot \delta = 0 \quad . \quad (15)$$

And from (14) and (15) $\qquad R_B = \dfrac{6EI}{l^3}(2\delta - li)$ . . . . (16)

$$M_B = \dfrac{2EI}{l^2}(3\delta - 2li)$$ . . . . (17)

Then $\qquad\qquad R_A = \text{whole load} - R_B$ . . . . . (18)

And $\quad M_A = M_B + \text{moment of whole load about A} - R_B \cdot l$. (19)

Given slopes i_A at A and i_B at B may easily be taken into account in equations (14) and (15), and any given difference in levels of the ends in equation (15).

Also equations (14) and (15) might have been written in the notation of Art. 82, application (*b*), $A\bar{x}/EI$ replacing δ and A/EI

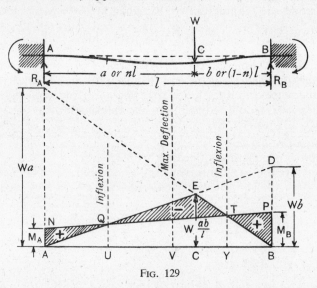

Fig. 129

replacing *i*. The factor $1/EI$ then disappears from the result, and (16) becomes

$$R_B = 6A(2\bar{x} - l)/l^3$$ . . . . . (20)

and (17) becomes $\qquad M_B = 2A(3\bar{x} - 2l)/l^2$ . . . . . (21)

A and $\bar{x}$ in (20) and (21) referring, of course, to the cantilever diagram, and differing from the A and $\bar{x}$ in equations (6) to (13A).

Values of F, M, *i*, and *y* anywhere may be found by methods and expressions used for the cantilever combining the effects of R_B, M_B, and the loads, or otherwise.

Example. A built-in beam of span *l* carries a load W at a distance *a*, from one end. Find the bending-moment diagram, points of inflexion, maximum deflection and that at the load.

The bending-moment diagram AEB, Fig. 129, for the simply supported beam is drawn as in Fig. 115 (*a*) and

$$\mu = -W\frac{b}{l}x + W(x-a) \quad . \quad . \quad . \quad . \quad (22)$$

the term $W(x-a)$ being ignored when $x < a$ (A to C). In order to draw the line NP, M_A and M_B are calculated from A, the area of AEB and its moment about the origin A or $\bar{x}$ the distance of the c.g. from A.

From the mensuration of the triangles

$$A = -\tfrac{1}{2}Wbl + \tfrac{1}{2}Wb^2 = -\tfrac{1}{2}Wb(l-b) = -\frac{Wab}{2} \quad . \quad (23)$$

$$A\bar{x} = -\tfrac{1}{2}Wal \times \tfrac{1}{3}l + \tfrac{1}{2}Wa^2 \times \tfrac{1}{3}a = -\frac{Wab(2a+b)}{6} \quad . \quad (24)$$

From (6)

$$M_B = \frac{2A}{l} - \frac{6A\bar{x}}{l^2} = \frac{Wa^2b}{l^2} \quad . \quad . \quad . \quad . \quad (25)$$

$$M_A = \frac{6A\bar{x}}{l^2} - \frac{4A}{l} = \frac{Wab^2}{l^2} \quad . \quad . \quad . \quad . \quad (26)$$

$$M_B - M_A = \frac{Wab(a-b)}{l^2} \quad \text{and} \quad M' = \frac{Wab^2}{l^2} + \frac{x}{l} \cdot \frac{Wab(a-b)}{l^2} \quad . \quad (27)$$

$$M = M' + \mu = \frac{Wab^2}{l^2} + \frac{xWab(a-b)}{l^3} - W\frac{b}{l}x + W(x-a)$$

$$= W\left\{\frac{ab^2}{l^2} - \frac{b^2(3a+b)}{l^3} \cdot x + (x-a)\right\} \quad . \quad . \quad . \quad (28)$$

the last term $(x-a)$ being omitted when $x < a$. (A to C).

The point of inflexion ($M = 0$) are, between A and C,

$$x = \frac{a}{3a+b}l \quad . \quad . \quad . \quad . \quad . \quad . \quad (29)$$

and between C and B (where $x > a$ and $(x-a)$ is included)

$$x = \frac{a+2b}{a+3b} \cdot l \quad . \quad . \quad . \quad . \quad . \quad (30)$$

These points are readily found graphically where the line NP cuts the bending-moment diagram AEB, viz. at Q and T. Since the slope at A is zero that distant x from A is

$$i = \frac{1}{EI}\int_0^x Mdx = \frac{W}{EI}\left\{\frac{ab^2x}{l^2} - \frac{x^2 \cdot b^2(3a+b)}{2l^3} + \tfrac{1}{2}(x-a)^2\right\} \quad . \quad (31)$$

where the last term $\tfrac{1}{2}(x-a)^2$ is omitted when $x < a$.

This slope is zero when $x = \frac{2a}{3a+b}l$. This is, of course, twice the value of x above at the point of inflexion. From the shaded bending-moment diagram in Fig. 129, it will be evident that since the slope is zero at A, it will reach a maximum at U and become zero again at V, where UV=AU for the negative area will then just equal the positive area ANQ. For higher values of x the negative slope will increase to its greatest value at Y and again reach zero at B.

The second point of inflexion may be found by equating i to zero but including the term $\frac{1}{2}(x-a)^2$ since $x>a$. This gives $x=\dfrac{a+b}{a+3b}l$. ($=$AY).

The deflection anywhere is found by integrating again

$$y=\int_0^x i\,dx=\frac{W}{EI}\left\{\frac{ab^2x^2}{2l^2}-\frac{x^3b^2(3a+b)}{6l^3}+\tfrac{1}{6}(x-a)^3\right\} \quad . \quad (32)$$

where again the last term $(x-a)^3/6$ is to be omitted when $x<a$. At the load, $x=a$,

$$y_C=\frac{Wa^3b^3}{3EIl^3} \quad . \quad . \quad . \quad . \quad . \quad . \quad (33)$$

And the maximum deflection is found by substituting the foregoing value of x, viz. $l\times 2a/(3a+b)$ for zero slope which gives

$$y_{max.}=\tfrac{2}{3}\frac{Wa^3b^2}{(3a+b)^2EI} \quad . \quad . \quad . \quad . \quad (34)$$

By writing $\quad M_B=\dfrac{Wa^2b}{l^2}=Wb-R_A(a+b)+\dfrac{Wab^2}{l^2} \quad . \quad . \quad (35)$

we find $\qquad\qquad R_A=Wb^2(3a+b)/l^3$ }

and similarly $\qquad\quad R_B=Wa^2(a+3b)/l^3$ } $\quad . \quad . \quad . \quad . \quad (36)$

Built-in Beams of Variable Section. Having considered in Art. 84 how simple beam-deflection problems are affected by a variable section, and in the present chapter the case of built-in beams of constant section, it will be sufficient to say that the modification in the work when the quantity I is not a constant consists in using M/I instead of M as a variable throughout.

89. Single Load and Couple. (*a*) *Single Load.* The problem of the single load W on an *encastré* beam has been solved at the end of the preceding article (Art. 88) as an example of the use of the general method, employing the area and moment of area of the bending-moment diagram. But it may also be solved easily by direct integration as in the case of the simply supported beam (Art. 79), the end conditions being very simple. We shall again employ Macauley's method of integration, ignoring where inapplicable in the equations for M . i and y terms which are only applicable beyond the values of x corresponding to the discontinuity at a single concentrated load W. We can again use Fig. 129 but will write nl in place of a and $(1-n)l$ in place of b, n and $1-n$ being fractions.

Starting from the fundamental equation for the bending moment at a distance x from the origin at A (Fig. 129)

$$EId^2y/dx^2 = M_A - R_A x + W(x-nl) \quad . \quad . \quad . \quad (1)$$

where $W(x-nl)$ is to be ignored for $x < nl$.

$$EIdy/dx = M_A x - \tfrac{1}{2}R_A x^2 + \tfrac{1}{2}W(x-nl)^2 + 0 \quad . \quad . \quad (2)$$

the constant being zero since $dy/dx = 0$ for $x = 0$ and the last term being ignored for $x < nl$. Putting $x = l$ for which $dy/dx = 0$

$$0 = M_A l - \tfrac{1}{2}R_A l^2 + \tfrac{1}{2}W(1-n)^2 l^2$$

hence, $R_A = 2M_A/l + W(1-n)^2$

$$EIdy/dx = M_A(x - x^2/l) - \tfrac{1}{2}W(1-n)^2 x^2 + \tfrac{1}{2}W(x-nl)^2 \quad . \quad (3)$$

the last term being ignored if $x < nl$. Integrating again,

$$EIy = M_A(\tfrac{1}{2}x^2 - x^3/3l) - W(1-n)^2 x^3/6 + W(x-nl)^3/6 + 0 \quad . \quad (4)$$

which is zero for $x = l$, hence

$$M_A = Wln(1-n)^2 \quad \text{(or } Wab^2/l^2) \quad . \quad . \quad . \quad . \quad (5)$$

$$R_A = W(1-n)^2(2n+1); \quad R_B = Wn^2(3-2n) \quad . \quad . \quad (6)$$

and substituting in (4)

$$EIy = W\{\tfrac{1}{2}n(1-n)^2 x^2 l - (1-n)^2(1+2n)x^3/6 + (x-nl)^3/6\} \quad . \quad (7)$$

and at C, where $x = nl$

$$EIy_C = \tfrac{1}{3}Wn^3(1-n)^3 l^3 \quad . \quad . \quad . \quad . \quad (8)$$

in agreement with (33) of Art. 88.   And differentiating twice

$$EIdy/dx = W\{n(1-n)^2 xl - \tfrac{1}{2}(1-n)^2(1+2n)x^2 + \tfrac{1}{2}(x-nl)^2\} \quad . \quad (9)$$

in agreement with (31) Art. 88.

$$M = EId^2y/dx^2 = W\{n(1-n)^2 l - (1-n)^2(1+2n)x + (x-nl)\} \quad . \quad (10)$$

in agreement with (28), Art. 88.   And at $x = nl$

$$M_C = -2Wln^2(1-n)^2 \quad . \quad . \quad . \quad . \quad (11)$$

At $x = 0$ $M_A = Wln(1-n)^2 \quad . \quad . \quad . \quad . \quad . \quad (12)$

At $x = l$ $M_B = W(1-n)n^2 \quad . \quad . \quad . \quad . \quad . \quad (13)$

The values of x at the points of inflection (for which $M = 0$) are found from (10) to be

$$x = ln/(1+2n) \quad \text{and} \quad x = l(2-n)/(3-2n) \quad . \quad . \quad (14)$$

as in (29) and (30), Art. 88.

(*b*) *Couple*. Let μ be the clockwise couple exerted at C, nl from A, Fig. 130. The unknown but equal reactions are R dcwn-wards at A and R upwards at B. There will also be external couples M_A at A and M_B at B. At a point distant x from A

$$M = EId^2y/dx^2 = M_A + Rx - \mu \quad . \quad . \quad . \quad . \quad (15)$$

I

where the last term (μ) is to be ignored for $x<nl$

$$EId y/dx=M_A x+\tfrac{1}{2}R x^2-\mu(x-nl) \quad . \quad . \quad . \quad (16)$$

the constant in the last term being such as to make it zero at $x=nl$ and the term being ignored for $x<nl$. At $x=l$

$$0=M_A l+\tfrac{1}{2}R l^2-\mu l(1-n)$$

$$R=2\{(1-n)\mu-M_A\}/l . \quad . \quad . \quad . \quad . \quad (17)$$

And substituting this value in (16)

$$EId y/dx=\{(1-n)\mu-M_A\}x^2/l+M_A x-\mu(x-nl) \quad . \quad . \quad . \quad (18)$$

$$EIy=\tfrac{1}{3}\{(1-n)\mu-M_A\}x^3/l+\tfrac{1}{2}M_A x^2-\tfrac{1}{2}\mu(x-nl)^2+0 \quad (19)$$

And putting $y=0$ for $x=l$ gives

$$M_A=\mu(1-n)(1-3n) \quad . \quad . \quad . \quad . \quad (20)$$

$$R=6\mu n(1-n)/l \quad . \quad . \quad . \quad . \quad . \quad (21)$$

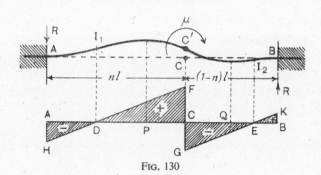

Fig. 130

And substituting for M_A and R in (15)

$$EId^2 y/dx^2=\mu(1-n)\{(1-3n)+6nx/l\}-\mu \quad . \quad . \quad (22)$$

And at $x=nl$ the bending moment at C on the portion CA is

$$M_{CA}=M_A+Rnl=\mu(1-n)(1-3n+6n^2) \quad . \quad . \quad (23)$$

$$M_{CB}=-\mu n(4-9n+6n^2) \quad . \quad . \quad . \quad . \quad . \quad . \quad (24)$$

$$M_B=\mu n(2-3n) \quad . \quad . \quad . \quad . \quad . \quad . \quad . \quad . \quad (25)$$

Note that the distribution of μ into M_{CA} and M_{CB} is not very simple. In the range AC or $x=0$ to $x=nl$, M=0 if

$$x/l=\tfrac{1}{6}(3n-1)/n \quad . \quad . \quad . \quad . \quad . \quad (26)$$

which gives a point of inflexion provided $n>\tfrac{1}{3}$. In the range CB or $x=nl$ to $x=l$, M=0 if

$$x/l=(4-3n)/(1-n) \quad . \quad . \quad . \quad . \quad (27)$$

Substituting for M_A in (19)

$$EIy=\tfrac{1}{2}\mu(1-n)\{(1-3n)l+2nx\}x^2/l-\tfrac{1}{2}\mu(x-nl)^2 \quad . \quad (28)$$

And at $x=nl$　　　$EIy_C=\frac{1}{2}\mu l^2 n^2(1-n)^2(1-2n)$ . . . . (29)

And differentiating (28)

$$EI\,dy/dx=\frac{1}{2}\mu(1-n)\{2(1-3n)x+6nx^2/l\}-\mu(x-nl)\ . \quad (30)$$

which is zero for a maximum value of y at

$$x/l=\frac{1}{3}(3n-1)/n \text{ or } 1-\frac{1}{3}n$$

(c) *Couple with support.* If the *encastré* beam is vertically supported at the point C (Fig. 130), which is the axis of the torque μ, the distribution of the bending moment and deformation of the beam are modified and the results are useful in further analysis. Let R_C be the vertical downward force at C necessary to keep the point C in the straight line AB (or $-R_C$ be the upward supporting force at C). From (8), writing R_C for W,

$$EIy_C=\frac{1}{3}R_C n^3(1-n)^3l^3 \text{ (downwards)}$$

And from (29)

$$EIy_C=\frac{1}{2}\mu l^2 n^2(1-n)^2(1-2n) \text{ (downwards)}$$

If $y_C=0$, equating the downward deflection at C due to μ to the upward deflection due to R_C, whether the numerical value be $+$ or $-$,

$$-\frac{1}{3}R_C n^3(1-n)^3l^3=\frac{1}{2}\mu l^2 n^2(1-n)^2(1-2n) \quad . \quad . \quad (31)$$

$$R_C=-\frac{3}{2}\frac{\mu}{l}\cdot\frac{1-2n}{n(1-n)} \text{ (downward)} \quad . \quad . \quad . \quad (32)$$

This will be downward if $n>\frac{1}{2}$.

And from (11) and (23)

$$M_{CA}=-2R_C ln^2(1-n)^2+\mu(1-n)(1-3n+6n^2)=\mu(1-n)\ . \quad (33)$$

$$M_{CB}=M_{CA}-\mu=-\mu n \quad . \quad . \quad . \quad . \quad (34)$$

At $x=0$, from (20) and (12), taking R_C in place of W,

$$\left.\begin{array}{l}M_A=\mu(1-n)(1-3n)-3\mu(1-2n)(1-n)/2=-\frac{1}{2}\mu(1-n)\\ \text{which is } -\frac{1}{2}M_{CA}\end{array}\right\}\ . \quad (35)$$

From (25) and (13)

$$\left.\begin{array}{l}M_B=\mu n(2-3n)-3\mu(1-2n)n/2=\frac{1}{2}\mu n\\ \text{which is } -\frac{1}{2}M_{CB}\end{array}\right\}\quad . \quad . \quad (36)$$

Variations in bending moment are linear and are shown in Fig. 131. Inflections are obviously at $\frac{1}{3}$ of AC from A and $\frac{1}{3}$ of CB from B.

A comparison of Figs. 131 and 130 is instructive. They are similar but in Fig. 131 the rates of change of bending moment in the two parts AC and CB are not equal as in Fig. 130, where the supporting forces (R) are numerically equal, one upward at B and the other downward at A. The downward restraining force R_C adds nR_C to the upward force R_B and diminishes the downward force R_A by $(1-n)R_C$, thus increasing the rate of change of M in the range CB and decreasing it in the range CA.   But in Fig. 131, as in Fig. 130, the total positive area is equal to the total negative area of the bending-moment diagram since the change of slope from A to B is zero.   The curves have points of inflexion I_1 above D and I_2

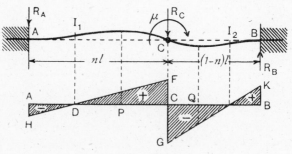

FIG. 131

above E, and zero slopes above P and Q where DP=AD and QE=EB.

Equations (35) and (36) should be noted as useful in later analysis (see Art. 94).   Equations (33) and (34) show the distribution of a moment µ between the two portions AC and CB of the beam.   It is

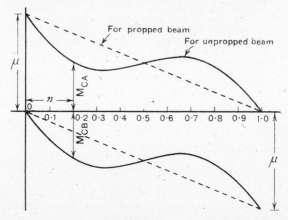

FIG. 132

divided in proportion to the flexural stiffnesses of the two parts or inversely as their flexibilities, that is, inversely as their lengths. (This is an example of the general case of elastic distribution of loads in Art. 21.   The common distortion is the rotation or inclination dy/dx or i_C at C.)

The values of M_{CA} and M_{CB} for the beam subject to the couple µ are shown in Fig. 132 by the full lines for the case where C is free to deflect (see (23) and (24)) and by the broken line for the case where C is kept in the line AB by a prop or vertical supporting force R_C at C (see (33) and (34)). For the unpropped beam, maxima and minima occur at $n = \frac{1}{3}$ and $n = \frac{2}{3}$, but in the central $\frac{4}{5}$ of the length the moment is fairly equally divided between the two parts.

The results (33) and (34) can be established by treating the parts AC and BC of the beam as cantilevers propped at their common point C and subject to such external moments there as give them a common rotation or inclination i_C at C.

Thus from (15), Art. 80, allowing for a difference of symbols, the upward propping force on the cantilever AC at C, due to a moment M_{CA} at C is $3M_{CA}/(2nl)$, and using (3) and (8) of Art. 80

$$EI_A i_C = M_{CA} nl - \frac{1}{2} \cdot \frac{3}{2} M_{CA} nl = \frac{1}{4} M_{CA} \cdot nl \quad . \quad . \quad (37)$$

where I_A is the value of I for the part CA.

Similarly, the *downward* vertical force at C for the cantilever CB is $3M_{CB}/\{2(1-n)l\}$ and

$$-EI_B i_C = M_{CB}(1-n)l - \frac{3}{4} M_{CB}(1-n)l = \frac{1}{4} M_{CB}(1-n)l \quad . \quad (38)$$

and equating the values of i_C in (37) and (38),

$$\frac{M_{CA}}{M_{CB}} = -\frac{1-n}{n} \times \frac{I_A}{I_B} \quad . \quad . \quad . \quad . \quad (39)$$

If $I_A = I_B$, this gives the result (33) and (34), for the moment μ is distributed so that $M_{CA} = (1-n)\mu$ and $M_{CB} = -n\mu$. Also

$$M_A = -\frac{3}{2} M_{CB}/(nl) \times nl + M_{CA} = -\frac{1}{2} M_{CA} \quad . \quad . \quad (40)$$

(as already shown at (16) of Art. 80).

Similarly, the bending moment at B will be of half the magnitude of M_{CB} at C and of opposite sign.

If I_A and I_B are not equal, the distribution of μ is nevertheless (as shown at (39)) in the ratio of the flexural stiffnesses of the two parts of the beam so that

$$M_{CA} = \frac{I_A/n}{I_A/n + I_B/(1-n)} \mu \quad \text{and} \quad M_{CB} = -\frac{I_B/(1-n)}{I_A/n + I_B/(1-n)} \mu \quad . \quad (41)$$

90. " Fixed-Free " Beam with Couple. It is convenient here, for later reference, to investigate the beam (or cantilever) fixed at one end (A) and freely supported at the other end (B) and acted upon by a couple μ at some intermediate point C which is free to deflect vertically. This is an extension of relations established in (14), (15), and (16) of Art. 80 for a couple μ at a distance nl from the fixed end and we continue to use the symbols of Art. 89 and Fig. 133.

$$M = EI d^2y/dx^2 = \mu - R/(l-x) - \mu \quad . \quad . \quad . \quad (1)$$

where the last term is ignored if $x < nl$.

Integrating twice and using the conditions $dy/dx=0$ for $x=0$ and $y=0$ for $x=0$ and for $x=l$ we find

$$Rl=3\mu n(2-n)/2 \qquad \qquad (2)$$

$$M_A=\mu-Rl=\tfrac{1}{2}\mu(2-6n+3n^2) \qquad (3)$$

$$M_{CB}=R(1-n)l=3\mu n(2-n)(1-n)/2 \qquad (4)$$

$$M_{CA}=M_{CB}+\mu=\tfrac{1}{2}\mu(2-6n+9n^2-3n^3) \qquad (5)$$

$$M=EId^2y/dx^2=\mu-3\mu n(2-n)(l-x)/(2l)-\mu. \qquad (6)$$

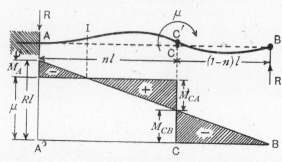

Fig. 133

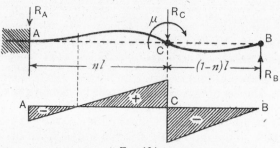

Fig. 134

where the last term is ignored for $x<nl$.

$$EIdy/dx=\mu x-3\mu n(2-n)(xl-\tfrac{1}{2}x^2)/(2l)-\mu(x-nl) \qquad (7)$$

$$EIy=\tfrac{1}{2}\mu x^2\{1-\tfrac{1}{2}n(2-n)(3-x/l)\}-\tfrac{1}{2}\mu(x-nl)^2. \qquad (8)$$

$$EIy_C=\tfrac{1}{2}\mu n^2 l^2(1-n)(2-4n+n^2) \qquad (9)$$

And between A and C, $M=0$ where $Rx=Rl-\mu$, *i.e.* where

$$x=l-\mu/R=-(3n^2-6n+2)l/\{3n(2-n)\} \qquad (10)$$

The location of the points inflexion at I and C′ will be evident from even a sketch of the bending-moment diagram, Fig. 133.

Now suppose the beam at point C (Fig. 134) is supported by a vertical force R_C which keeps C in the line AB. We could proceed to find what value of R_C will give a deflection equal and opposite to y_C (see (9)) and then modify the foregoing results for the combined effects of μ and R_C. But we will deduce the necessary results by determining the moment distribution by considering AC as a cantilever propped at C and subject to a moment M_{CA} at C. And CB as a simply supported beam subject to a moment M_{CB} at C. The remaining conditions are that $M_{CA} - M_{CB} = \mu$ and dy/dx at C has the same magnitude for the parts AC and CB.

As in (37) of Art. 89, for the cantilever AC,

$$EI_A \cdot i_C = \tfrac{1}{4} M_{CA} nl \quad . \quad . \quad . \quad . \quad . \quad (11)$$

And from (19) of Art. 81

$$EI_B \cdot i_C = -\tfrac{1}{3} M_{CB}(1-n)l \quad . \quad . \quad . \quad . \quad (12)$$

and equating (11) and (12)

$$\frac{M_{CA}}{M_{CB}} = -\tfrac{4}{3}\frac{1-n}{n} \times \frac{I_A}{I_B} \quad . \quad . \quad . \quad . \quad (13)$$

And

$$M_{CA} = \frac{4I_A/n}{4I_A/n + 3I_B/(1-n)}\mu \quad . \quad . \quad . \quad . \quad (14)$$

$$M_{CB} = \frac{3I_B/(1-n)}{4I_A/n + 3I_B/(1-n)} \cdot \mu \quad . \quad . \quad . \quad (15)$$

If $I_A = I_B$

$$M_{CA} = \frac{4(1-n)}{4-n}\mu; \quad M_{CB} = -\frac{3n}{4-n}\mu \quad . \quad . \quad . \quad (16)$$

This distribution of μ does not differ widely from that for the beam *encastré* at each end, viz. inversely as the lengths of the two parts as shown at (33) and (34), Art. 89. It involves a rather greater proportion in the part AC which is more constrained and therefore stiffer, *e.g.* for $n=0\cdot4$, $\tfrac{2}{3}$ instead of $0\cdot6$. For $n=0\cdot6$, $\tfrac{4}{9}$ instead of $0\cdot4$.

Equating the known value of M_{CB} to the moment of R_B about C,

$$M_{CB} = -\frac{3n}{4-n}\mu = -R_B \times (1-n)l$$

$$R_B = \frac{3n}{(4-n)(1-n)} \cdot \frac{\mu}{l} \quad . \quad . \quad . \quad . \quad . \quad (17)$$

And since $M_A = -\tfrac{1}{2}M_{CA}$, the total increase in bending moment from A to C is $M_{CA} - M_A = \tfrac{3}{2}M_{CA}$ and the rate of change is the downward force R_A or

$$R_A \times nl = \tfrac{3}{2} \cdot M_{CA} = \tfrac{3}{2} \times \frac{4(1-n)}{4-n}\mu$$

$$R_A = \frac{6(1-n)}{n(4-n)}\frac{\mu}{l} \quad . \quad . \quad . \quad . \quad (18)$$

And if we take R_C positive downward it must balance $R_B - R_A$, or, using (17) and (18),

$$R_C = R_B - R_A = -\frac{3(2-4n+n^2)}{n(4-n)} \qquad . \quad . \quad . \quad (19)$$

which is positive if $n > (2 - \sqrt{2})$, *i.e.* $n > 0.586$.

And since

$$M_A = -\tfrac{1}{2}M_{CA} = -\frac{2(1-n)}{4-n}\mu \qquad . \quad . \quad . \quad (20)$$

we can easily draw the bending-moment diagram as shown in Fig. 134. The bending moment anywhere is

$$M = EId^2y/dx^2 = M_A + R_A x - \mu$$
$$= -\frac{2\mu(1-n)}{4-n}\left(1 - \frac{3}{n}\frac{x}{l}\right) - \mu \qquad . \quad . \quad . \quad (21)$$

the last term being ignored if $x < nl$. M is zero for $x/l = n/3$ and for $x = l$.

91. Continuous Beams. Theorem of Three Moments. A beam resting on more than two supports and covering more than one span is called a continuous beam. Beams supported at the ends and propped at some intermediate point have already been noticed (Arts. 79, 81, 89, and 90), and form simple special cases of continuous beams.

Considering first a simple case of a continuous beam, let AB and BC, Fig. 135, be two consecutive spans of length l_1 and l_2 of a con-

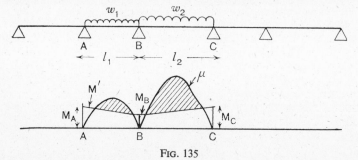

Fig. 135

tinuous beam, the uniformly spread loads on l_1 and l_2 being w_1 and w_2 per unit length respectively. Then for either span, as in Art. 86, the bending moment is the algebraic sum of μ, the bending moment for a freely supported beam of the same span and that caused by the fixing moments at the supports, or, as in Art. 86 (8),

$$M = EI\frac{d^2y}{dx^2} = \mu + M'$$

M' being generally of opposite sign to μ. First apply this to the span BC, taking B as origin and x positive to the right, μ being equal to $-\frac{1}{2}w_2(l_2x-x^2)$, being reckoned negative when producing concavity upwards, by (7) and (8), Art. 86,

$$EI d^2y/dx^2 = -\tfrac{1}{2}w_2l_2x + \tfrac{1}{2}w_2x^2 + M_B + (M_C - M_B)x/l_2 \quad . \quad (1)$$

and integrating

$$EI dy/dx = -\tfrac{1}{4}w_2l_2x^2 + \tfrac{1}{6}w_2x^3 + M_B . x$$
$$+ (M_C - M_B)x^2/(2l_2) + EI . i_B \quad . \quad . \quad (2)$$

where i_B is the value of dy/dx at B, where $x=0$.

Integrating again, y being 0 for $x=0$

$$EI y = -\frac{w_2l_2}{12} . x^3 + \frac{w_2}{24}x^4 + \frac{M_B}{2} . x^2$$
$$+ (M_C - M_B)\frac{x^3}{6l_2} + EI . i_B . x + 0 \quad . \quad . \quad (3)$$

and when $x=l_2$, $y=0$, hence dividing by l_2

$$EI . i_B = w_2l_2^3/24 - M_Bl_2/2 - (M_C - M_B)l_2/6$$

or $\qquad 6EI . i_B = w_2l_2^3/4 - 2M_Bl_2 - M_Cl_2 \quad . \quad . \quad . \quad (4)$

Now, taking B as origin, and dealing in the same way with the span BA, x being positive to the left, we get similarly (changing the sign of i_B)

$$-6EI . i_B = w_1l_1^3/4 - 2M_Bl_1 - M_A . l_1 \quad . \quad . \quad . \quad (5)$$

and adding (4) and (5)

$$M_Al_1 + 2M_B(l_1+l_2) + M_C . l_2 - \tfrac{1}{4}(w_1l_1^3 + w_2l_2^3) = 0 \quad . \quad (6)$$

This is Clapeyron's Theorem of Three Moments for the simple loading considered. If there are n supports and $n-1$ spans, or $n-2$ pairs of consecutive spans, such as ABC, $n-2$ equations, such as (6), may be written down. Two more will be required to find the bending moments at n supports, and these are supplied by the end conditions of the beam, *e.g.* if the ends are freely supported, the bending moment at each end is zero.

If an end, say at A, were fixed horizontally, $i_A = 0$ and an equation similar to (5) for the end span would be

$$2M_A + M_B - w_1l_1^2/4 = 0 \quad . \quad . \quad . \quad . \quad (7)$$

When the bending moment at each support is known, the reactions at the supports may be found by taking the moments of internal and external forces about the various supports, or from Art. 86 (4), the shearing force on a section just to the right of A_1,

$$F_A = \frac{M_B - M_A}{l} - \frac{wl}{2} \quad . \quad . \quad . \quad . \quad (8)$$

The shearing force immediately to each side of a support being

I*

found, the pressure on that support is the algebraic difference of the shearing forces on the two sides. As the shearing force generally changes sign at a support, the magnitude of the reaction is generally the sum of the magnitudes of the shearing forces on either side of the support without regard to algebraic sign.

Example 1. A beam rests on five supports, covering four equal spans, and carries a uniformly spread load. Find the bending moments, reactions, etc., at the supports.

Since the ends are free (Fig. 136), $M_A = 0$, and $M_E = 0$.

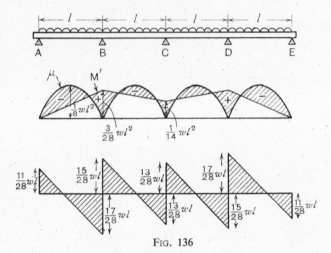

FIG. 136

And from the symmetry evidently $M_D = M_B$.

Applying the equation of three moments (6) to the portions ABC and BCD

$$0 + 2M_B . 2l + M_C . l - \tfrac{1}{2}wl^3 = 0$$

and $$M_B . l + 2M_C . 2l + M_B l - \tfrac{1}{2}wl^3 = 0$$

hence $$4M_B l + M_C l - \tfrac{1}{2}wl^3 = 0$$

and $$4M_B l + 8M_C l - wl^3 = 0$$

$$7M_C . l = \tfrac{1}{2}wl^3 \qquad M_C = \tfrac{1}{14}wl^2 \qquad M_B = \tfrac{3}{28}wl^2 = M_D$$

Taking moments about B

$$-R_A . l + \frac{wl^2}{2} = \tfrac{3}{28}wl^2 \qquad\qquad R_A = \tfrac{11}{28}wl = R_E$$

Taking moments about C

$$\tfrac{22}{28}wl^2 + R_B . l - 2wl^2 = -\tfrac{1}{14}wl^2 \qquad R_B = \tfrac{8}{7}wl = R_D$$

$$R_C = 4wl - \tfrac{11}{14}wl - \tfrac{16}{7}wl = \tfrac{13}{14}wl$$

The shearing-force diagram for Fig. 136 may easily be drawn by setting up $\tfrac{11}{28}wl$ at A, and decreasing the ordinates uniformly by an amount wl to $-\frac{17}{28}wl$ at B, increasing there by $\frac{8}{7}wl$, and so on, changing at a uniform rate over each span, and by the amount of the reactions at the various supports.

The bending-moment diagram (Fig. 136) may conveniently be drawn by drawing parabolas of maximum ordinate $\frac{1}{8}wl^2$ on each span, and erecting ordinates M_B, M_C, . M_D, and joining by straight lines. The algebraic sum of μ and M' is given by vertical ordinates across the shaded area in Fig. 136. An algebraic expression for the bending moment in any span may be written from (8), Art. 86, as follows:

Span AB, origin A,

$$M = -\tfrac{1}{2}w(lx - x^2) + \tfrac{3}{28}wlx = -\tfrac{1}{2}wx(\tfrac{11}{14}l - x)$$

Span BC, origin B,

$$M = -\tfrac{1}{2}w(lx - x^2) + \tfrac{3}{28}wl^2 - \tfrac{1}{28}wlx = -\tfrac{1}{2}w(\tfrac{15}{14}lx - \tfrac{3}{14}l^2 - x^2)$$

Example 2. A continuous girder ABCD covers three spans, AB 60 ft., BC 100 ft., CD 40 ft. The uniformly spread loads are 1 ton, 2 tons, and 3 tons per foot run on AB, BC, CD respectively. If the girder is of the same cross-section throughout, find the bending moments at the supports B and C, and the pressures on each support. Solve the problem also if the end A is fixed in the line ABCD.

For the spans ABC,

$$0 + 320M_B + 100M_C = \tfrac{1}{4} \times 1{,}000(216 + 2{,}000) = 554{,}000 \qquad (a)$$

hence $\qquad 16M_B + 5M_C = 27{,}700$ ton-ft.

For the spans BCD,

$$100M_B + 280M_C + 0 = \tfrac{1}{4} \times 1{,}000(2{,}000 + 192) = 548{,}000 \qquad (b)$$

hence $\qquad 5M_B + 14M_C = 27{,}400$ ton-ft.

From which $\qquad M_B = 1{,}260\!\cdot\!3$ ton-ft. $\quad M_C = 1{,}507\!\cdot\!0$ ton-ft.

Taking moments about B, $R_A \times 60 - 60 \times 30 = -1{,}260\!\cdot\!3$
$$R_A = 9 \text{ tons}$$

,, ,, C, $9 \times 160 + 100R_B - 60 \times 130 - 200 \times 50$
$$= -1{,}507 \qquad R_B = 148\!\cdot\!5 \text{ tons}$$

,, ,, C, $40R_D = 120 \times 20 = -1{,}507$
$$R_D = 22\!\cdot\!3 \text{ tons}$$

,, ,, B, $22\!\cdot\!3 \times 140 + 100R_C - 120 \times 120 - 200 \times 50$
$$= -1{,}260 \qquad R_C = 200\!\cdot\!1 \text{ tons}$$

If the beam is fixed at A the first equation of three moments (a) has $60M_A$ added to the left side. The second equation (b) is unchanged, and a third equation is found in (7) of Art. 91, namely

$$2M_A + M_B = 1 \times 60^2/4 = 900 \text{ ton-ft.} \qquad (c)$$

Solving the three equations we find

$M_A = -201 \cdot 4$ ton-ft.; $M_B = 1,302 \cdot 8$ ton-ft.; $M_C = 1,492$ ton-ft.

Hence, by moments about B, C, and D,

$R_A = 4 \cdot 93$ tons; $R_B = 153 \cdot 18$ tons; $R_C = 199 \cdot 19$ tons; $R_D = 22 \cdot 7$ tons.

92. Continuous Beams ; any Loading. Let the diagrams of bending moment APB and BQC be drawn for any two consecutive spans AB or l_1, and BC or l_2 (Fig. 137), of a continuous beam as if each span were bridged by independent beams freely supported at their ends. Let the area APB be A_1, and the distance of its centroid from the point A be $\bar{x}_1$, so that $A_1\bar{x}_1$ is the moment of the area

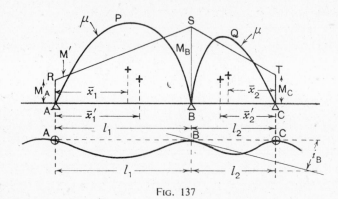

Fig. 137

about the point A. Let the area under BQC be A_2, and the distance of its centroid from C be $\bar{x}_2$, the moment about C being $A_2\bar{x}_2$. (In accordance with the signs adopted in Art. 78, and used subsequently, the areas A_1 and A_2 will be negative quantities for downward loading, bending moments which produce upwards convexity being reckoned positive.) Draw the trapezoids ARSB and BSTC as in Art. 86, to represent M′, the bending moments due to the fixing couples. Let A_1' and A_2' be the areas of ARSB and BSTC respectively, and $\bar{x}_1'$ and $\bar{x}_2'$ the distances of their centroids from A and C respectively.

From A as origin, x being measured positive towards B, using the method of Art. 82 equation (3) between limits $x = l_1$ and $x = 0$, the supports at A and B being at the same level

$$\left(x\frac{dy}{dx} - y\right)_0^{l_1} = l_1 i_B = \frac{1}{EI}\int_0^{l_1}(\mu + M')x\,dx = \frac{1}{EI}(A_1\bar{x}_1 + A_1'\bar{x}_1'). \quad (1)$$

i_B being the slope $\left(\dfrac{dy}{dx}\right)$ at B.

From C as origin, x being measured positive toward B, C and B being at the same level,

$$\left(x\frac{dy}{dx}-y\right)_0^{l2}=l_2i_B=\frac{1}{EI}(A_2\bar{x}_2+A_2'\bar{x}_2') \quad . \quad . \quad . \quad (2)$$

Equating the slope at B from (1) and (2) with sign reversed on account of the reversed direction of x

$$(A_1\bar{x}_1+A_1'\bar{x}_1')/l_1 = -(A_2\bar{x}_2+A_2'\bar{x}_2')/l_2 \quad . \quad . \quad (3)$$

And as in Art. 88 (4A), by joining AS and taking moments about A

$$A_1\bar{x}_1'=l_1^2(M_A+2M_B)/6$$

and similarly

$$A_2'\bar{x}_2'=l_2^2(M_C+2M_B)/6$$

hence (3) becomes

$$A_1\bar{x}_1/l_1+A_2\bar{x}_2/l_2+\tfrac{1}{6}M_A \cdot l_1+\tfrac{1}{3}M_B(l_1+l_2)+\tfrac{1}{6}M_Cl_2=0$$

or $6A_1\bar{x}_1/l_1+6A_2\bar{x}_2/l_2+M_A \cdot l_1+2M_B(l_1+l_2)+M_Cl_2=0$. (4)

This is a general form of the Equation of Three Moments, of which equation (6) of the previous article is a particular case easily derived by writing $A_1=-\tfrac{2}{3} \cdot \dfrac{wl_1^2}{8} \cdot l_1$, and $x_1=\dfrac{l_1}{2}$, etc., the areas A_1 and A_2 being negative for bending producing concavity upwards. For a beam on n supports this relation (4) provides $n-2$ equations, and the other necessary two follow from the manner of support at the ends.   If either end is fixed horizontally, an equation of moments for the adjacent span follows from the method of Art. 88.   If A is an end fixed horizontally, and AB the first span, from area moments *about* B, an equation similar to (5), Art. 88, is

$$2M_A+M_B+\frac{6A_1(l_1-\bar{x}_1)}{l_1^2}=0 \quad (A_1 \text{ being generally negative}) \quad . (4A)$$

If both ends are fixed horizontally, a similar equation holds for the other end.   If, say, the end A is fixed at a downward slope i_A towards B, the right-hand side of this equation would be $-6EIi_A/l_1$ instead of zero.   If either end overhangs an extreme support the bending moment at the support is found as for a cantilever.

If some or all the supports sink, the support B falling δ_1 *below* A and δ_2 *below* C, a term corresponding to y appears in (1) and (2), so that (3) becomes

$$(A_1\bar{x}_1+A_1'\bar{x}_1'+EI\delta_1)/l_1 = -(A_2\bar{x}_2+A_2'\bar{x}_2'+EI\delta_2)/l_2 \quad . \quad (3A)$$

and (4) becomes

$$6A_1\bar{x}_1/l_1+6A_2\bar{x}_2/l_2+M_A \cdot l_1+2M_B(l_1+l_2)$$
$$+M_C \cdot l_2+6EI\left(\frac{\delta_1}{l_1}+\frac{\delta_2}{l_2}\right)=0 \quad . \quad . \quad (5)$$

Wilson's Method. A simple and ingenious method of solving general problems on continuous beams, published by G. Wilson,[1] consists of finding the reactions at the supports by equating the upward deflections caused at every support by all the supporting forces, to the downward deflections which the load would cause at those various points if the beam were supported at the ends only. This provides sufficient equations to determine the reactions at all the supports except the end ones. The end reactions are then found by the usual method of taking moments of all upward and downward forces about one end, and in the case of free ends, equating the algebraic sum to zero. To take a definite case, suppose the beam to be supported at five points A, B, C, D, and E, Fig. 138, all at the same level. Let the distances of B, C, D, and E from A be b, c, d, and e respectively. Let the deflections at A, B, C, D, and E due to the load on the beam if simply supported at A and E be o, y_B, y_C, y_D, and o respectively. These may be calculated by the methods of Arts. 79, 81, 82, 83, according to the manner in which the beam is loaded.

Now let the upward deflection at B, C, and D, if the beam were

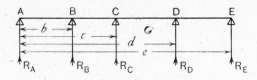

FIG. 138

supported at the ends, due to 1 lb. or 1 ton or other unit force at B be

$$_b\delta_B, \ _b\delta_C, \text{ and } _b\delta_D \text{ respectively}$$

and those at B, C, and D due to the unit force at C be

$$_c\delta_B, \ _c\delta_C, \text{ and } _c\delta_D \text{ respectively}$$

and due to unit force at D be

$$_d\delta_B, \ _d\delta_C, \text{ and } _d\delta_D \text{ respectively}.$$

Then all the supports being at zero level, if R_B, R_C, and R_D are the reactions at B, C, and D respectively, equating downward and upward deflections at B, C, and D for the beam supported at the ends A and E only

$$y_B = (R_B \times _b\delta_B) + (R_C \times _c\delta_B) + (R_D \times _d\delta_B) \quad . \quad . \quad . \quad (6)$$

$$y_C = (R_B \times _b\delta_C) + (R_C \times \delta_C) + (R_D \times _d\delta_C) \quad . \quad . \quad . \quad (7)$$

$$y_D = (R_B \times _b\delta_D) + (R_C \times _c\delta_D) + (R_D \times _d\delta_D) \quad . \quad . \quad . \quad (8)$$

[1] *Proc. Roy. Soc.*, vol. 62, Nov., 1897.

Note that $_c\delta_B = _b\delta_C$, $_d\delta_B = _d\delta_D$, $_c\delta_D = _d\delta_C$, which becomes apparent by changing b into x, x into b and a into $a+b-x$ in (7), Art. 81.

From three simple simultaneous equations (6), (7), and (8), R_B, R_C, and R_D can be determined. R_E may be found by an equation of moments about A.

$R_E \times e =$ (moment of whole load about A) $- b\,R_B - cR_C - dR_D$

and $\quad R_A =$ whole load $- R_B - R_C - R_D - R_E$.

The exercise at the end of Art. 81 is a simple example of this method, there being only one support, and therefore only one simple equation for solution.

Wilson's method may be used for algebraic calculations when the loading is simple, so that the upward and downward deflections may be easily calculated, but it is equally applicable to irregular types of loading where downward deflections at several points are all determined in one operation graphically.

When the reactions are all known, the bending moment and shearing force anywhere can be obtained by direct calculation from the definitions (Art. 39).

Sinking of any support can evidently be taken into account in this method very simply. If the support at B, for example, sinks a given amount, that amount of subsidence must be subtracted from the left-hand side of equation (6).

If one end of the beam is fixed, the deflections must be calculated as for a propped cantilever (Arts. 80 and 82). If both ends, they must be calculated as indicated in Arts. 87 and 88.

Example 1. Find the reactions in Example 1 of Art. 91 by Wilson's Method. Using Fig. 136 the beam being supported at A and E only, and A being the origin, by (9) Art. 79.

$$y_B = \frac{wl^4}{24EI}(1-8+64) = \tfrac{57}{24}\frac{wl^4}{EI} = y_D \text{ from the symmetry.}$$

And by (11), Art. 79

$$y_C = \tfrac{5}{384} \cdot \frac{256l^4}{EI} = \tfrac{10}{3}\frac{wl^4}{EI}$$

And using (7) and (8), Art. 81, the upward deflections due to the props are, at B

$$\frac{l^3}{EI}\left\{ \frac{R_B \times 9 \times 1}{3 \times 4} - \frac{R_C \times 2}{4}(\tfrac{1}{6}-\tfrac{4}{6}-\tfrac{4}{3}) - \frac{R_D}{4}(\tfrac{1}{6}-\tfrac{9}{6}-\tfrac{3}{3}) \right\}$$

$$= \frac{l^3}{EI}(\tfrac{4}{3}R_B + \tfrac{11}{12}R_C), \text{ since by symmetry } R_B = R_D$$

And at C

$$\frac{l^3}{EI}\left\{ -\frac{2R_B \cdot 2}{4}(\tfrac{4}{3}-\tfrac{9}{6}-\tfrac{3}{3}) + \frac{R_C \cdot 16}{12} \right\} = \frac{l^3}{EI}(\tfrac{11}{6}R_B + \tfrac{4}{3}R_C)$$

Equating upward and downward deflections at B and C

$$\tfrac{57}{24}wl = \tfrac{4}{3}R_B + \tfrac{11}{12}R_C$$
$$\tfrac{10}{3}wl = \tfrac{11}{6}R_B + \tfrac{4}{3}R_C$$

from which $R_B = R_D = \tfrac{8}{7}wl$ and $R_C = \tfrac{13}{14}wl$.

$$R_A = R_E = \tfrac{1}{2}(4wl - 2 \times \tfrac{8}{7}wl - \tfrac{13}{14}wl) = \tfrac{11}{28}wl$$
$$M_B = -\tfrac{11}{28}wl^2 + wl^2/2 = \tfrac{3}{28}wl^2$$
$$M_C = 2wl^2 - \tfrac{8}{7}wl^2 - \tfrac{11}{28}wl \times 2l = \tfrac{1}{14}wl^2$$

The bending moment anywhere can be simply stated, the diagrams of bending moment and shearing being as shown in Fig. 136.

Example 2.   A continuous beam 30f t. long is carried on supports at its ends, and is propped to the same level at points 10 ft. and 22 ft. from the left-hand end.   It carries loads of 5 tons, 7 tons, and 6 tons at distances of 7 ft., 14 ft., and 24 ft. respectively from the left-hand end.   Find the bending moment at the props, the reactions at the four supports, and the points of contraflexure.

Firstly, by the General Equation of Three Moments.   For the spans ABC, Fig. 139, with the notation of Art. 92.

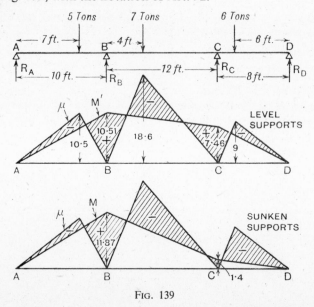

Fig. 139

Moment of the bending-moment diagram area on AB about A

$$A_1\bar{x}_1 = (\tfrac{1}{2} . 7 . \tfrac{21}{2} . \tfrac{2}{3} . 7) + (\tfrac{1}{2} . 3 . \tfrac{21}{2} . 8) = \tfrac{343}{2} + 126 = 297 \cdot 5 \text{ ton-(ft.)}^3.$$

Moment of the bending-moment diagram on BC about C

$$A_2\bar{x}_2 = (\tfrac{1}{2} . 4 . \tfrac{56}{3} . \tfrac{28}{3}) + (\tfrac{1}{2} . 8 . \tfrac{56}{3} . \tfrac{16}{3}) = \tfrac{3136}{9} + \tfrac{3584}{9} = 746 \cdot \dot{6} \text{ ton-(ft.)}^3.$$

This must be taken as negative in accordance with the signs adopted at the end of Art. 78. Then from (4) of Art. 92, since $M_A = 0$

$$-(6 \times 29 \cdot 75) - \frac{6 \times 746 \cdot \dot{6}}{12} + 0 + 2M_B \times 22 + 12M_C = 0$$

or $\qquad\qquad\qquad 44M_B + 12M_C = 551 \cdot 83 \quad . \quad . \quad . \quad . \quad (9)$

For the spans BCD

About B, $\qquad A_1 \bar{x}_1 = (\frac{1}{2} . 4 . \frac{5 \cdot 6}{3} . \frac{2}{3} . 4) + (\frac{1}{2} . 8 . \frac{5 \cdot 6}{3} . \frac{2 \cdot 0}{3}) = 597 \cdot \dot{3}$

About D, $\qquad A_2 \bar{x}_2 = (\frac{1}{2} . 2 . 9 . \frac{2 \cdot 0}{3}) + (\frac{1}{2} . 6 . 9 . 4) = 168$

Taking these as negative, from (4), M_D being 0

$$-\frac{6 \times 597 \cdot \dot{3}}{12} - \frac{6 \times 168}{8} + 12M_B + 2M_C \times 20 + 0 = 0$$

or $\qquad\qquad\qquad 12M_B + 40M_C = 424 \cdot \dot{6} \quad . \quad . \quad . \quad . \quad (10)$

And from the equations (9) and (10)

$\qquad M_B = 10 \cdot 51$ ton-ft. $\qquad\qquad M_C = 7 \cdot 46$ ton-ft.

Taking moments to the left of B

$\qquad 5 \times 3 - 10R_A = 10 \cdot 51 \qquad\qquad R_A = 0 \cdot 449$ ton

Taking moments to left of C

$\quad 5 \times 15 + 7 \times 8 - 22 \times 0 \cdot 45 - 12R_B = 7 \cdot 46 \qquad R_B = 9 \cdot 471$ tons

Taking moments to right of C

$\qquad\qquad 6 \times 2 - 8R_D = 7 \cdot 46 \qquad R_D = 0 \cdot 567$ ton

$\qquad\qquad R_C = 5 + 7 + 6 - 0 \cdot 45 - 9 \cdot 47 - 0 \cdot 57 = 7 \cdot 51$ tons

Inflexions. Taking A as origin and taking convexity upward as positive bending. From 5-ton load to B

bending moment $= 5(x-7) - 0 \cdot 449x = 4 \cdot 551x - 35$, which vanishes, for $x = 7 \cdot 9$ ft.

From B to 7-ton load, bending moment is

$4 \cdot 551x - 35 - 9 \cdot 471(x - 10) = 59 \cdot 71 - 4 \cdot 92x$, which vanishes, for $x = 12 \cdot 14$ ft.

From 7-ton load to C the bending moment is

$59 \cdot 71 - 4 \cdot 92x + 7(x - 14) = 2 \cdot 08x - 38 \cdot 29$, which vanishes, for $x = 18 \cdot 5$ ft.

From C to 6-ton load the bending moment is

$2 \cdot 08x - 38 \cdot 29 - 7 \cdot 51(x - 22) = 126 \cdot 9 - 5 \cdot 43x$, which vanishes, for $x = 23 \cdot 4$ ft.

Secondly, by Wilson's Method. With end supports only, the downward deflections by (7) and (10) of Art. 81 are, at B

$$\frac{1}{6EI \times 30}[\{ 5 \times 7 \times 20(529 + 322 - 400)\}$$

$$+ \{7 \times 16 \times 10(196 + 448 - 100)\} + \{6 \times 6 \times 10(576 + 288 - 100)\}]$$

or $y_B = \dfrac{1}{180EI}(315,700+609,280+275,040) = \dfrac{1,200,020}{180EI}$

$y_C = \dfrac{1}{6EI \times 30}[\{5 \times 7 \times 8(529+322-64)\}$
$+\{7 \times 14 \times 18(256+448-64)\}+\{6 \times 6 \times 22(576+288-484)\}]$

or $y_C = \dfrac{1}{180EI}(220,360+501,760+300,960) = \dfrac{1,023,080}{180EI}$

With end supports only, the upward deflections due to the props at B and C are

At B, $\dfrac{1}{6EI \times 30}[\{2R_B \times 100 \times 400\}+\{R_C \times 8 \times 10(484+352-100)\}]$

$= \dfrac{1}{180EI}(80,000R_B+58,880R_C)$

At C, $\dfrac{1}{6EI \cdot 30}[\{R_B \times 10 \times 8(400+400-64)\}+\{2R_C \times 64 \times 484\}]$

$= \dfrac{1}{180EI}(58,880R_B+61,952R_C)$

Equating the upward and downward deflections at B and C

$$80,000R_B+58,880R_C=1,200,020 \quad . \quad . \quad . \quad (11)$$
$$58,880R_B+61,952R_C=1,023,080 \quad . \quad . \quad . \quad (12)$$

which equations give the values

$$R_B=9\cdot47 \text{ tons} \quad R_C=7\cdot51 \text{ tons}$$

confirming the previous results.   The reactions at the ends, bending moments at the supports, and position of the points of inflexion follow by direct calculation very simply (see Fig. 139).

Example 3.   If the cross-section of the continuous beam in Example 2 above has a moment of inertia of 300 inch units, and the support B sinks $\frac{1}{20}$ in. and the support C sinks $\frac{1}{10}$ in., find the bending moments and reactions at the supports, E being 13,000 tons per sq. in.

Firstly, by Wilson's Method.   The downward deflection at B due to the load would be

$$\frac{1}{EI}\left(\frac{1,200,020}{180}\right) \text{ ft.} \quad \text{or} \quad \frac{\text{ton-(ft.)}^3}{\text{ton-(ft.)}^2}$$

if E and I are in foot and ton units.   If E and I are in inch units the deflection at B would be

$$\frac{1,728}{EI} \times \frac{1,200,020}{180} \text{ in., the dimensions being } \frac{\text{ton-(in.)}^3}{\text{ton-(in.)}^2}$$

The upward deflection at B due to the props has to balance

0·05 in. less than this amount, hence

$$\frac{1,728}{180EI}(80,000R_B+58,880R_C)=\frac{1,728}{180EI}(1,200,020)-0·5$$

or corresponding to (11), putting $I=300$ and $E=13,000$

$$80,000R_B+58,880R_C=1,200,020-20,312=1,179,708 \quad . \quad (13)$$

and corresponding to (12) with 0·1 in. subsidence at C

$$58,880R_B+61,952R_C=1,023,080-40,625=982,455 \quad . \quad (14)$$

From the simple equations (13) and (14)

$$R_C=6·13 \text{ tons} \qquad R_B=10·23 \text{ tons}$$

And by an equation of moments about A, $\quad R_D=1·33$ tons, and by an equation of moments about D, $\quad R_A=0·31$ ton.

Secondly, by the General Equation of Three Moments. From equation (5), Art. 92, an equation corresponding to equation (9), the units of which are ton-(feet)², may be formed. Using such units this becomes

$$144(44M_B+12M_C)+6\times13,000\times300\left(\frac{0·05}{120}-\frac{0·05}{144}\right)=551·83\times144$$

or $$44M_B+12M_C=551·83-11·3 \quad . \quad . \quad . \quad . \quad (15)$$

And corresponding to (10)

$$12M_B+40M_C=424·6-\frac{6\times13,000\times300}{144}\left(\frac{0·05}{144}+\frac{0·1}{96}\right)$$

or $$12M_B+40M_C=199. \quad . \quad . \quad . \quad . \quad (16)$$

And from (15) and (16)

$$M_B=11·87 \text{ ton-ft.} \qquad M_C=1·404 \text{ ton-ft.}$$

From an equation of moments to the left of B, $\quad R_A= 0·31$ ton
,,   ,,   ,,   ,, right of C, $\quad R_D= 1·33$ tons
,,   ,,   ,,   ,, right of B, $\quad R_C= 6·13$,,
,,   ,,   ,,   ,, left of C, $\quad R_B=10·23$,,
confirming the previous results.

The diagram of bending moments is shown in the lower part of Fig. 139. The serious changes in the magnitude of the bending moments at B, C, and under the 6-ton load may be noted; also the change in position of the points of inflexion to the right and left of C, involving change in signs of the bending moment over some length of the beam: all these changes arise from the slight subsidence of the two supports at B and C.

93. Continuous Beams of Varying Section. The methods of the previous article may be applied to cases where the moment of inertia of cross-section (**I**) varies along the length of span. The modifications in the first method will consist in dividing all bending-moment terms by the variable I before making the summation of the various terms in $\int_0^l \mathrm{M}x\,dx$ and writing E in place of EI. The complete method is more fully explained in the author's " Strength of Materials."

Fixing the girder ends at any inclination may also be taken into account as indicated in Arts. 88 and 92.

Wilson's Method of solving problems in continuous beams by equating the downward deflections produced by the load to the upward deflections produced by the supporting forces, supposing the beam to be supported at the ends only, may be applied in cases where the value of I varies, provided the deflections for the necessary equations are determined in accordance with the principles in Art. 84. Generally, a graphical method will be the simplest for determining the deflections. Full details of a numerical example will be found in Wilson's paper already referred to, where the deflections are found by a novel graphical method.

Example. Example 2 (first part) of Art. 91 may be modified by taking I for the span BC as twice I for the spans AB and CD. (In practice such variation is far commoner than continuous variation along the length of a beam.)

Let I be the second moment of the area of section in AB and CD; then 2I will be the second moment in BC.

The Theorem of Three Moments, Art. 91 (6), becomes

$$\mathrm{M_A}l_1/\mathrm{I} + 2\mathrm{M_B}\{l_1/\mathrm{I} + l_2/2\mathrm{I}\} + \mathrm{M_C}l_2/2\mathrm{I} = \tfrac{1}{4}(w_1 l_1^3/\mathrm{I}_1 + w_2 l_2^3/2\mathrm{I}) \quad (1)$$

$$\mathrm{M_A}l_1 + 2\mathrm{M_B}(l_1 + \tfrac{1}{2}l_2) + \tfrac{1}{2}\mathrm{M_C}l_2 = \tfrac{1}{4}(w_1 l_1^3 + \tfrac{1}{2}w_2 l_2^3) \quad . \quad . \quad (2)$$

Similarly

$$\tfrac{1}{2}\mathrm{M_B}l_2 + 2\mathrm{M_C}(\tfrac{1}{2}l_2 + l_3) + \mathrm{M_D}l_3 = \tfrac{1}{4}(\tfrac{1}{2}w_2 l_2^3 + w_3 l_3^3) \quad . \quad . \quad (3)$$

and since $\mathrm{M_A} = \mathrm{M_D} = 0$, (2) and (3) give

$$0 + 220\mathrm{M_B} + 50\mathrm{M_C} = \tfrac{1}{4} \times 1{,}000(216 + 1{,}000) = 304{,}000$$

$$50\mathrm{M_B} + 2\mathrm{M_C} \times 90 + 0 = \tfrac{1}{4} \times 1{,}000(1{,}000 + 192)$$

From which $\mathrm{M_B} = 1{,}073$ ton-ft. and $\mathrm{M_C} = 1{,}358$ ton-ft.

Taking moments to the left of B and to the left of C

$$60 \text{ tons} \times 30 \text{ ft.} - 60 \text{ ft.} \times \mathrm{R_A} = \mathrm{M_B} = 1{,}073 \text{ ton-ft.}$$

$$\mathrm{R_A} = 12 \cdot 12 \text{ tons}$$

$$60 \text{ tons} \times 130 \text{ ft.} + 200 \text{ tons} \times 50 \text{ ft.} - 12 \cdot 12 \text{ tons} \times 160 \text{ ft.} - \mathrm{R_B} \times 100 \text{ ft.}$$
$$= 1{,}358 \text{ ton-ft.}$$

$$\mathrm{R_B} = 45 \cdot 03 \text{ tons.}$$

To the right of C

$$120 \text{ tons} \times 20 \text{ ft.} - 40\mathrm{R_D} = \mathrm{M_C} = 1{,}358 \text{ ton-ft}$$

$$\mathrm{R_D} = 26 \cdot 05 \text{ tons.}$$

To the right of B

200 tons × 50 ft. + 120 tons × 120 ft. − 26·05 tons × 140 ft. − R_C ×
  100 ft. = 1,073 ton-ft.

$$R_C = 196·8 \text{ tons.}$$

(The sum of the four supporting forces is equal to the total load.)

94. Moment Distribution Method. The bending moment at the supports of a continuous beam may be found by an ingenious method of successive approximation introduced by Prof. Hardy Cross [1] about 1929. It has a wider application than only to straight beams. Applied to a beam it is similar in principle to the elegant and far-reaching " method of relaxation " developed by Southwell.[2] The distribution method is direct and does not involve the solution of a number of simultaneous equations. The approximation can be carried as far as desired and approaches exact results more closely the further the process is carried.

We first imagine the continuous beam to consist of separate spans but the successive lengths which bridge the gaps between the supports to be not simply supported but clamped or fixed in direction at their ends, *i.e.* at the supports. Then if the loads are applied the clamps which keep the ends fixed in direction will be subject to torques or moments and will themselves exert equal and opposite moments on the ends of the successive lengths of the beam. The magnitude of such moments is known from the study of the beam *encastré* at its ends (Arts. 85 to 89). Actually the continuous beam may be free from such constraints but the initial supposition of them simplifies the problem. Having noted the two supposed external moments on either side of a particular support we should find that the two are not normally in equilibrium though they may be of opposite sign. We then (in imagination) proceed to unlock, or free from the constraint of the clamps, the beam above one selected support by the application of a moment equal and opposite to the unbalanced moment on the two sides of the supports. (It may facilitate the conception to imagine the two contiguous lengths of beam as connected by a " joint " to which the clamping and releasing moments are applied.) The distribution of this external balancing moment between the two lengths of beam on either side of the " joint " at the selected support will be in accordance with that found in (33) and (34) of Art. 89 or with (41) of Art. 89.

---

[1] " The Method of Distribution of Fixed End Moments " in *Journl. Am. Concrete Inst.*, Dec., 1929. " Analysis of Continuous Frames by Distributing Fixed End Moments," *Proc. Am. Soc. Civ. Eng.*, 1930, and *Trans. Am. Soc. C.E.*, 1932, vol. 96 (Paper 1793). Some instructive numerical examples may be found in Cassie's *Structural Analysis*, Longmans.

[2] *Relaxation Methods in Engineering Science*, Oxford Press; and *Proc. Roy. Soc.*, A. No. 872, vol. 151 (1933); also No. 878, vol. 153 (1935).

And the application of this external moment not only balances the external moments on the joint selected for relaxation from constraint but induces moments on the " joints " at the far ends of the two lengths of the beam which meet at the selected joint. Such induced moments are in accordance with (35) and (36) or (40) of Art. 89.

This modifies the total external moment on these two next joints. We then proceed to lock the released joint again and to release or unlock one of these next joints or some other one in a similar way and thereby to induce moments in other " next joints." But these induced moments will be of diminishing magnitude as the process of release progresses until finally all freely supported joints are in equilibrium as nearly as may be necessary, neglecting any insignificant degree of unbalance. The imaginary constraints are no longer necessary. By adding algebraically the moments originally allocated for complete fixture of direction and those added for subsequent relaxation of joints we obtain the moments finally operative when each joint is either freely supported or " direction-fixed " according as is specified in the conditions of any particular problem.

The process will best be understood by considering in detail a definite case. Let all the external moments applied to the beam or its parts be taken as positive when clockwise. (We can later say whether the *bending moment* on the beam is positive or negative according to any convention we adopt, such as that in Arts. 42 and 78.)

Example 1. Determine the bending moments at the support in Example 2 of Art. 91, Fig. 140.

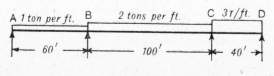

Fig. 140

If we imagine the beam fixed horizontally at A and D and on both sides of B and C we can use (7) of Art. 85 to write down the end bending moments of each span which are all of the form $wl^2/12$. Using ton-feet units,

$M_{BA} = M_{AB} = 1 \times 60^2/12 = 300$ ton-ft.; $M_{BC} = M_{CB} = 2 \times 100^2/12 =$ 1,667 ton-ft.; $M_{CD} = M_{DC} = 3 \times 40^2/12 = 400$ ton-ft.

The necessary external end moments are entered with their appropriate signs in the third line of Table I.

TABLE I

Joint balanced and moment required		A	B		C		D
		Distribution fractions . $\frac{5}{8}$	$\frac{3}{8}$	$\frac{2}{7}$	$\frac{5}{7}$		
		−300	+300	−1,667	+1,667	−400	+400
B	+1367	+427	+854	+512	+256	—	—
D	−400	—	—	—	—	−200	−400
C	−1,323	—	—	−189	−378	−945	−472
A	−127	−127	−63	—	—	—	—
D	+472	—	—	—	—	+236	+472
C	−236	—	—	−33	−67	−169	−84
B	+285	+89	+178	+107	+53	—	—
D	+84	—	—	—	—	+42	+84
C	−95	—	—	−13	−27	−68	−34
A	−89	−89	−44	—	—	—	—
B	+57	+18	+36	+21	+10	—	—
D	+34	—	—	—	—	+17	+34
C	−27	—	—	−4	−8	−19	−9
A	−18	−18	−9	—	—	—	—
B	+13	+4	+8	+5	+2	—	—
D	+9	—	—	—	—	+4	+9
C	−6	—	—	−1	−2	−4	−2
A	−4	−4	−2	—	—	—	—
B	+3	+1	+2	+1	0	—	—
D	+2	—	—	—	—	+1	+2
A	−1	−1	0	—	—	—	—
Totals . . .		0	+1,260	−1,261	+1,506	−1,505	0

All these initial bending moments are positive ($+wl^2/12$) and will require clockwise fixing moments at the right-hand end of spans and counter-clockwise moments at the left-hand ends. Accordingly, as we are regarding clockwise external moments as positive we have positive signs at the right-hand (*e.g.* +1,667, etc.) and negative signs at the left-hand ends (−300, −1,667 and −400).

The order in which the joints are relaxed is not important. Let us first release B. It has upon it a net moment +300−1667 = −1,367 (*i.e.* 1,367 counter-clockwise). In order to balance this and put the joint in equilibrium we impose, in imagination, a clockwise or + moment of 1,367 units. This will be distributed as shown at (33) and (34) of Art. 89. (For B is a point in the *encastré* beam AC and is supported to the level AC.) And as I is constant the distribution is inversely as the lengths AC and CB. Thus to the left of

B the fraction of the moment is $100/(100+60)$ or $\frac{5}{8}$ and to the right $\frac{60}{160}$ or $\frac{3}{8}$. These fractions are entered in the second line of Table I. The allocation of $+$ moment to the nearest whole number is $\frac{5}{8}$ of $1,667 = +854$ to the left and $\frac{3}{8}$ of $1,667$ or $+512$ to the right and this leaves the joint B in equilibrium. These moments are entered in the fourth line, and a horizontal line, indicating balance, is drawn underneath them. But imposing these moments on either side of B induces moments of half the magnitudes at the opposite ends of AB and BC as was noted at (35) and (36) of Art. 89. The inducing of *bending moments* of opposite sign implies the action of an external couple of like sign. Hence we carry over to joint A and enter in the fourth line a moment of $\frac{1}{2}$ of $854 = 427$ units and to joint C a moment of $\frac{1}{2}$ of $+512 = 256$ units.

Secondly, let us release joint D by the imposition of a moment -400 which puts D in equilibrium but induces a moment of $\frac{1}{2}$ of $-400 = -200$ units at C. (At this stage C and A are unbalanced.) Thirdly we balance C. The unbalanced moment is $+1,667+256-400-200 = -1,323$ and requires a moment of $-1,323$ units. The distribution fraction to the left is $\frac{40}{140} = \frac{2}{7}$ and to the right is $\frac{5}{7}$. To the right, $\frac{5}{7}$ of $-1,323 = -945$ units. To the left $\frac{2}{7}$ of $-1,323 = -378$ units. The induced moments are $\frac{1}{2}$ of $-945 = -472$ units on D and $\frac{1}{2}$ of $-378 = -189$ units on B. Fourthly, having locked C, we relax (or balance) A. The unbalanced moment there is $-300+427 = +127$ units, which require a torque of -127 units on A and this induces a moment of half this magnitude or -63 units at B. With A again locked the joint D is next balanced by imposing $+472$ units of torque upon it, thus inducing a moment of $+236$ units to the right of C which is in turn balanced by $\frac{2}{7}$ of $-236 = -67$ to the left of C and $\frac{5}{7}$ of $-236 = -169$ to the right of C, giving induced moments of -33 on the right of B and -84 at D. The remainder of the process can be followed from Table I, which has been carried further than necessary for practical purposes in order to demonstrate the process and the approach to an exact solution of the problem. The moments are stated to the nearest whole number. Comparison with the solution of Example 2 of Art. 91 shows that there is close agreement, any slight difference arising from the fact that the moments have not been calculated to an accuracy beyond the nearest whole number. The supporting forces can be calculated as in Art. 91 from the moments at A, B, C, and D. After the balancing of moments on each selected joint, horizontal lines drawn as in Table I below the moment numbers to indicate balance up to that stage in the process may prove helpful to the beginner. And a dash or a zero in otherwise vacant spaces in the Table may help to avoid confusion or error.

If the beam is fixed at A we proceed as before except that we do not release the beam at A. The figures for this case are entered in Table II. For the first three steps they are the same as for Table I and in all subsequent steps the balancing of A is omitted. The results agree very closely with those given in Example 2 of Art. 91 (where the value of the supporting forces are given).

TABLE II

Joint balanced and moment required	A		B		C		D
	Distribution fractions . $\frac{5}{8}$		$\frac{3}{8}$		$\frac{2}{7}$	$\frac{5}{7}$	--
		−300	+300	−1,667	+1,667	−400	+400
B	+1,367	+427	+854	+512	+256	0	0
D	−400	0	0	0	0	−200	−400
C	−1,323	0	0	−189	−378	−945	−472
D	+472	0	0	0	0	+236	+472
C	−236	0	0	−33	−67	−169	−84
B	+222	+69	+139	+83	+41	0	0
D	+84	0	0	0	0	+42	+84
C	−83	0	0	−12	−24	−59	−29
D	+29	0	0	0	0	+14	+29
C	−14	0	0	−2	−4	−10	−5
B	+14	+4	+9	+5	+2	0	0
D	+5	0	0	0	0	+2	+5
C	−4	0	0	0	−1	−3	−1
D	+1	0	0	0	0	0	+1
Totals . .		+200	+1,302	−1,303	+1,492	−1,492	0

Change in Section. When a continuous beam is of different section in different spans but of constant section throughout each span, we can easily find the bending moments by the method of moment distribution. The only alteration to be made from the previous examples is in the distribution fractions due to the modification of the relative flexural stiffness (I/l) of contiguous lengths of beam. The formulae for these fractions have been established in (39) and (41), Art. 89.

Example 2. The example of Art. 93 based on Example I of the present article with a modified (doubled) value of I on the span BC will illustrate the procedure. The solution differs from Table I in the distribution fractions. At B the imposed moments are distributed between the lengths AB and BC in the ratio of their flexural stiffness I/l, that is, in the ratio of $I/60$ to $2I/100$ or 5 to 6. Thus $\frac{5}{11}$ goes to stress AB and $\frac{6}{11}$ to BC. At C the ratio is $2I/100$ to

250   THEORY OF STRUCTURES   [Ch. VIII

I/40 or 4 to 5, that is $\frac{4}{9}$ on CB and $\frac{5}{9}$ on CD. These fractions are
entered on the second line of Table III. The work is then as in
Table I, but space is saved by entering the releases of two joints
(not next to one another) in a single line.

TABLE III

Joints balanced and moments required		A	B		C	D
	Distribution fractions .	$\frac{5}{11}$	$\frac{6}{11}$	$\frac{4}{9}$	$\frac{5}{9}$	
		−300	+300	−1,667	+1,667	−400	+400
B	+1,367	+310	+621	+746	+373	0	0
C	−1,640	0	0	−364	−729	−911	−455
B	+364	+82	+165	+199	+99	0	0
A, −92; D, +55		−92	−46	0	0	+27	+55
C	−126	0	0	−28	−56	−70	−35
B, +74; D, +35		+17	+34	+40	+20	+17	+35
A, −17; C, −37		−17	−8	−8	−16	−21	−10
B, +16; D, +10		+3	+7	+9	+4	+5	+10
A, −3; C, −9		−3	−1	−2	−4	−5	−2
B, +3; D, +2		0	+1	+2	+1	+1	+2
C	−2				+1	−1	
Totals . .		0	+1,073	−1,073	+1,358	−1,358	0

The results agree with the example of Art. 93, solved by the
Theorem of Three Moments.

Example 3. To illustrate the application to discontinuous
loading, solve Example 2 of Art. 92, Fig. 139.

The initial moments with all the lengths of beam *encastré* at both
ends (at supports) are calculated as in (25) and (26) of Art. 88 or
(12) and (13) of Art. 89 as follows:

$M_{AB}=(5\times7\times9)/100=3.15$; $M_{BA}=(5\times49\times3)/100=7.35$; $M_{BC}=$
$(7\times4\times64)/144=12.4$; $M_{CB}=(7\times8\times16)/144=6.2$; $M_{CD}=$
$(6\times2\times36)/64=6.75$; $M_D=(6\times6\times4)/64=2.25$.

These are entered on the third line of Table IV. The ratio
distribution at B is inversely as AB to BC or 12 to 10=5 to 6.
That is $\frac{5}{11}$ is allocated to AB and $\frac{6}{11}$ to BC, and at C, $\frac{8}{20}$=0.4 to
CB and 0.6 to CD as entered on the second line of Table IV.
(Underlining indicates release and balance.)

The result agrees with that of Example 2 of Art. 92.

Abbreviation for Free Ends. The procedure can be shortened if
one or both ends of the continuous beam are freely supported. The
bending moment at such an end is zero and at the other end of the

outer span the beam can be initially regarded as fixed so that the span is bridged by a cantilever. The general case of distribution is shown at (13), (14), and (15) of Art. 90 and the case of the beam of uniform section at (16) of Art. 90. A solution of Example 3 above by this shortened procedure will illustrate it.

TABLE IV

Joints released and moments required	A	B		C		D
	Distribution fractions . $\frac{6}{11}$		$\frac{5}{11}$	0·4	0·6	
	−3·15	+7·35	−12·44	+6·22	−6·75	+2·25
B, +5·09; D, −2·25	+1·39	+2·78	+2·31	+1·15	−1·12	−2·25
A, +1·76; C, +0·5	+1·76	+0·88	+0·10	+0·20	+0·30	+0·15
B, −0·98; D, −0·15	−0·26	−0·53	−0·45	−0·22	−0·07	−0·15
A, +0·26; C, +0·29	+0·26	+0·13	0+·06	+0·12	+0·17	+0·08
B, −0·19; D, −0·08	−0·05	−0·10	−0·09	−0·04	−0·04	−0·08
A, +0·05; C, +0·08	+0·05	+0·02	+0·01	+0·03	+0·05	+0·02
B, −0·03; D, −0·02	−0·01	−0·02	−0·01	0	−0·01	−0·02
A, +0·01; C, +0·01	+0·01				+0·01	
Totals . .	0	+10·51	−10·51	+7·46	−7·46	0

If B and C (Fig. 139) are locked, by equating the downward deflections caused by the loads to the upward deflections at A and D caused by the end supporting forces R_A and R_D, we can find these forces. Using equation (5) of Art. 80 (omitting EI on both sides),

$$R_A 10^3/3 = 5 \times 3^3/3 + 5 \times 3^2 \times 7/2$$
$$R_A = 0·6075 \text{ ton}$$
$$R_D \times 8^3/3 = 6 \times 2^3/3 + 6 \times 2^3/2$$
$$R_D = 33/64 \text{ ton}$$
$$M_{BA} = -0·6075 \times 10 + 5 \times 3 = +8·93 \text{ ton-ft.}$$
$$M_{CD} = -(33/64) \times 8 + 6 \times 2 = -7·875 \text{ ton-ft.}$$

involving a clockwise external moment on AB at B and a counterclockwise external moment on CD at D.

The distribution fractions are, for ABC $n = \frac{12}{22} = \frac{6}{11}$ (which is the fraction BC/AC). And from (16) of Art. 90 the fraction of the moment at B which is taken by BC is $4(1-n)/(4-n) = (4 \times 5 \times 11)/(11 \times 38) = \frac{10}{19}$. The fraction taken by BA is $-3n/(4-n) = -\frac{9}{19}$.

For BCD $n = \frac{12}{20} = \frac{3}{5}$ or 0·6.

Fraction of moment at C taken by CB $= 4(1-n)/(4-n) = \frac{8}{7}$

Fraction ,, ,, ,, CD $= -\frac{9}{17}$.

The initial moments M_{BC} and M_{CB} are as before when joints B and C are locked. Having now some familiarity with the process we can unlock and unbalance B and C simultaneously provided we carry over the induced moments. Thus we reduce the amount of unbalance more quickly as shown in Table V.

TABLE V

Joints released and moments required	A	B		C		D
Distribution fractions .		$\frac{9}{19}$	$\frac{10}{19}$	$\frac{8}{17}$	$\frac{9}{17}$	
	0	+8·930	−12·444	+6·222	−7·875	0
B, +3·514; C, +1·653		+1·664	+1·850	+0·778	+0·875	
			+0·389	+0·925		
B, −0·389; C, −0·925		−0·184	−0·205	−0·435	−0·495	
			−0·217	−0·102		
B, +0·217; C, +0·102		+0·103	+0·114	+0·048	+0·054	
			+0·024	+0·057		
B, −0·034; C, −0·056		−0·011	−0·013	−0·027	−0·030	
Totals . .	0	+10·502	−10·502	+7·466	−7·466	0

The results are as before. The proviso of unlocking only one joint at a time is only an aid to the imagination. More can be unlocked simultaneously if the induced moments are properly distributed. These induced moments in turn require balancing but with quickly diminishing values the table is shortened. It is a matter of individual choice how many joints are released simultaneously in a long beam with many supports.

Though the method of moment distribution has been developed for unsymmetrical practical cases it can give simple and exact solutions to the simple standard cases. Thus for Fig. 136 (Example 1, Art. 91) omitting the factor wl^2, if B, C, and D are locked, we should have clockwise moments of $+\frac{1}{8}$ and $-\frac{1}{12}$ to the left and right of B respectively, $+\frac{1}{12}$ and $-\frac{1}{12}$ to the left and right of C respectively. Releasing B by a moment $-(\frac{1}{8}-\frac{1}{12})=-\frac{1}{24}$ divided between AB and BC in the ratio 3 to 4 ((16), Art. 90) gives a moment $\frac{1}{8}-\frac{1}{56}=\frac{3}{28}$ to the left of B and $-\frac{1}{12}-\frac{1}{42}=-\frac{3}{28}$ to the right of B and an induced moment of $-\frac{1}{84}$ at C, which, added to $\frac{1}{12}$ gives $\frac{1}{14}$ to the left of C and from the symmetry there is a moment of $-\frac{1}{14}$ to the right of C. Thus all the " joints " are balanced and the moments are as found in Example 1 of Art. 91.

In other cases of symmetrical supports, lengths, loading and release of joints the final moments are approached by series with terms, which may be in geometrical progression which when summed to infinity give exactly the same values as those obtained by the theorem of three moments. For example, take a continuous beam of three equal spans $l=AB=BC=CD$ with only BC loaded (uniformly), A and D fixed horizontally. Considering all the joints locked we have clockwise moments of $+\frac{1}{12}wl^2$ at C and $-\frac{1}{12}wl^2$ at B. Balancing these by moments of $+\frac{1}{12}wl^2$ and $-\frac{1}{12}wl^2$ equally divided at B and C we get induced moments $+\frac{1}{48}wl^2$ at A and C and $-\frac{1}{48}wl^2$ at B and D. Balancing these at B and C we get at A a moment

$$\tfrac{1}{48}wl^2(1+\tfrac14+\tfrac{1}{16}+ \text{ etc.})$$

which has a total value $\frac{1}{48}wl^2\times\frac43=\frac{1}{36}wl^2$ clockwise, which is there a negative bending moment.

To the left of B a moment

$$\tfrac{1}{24}wl^2(1+\tfrac14+\tfrac{1}{16}+ \text{ etc.})=\tfrac43\times\tfrac{1}{24}wl^2=\tfrac{1}{18}wl^2$$

clockwise which is a positive bending moment. These values are exact.

95. Advantages and Disadvantages of Continuous Beams.

An examination of Figs. 136 and 139 and other diagrams of bending moment for continuous girders which the reader may sketch, shows that generally (1) the greatest bending moment to which the beam is subjected is less than that for the same spans if the beam were cut at the supports into separate pieces; (2) disregarding algebraic sign, the average bending moment throughout is smaller for the continuous beam, and less material to resist bending is therefore required; (3) in the continuous beam the bending moment due to external load is not greatest at points remote from the supports, but at the supports; hence, in girders of variable cross-section, the heavy sections are not placed in positions where their effect in producing bending stress is greatest.

On the other hand, a small subsidence of one or more supports may cause serious changes in the bending moment and bending stresses at particular sections, as well as changes of sign in bending moment and bending stresses over considerable lengths, with change in position of the points of contraflexure. These changes, resulting from very small changes in level of a support, form serious objections to the use of continuous girders. Another practical objection in the case of built-up girders is the difficulty in attaining the conditions of continuity during construction or renewal, or of determining to what degree the conditions are attained. In a loaded continuous girder two points of contraflexure usually occur between two consecutive supports; if at these two points the girder is hinged instead of being continuous, the bending moment there remains zero, and changes in load or subsidence of a support do not produce changes in sign of the bending moment and bending stresses. This is the principle of the cantilever bridge (see Art. 139). although the girder is not solid, but of the braced type dealt with in later chapters: the portions between the hinges are under the conditions of a beam simply supported at its ends, and the portions adjoining the piers are practically cantilevers which carry the simply supported beams at their ends. The points of zero bending moment being fixed, the bending-moment diagrams become very simple. For cantilever bridges and continuous braced girders, see Chapter XIV.

EXAMPLES VIII

1. A beam is firmly built in at each end and carries a load of 12 tons uniformly distributed over a span of 20 ft. If the moment of inertia of the section is 220 inch units and the depth 12 in., find the maximum intensity of bending stress and the deflection. (E=13,000 tons per sq. in.)

2. A built-in beam carries a distributed load which varies uniformly from nothing at one end to a maximum w per unit length at the other. Find the bending moment and supporting forces at each end and the position where maximum deflection occurs.

3. A built-in beam of span l carries two loads each W units placed $\frac{1}{3}l$ from either support. Find the bending moment at the supports and centre, the deflection at the centre and under the loads, and find the points of contra-flexure.

4. A built-in beam of span l carries a load W at a distance $\frac{1}{3}l$ from one end. Find the bending moment and reactions at the supports, the deflection at the centre and under the load, the position and amount of the maximum deflection, and the position of the points of contrary flexure.

5. A built-in beam of 20-ft. span carries two loads, each 5 tons, placed 5 ft. and 13 ft. from the left-hand support. Find the bending moments at the supports.

6. A built-in beam of span l carries a uniformly distributed load w per unit of length over half the span. Find the bending moment at each support, the points of inflexion, the position and magnitude of the maximum deflection.

7. The moment of inertia of cross-section of a beam built in at the ends varies uniformly from I_0 at the centre to $\frac{1}{2}I_0$ at each end. Find the bending moment at the end and middle, and the central deflection when a load W is supported at the middle of the span.

8. Solve the previous problem when the load W is uniformly distributed over the span.

9. A continuous beam rests on supports at its ends and two other supports on the same level as the ends. The supports divide the length into three equal spans each of length l. If the beam carries a uniformly spread load w per unit length, find the bending moments and reactions at the supports.

10. A continuous beam covers three consecutive spans of 30 ft., 40 ft., and 20 ft., and carries loads of 2, 1, and 3 tons per foot run respectively on the three spans. Find the bending moment and pressure at each support. Sketch the diagrams of bending moment and shearing force.

11. A continuous beam ABCD 20 ft. long rests on supports A, B, C, and D, all on the same level, AB=8 ft., BC=7 ft., CD=5 ft. It carries loads of 7, 6, and 8 tons at distances 3, 11, and 18 ft. respectively from A. Find the bending moment at B and C, and the reactions at A, B, C, and D. Sketch the bending-moment diagram. (The results should be checked by using both methods given in Art. 92 and that in Art. 94.)

12. Solve Problem No. 9, (*a*) if one end of the beam is firmly built in, (*b*) if both ends are built in.

13. Solve Problem No. 11, the end A being fixed horizontally.

14. Solve Problem No. 11, if the support B sinks $\frac{1}{10}$ in., I being 90 (in.)^4 and E = 13,000 tons per sq. in.

CHAPTER IX

FLEXURAL STRAIN ENERGY

96. Elastic Strain Energy. Calculations of elastic distortion and stress in a loaded structure or structural element, whether solid or framed, can often be made from expressions for elastic strain energy stored in the body as a result of loading (see Art. 28). We need only consider cases in which the stresses are within the limits of Hooke's Law (Art. 5), *i.e.* the strains are proportional to the stresses and to the loads and in which the work done in transferring energy to the material is done by the loads and not in part by the supporting forces. In the present chapter we indicate some applications of strain energy methods to problems on beams. The alternative methods are generally less obvious than those employed in the preceding chapters and are not necessarily to be preferred, but in some cases they are neat and short and some acquaintance with them is desirable.

Strain Energy of Beams. When a beam is bent within the elastic limits, the material is subjected to varying degrees of tensile and compressive bending stress, and therefore possesses elastic strain energy (Art. 28), *i.e.* it is a spring, although it may be a stiff one. The total flexural strain energy may be calculated in various ways; it may conveniently be expressed in the form

$$c \times \frac{p^2}{E} \times \text{volume of the material of the beam} \quad . \quad . \quad (1)$$

where p is the maximum intensity of direct stress to which the beam is subjected anywhere, and c is a coefficient depending upon the manner in which the beam is loaded and supported, but which is always less than the value $\frac{1}{2}$, which is the constant for uniformly distributed stress (see Art. 28). If f is the intensity of stress at the elastic limit of the material, then

$$c \times \frac{f^2}{E} \times \text{volume}$$

is the proof resilience of the beam. Note that capacity to absorb energy depends not only upon the safe limit of elastic stress f but also inversely upon the value of Young's Modulus. In this respect combined with lightness, wood and other materials may compare favourably with metals.

For a beam of any kind supporting only a concentrated load W, the resilience is evidently

$$\tfrac{1}{2} \cdot W \times (\text{deflection at the load}) \quad . \quad . \quad . \quad (2)$$

e.g. a cantilever carrying an end load W has a deflection

$$\frac{Wl^3}{3EI} \text{ (see (2), Art. 80)}$$

hence the strain energy is

$$c \times \frac{p^2}{E} \times \text{volume} = \tfrac{1}{2} \cdot \frac{W^2 l^3}{3EI}$$

For any symmetrical shape of cross-section if d is the depth, from Art. 46

$$p = Wl \div (2I/d) \text{ and area of section} = I/k^2$$

where k is the radius of gyration about the neutral axis. Substituting, this value of p

$$c \times \frac{W^2 l^2 d^2}{4EI^2} \times \text{volume} = \frac{W^2 l^3}{6EI}$$

$$c = \tfrac{2}{3} \frac{k^2}{d^2}$$

Strain energy $= \tfrac{2}{3} \dfrac{k^2}{d^2} \dfrac{p^2}{E} \times \text{volume}.$

For a rectangular section $k^2/d^2 = \tfrac{1}{12}$ and

$$\text{strain energy} = \tfrac{1}{18} \frac{p^2}{E} \times \text{volume} \quad . \quad . \quad . \quad (3)$$

or $\tfrac{1}{18} \dfrac{p^2}{E}$ per unit volume. For a circular section $k^2/d^2 = \tfrac{1}{16}$ and the strain energy is $\tfrac{1}{24} \dfrac{p^2}{E}$ per unit volume. For I sections the value of k/d is usually about 0·4.

The same coefficients, etc., as those above for a cantilever will evidently hold for a beam simply supported at its ends, and carrying a load midway between them.

If all the dimensions are in inches and the loads in tons, the strain energy will be in inch-tons.

Strain Energy from Bending Moment. If with the notation of Art. 78, in a short length of beam dx, over which the bending moment is M, the change of slope is di, the elastic strain energy of that portion is

$$\tfrac{1}{2} \cdot M \cdot di \quad . \quad . \quad . \quad . \quad . \quad . \quad (4)$$

and over a finite length the strain energy U is

$$U = \tfrac{1}{2} \int M di \quad . \quad . \quad . \quad . \quad . \quad . \quad (5)$$

K

which may also be written

$$U = \tfrac{1}{2}\int M\frac{di}{dx}dx = \tfrac{1}{2}\int M\frac{d^2y}{dx^2}dx = \tfrac{1}{2}\int \frac{M^2}{EI}dx \quad . \quad . \quad . \quad (6)$$

or, if EI is constant

$$U = \frac{1}{2EI}\int M^2 dx \quad . \quad . \quad . \quad . \quad . \quad . \quad (7)$$

$\tfrac{1}{2}\int M^2 dx$ as the moment of the area of the bending-moment diagram about its base is often easily calculable.

From these forms the strain energy of any beam may be found when the bending-moment diagram is known.

For a beam of uniform section and length *l*, subjected to " simple bending " (see Arts. 46 and 77), for which the bending moment and curvature are constant, the strain energy, from (4) or (7), is

$$\tfrac{1}{2}M \times \text{change in inclination of extreme tangents} = \tfrac{1}{2}\frac{M^2l}{EI} \quad . \quad (8)$$

If such a beam is rectangular in section, the breadth being *b* and the depth *d*, $p = M \div \tfrac{1}{6}bd^2$, and in the form (1), the strain energy, from (7), is

$$c \times \frac{p^2}{E} \times \text{volume} \quad \text{or} \quad c \times \frac{36M^2}{Eb^2d^4} \times bdl = \tfrac{1}{2} \cdot \frac{M^2l \times 12}{Ebd^3}$$

hence $\quad c = \tfrac{1}{6}$, and the strain energy $= \tfrac{1}{6}\dfrac{p^2}{E} \cdot bdl$

The same coefficient ($\tfrac{1}{6}$) will hold for any of the rectangular beams of uniform bending strength, in which the same maximum intensity of skin stress *p* is reached at every cross-section, and which bend in circular arcs. For circular sections the corresponding coefficient is $\tfrac{1}{8}$.

For a bending moment varying uniformly from a maximum to zero the coefficient $c = \tfrac{1}{18}$ has already been obtained at (3) from (2) but it is readily found alternatively by writing $M = Wx$ in (7) and integrating.

In the case of a distributed load *w* per unit length of span, the strain energy corresponding to (2) may be written

$$\tfrac{1}{2}\int wy\,dx \quad . \quad . \quad . \quad . \quad . \quad . \quad . \quad (9)$$

where *y* is the deflection at a distance *x* from the origin.

Beam Deflections calculated from Strain Energy. In equation (2) the deflection has been used to calculate the elastic strain energy. Similarly, if the strain energy is calculated from the bending moments by (5) or (7), the deflections may be obtained from the strain energy. For example, in the case given in Art. 81, of a non-central load W on a simply supported beam, using the notation of Art. 81 and Fig. 115 (*a*), integrating over the whole span, using (7)

$$U = \tfrac{1}{2} \cdot y_C \cdot W = \tfrac{1}{2} \int_0^l \frac{M^2}{EI} dx$$

$$= \frac{1}{2EI} \int_0^a \left(-\frac{bWx}{l} \right)^2 dx + \frac{1}{2EI} \int_a^l \left\{ -\frac{bWx}{l} + W(x-a) \right\}^2 dx \quad . \quad (10)$$

$$= \frac{1}{2EI} \int_0^a \left(\frac{bWx}{l} \right)^2 dx + \frac{1}{2EI} \int_a^l \left\{ \frac{Wa(l-x)}{l} \right\}^2 dx$$

$$= \frac{W^2 a^2 b^2}{6EIl} \quad . \quad . \quad . \quad . \quad . \quad . \quad . \quad . \quad . \quad (11)$$

$$y_C = \frac{Wa^2 b^2}{3EIl} \quad . \quad . \quad . \quad . \quad . \quad . \quad . \quad (12)$$

which agrees with (8), Art. 81.

Taking as a second example the case (*b*), Art. 79, and Fig. 109, of a uniformly spread load *w* per unit span on a beam simply supported at each end, at a distance *x* from either support,

$$M = -\frac{w}{2}(lx - x^2) \quad \text{(see Fig. 49)}$$

To find the deflection at a distance *a* from an origin at the left-hand end, we introduce an important principle by considering the effect of a very small load W placed at that section. Over the length *a* from the origin it would cause an additional bending moment

$$EI\frac{d^2y}{dx} \quad \text{or} \quad EI\frac{di}{dx} = -\frac{l-a}{l}Wx$$

and over this portion

$$di = -\frac{l-a}{l}\frac{Wx}{EI}dx$$

and for the remaining range (*l*−*a*) the additional bending moment would be

$$-\frac{W(l-a)}{l}x + W(x-a) = -\frac{Wa}{l}(l-x)$$

and

$$di = -\frac{Wa}{EIl}(l-x)dx$$

Hence from (5) the total increase of strain energy in the whole beam, due to W would be

$$U = \tfrac{1}{2} \int M di = \tfrac{1}{2}\frac{W}{EIl} \cdot \frac{w}{2} \left\{ (l-a) \int_0^a x^2(l-x)lx + a \int_a^l x(l-x)^2 dx \right\} . \quad (13)$$

$$= \frac{Wwa(l-a)(l^2 + al - a^2)}{48EI} \quad . \quad . \quad . \quad . \quad . \quad . \quad (14)$$

And equating to the energy $\frac{1}{2}W \cdot y$ we find

$$y = \frac{wa(l-a)(l^2+la-a^2)}{24EI} \quad . \quad . \quad . \quad . \quad (15)$$

which agrees with (9), Art. 79, when x is written instead of a.

Note that this deflection is independent of the small load W, the effect of which was considered on the supposition that its effect on y may be neglected.

General Formula for Deflection. Generalising this method of adding an imaginary small load, take $W=1$ and let m be the bending moment at any section due to unit load at the particular section the deflection at which is y, then $di = m \cdot dx/EI$

$$\tfrac{1}{2} \times 1 \times y = \tfrac{1}{2}\int M di = \tfrac{1}{2}\int \frac{Mm}{EI}dx \quad \text{or} \quad y = \int \frac{Mm}{EI}dx \quad . \quad (16)$$

the integration being over the whole length of the beam and if necessary divided into separate ranges with convenient origins or effected graphically in suitable cases. In the particular case of the deflection under a load W, $M=Wm$, and

$$y = W \int \frac{m^2}{EI}dx \quad . \quad . \quad . \quad . \quad . \quad . \quad (17)$$

For example, in the case of a cantilever with a load W at the free end, $M=Wx$ and $m=x$ if the origin be taken at the free end and the deflection at the loaded free end is

$$y = W \int \frac{m^2}{EI}dx = \frac{W}{EI}\int_0^l x^2 dx = \frac{Wl^3}{3EI} \quad . \quad . \quad (18)$$

But formula (11) applies to beams with any type of support and with varying section.

Clerk Maxwell's Reciprocal Deflection Theorem.[1] For a single load W,

$$M = Wm'$$

where m' is the bending moment due to unit load at C (Fig. 115 (a)). Hence (16) becomes

$$y = W \int \frac{mm'}{EI}dx \quad . \quad . \quad . \quad . \quad . \quad (19)$$

the summation being over the whole length of the beam, and from the nature of the product mm' (viz. the product of ordinates of two triangular bending-moment diagrams) it is evident that *the deflection at* X *due to* W *at* C *is equal to the deflection at* C *due to* W *at* X. And this is true for any form of beam, *e.g.* the cantilever and built-in

---

[1] *Phil. Mag.*, Vol. 27, 1864. The theorem was extended by Rayleigh, *Scientific Papers*, Vol. 1, or *London Math. Soc.*, 1873.

beam. Even so it is only a particular case of a theorem applicable
to any elastic system. It frequently simplifies beam deflection
problems, *e.g.* this theorem shows that (5), of Art. 80, would give
the deflection at C in Fig. 111 due to W at A, as well as the deflection at A due to W at C. We have already noticed from algebraic
results that it holds for the beam supported freely at its ends in
Art. 92 (see equations (6), (7), and (8) and the note below them).

Castigliano's First Theorem. This is applicable and may be used
to obtain beam deflections. Limiting its application to a beam, it
may be stated as follows. The partial differential coefficient of the
total strain energy with respect to a load (W) is equal to the movement of the load *in its line of action*. Or if the total strain energy
be U

$$y = \frac{\partial U}{\partial W} \quad . \quad . \quad . \quad . \quad . \quad (20)$$

For example, if U be calculated from (7) then deflection may be
found from (13). Thus an alternative procedure to that in Art. 80,
section (*a*), is, since $M = W(l-x)$ for the cantilever in Fig. 110,
from (7)

$$U = \frac{W^2}{2EI} \int_0^l (l-x)^2 = \tfrac{1}{6} \frac{W^2 l^3}{EI}$$

and hence from (20)

$$y_A = \frac{l^3}{6EI} \frac{\partial (W^2)}{\partial W} = \frac{2Wl^3}{6EI} = \frac{Wl^3}{3EI}$$

as in (2), Art. 80.

Or, for a beam supported at its ends, from equation (11) we might
have written

$$y = \frac{\partial U}{\partial W} = \frac{a^2 b^2}{6EIl} \frac{\partial W^2}{\partial W} = \frac{2Wa^2 b^2}{6EIl} = \frac{Wa^2 b^2}{3EIl}$$

There is no apparent advantage in using Castigliano's theorem
instead of the energy equation (10); both these methods are applicable particularly to deflections at a load.

Castigliano's theorem is applicable also to couples and rotations.
Thus the partial differential coefficient of the total strain energy U,
with respect to a couple M_1 exerted upon the beam is equal to the
rotation of the beam axis at the axis of the couple M_1, or if i_1 is the
rotation of the beam at the axis of M_1

$$i_1 = \frac{\partial U}{\partial M_1} \quad . \quad . \quad . \quad . \quad . \quad (21)$$

For example, if a bending couple M_1 be applied to a cantilever at
its free end in addition to a load W, using Fig. 110 but taking the

origin now at the free end for greater convenience, $M = Wx + M_1$

$$U = \frac{1}{2EI}\int_0^l M^2 dx = \frac{1}{2EI}\int_0^l (Wx+M_1)^2 dx = \frac{1}{2EI}\int_0^l (W^2x^2$$

$$+2WxM_1 + M_1{}^2)dx = \frac{1}{2EI}(W^2l^3/3 + WM_1 l + M_1{}^2)$$

$$i_1 = \frac{\partial U}{\partial M_1} = \frac{1}{2EI}(Wl_1{}^2 + 2M_1 l) \quad \text{or} \quad \frac{Wl^2}{2EI} + \frac{M_1 l}{EI}$$

the slope at the free end; the two terms of which agree with (1) and (9) of Art. 80. If $M_1 = 0$, $Wl^2/2EI$ gives the rotation of the free end due to W.

And $$y_1 = \frac{\partial U}{dW} = \frac{1}{2EI}\left(\frac{2Wl^3}{3} + M_1 l^2\right) = \frac{Wl^3}{3EI} + \frac{M_1 l^2}{2EI}$$

the deflection at the free end. The two terms agree with (2) and (11) of Art. 80. If $W = 0$, $M_1 l^2/2EI$ gives the deflection due to M_1.

Note that if M_1 is zero we should nevertheless need to introduce this term in order to find the partial differential coefficient $\partial U/\partial M$ and then make $M_1 = 0$ in order to find the rotation $Wl^2/2EI$ due to W. Similarly if W is zero we must introduce the term W in order to find the partial differential coefficient $\partial U/\partial W$ and then make $W = 0$ in order to find the deflection $M_1 l^2/2EI$ due to M_1.

This illustrates that in using Castigliano's theorem, unless actually part of the load system, a force must be introduced corresponding in position and direction to the required deflection, and subsequently made equal to zero. And if it is not part of the load system, a couple, with its axis at the point at which an inclination or rotation is required, must be introduced and subsequently made equal to zero.

Thus by the device of introducing temporarily a fictitious force or couple the deflection or rotation at any unloaded point may be determined.

Minimum Strain Energy. An important case of equation (20) occurs when a beam is resting on a prop which reduces the deflection to zero. For then

$$\frac{\partial U}{\partial P} = 0 \qquad \cdots \cdots \qquad (22)$$

where P is the force exerted by the prop. The equation (22) may then be solved for the unknown value of P. This is exemplified in Art. 98.

The statement $\partial U/\partial P = 0$ implies that of all possible values of P for equilibrium, the actual is one that which gives the minimum value of U, *i.e.* the least flexural strain energy in the beam under the forces of loads and support. It applies also to any constraining moment, say, M_1 in the form

$$\partial U / \partial M_1 = 0 \quad . \quad . \quad . \quad . \quad (23)$$

97. Elastic Energy in Shear Strain. When material suffers shear strain within the elastic limit, elastic strain energy is stored just as in the case of direct stress and strain. For simple distributions of shear stress the elastic strain energy is easily calculated. Let Fig. 9 represent a piece of material of length l perpendicular to the plane of the diagram, having uniform shear stress of intensity q on the face BC, causing shear strain φ and deflection BB″.

Then the strain energy evidently is

$$\tfrac{1}{2} \times (\text{force}) \times (\text{distance}) = \tfrac{1}{2} \times (\text{BC} \cdot l \cdot q) \times \text{BB}'' = \tfrac{1}{2} \cdot \text{BC} \cdot l \cdot q \cdot \text{AB}\varphi$$

$$= \tfrac{1}{2} \cdot \text{BC} \cdot l \cdot \text{AB} \cdot \frac{q^2}{N}$$

$$= \tfrac{1}{2} \cdot \frac{q^2}{N} \times \text{volume or } \tfrac{1}{2}\frac{q^2}{N} \text{ per unit of volume}$$

where N is the modulus of rigidity.

Note the similarity to the expression $\tfrac{1}{2}\dfrac{p^2}{E}$ per unit volume, which is the strain energy for uniformly distributed direct stress (Art. 28).

Deflection of a Beam due to Shearing. In addition to the ordinary deflections due to the bending moment calculated in Chapter VI, there is in any given case other than " simple bending " (Art. 44) a further deflection due to the vertical shear stress on transverse sections of a horizontal beam. This was not taken into account in the calculations of Chapter VI, and the magnitude of it in a few simple cases may now be estimated.

In the case of a cantilever of length l carrying an end load W (Fig. 43), if the shearing force F($=$W) were uniformly distributed over vertical sections, the deflections due to shear at the free end would be

$$l \times (\text{angle of shear strain})$$

or

$$\varphi \cdot l = \frac{q}{N}l \quad \text{or} \quad \frac{Wl}{AN}$$

where A is the area of cross-section. If the section were rectangular, of breadth b and depth d, the deflection with uniform distribution would be $\dfrac{Wl}{bd \cdot N}$.

But we have seen (Art. 53) that the shear stress is not uniformly distributed over the section, but varies from a maximum at the neutral surface to zero at the extreme upper and lower edges of the section. The consequence is that the deflection will be rather more than $\dfrac{Wl}{AN}$. We can get some idea of its amount in particular cases from the distribution of shear stress calculated in Art. 53. But it should be remembered that such calculations are based on the simple theory of bending (see Art. 47), and are approximate only. While the simple (or Bernoulli-Euler) theory gives the deflections due to the bending moment with sufficient accuracy, the portion of the total deflection which is due to shearing cannot generally be estimated with equal accuracy from the distribution of shear stress deduced in Art. 53. In a great number of practical cases, however, the deflection due to shearing is negligible in comparison with that caused by the bending moment. Assuming the distribution of shear stress to be as calculated in Art. 53, and constant over a narrow strip of the cross-section parallel to the neutral axis of the section, a few deflections due to shear will now be calculated for cases where the shearing force is uniform, and for which the simple theory of bending is approximately correct (see Art. 44).

Cantilever of Rectangular Section with End Load. The breadth being b and the depth d, a longitudinal strip of length l, width b, and thickness dy, parallel to the neutral surface and distant y from it, will store strain energy

$$\tfrac{1}{2} \cdot \frac{q^2}{N} \cdot b \cdot l \cdot dy$$

due to shear strain. And from (4), Art. 53

$$q = \frac{6F}{bd^3}\left(\frac{d^2}{4} - y^2\right)$$

where $F = W$, the end load.

Hence

$$q^2 = \frac{36W^2}{b^2d^6}\left(\frac{d^4}{16} + y^4 - \frac{d^2y^2}{2}\right)$$

The total shearing resilience in the cantilever is

$$\frac{bl}{2N}\int_{-\frac{d}{2}}^{\frac{d}{2}} q^2 dy = \frac{18W^2l}{Nbd^6}\int_{-\frac{d}{2}}^{\frac{d}{2}}\left(\frac{d^4}{16} - \frac{d^2y^2}{2} + y^4\right)dy \quad . \quad . \quad (1)$$

or

$$\frac{36W^2l}{Nbd^6}\left[\frac{yd^4}{16} - \frac{y^3d^2}{6} + \frac{y^5}{5}\right]_0^{\frac{d}{2}} = \frac{3}{5}\frac{W^2l}{Nbd}$$

If δ be the deflection at the free end due to shearing, the shear strain energy is $\tfrac{1}{2} \cdot W \cdot \delta = \tfrac{3}{5}\dfrac{W^2l}{Nbd}$, hence

$$\delta = \tfrac{6}{5}\frac{Wl}{Nbd} = \tfrac{6}{5} \times \left(\frac{\text{mean value of } q}{N}\right) \times (l)$$

which is 20 per cent. greater than it would be with uniformly distributed shear stress.

Similarly, for a beam simply supported at its ends and of length l, carrying a central load W, putting $l/2$ for l, and $W/2$ for W, the shearing deflection is

$$\tfrac{3}{10} \cdot \frac{Wl}{Nbd}$$

or the total deflection due to bending and shearing is

$$\frac{Wl^3}{48EI} + \tfrac{3}{10}\frac{Wl}{Nbd} = \frac{Wl^3}{4Ebd^3}\left\{1 + \tfrac{6}{5}\frac{E}{N}\left(\frac{d}{l}\right)^2\right\}$$

or if $E/N = \tfrac{5}{2}$, this becomes

$$\frac{Wl^3}{4Ebd^3}\left\{1 + 3\left(\frac{d}{l}\right)^2\right\}$$

or for the cantilever

$$\frac{4Wl^3}{Ebd^3}\left\{1 + \tfrac{3}{4}\left(\frac{d}{l}\right)^2\right\}$$

The second term is negligible if (l/d) is large, which is generally the case in practice. This expression for the shearing deflection is in fair agreement with the more exact expression deduced by St. Venant [1] provided the breadth is not great compared with the depth.

Distributed Loads. With a distributed load the simple theory of bending does not hold with the same accuracy as when the vertical shearing force on the cross-sections is constant throughout the length (see Art. 47). Neglecting this, however, for a beam of rectangular section, the deflection due to shear strain of an element of length dx would be

$$\tfrac{6}{5}\frac{F}{Nbd}dx$$

In the case of a uniformly distributed load w per unit length at a distance x from the free end $F = wx$, hence the total deflection is

$$\tfrac{6}{5}\frac{w}{Nbd}\int_0^l x\,dx = \tfrac{3}{5}\frac{wl^2}{Nbd} \quad \text{or} \quad \tfrac{3}{5}\frac{wl}{Nbd}$$

the effect of a distributed load being half that of the same load concentrated at the end. The same coefficient will evidently hold good for a beam freely supported at its ends, and uniformly loaded, compared to similar beam carrying the same load concentrated midway between the supports.

I-*Section Girders.* The cases in which the shearing deflections are of more importance are the various built-up sections of which

[1] See Todhunter and Pearson's "History of Elasticity," vol. ii, Arts. 91 and 96.

K *

girders are made, particularly when the depth is great in proportion to the length. In an **I**-girder section, for example, the intensity of shear stress in the web is (see Art. 53) much greater than the mean intensity of shear stress over the section. A common method of roughly estimating the total deflection of large built-up girders is to calculate for ordinary bending deflection, using a value of E about 25 per cent. below the usual value to allow for shearing, etc.

Any Section. For any solid section instead of (1) the elastic energy $\frac{1}{2}W\delta$ would be

$$\tfrac{1}{2}W\delta = \frac{l}{2N}\int_{\frac{d}{2}}^{\frac{d}{2}} q^2 z \, dy \qquad \ldots \qquad (2)$$

where z is the breadth of the section at a depth y, as in Art. 53, and $q = \dfrac{F}{Iz}\displaystyle\int_{y}^{\frac{d}{2}} yz \, dy$, as in Art. 53,[1] hence the strain energy

$$\tfrac{1}{2} \cdot W \cdot \delta = \frac{l}{2N}\int_{\frac{d}{2}}^{\frac{d}{2}}\left\{\frac{F^2}{I^2 z}\left(\int_{y}^{\frac{d}{2}} yz\,dy\right)^2\right\}dy \qquad \ldots \qquad (3)$$

or for the cantilever symmetrical about the neutral axes of the sections with end load W, where $F = W$

$$\tfrac{1}{2} \cdot W \cdot \delta = \frac{W^2 l}{I^2 N}\int_{0}^{\frac{d}{2}}\frac{1}{z}\left(\int_{y}^{\frac{d}{2}} yz\,dy\right)^2 dy \quad \text{and} \quad \delta = \frac{2Wl}{I^2 N}\int_{0}^{\frac{d}{2}}\frac{1}{z}\left(\int_{y}^{\frac{d}{2}} yz\,dy\right)^2 dy$$

For a simply supported beam of span l and central load W, the deflection would be $\frac{1}{4}$ of the above expression.

For sections the width (z) of which cannot be simply expressed as a function of the distance (y) from the neutral surface, a graphical method will be most convenient. The values of q may be found as in Art. 53 and Fig. 75. A diagram, somewhat similar to Fig. 75, may then be plotted, the ordinates of which are proportional to $q^2 \times z$, by squaring the ordinates of Fig. 75 and multiplying each by the corresponding width of the section. The total area of this diagram would represent $\displaystyle\int_{-\frac{d}{2}}^{\frac{d}{2}} q^2 z \, dy$, and the deflection of, say, a cantilever may be found from it by multiplying by l/N and dividing by W. If the diagram of q is not required it is rather more con-

---

[1] In the case of a varying section, for q substitute the value given in the first footnote to Art. 53, and for $d/2$ write y_1, which is not a constant but the extreme value of y for any section, and for the right-hand side of (2) write $\dfrac{1}{2N}\displaystyle\int_{0}^{l}\left\{\int_{-y_1}^{y_1} q^2 z\,dy\right\}dx.$
This may be found if I and y_1 are known as functions of x, the length of beam. A different method of obtaining a rather more general result is given by Prof. S. E. Slocum in the *Journal of the Franklin Institute*, April, 1911.

venient to proceed as follows (see Fig. 141).   Draw the ordinary
modulus figure for the section as shown at (*a*), and plot a diagram
(*b*) showing *q . z* instead of *q*, on the depth of the beam as a base-
line.   Equation (3), Art. 53, shows that at any height *y* from the
neutral axis

$$qz = \frac{W}{I} \times \left(\text{area of modulus figure between } y \text{ and } \frac{d}{2} \right)$$

from which equation the ordinates of (*b*) may be found by measuring
areas on Fig. (*a*).   Square the ordinates of this diagram (*b*), and

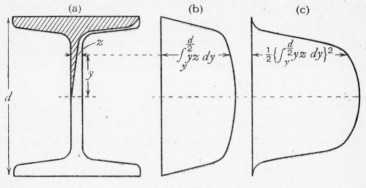

(a)   (b)   (c)

$$\int_y^{\frac{d}{2}} yz \, dy$$

$$\tfrac{1}{2} \left\{ \int_y^{\frac{d}{2}} yz \, dy \right\}^2$$

FIG. 141

divide each by the width *z* and plot the results as ordinates of the
diagram (*c*) on the depth *d* as a base.   The area of the resulting

figure (*c*) represents $\displaystyle\int_{-\frac{d}{2}}^{\frac{d}{2}} q^2 z \, dy$ as before, and the deflection (see (2)

above) is found by multiplying[1] by *l*/N and dividing by W for a
cantilever with an end load, and is ¼ of this for a beam of length *l*
supported at its ends and carrying a central load W, provided W is
used as above in finding *qz*, or ½ this if W/2, the actual shearing
force, is used in finding *qz*.

It is, of course, not necessary actually to plot the diagram (*b*).

Scales.   Fig. 141 (*a*) being drawn full size, the width of the
modulus figure represents $2yz/d$.   If *p* sq. in. of modulus figure
area at (*a*) are represented by 1-in. ordinates on (*b*), the ordinates

represent $\displaystyle\int_y^{\frac{d}{2}} yz \, dy$ on a scale of 1 in. $= p \times \dfrac{d}{2}$ (in.)³.   If the ordinates

---

[1] In the case of a beam, the section of which varies along its length, we might
divide the whole into a number of short lengths δ*l*, and find graphically $\displaystyle\int_{-y_1}^{y_1} q^2 z \, dy$
for each; then by multiplying each value by δ*l*, and dividing the sum by NW, we
could find the deflection (see preceding footnote).

of (*b*) in inches are squared and divided by *nz*, say, for convenience, and then plotted in inches, on Fig. (*c*), the area of Fig. (*c*) represents

$$\int_{-\frac{d}{2}z}^{\frac{d}{2}} \frac{1}{z}\left(\int_{y}^{\frac{d}{2}} yz\,dy\right)^2 dy$$ on a scale of 1 sq. in. $= n\left(p \cdot \frac{d}{2}\right)^2$, the units

being (inches)[6].

To obtain, say, the cantilever deflection, it is only necessary to multiply the result in (inches)[6] by $\frac{Wl}{I^2N}$, the unit of which are (inches)$^{-5}$, when inch units are used for *l*, I, and N, to obtain the deflection in inches. For the centrally loaded beam the factor would be $\frac{1}{4}\frac{Wl}{I^2N}$.

Fig. 141, when drawn full size, represents the British Standard Beam section, No. 10, for which $d=6$ in., $1=43\cdot61$ (in.)[4], and the web is 0·41 in. thick : the area of the diagram (*c*) represents 761 (in.)[6], and the shearing deflection of a cantilever would be 0·416W*l*/N in.

The deflection due to shearing of an **I** beam with square corners such as Fig. 75 may be found by integration in two ranges over which the breadth is constant (see example below), and this method might be used as an approximation for any **I** section by using mean values for the thickness of the flanges and web: an example is given below.

Simple Approximation for **I** *Sections.* Owing to the limitations of the simple theory of bending, none of these calculations can be regarded as correct, and perhaps the simplest approximation may also be the best, viz. to calculate the deflection due to shear as if the web carried the whole shearing force with uniform distinction, so that for a cantilever

$$\delta = \frac{Wl}{AN}$$

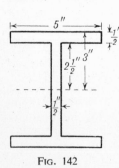

and for a beam simply supported at its ends

$$\delta = \frac{Wl}{4AN}$$

where A is the area *of the* web and *l* is the length of the beam, all the linear units being, say, inches.

FIG. 142

Example. Find the ratio of the deflections due to shearing and bending in a cantilever of **I** section, 6 in. deep and 5 in. wide, the flanges and web each $\frac{1}{2}$ in. thick, carrying an end load, E/N being taken as $\frac{5}{2}$. $1=43\cdot125$ (in.)[4] (see Fig. 142). In the flanges

$$q = \frac{W}{I}\int_y^3 y\,dy = \frac{W}{2I}(9 - y^2)$$

$$q^2 = \frac{W^2}{4I^2}(81 - 18y^2 \times y^4)$$

In the web

$$q = \frac{W}{\frac{1}{2}I}\left(\int_{2\frac{1}{2}}^3 5y\,.\,dy + \int_y^{2\frac{1}{2}} \frac{1}{2}\,.\,y\,dy\right) = \frac{2W}{I}\left(\frac{135}{16} - \frac{y^2}{4}\right) = \frac{W}{I}\left(\frac{135}{8} - \frac{y^2}{2}\right)$$

$$q^2 = \frac{W}{I^2}\left(\frac{18225}{64} - \frac{135}{8}y^2 + \frac{y^4}{4}\right)$$

Taking both sides of the neutral axis, the total shearing resilience is by (2)

$$\tfrac{1}{2}W\,.\,\delta = \frac{l}{2N}\int_{-3}^3 q^2 z\,dy = 2\frac{l}{2N}\left\{\frac{5W^2}{4I^2}\int_{2\frac{1}{2}}^3 (81 - 18y^2 + y^4)dy \right.$$

$$\left. + \frac{W^2}{2I^2}\int_0^{2\frac{1}{2}}\left(\frac{18225}{64} - \frac{135}{8}y^2 + \frac{y^4}{4}\right)dy\right\}$$

$$\delta = \frac{2lW}{NI^2}(1\cdot65 + 314\cdot5) = \frac{632Wl}{I^2N} = 0\cdot340\frac{Wl}{N}$$

(This agrees closely with the result given for Fig. 141, being less in about the same proportion that the web thickness is greater, I being nearly the same in each.)

Ratio of deflections $\frac{shearing}{bending} = \frac{632Wl}{I^2N} \times \frac{3EI}{Wl^3} = \frac{1896}{I}\,.\,\frac{E}{N}\,.\,\frac{1}{l^2}$, and taking $I = 43\cdot125$ and $N/E = \frac{5}{2}$, this ratio is $110/l^2$ nearly. For a simply supported beam of span l the ratio would be $440/l^2$, and if the span were 10 times the depth, or 60 in., the ratio would be $\frac{440}{3600}$, or over 12 per cent.

98. Statically Indeterminate Beams. If a body has force exerted upon it in the form of known loads and is restrained from bodily motion by other supporting forces or reactions called into play by the loads, it is possible to find these reactive forces by the ordinary rules of statics provided the supporting forces are not too numerous. For example, if a table is supported on three legs, or a beam rests on two sharply defined supports, it is easy to find the supporting forces. Moreover, these do not depend much upon the way in which the body deforms so long as strains remain small. Thus, *e.g.* the upward reactions on the ends of a beam carrying a central load will each be equal to half the load whether the beam is of the same cross-section throughout or varies widely. But if the table has four legs or if the beam is propped at a third point, the ordinary rules of statics will no longer serve to determine the distribution of the load on the supports nor the magnitudes of the reactions. These depend upon the proportions of the structure, the deformations produced by the combination of loading and reactive forces (including forces which constitute couples) and upon relative movements of supports.   Thus a fourth leg can be added to a loaded three-legged table, or a prop to a loaded beam, so as just to touch the structure and fill a gap and take no load.   A structure with more supports than are necessary for equilibrium is " statically indeterminate " so far as its supports or reactive constraints are concerned.   If a support is raised it will take an increasing load until it may (like a screwjack) remove the structure from contact with another support, and make it statically determinate again on fewer supports.

Without noting the fact, we have already considered several statically indeterminate problems in the propped cantilever (Art. 80), the beam supported at its end and propped at an intermediate point (Art. 81), and built-in and continuous beams in Chapter VIII. Such examples will now be used to show certain general principles applicable to statically indeterminate beams but we may here confine our attention to straight beams, merely noticing that statically indeterminate problems are of much wider scope, *e.g.* in arched beams and other metal structures.

In the propped cantilever (Art. 80) we found the load on the prop by equating the downward deflection at the free end, if the cantilever were unpropped, to the upward deflection of the same point of the beam due to the upward thrust exerted by the supporting force of the prop.   But, alternatively, we could have considered the beam as supported freely at both ends and then found the couple necessary at one end to produce a slope equal and opposite to that produced by the load in the simply supported condition of the beam and thus to produce zero slope when the load and the rotational constraint act together.

The principle of this method is that of (1) removing from the actual system one or more constraints (*i.e.* reactive forces or moments) and finding the deformation caused by the load (under statically determinate conditions), and (2) reimposing the constraints and finding their necessary magnitudes in order to reduce the deformation at one or more points to amounts (such as zero) prescribed by the conditions of the problem.   Thus the removal of a single prop and its reimposition sufficiently to neutralise a deflection at some fixed point, will give one equation to find the one unknown supporting force.

In a built-in beam the removal of two constraining moments at the ends would allow the beam at its ends to rotate to a slope calculated for a beam with freely supported ends.   The reimposition of moments M_A and M_B (Arts. 86, 87, 88) at the ends sufficient to reduce the slope to zero at *two* places gives two equations to find the magnitudes of the two unknown moments M_A and M_B. The actual process in Arts. 85, 87, and 88 was not carried out in two stages but the unknown bending moments, M_A and M_B were found by inserting the two conditions $i_A = 0$ and $i_B = 0$ which has the same effect but does not so clearly suggest the principle of the super-positions of two systems of forces. Similarly, the problem of the propped cantilever, Art. 80, might be solved in one stage by inte-gration of the equation $EId^2y/dx^2 = M$ where the contribution of the unknown force P at the prop is included in the expression for M.

Again the continuous beam problem (Chapter VIII) was solved in Art. 91 by making the slopes at the ends of a span equal to those in the adjoining spans at the junctions. But it was also solved in Art. 92 by Wilson's method of equating the upward deflection due

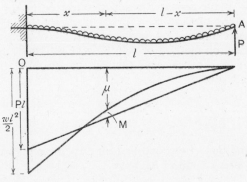

FIG. 143

to the supporting forces of props to the downward deflections which would result from the load if the props were removed.

All these cases illustrate the method of solving statically inde-termine problems by equating opposite deformations produced by component determinate systems of forces which when superposed give the actual statically indeterminate system.

This is not the only method and we shall briefly indicate others by pointing out three ways of solving the problem of a cantilever of uniform section carrying a uniform load of w per unit length and propped at its otherwise free end to the level of the fixed end. See Fig. 143 for bending-moment diagram; μ stands for the bending moment for the beam without the prop P at the free end and M for that when the beam has the prop supplying the upward supporting force P; so that

$$\mu = \tfrac{1}{2}w(l-x)^2 \quad . \quad . \quad . \quad . \quad . \quad . \quad (1)$$

$$M = \mu - P(l-x) = \tfrac{1}{2}w(l-x)^2 - P(l-x) \quad . \quad . \quad . \quad (2)$$

Method A.   (The most direct and obvious for a simple continuous loading.) $i=0$ and $y=0$ for $x=0$

$$EI\frac{d^2y}{dx^2}=M=\frac{w}{2}(l^2-2lx+x^2)-P(l-x)$$

$$EI\frac{dy}{dx}=\frac{w}{2}(l^2x-lx^2+\tfrac{1}{3}x^3)-P(lx-\tfrac{1}{2}x^2)+0$$

$$EI\,.\,y=\tfrac{1}{2}w(\tfrac{1}{2}l^2x^2-\tfrac{1}{3}lx^3+\tfrac{1}{24}x^4)-P(\tfrac{1}{2}lx^2-\tfrac{1}{6}x^3)+0$$

And since $y=0$ for $x=l$,

$$P=\frac{wl^4}{8}\div\frac{l^3}{3}=\tfrac{3}{8}wl$$

and substitution in the foregoing lines gives y, dy/dx and M completely.

Method B.   If the downward deflection at A for the unpropped cantilever and the upward deflection caused by the upward thrust of the prop are expressed by means of Art. 80 (*c*) and (*a*) or by the slope and deflection method of Art. 82 by Castigliano's theorem of Art. 96, or in any other way, then an equation of the opposite deflections at A gives

$$y_A=\frac{wl^4}{8EI}=\frac{Pl^3}{3EI}$$

$$P=\tfrac{3}{8}wl$$

And slopes and deflections can be found by the methods of Art. 82 or of Art. 96 or by method A above.

Method C.   Using the minimum strain energy method of (22) Art. 96, the strain energy U is

$$U=\frac{1}{2EI}\int_0^l M^2dx$$

$$\frac{\partial U}{\partial P}=\frac{1}{EI}\int_0^l M\frac{\partial M}{\partial P}dx\quad\text{where M is given by (2),}$$

and since $\partial M/\partial P=(l-x)$,

$$\frac{\partial U}{\partial P}=\frac{1}{EI}\int_0^l\left\{\frac{w}{2}(l-x)^2-P(l-x)\right\}(l-x)dx$$

$$=\frac{1}{EI}\left(\frac{wl^4}{8}-\frac{Pl^3}{3}\right)$$

And from (22), Art. 96, the condition of no deflection at A is $\partial U/\partial P=0$, hence $wl^4/8-Pl^3=0$ or

$$P=\tfrac{3}{8}wl$$

The slopes and deflections following as in other methods.

Finally, we could solve the problem by the method of moment

distribution (Art. 94).　If we lock the beam at O and A (Fig. 143) the clockwise external moments at O and A are $-\frac{1}{12}wl^2$ and $+\frac{1}{12}wl^2$ respectively.　If we then release A by a moment $-\frac{1}{12}wl^2$ and add to O the induced moment $-wl^2/24$ we have $M_O = \frac{1}{8}wl^2$ and $M_A = 0$. Hence from moments about O,

$$-Pl + \tfrac{1}{2}wl^2 = +\tfrac{1}{8}wl^2 \text{ and } P = \tfrac{3}{8}wl.$$

EXAMPLES IX

1. If the limits of safe bending stress for steel and ash are in the ratio 8 to 1, and Young's moduli of elasticity for the two materials are in the ratio 20 to 1, compare the proof resilience per cubic inch of steel with that for ash and where both are bent in a similar manner.　If steel weighs 480 lb. per cu. ft. and ash 50 lb. per cu. ft., compare the proof resilience of steel with that of an equal weight of ash.

2. A beam of I section is 20 in. deep and $7\frac{1}{2}$ in. broad, the thickness of web and flanges being 0·6 in. and 1 in. respectively.　If the beam carries a load at the centre of a 20-ft. span, find approximately what proportion of the total deflection is due to shearing if the ratio $E/N = 2·5$.

3. Solve Problem No. 7, Examples VII, by Castigliano's first theorem (Art. 96).

CHAPTER X

DIRECT AND BENDING STRESSES

99. Combined Bending and Direct Stress. It often happens that the cross-section of a pillar or a tie-rod mainly subjected to a longitudinal thrust or pull has, in addition bending stresses across it, the pillar or tie-rod suffering flexure in an axial plane; or that the cross-section of a beam resisting flexure has brought upon it further direct stress due to an end thrust or pull, the loads on the beam not being all transverse ones, such as were supposed in Chapters iv and v, but such as make the beam also a strut or a tie. In either case the resultant longitudinal intensity of stress at any point in a cross-section will be the algebraic sum of the direct stress of tension or compression and the direct stresses due to bending. If p is the intensity of stress anywhere on a section subjected to an end load

$$p = p_0 + p_b \qquad \ldots \quad \ldots \quad (1)$$

where p_0 is the total end load divided by the area of cross-section, and p_b is the intensity of bending stress as calculated from the bending moments for purely transverse loading in Art. 46, and is of the same sign as p_0 in part of the section and of opposite sign in another part. The stress intensity p will change sign somewhere in the section if the extreme values of p_b are of greater magnitude than p_0, but the stress will not be zero at the centroid of the section as in the case of a beam bent only by transverse forces. The effect of the additional direct stress p_0 is to change the position of the neutral surface or to remove it entirely.

100. Eccentric Longitudinal Loads. If the line of action of the direct load on a prismatic bar is parallel to the axis of the bar, and intersects an axis of symmetry of the cross-section at a distance h from the centroid of the section, bending takes place in the plane of the axis of the bar and the line of action of the eccentric load. Thus, Fig. 144 represents the cross-section of a bar, the load P passing through the point C, and O is the centroid of the section. Let A be the area of cross-section, and y_1 distance OD from the centroid O to the extreme edge D in the direction OC, and let I be the moment of inertia of the area of section about the central axis FG perpendicular to OC. Then, in addition to the direct tension or compression P/A or p_0, there is a bending moment $M = P \cdot h$ on the section, the intensity of stress at any point distant y from FG being

$$p = p_0 + p_b = \frac{A}{P} + \frac{P \cdot h \cdot y}{I} \quad \text{(Art. 46)}$$

or since $I = Ak^2$, where k is the radius of gyration about FG

$$p = \frac{P}{A} + \frac{Phy}{Ak^2} = \frac{P}{A}\left(1 + \frac{h \cdot y}{k^2}\right) \quad \text{or} \quad p_0\left(1 + \frac{hy}{k^2}\right) \quad . \quad . \quad (1)$$

y being positive for points on the same side of FG as C, and negative on the opposite side. The intensity varies uniformly with the dimension y, as shown in Figs. 144, 145.

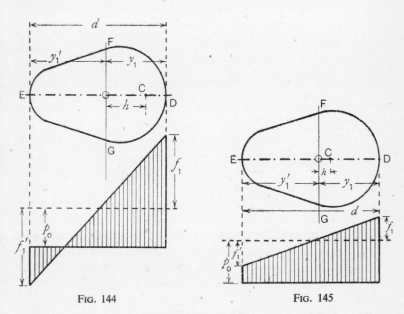

FIG. 144   FIG. 145

The extreme stress intensities at the edges of the section will be

$$p_0 + f_1 \quad \text{and} \quad p_0 - f_1'$$

where f_1 and f_1' are the opposite extreme values of p_b, or if y_1 and y_1' are the distances of the extreme edges from the centroid O, the extreme stress intensities of stress are

$$p = p_0\left(1 + \frac{hy_1}{k^2}\right) \quad \text{and} \quad p = p_0\left(1 - \frac{hy'_1}{k^2}\right) \quad . \quad . \quad (2)$$

on the extreme edges D and E, the former being on the same side of the centroid as C, and the latter on the opposite side.   If the section is symmetrical about FG

$$y_1 = y_1' = d/2$$

Evidently $p = 0$ for $y = -k^2/h$ if this distance is within the area of cross-section, *i.e.* if k^2/h is less than y_1' the distance from the centroid to the edge E opposite to C.   An axis parallel to FG and distant k^2/h from it on the side opposite to C might be called the neutral axis of the section, for it is the intersection of the area of cross-section by a surface along which there is no direct longitudinal stress. The uniformly varying intensity of stress where h is greater than k^2/y_1' is shown in Fig. 144. If k^2/h is greater than y_1', *i.e.* if h is less than k^2/y_1' the stress throughout the section is of the same kind as p_0; this uniformly varying distribution of stress is shown in Fig. 145. With loads of considerable eccentricity, it should be noted, such metals as cast iron, which are strong in compression, may ultimately fail in tension under a compressive load.

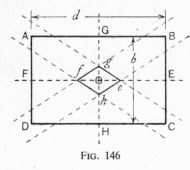

FIG. 146

Rectangular Section. In the rectangular section of breadth b and depth d, shown in Fig. 146, in order that the stress on the section shall be all of the same sign, the maximum deviation in the direction OE of the line of action of the resultant stress from the line GH through the centroid is

$$h = k^2 \div y = \tfrac{1}{12}d^2 \div \frac{d}{2} = \frac{d}{6}$$

From this result springs the well-known rule for masonry, in which no tension is allowed—that across a rectangular joint the resultant thrust across the joint must fall within $\tfrac{1}{6}$ of the thickness from the centre line of the joint, or *within the middle third.* The limiting deviation in the direction OG under the same conditions is $\tfrac{1}{6}b$.

Core or Kernel of a Section. If the line of action of the stress is on neither of the centre lines of the section, the bending is unsymmetrical, and may conveniently be resolved in the planes of the two principal axes as in Art. 52. If the line of action of P fall in the quarter GOEB say, at a point the co-ordinates of which, referred to OE and OG as axes, are x and y measured positive toward E and G respectively, the bending moment about OE is P . y, and about OG is P . x, and the stress at any point in the section the co-ordinates of which are x', y', is

$$p = \frac{P}{bd} + \frac{P \cdot y \cdot y'}{\tfrac{1}{12}db^3} + \frac{P \cdot x \cdot x'}{\tfrac{1}{12}bd^3} = \frac{12P}{bd}\left(\frac{1}{12} + \frac{y \cdot y'}{b^2} + \frac{x \cdot x'}{d^2}\right) \quad . \quad (3)$$

The least value of this is evidently always at D, where $x' = -d/2$ and $y' = -b/2$ when the least value of p is

$$\frac{6P}{bd}\left(\tfrac{1}{6} - \frac{y}{b} - \frac{x}{d}\right)$$

This just reaches zero when

$$\frac{y}{b}+\frac{x}{d}=\tfrac{1}{6}, \quad \text{or} \quad y=-\frac{b}{d}x+\frac{b}{6} \ .$$

the equation to the straight-line joining points *g, b*/6 from O along OG, and *e, d*/6 from O along OE.   Similar limits will apply in other quarters of the rectangle, and the stress will be of the same sign in all parts of the section, provided the line of the resultant load falls within a rhombus *egfh*, the diagonals of which lie along EF and GH, and are of length *d*/3 and *b*/3 respectively.   This rhombus is called the *core* or *kernel* of the section.

Circular Section.   In the case of a circular section of radius R, the deviation which just produces zero stress at one point of the perimeter of the section and double the average intensity diametrically opposite is

$$h=k^2 \div R = \frac{R^2}{4} \div R = \tfrac{1}{4}R$$

and for a hollow circular section of internal radius *r* and external radius R the deviation would be

$$h=\frac{R^2+r^2}{4R}$$

which approaches the limit $\tfrac{1}{2}R$ in the case of a thin tube.

Other Sections.   A more general form of (3) is evidently

$$p=\frac{P}{A}\left(1+\frac{yy'}{k_x^2}+\frac{xx'}{k_y^2}\right) \quad \cdots \cdots \quad (4)$$

where k_x and k_y are the radii of gyration of the area of section about the axes of *x* and *y* respectively, and for zero stress at a point the co-ordinates of which are *x', y'*

$$\frac{yy'}{k_x^2}+\frac{xx'}{k_y^2}=-1 \quad \cdots \cdots \cdots \quad (5)$$

For a symmetrical **I** section of breadth *b* in the direction of *x*, and depth *d* in the direction of *y*, the four corners will be limiting points of zero stress, and the limits of deviation of load from the centroid for no change in sign of the stress will be the bounding line

$$y=-\frac{k_x^2}{k_y^2}\cdot\frac{b}{d}x-\frac{2k_x^2}{d} \quad \cdots \cdots \quad (6)$$

and three others forming a rhombus having the principal axes as diagonals.   Similar bounding lines will fix the deviation limits or cores for various other sections the boundaries of which can be circumscribed by polygons.

For a symmetrical **I** section such as Fig. 36, if the axis OY is taken as the vertical principal axis of the section, for a corner

$$x' = \frac{b}{2} \text{ and } y' = \frac{d}{2}$$

If x and y are the co-ordinates of the centre of the loading, the unit stress from (4) is

$$p = \frac{P}{A}\left(\frac{yd}{2k_x{}^2} + \frac{xb}{2k_y{}^2} + 1\right) \quad \text{or} \quad \frac{p}{p_0} - 1 = \frac{yd}{2k_x{}^2} + \frac{xb}{2k_y{}^2} \quad . \quad (7)$$

For various values of p/p_0 equation (7) would represent a series of straight lines on which the load centre would lie; the inclination of the lines to the axis OX would be at an angle θ such that

$$\tan \theta = -\frac{k_x{}^2}{k_y{}^2} \cdot \frac{b}{d} \quad \ldots \quad \ldots \quad (8)$$

and equation (6) is the particular line for $p=0$. The minimum eccentricity of loading to give any ratio p/p_0 at the corner of the section would occur when a line joining the centroid to the load centre is perpendicular to the lines represented by (7), *i.e.* inclined to the axis OX at an angle the tangent of which is

$$\frac{k_y{}^2}{k_x{}^2} \cdot \frac{d}{b} \quad \ldots \quad \ldots \quad \ldots \quad (9)$$

Common examples of eccentric loads occur in tie-bars " cranked " to avoid an obstacle, frames of machines, such as reciprocating engines, members of steel structures, and columns or pillars of all kinds; but it is to be remembered that, particularly in the case of pillars, the deviation h is a variable along the length if flexure takes place. Frequently, however, in columns which are short in proportion to their cross-sectional dimensions, and in which the deviation h of resultant thrust from the axis is considerable, this variation in h is negligible.

Masonry Seating for Beam Ends. If we assume the forces exerted by the walls on a cantilever or a built-in beam to consist of a uniform upward pressure equal to the total vertical reaction R and equal upward and downward pressures varying in intensity uniformly along the length from zero at the centre of the seating to maxima at the ends, giving a resultant couple or fixing moment, formula (1) may be applied to calculate the maximum intensity of pressure on the masonry. If b be the (constant) breadth of the beam and d the length of the seating, $p_0 = \dfrac{R}{b \cdot d}$. The moment of the seating pressures about the centroid of the seating is nearly the same as the bending moment at the entrance to the wall if the seating is short, exceeding it by $R \times d/2$. Taking the case of a cantilever of length l carrying an end load W (Fig. 43), the moment is $W(l + d/2)$;

writing this for P . *h*, and *b* . *d* for A, and $\frac{1}{6}bd$ for Ak^2/y_1 in (1) or (2), the extreme intensity of pressure at the entrance to the wall is

$$p_{max}=\frac{W}{bd}+\frac{6W(l+d/2)}{bd^2}=\frac{2W}{bd}(2+3l/d)$$

which serves to calculate the maximum pressure intensity if *d* is known, or to determine *d* for a specified value (say about 500 lb. per sq. in.) of the working intensity of crushing stress on the seating.

Example 1.   In a rectangular cross-section 2 in. wide and 1 in. thick the axis of a pull of 10 tons deviates from the centre of the section by $\frac{1}{10}$ in. in the direction of the thickness, and is in the centre of the width.   Find the extreme stress intensities.

The extreme bending stresses are

$$f=\frac{M}{Z}=\frac{\frac{1}{10}\times 10}{\frac{1}{6}\times 2\times 1}=3 \text{ tons per sq. in.}$$

tension and compression along the opposite long edges of the section.   To these must be added algebraically a tension of

$$\tfrac{10}{2}=5 \text{ tons per sq. in.}$$

hence, on the side on which the pull deviates from the centroid the extreme tension is

$$5+3=8 \text{ tons per sq. in.}$$

and on the opposite side the tension is

$$5-3=2 \text{ tons per sq. in.}$$

Here a deviation of the load a distance of $\frac{1}{10}$ of the thickness from the centroid increases the maximum intensity of stress to 60 per cent. over the mean value.

Example 2.   A short cast-iron pillar is 8 in. external diameter, the metal being 1 in. thick, and carries a load of 20 tons.   If the load deviates from the centre of the column by $1\frac{3}{4}$ in., find the extreme intensities of stress.   What deviation will just cause tension in the pillar?

The area of section is $\frac{\pi}{4}(64-36)=22\cdot 0$ sq. in.

The moment of resistance to bending is equal to

$$20\times 1\tfrac{3}{4}=35 \text{ ton-in.}$$

hence the extreme intensities of bending stress are

$$35\div\frac{\pi}{32}\cdot\left(\frac{8^4-6^4}{8}\right)=\frac{35\times 8\times 32}{\pi\times 2{,}800}=1\cdot 017 \text{ tons per sq. in.}$$

The additional compressive stress is

$$\tfrac{20}{22}=0\cdot 909 \text{ ton per sq. in.}$$

hence the maximum compressive stress is $1\cdot 017+0\cdot 909=1\cdot 926$ tons per sq. in., and the minimum compression is $0.909-1.017=$ -0.108, i.e. 0.108 ton per sq. in. tension.

If there is just no stress on the side remote from the eccentric load the deviation would be

$$1.75 \times \frac{0.909}{1.017} = 1.56 \text{ in.}$$

Example 3. A short stanchion of symmetrical **I** section withstands a thrust parallel to its axis such that the stress would be 2 tons per sq. in. if the thrust were truly axial. Determine the eccentricity which would be sufficient to produce a stress of 10 tons per sq. in. if the section is 9 in. deep, 7 in. wide, 17.06 sq. in. area, the principal moments of inertia being 229.5 (in.)^4 and 46.3 (in.)^4, the former being about an axis in the direction of the breadth.

$$\text{Taking } k_x{}^2 = \frac{I_x}{A} = \frac{229.5}{17.06} = 13.45, \ k_y{}^2 = \frac{46.3}{17.06} = 2.714$$

and in equation (7), $\frac{p}{p_0} = \frac{10}{2} = 5$; this gives

$$5-1 = 4 = \frac{4.5y}{13.45} + \frac{3.5x}{2.714} \text{ or } y = -3.854x - 11.96$$

as the locus of the centre of pressure to produce the extreme stress at one corner. The inclination of this locus to the horizontal principal axis is

$$\tan^{-1}(-3.854) = 180 - 75.55 = 104.45°$$

and for $x=0$, $y = -11.96$ in.

Hence the distance of the line from the centroid is

$$11.96 \cos 75.55° = 3.00 \text{ in.}$$

in a direction inclined $14.45°$ to the horizontal axis. If the centre of pressure were on the horizontal axis of the **I** section, the deviation to produce the same extreme stress would be

$$\frac{11.96}{3.854} = 3.1 \text{ in.}$$

Example 4. A cantilever 8 in. broad is at the wall subjected to a shearing force of 20 tons and a bending moment of 400 ton-in. Assuming a uniformly varying pressure between the beam and its seating, find what length of the beam must be built into the wall in order that the pressure shall not exceed $\frac{1}{4}$ ton per sq. in.

Taking the upward pressure to support the shearing force and the upward pressure constituting part of the fixing couple, if d is the length required

$$\frac{1}{4} = \frac{20}{8d} + \frac{400 + (20 \times d/2)}{\frac{1}{6} \times 8 \times d^2}$$

$$d^2 - 40d - 1,200 = 0$$

Hence $d=60$ in., *i.e.* the beam must be built into the wall for a length of 5 ft.

101. The S-Polygon. A useful method of dealing with the extreme stresses produced in unsymmetrical bending (whether produced by an eccentric longitudinal load, a transverse load, or by a pure moment or couple) may conveniently now be noticed.

From equation (1) of Art. 52, with the notation of that article and Fig. 71, the bending stresses produced at any point (such as Q in

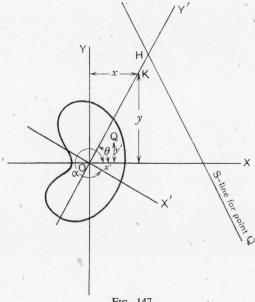

Fig. 147) the co-ordinates of which are x', y', by a bending moment M in the plane OY' (Figs. 71 and 147) is

$$p_b = M\left(\frac{y' \cos \alpha}{I_x} - \frac{x \sin \alpha}{I_y}\right) \quad \ldots \quad (1)$$

or

$$p_b = M \div \frac{I_x I_y}{y' I_y \cos \alpha - x' I_x \sin \alpha} \quad \ldots \quad (2)$$

or

$$p_b = M/S, \text{ say} \quad \ldots \quad \ldots \quad \ldots \quad (3)$$

where S is the section modulus (of which Z in Art. 46 is the particular value for $\alpha=0$), and

$$S = \frac{I_x I_y}{y' I_y \cos \alpha - x' I_x \sin \alpha} = \frac{A k_x^2 k_y^2}{y' k_y^2 \cos \alpha - x' k_x^2 \sin \alpha} \quad . \quad (4)$$

where A is the area of cross-section of the beam or column.

If the plane of the bending moment M makes an angle θ with OX, we may write $\alpha = \theta - 90$, and making this substitution in (4) and inverting both sides

$$\frac{1}{S} = \frac{1}{A}\left(\frac{y' \sin \theta}{k_x^2} + \frac{x' \cos \theta}{k_y^2}\right) \quad . \quad . \quad . \quad (5)$$

This is the polar equation for a straight line, with a radius vector S, inclined θ to the initial line OX; the tangent of the angle which the straight line makes with OX is

$$-\frac{k_x^2}{k_y^2} \cdot \frac{x'}{y'} \quad \text{or} \quad -\frac{I_x}{I_y} \cdot \frac{x'}{y'} \quad . \quad . \quad . \quad (6)$$

and the intercept on OY is

$$\left. \begin{array}{c} +\dfrac{Ak_x^2}{y'} \quad \text{or} \quad \dfrac{I_x}{y'} \\[2ex] \dfrac{Ak_y^2}{x'} \quad \text{or} \quad \dfrac{I_y}{x'} \end{array} \right\} \quad . \quad . \quad . \quad . \quad (7)$$

and on OX is

From which the line can easily be drawn and the value of S measured for any inclination θ of the plane of bending to OX. The line is defined by (7) or (6) and (7), and is, of course, dependent only on the position (x', y') of Q and the shape and size of the section, and is independent of the position θ of the plane of bending OY'. It may conveniently be called the S-line for the point Q. To find the bending stress produced at Q by a bending moment M in the plane OY' or OK, it is only necessary to measure the intercept or radius vector OH, which gives the value of S, and to substitute this in equation (3). The radius vector is of course of infinite length when parallel to the S-line for Q, *i.e.* from (6), when

$$\tan \theta = -\frac{k_x^2}{k_y^2} \cdot \frac{x'}{y'} \quad \text{or} \quad -\frac{I_x}{I_y} \cdot \frac{x'}{y'}. \quad . \quad . \quad (8)$$

for then Q is on the neutral axis of the section, which is in agreement with (6), Art. 52.

If any section be circumscribed by a polygon, without re-entrant angles, the apices of this polygon are points which might, for different directions of bending, form extreme points of the section, and hence be in fibres of maximum bending stress. The S-lines drawn for each apex in turn form a polygon which has been described and called by Prof. L. J. Johnson [1] the S-polygon. When the S-polygon has been drawn for any particular section, since for all extreme (and other) points by (3) the bending stress p_b is inversely proportional to the radius vector S, it is easy to pick out (by nearness to O) the plane of bending which for a given bending moment causes the maximum

[1] " An Analysis of General Flexure in a Straight Bar of Uniform Cross Section," *Trans. Am. Soc. of Civil Engineers*, vol. lvi (1906), p. 169.

stress p_b at any point, and to calculate the value of p_b (viz. M/S) by measuring S to scale.[1]

And, similarly, it is easy to pick out the point on the section, and the plane of bending, which for a given value of M give the maximum bending stress anywhere in the section.   Both are determined by drawing from O the perpendicular on to the nearest side of the S-polygon.

In the case of sections having partially curved boundaries containing points which are extreme ones for some planes of bending (*e.g.* the section shown in Fig. 72), the curved boundary may be looked upon as the limit of an inscribed (or of a circumscribed) polygon.   Successive apices of such a polygon would have corresponding sides in the S-polygon, and if the successive apices of the inscribed polygon be taken close together, the successive S-lines will differ little in slope and position and in the limit they will define a curved side in the S-polygon.   If necessary such a curved side could be drawn approximately, but in sections such as unequal angles, Z-bars, T-bars, it will generally be sufficiently near to treat the outer corners as square instead of being rounded off.

It is evident from (4) that the dimensions of S are the cubes of lengths, say, (inches)³.   It will often be convenient to draw a cross-section full size, and the S-polygon to a scale of one (in.)³ to 1 in., though any scales may be employed for either the cubic or linear quantities.

A convenient way of drawing the polygon is to set off each S-line by means of its intercepts given by (7), and the S-lines may be denoted by small letters corresponding to a capital letter used to denote the points in the boundary of the section to which they correspond.   The apices of the polygon are denoted by the two small letters on the pairs of S-lines meeting there.

Another method of drawing the S-polygon for any section is to locate its apices or intersections of the successive S-lines for the successive apices of the polygon circumscribing the section.   This may be done by the following formulae for the co-ordinates.   Let x_a, y_a, be the co-ordinates of a point A, and x_b, y_b, be those of a point B, AB being a side of the polygon circumscribing the section.

Then for the point A the S-line equation (5) may be written

$$y = -\frac{k_x^2}{k_y^2} \cdot \frac{x_a}{y_a} x + A\frac{k_x^2}{y_a} \quad \cdots \cdots \quad (9)$$

---

[1] The minimum value of S, of course, occurs when the radius vector is measured perpendicular to the S-line, *i.e.* when

$$\tan \theta = +\frac{k_y^2}{k_x^2} \cdot \frac{y'}{x'}$$

This is not necessarily in the direction joining O to Q, except when $k_y = k_x$, *i.e.* in doubly symmetrical sections.

and its intersection with the corresponding line for B is given by the co-ordinate x_{ab}, y_{ab}, where

$$x_{ab} = \frac{I_y(y_b - y_a)}{x_a y_b - x_b y_a} \quad \text{or} \quad \frac{A k_y^2(y_b - y_a)}{x_a y_b - x_b y_a} \qquad (10)\,[1]$$

$$y_{ab} = \frac{I_x(x_a - x_b)}{x_a y_b - x_b y_a} \quad \text{or} \quad \frac{A k_x^2(x_a - x_b)}{x_a y_b - x_b y_a} \qquad (11)\,[1]$$

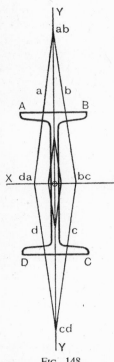

FIG. 148

The similarity of the S-line defined by (5) or (7) to the line (5) of Art. 100 will be noted. The two lines have the same slope as given at (6), but line (5) of Art. 100 makes intercepts

$$-\frac{k_x^2}{y'} \text{ on OY, and } -\frac{k_y^2}{x'} \text{ on OX} \qquad (12)$$

in place of those given in (7). Thus the lines forming the sides of the core are parallel to those of the S-polygon, but on opposite sides of the origin O. The core and the S-polygon are therefore similar figures, and the core might be used in place of the S-polygon, S being found by multiplying the radius vector of the core on the *opposite* side of O to the point concerned by A, the area of the section, or modifying the scale.

Fig. 148 shows the S-polygon for a British Standard Beam Section (No. 8, 6×3 in.) ABCD (see Appendix), the side *a* corresponding to A, and so on. It is easily drawn from the intercepts (7) to which, in fact, the formulae (11) and (10) reduce when $x_a = -x_b$ and $y_a = y_b$, etc.

The intercepts are in such a case the principal moduli of the section denoted by Z, as in Art. 46, and given in steel section tables. The inner or smaller rhombus shows the core of the section.

[1] If OX and OY are not the principal axes of the section, for which $\Sigma(xy\,dydx) = 0$, as here supposed, the values are

$$x_{ab} = \frac{I_y(y_b - y_a) + (x_a - x_b)\,\Sigma(xy\,dxdy)}{x_a y_b - x_b y_a}$$

$$y_{ab} = \frac{I_x(x_a - x_b) - (y_a - y_b)\,\Sigma(xy\,dxdy)}{x_a y_b - x_b y_a}$$

The product of inertia $\Sigma(xy\,dydx)$ being not zero in this case. This may be preferable for the information given in some tables; those relating to British Standard Sections, however, contain sufficient information to allow the use of the simpler formulæ (10) and (11), which involve less arithmetic computation, but x_a, y_a, etc., must sometimes be measured, whereas for one pair of axes (not necessarily principal axes) they may be obtained from the tables with or without simple subtraction.

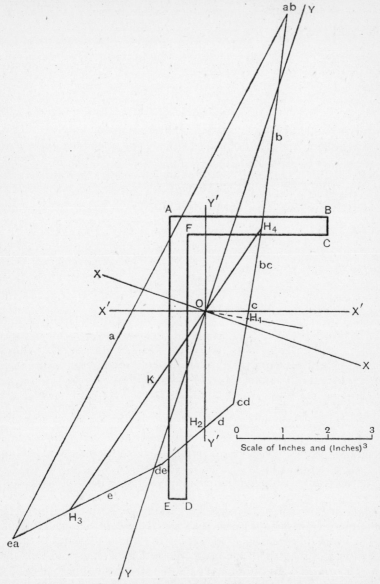

FIG. 149

A more useful example of the S-polygon is shown in Fig. 149 for a $6 \times 3\frac{1}{2} \times \frac{3}{8}$ in. British Standard Angle (see Appendix). The corners D, F, and C have been taken for simplicity as square. This polygon was drawn by setting out the angle section ABCFDE, and the axes OX′ and OY′ from the details in the tables, and then setting out the principal axes OX and OY at the inclination to OX′ and OY′ respectively of 19°, or $\tan^{-1} 0·344$, given in the standard tables. The apices of the S-polygon were then calculated by the formulae (10) and (11) from the co-ordinates of A, B, C, D, and E with respect to OX and OY, measured from the drawing. The work was checked by calculation from (7) of intercepts on OX and OY. If desired, a more exact result could be obtained by putting in the curves at C and D as in Fig. 149, and drawing their common tangent and regarding it, instead of a line CD, as one of the five sides of a

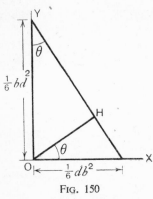

FIG. 150

circumscribing polygon of the section; but for all practical purposes a circumscribing polygon ABCDE is sufficiently accurate. From the S-polygon (Fig. 149) it is immediately apparent that the least resistance to bending ($p_b \times$ S) is for a plane of bending between OX and OX′, and the least value of S is evidently found by dropping a perpendicular OH_1 from O on to the line c.

The following examples illustrate the simplicity and usefulness of the S-polygon for certain problems. Other examples will be found in Prof. L. J. Johnson's paper previously referred to, and in a paper by Prof. Cyril Batho.[1]

Example 1. Find for a beam the section of which is a rectangle of depth d and breadth b the position of the plane of bending in which the greatest bending stress will be produced by a given bending moment, and the bending moment necessary to produce a bending stress p_b. Also the maximum stress which may be produced by a longitudinal thrust P with an eccentricity h. Fig. 150 represents a quarter of the rhombus, the whole of which forms the S-polygon for the rectangular section, the hypotenuse of the right-angled triangle being the S-line for one corner of the section. The minimum value of S is represented by OH, the perpendicular from O on to the hypotenuse. The required plane of bending is therefore through the axis of the beam and OH, *i.e.* inclined to OX, the shorter principal axis at an angle θ, which from the simple geometry of the figure is evidently $\tan^{-1} b/d$. Also OH, from the geometry of the right-angled triangle, represents a value

$$S = \tfrac{1}{6} \frac{b^2 d^2}{\sqrt{(b^2 + d^2)}}$$

[1] " The Effect of End Connections on the Distribution of Stress in certain Tension Members," *Journl. Franklin Inst.*, Aug., 1915.

Hence the minimum bending moment to produce a bending stress of intensity p_b is

$$M = \frac{p_b}{6} \frac{b^2 d^2}{\sqrt{(b^2 + d^2)}}$$

(Note that the value required in a plane through the beam axis and the shorter axis of the section is $p_b \times db^2/6$, which is $\sqrt{\{1 + (d/b)^2\}}$ times the minimum value.)

Also if the eccentric thrust P acts in this most effective position, *i.e.* in the axial plane OH, its moment is Ph, and it produces a bending stress $Ph/S = 6Ph\sqrt{(b^2 + d^2)}/(b^2 d^2)$ in addition to the direct stress P/bd. Hence the maximum stress intensity is

$$\frac{P}{bd}\left\{1 + \frac{6h\sqrt{(b^2 + d^2)}}{bd}\right\}$$

Example 2.   Find the bending moment which an angle section $6 \times 3 \times \frac{3}{8}$ in. will resist in every plane (perpendicular to the section) without the bending stress exceeding 6 tons per sq. in.

From Fig. 149 the shortest perpendicular OH_1 from O on the S-polygon measures 0·94 in. when drawn to a scale 1 in. = one (in.)³, hence the minimum value of S = 0·94 (in.)³, and by (3)

$$M = 6 \times 0.94 = 5.64 \text{ ton-in.}$$

(Compare the result in Example 1 of Art. 52 for a plane through O parallel to the long leg of the angle. $OH_2 = 2.45$ (in.)³, and indicates a moment of $6 \times 2.45 = 14.7$ ton-in.   This moment is quite 15 ton-in. if the S-polygon is drawn for a polygon circumscribing the angle with the corners D and C rounded as in Fig. 72.)

Example 3.   A structural member made of a $6 \times 3\frac{1}{2} \times \frac{3}{8}$ in. angle carries a thrust of 10,000 lb. applied at a point K (Fig. 149) $\frac{3}{16}$ in. from AE at a level $3\frac{3}{8}$ in. vertically below A.   Find the maximum compressive and tensile unit stresses in the section.

OK is the plane of the bending moment produced by the eccentric thrust.   This meets the *e* line at H_3, and OH_3 scales 5·15 (in.)³, while OK = 1·68 in.   Hence from (3)

$$p_b = \frac{M}{S} = \frac{10,000 \times 1.68}{5.15} = 2,920 \text{ lb. per sq. in.}$$

which is a compressive stress, OH_3 being on the same side of O as K is.   The mean direct stress is

$$\frac{P}{\text{area}} = \frac{10,000}{3.422} = 3,080 \text{ lb. per sq. in.}$$

Hence from (1) Art. 99 (at E)

max. compressive unit stress $= p_b + p_0 = 3,260 + 2.920$
$$= 6,180 \text{ lb. per sq. in.}$$

The length OH_4 in KO produced scales $2·17$ (in.)^3

Hence (at B)

$$\text{(tensile)} \quad p_b = \frac{10,000 \times 1·68}{2·17} = 7,850 \text{ lb. per sq. in.}$$

Hence (at B)

max. tensile unit stress $= 7,850 - 2,920 = 4,930$ lb. per sq. in.

The position of K is about the probable centre of a thrust trans-mitted to the angle bar by a $\frac{3}{8}$-in. gusset plate.

102. Pillars, Columns, Stanchions, and Struts. These terms are usually applied to prismatic and similar-shaped pieces of material under compressive stress. The effects of uniformly distributed compressive stress are dealt with in Chapter II on the supposition that the length of the strut is not great. The uniformly varying stress resulting from combined bending and compression on a short prismatic piece of material is dealt with in Arts. 99 and 100. There remain the cases in which the strut is not short, in which the strut fails under bending or buckling due to a central or to an eccentric load. Theoretical calculation for such cases is of two kinds: first, exact calculation for ideal cases which cannot be even approxi-mately realised in practice, and secondly, empirical calculation, which cannot be rigidly based on rational theories, but which can be shown to be reasonable theoretically, as well as in a fair measure of agreement with experiments. Calculations of each kind will be dealt with in the following articles, and the objections and uncer-tainties attaching to each will be pointed out, but the stresses and strains produced in struts by known loads cannot be estimated by any method with the same degree of approximation as in the case of beams or tie-rods, for reasons which will be indicated.

103. Euler's Theory : Long Pillars. This refers to pillars which are very long in proportion to their cross-sectional dimensions, which are perfectly straight and homogeneous in quality, and in which the compressive loads are perfectly axially applied. Under such ideal conditions it is shown that the pillar would buckle and collapse under a load much smaller than would produce failure by crushing in a short piece of the same cross-section, and that until this critical load is reached it would remain straight. This evidently could not apply to any pillar so short that the elastic limit is reached before the buckling load.

The strength to resist buckling is greatly affected by the condition of the ends, whether fixed or free. A fixed end means one which is so supported or clamped as to constrain the direction of the strut at that point, as in the case of the ends of a built-in or *encastré* beam, while a free end means one which by being rounded or pivoted or hinged is free to take up any angular position due to bending of the strut.   If the collapsing load for a strut with one kind of end support is found, the corresponding loads for other conditions may be deduced from it.

Case I, Fig. 151.   Notation as in the figure.   Let P be the load at which instability occurs and the column is in equilibrium in a curve under the action of P and its own flexural elastic resisting forces. One end O is fixed, and the other end, initially at R, is free to move laterally and to take up any angular position. The fixing will of course involve at O an external moment ($M_0 = P \times a$) and a longitudinal reaction P. Taking the fixed end O as origin, measuring x along the initial position of the strut OR, and bending deflections y perpendicular to OR, the bending moment at Q' is $P(a-y)$ if the moment is reckoned positive for convexity towards the initial position OR; then, neglecting any effects of direct compression and using the relations for ordinary transverse bending, the curvature

$$\frac{M}{EI} = \frac{P(a-y)}{EI} = \frac{d^2y}{dx^2} \text{ (approximately, as in Art. 62)}$$

where I is the least moment of inertia of the cross-section, which is assumed to be the same throughout the length

$$\frac{d^2y}{dx^2} + \frac{P}{EI} \cdot y = \frac{P}{EI} \cdot a . \quad . \quad . \quad (1)$$

The solution to this well-known differential equation is[1]

$$y = a + B \cos \sqrt{P/EI} \cdot x + C \sin \sqrt{P/EI} \cdot x . \quad (2)$$

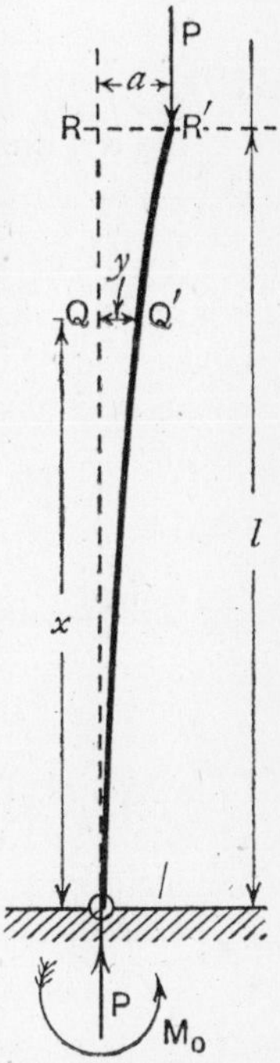

where B and C are constants of integration which may be found from the end conditions.   When $x=0$, $y=0$, hence

$$0 = a + B + 0 \quad \text{or} \quad B = -a$$

And when $x=0$, $dy/dx=0$, hence, differentiating (2)

$$dy/dx = \sqrt{P/EI}(-B \sin \sqrt{P/EI}x + C \cos \sqrt{P/EI}x)$$

and $0 = \sqrt{P/EI}(-0 + C)$ hence C=0

and (2) becomes

$$y = a(1 - \cos x \sqrt{P/EI} . \quad . \quad . \quad . \quad . \quad . \quad (2A)$$

This represents the deflection to a curve of cosines or sines, and

FIG. 151

[1] See Lamb's *Infinitesimal Calculus.*

L

holds for all values of x to $x=l$. In particular, at the free end $x=l$ and $y=a$, hence

$$a=a-a \cos l\sqrt{P/EI}$$

or
$$-a \cos l\sqrt{P/EI}=0$$

From this it follows that either $a=0$ or the cosine is zero. In the former case evidently no bending takes place; in the latter case, if bending takes place

$$\cos l\sqrt{P/EI}=0 \quad . \quad . \quad . \quad . \quad . \quad . \quad (3)$$

and
$$l\sqrt{P/EI}=\pi/2 \text{ or } 3\pi/2 \text{ or } 5\pi/2, \text{ etc.}$$

Taking the first value $\pi/2$, which gives the least magnitude to P

$$l^2 \frac{P}{EI}=\frac{\pi^2}{4} \quad \text{or} \quad P=\frac{\pi^2 EI}{4l^2} \quad . \quad . \quad . \quad . \quad (4)$$

This gives a collapsing load, and for a long column is much within the elastic limit of compressive stress. Writing $A \cdot k^2$ for I, where A is the constant area of cross-section and k is the least radius of gyration

$$P=\frac{\pi^2 EA}{4}\left(\frac{k}{l}\right)^2$$

or the average intensity of compressive stress is

$$p_0=\frac{P}{A}=\frac{\pi^2 E}{4}\left(\frac{k}{l}\right)^2 \quad . \quad . \quad . \quad . \quad . \quad (5)$$

Case II, *Fig.* 152. Both ends on pivots or frictionless hinges or otherwise free to take up any angular position. If half the length of the strut be considered, its ends and loading evidently satisfy the conditions of Case I; hence the collapsing load

$$P=\pi^2 EI/4(\tfrac{1}{2}l)^2=\pi^2 EI/l^2 \quad . \quad . \quad . \quad . \quad (6)$$

and
$$p_0=P/A=\pi^2 E(k/l)^2 \quad . \quad . \quad . \quad . \quad . \quad (7)$$

This case of hinged ends in fixed positions is so often taken as the standard for reference that we may solve it independently, instead of Case I, briefly as follows. From Fig. 152 at X,

$$M=EI\frac{d^2y}{dx^2}=-P \cdot y$$

$$\frac{d^2y}{dx^2}+\frac{P}{EI} \cdot y=0$$

$$y=A \cos \sqrt{P/EI}x+B \sin \sqrt{P/EI}x$$

and since $dy/dx=0$ for $x=0$, $B=0$

$$y=A \cos \sqrt{P/EI}x \quad \text{or} \quad a \cos \sqrt{P/EI}x$$

where $y=a$ for $x=0$.

And since $y=0$ for $x=l/2$

$$a \cos \sqrt{P/EI}\,l/2 = 0$$

And unless $a=0$ the cosine is zero the lowest value of satisfying this is given by

$$\sqrt{P/EI}\,l/2 = \pi/2$$

or
$$P = \pi^2 EI/l^2 \text{ as in (6)}.$$

*Case II*A. The same evidently holds good if one end were fixed in direction and position as in Fig. 151 or 153 and the other end were guided in direction but not fixed in position, *i.e.* free to move sideways, for the half length would again correspond to Case I.

Case III, Fig. 153. Both ends rigidly fixed in position and direction. If the length of the strut be divided into four equal parts,

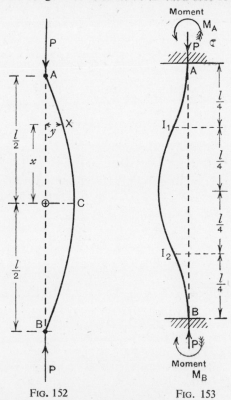

FIG. 152   FIG. 153

evidently each part is under the same end and loading conditions as in Case I, hence the collapsing load

$$P = \pi^2 EI/4(\tfrac{1}{4}l)^2 = 4\pi^2 EI/l^2 \quad . \quad . \quad . \quad . \quad (8)$$

and
$$p_0 = P/A = 4\pi^2 E(k/l)^2 \quad . \quad . \quad . \quad . \quad . \quad (9)$$

Thus the ideal strut fixed at both ends is four times as strong as one freely hinged at both ends. These two are the most important cases.

Case IV, Fig. 154. One end B rigidly fixed, and the other A hinged without friction, *i.e.* free to take any angular position, but

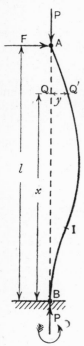

not to move laterally. Evidently, if bending takes place, some horizontal force F at the hinge will be called into play, since lateral movement is prevented there ; also an equal and opposite horizontal balancing force F (not shown) at B. Take B as origin. The bending moment at Q', reckoning positive those moments which tend to produce convexity towards BR, is $F(l-x)-P \cdot y$, hence

$$EI\frac{d^2y}{dx^2}=F(l-x)-Py$$

or,
$$\frac{d^2y}{dx^2}+\frac{P}{EI} \cdot y=\frac{F}{EI}(l-x)$$

the solution of which is
$$y=B \cos x\sqrt{P/EI}+C \sin x\sqrt{P/EI}+F(l-x)/P \quad . \quad . \quad . \quad . \quad (10)$$

Finding the constants as before

$y=0$ for $x=0$ gives $0=B+0+Fl/P$ and $B=-Fl/P$

$dy/dx=0$ for $x=0$ gives $0=0+C\sqrt{P/EI}-F/P$ and $C=F\sqrt{EI/P}/P$

and substituting these values in (10)

$$y=(F/P)(-l \cos x\sqrt{P/EI}+\sqrt{EI/P} \sin x\sqrt{P/EI}+l-x)$$

for all values of x. And putting $y=0$ for $x=l$

$$0=(F/P)(-l \cos l\sqrt{P/EI}+\sqrt{EI/P} \sin l\sqrt{P/EI})$$

hence, either $F=0$, in which case there is no bending, or

$$\tan l\sqrt{P/EI}=l\sqrt{P/EI}$$

an equation in $l\sqrt{P/EI}$, which may be easily solved by a table giving the values of tangents and of angles in radians. The solution for which P is least (other than $P=0$) is approximately

$$l\sqrt{P/EI}=4 \cdot 5 \text{ radians}$$

from which
$$P=20\tfrac{1}{4} EI/l^2 \quad . \quad . \quad . \quad . \quad . \quad . \quad (11)$$

and
$$p_0=P/A=20\tfrac{1}{4} E(k/l)^2 \quad . \quad . \quad . \quad (12)$$

By substituting the known values of y in the original equation, and equating d^2y/dx^2 to zero, we find approximately $4 \cdot 5=\tan 4 \cdot 5x/l$, which is satisfied by $x=l$ or $x=0.30l$, *i.e.* the point of inflexion I (Fig. 154) is $0.30l$ from B and $0.70l$ (approximately) from A, 0.35 of the length being under conditions similar to Case I.

The ultimate strength of the strut in each case is inversely proportional to the square of its length, and comparison between the four cases above shows that the strengths are inversely proportional in Figs. 151, 152, 153, and 154 to the square of the numbers 1, $\frac{1}{2}$, $\frac{1}{4}$, and 0.35 (approximately), the fraction of the lengths between a point of inflexion and a point of maximum curvature. The strengths in the same order are therefore proportional to the numbers 1, 4, 16, and 8 (approximately).

104. Use of Euler's Formulae. Since actual struts deviate from many of the conditions for the ideal cases of Art. 103, the use of the formulae there derived must be modified to take account of such deviations, beyond the ordinary margin of a factor of safety, the effect of very small deviations from the ideal conditions being very great (see Art. 107).

" *Fixed* " *and* " *Free* " *Ends.* Most actual struts will not exactly fulfil the condition of being absolutely fixed or perfectly free at the ends, and, in applying Euler's rules, allowance must be made for this. An end consisting of a broad flat flange bolted to a fairly rigid foundation will approximate to the condition of a perfectly " fixed " end, and an end which is attached to part of a structure by some form of pin-joint will approximate to the " free " condition; in other cases the ends may be so fastened as to make the strength conditions of the strut intermediate between two of the ideal cases of Art. 103, and sometimes to make the conditions different for different planes of bending.

Elastic Failure. Euler's rules have evidently no application to struts so short that they fail by reaching the yield point of crushing or compressive stress before they reach the values given in Art. 103. For example, considering, say, a mild-steel strut freely hinged at both ends (Case II, Art. 103), and taking $E=13,000$ tons per sq. in., and the yield point 21 tons per sq. in., the shortest length to which formula (7) could *possibly* apply would be such that

$$p_0=21=\pi^2 \cdot 13,000 \cdot (k/l)^2$$

l being about 80 times k, which would be about 20 diameters for a solid circular section, and 28 diameters for a thin tube. Since these rules only contemplate very long struts, it is to be expected that they would not give very accurate values of the collapsing load until lengths considerably greater than those above mentioned have been reached. For shorter struts than these Euler's rules are not applicable, and will, if used, evidently give *much* too high a value of the collapsing load; such shorter or medium-length struts are, however, of very common occurrence in structures and machines. The values of p_0 for columns of mild steel and cast iron with freely hinged ends, as calculated by (7), Art. 103, are shown in Fig. 155.

105. Rankine's and Other Empirical Formulae.

Rankine. For a strut so very short that buckling is practically impossible the ultimate compressive load is

$$P_c = f_c \times A \quad . \quad . \quad . \quad . \quad . \quad (1)$$

where A is the area of cross-section and f_c is the ultimate intensity of compressive stress, a quantity difficult to find experimentally because in short specimens frictional resistance to lateral expansion augments longitudinal resistance to compression, and in longer specimens failure takes place by buckling; f_c may well be taken as the intensity of stress at the yield point in compression.

The ultimate load for a *very* long strut is given fairly accurately by Euler's rules (see Art. 103). Let this load be denoted by P_e; then, taking the case of a strut hinged at both ends (Case II, Art. 103)

$$P_e = \frac{\pi^2 EI}{l^2} = \pi^2 EA \left(\frac{k}{l}\right)^2 \quad . \quad . \quad . \quad . \quad (2)$$

If P is the crippling load of a strut of *any* length l and cross-section A, the equation

$$\frac{1}{P} = \frac{1}{P_c} + \frac{1}{P_e} \quad . \quad . \quad . \quad . \quad . \quad (3)$$

evidently gives a value of P which holds well for a very short strut, for $1/P_e$ then becomes negligible, or $P = P_c$ very nearly, and also holds for a very long strut, for $1/P_c$ then becomes negligible in comparison with $1/P_e$ and $P = P_e$ very nearly. Further, since the change in P is caused by increasing l, for a constant value of A must be a continuous change, it is reasonable to take (3) as giving the value of P for any length of strut.

For a strut with both ends freely hinged, the equation (3) may be written

$$P = \frac{1}{\dfrac{1}{f_c . A} + \dfrac{l^2}{\pi^2 EI}} = \frac{f_c A}{1 + \dfrac{f_c . l^2}{\pi^2 E k^2}} = \frac{f_c . A}{1 + a\left(\dfrac{l}{k}\right)^2} \quad . \quad . \quad (4)$$

where $a = \dfrac{f_c}{\pi^2 E}$, a constant for a given material, or if p_0 is the mean intensity of compressive stress on the cross-section

$$p_0 = \frac{P}{A} = \frac{f_c}{1 + a\left(\dfrac{l}{k}\right)^2} \quad . \quad . \quad . \quad . \quad (5)$$

In the case of a strut " fixed " at both ends the constant is $a/4$, or half the length may be used for l in (5), and for a strut fixed at one end with angular freedom at the other the constant is $a/2$ [1] (approximately), or $l/\sqrt{2}$ may be used for l in (5), and for a strut fixed at one end and free to move in direction and position at the other it is $4a$ (see Cases III, IV, and I, Art. 103). The above are Rankine's rules for struts; they are really empirical, and give the closest agreement with experiments on a series of struts of different ratios l/k when the constants are determined from such experiments rather than from the values of E and f_c for a short length. The values f_c and $f_c/\pi^2 E$ of the constants in (4) may be called the " theoretical " constants; the value of a would evidently be less than $f_c/\pi^2 E$ for ends with hinges which are not frictionless, and which consequently help to resist bending.

Gordon's Rule. Rankine's rule is a modification of an older rule of Gordon's, viz.

$$P = f_c A \div \{1 + c(l/d)^2\} \quad . \quad . \quad . \quad . \quad (6)$$

where d is the least breadth or diameter of the cross-section in the direction of the least radius of gyration, and c is a constant which will differ not only for different materials and end fixings, but with the shape of cross-section.

Rankine's Constants. The usually accepted values of f_c and a in Rankine's formula are about as follow:

Material	f_c tons per sq. in.	a
Mild steel . .	21	$\frac{1}{7500}$
Wrought iron .	16	$\frac{1}{9000}$
Cast iron. . .	36	$\frac{1}{1600}$

The above constants for wrought and cast iron are those given as average values by Rankine, and widely adopted. The value of f_c for mild steel taken as the yield point may be rather lower than that given above, and rather higher for many kinds of machinery steel, the value of a being altered in about the same proportion. The values of p obtained from Rankine's formula (5) with the above constants will generally be rather above the values of Euler's " ideal " strut, and therefore obviously too high for very long columns with absolutely free ends, because the values of a (generally deduced from experiments in which the ends are not absolutely free) are smaller than the " theoretical " value $f_c/\pi^2 E$. The average intensities of stress, or load per unit area of cross-section occurring at the ultimate

[1] $a/2$ is simpler and more correct than the value $4a/9$ often given (see Case IV, Art. 103).

load for mild steel and cast-iron struts of various strength with free ends, as calculated by Rankine's formula, and the above constants, are shown in Fig. 155.

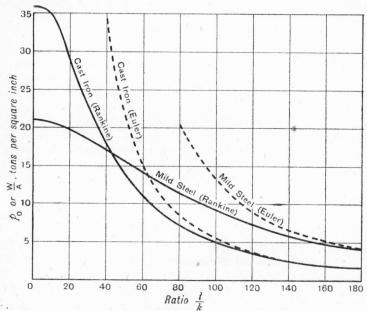

FIG. 155.—Ultimate strength of struts

Choice of a Formula.[1] If the ratio l/k exceeds about 150, which it rarely if ever does, Euler's values may be used to give the breaking loads, and factors of safety on the average intensity of stress of 5 for steel and wrought iron, 6 for cast iron, and 10 for timber may be used to give the working loads. For shorter struts Rankine's formula may be used with factors of safety of about 3 or 4 for steel.

It may be noted that the specifications of the American Bridge Co. for dead loads give the permissible loads in pounds per square inch of cross-section, as

$$p = 15,000 \div \{ 1 + (l/k)^2/13,500 \} \quad \text{(for soft steel)}$$

and $\quad p = 17,000 \div \{ 1 + (l/k)^2/11,000 \} \quad \text{(for medium steel)}$

where l is the length of a structural strut centre to centre of the pins at its ends.

[1] Papers on Struts will be found in *Proc. Inst. Mech. Eng.*, 1905; in *Trans. Am. Soc. C.E.*, vol. 76 (1913); and in *Engineering*, July 14th, 1905; Jan. 10th, 1908; July 2nd, 1909; Jan. 14th, 1910; and March 31st, 1911, by Dr. W. E. Lilly. Also in *Engineering*, July 26th and Aug. 2nd, 1912, by Mr. H. V. Hutt; Aug. 22nd, 1912, by Mr. R. V. Southwell; Oct. 2nd, 1914, Sept. 21st and Nov. 30th, 1917, by the author. See also Jan. 24th and 31st, 1919, author and Bisacre. See also *I.C.E. Selected Engineering Paper* No. 28, " The Strength of Struts," by Prof. A. Robertson (1925).

Various other values of the constants in Rankine's formula are in use depending upon the quality of the material, the type of end connections and factor of safety used.

Euler's formula, for cases in which it may reasonably be used, has the advantage of directness; the necessary area of cross-section may be found for a given load from (4), (6), (8), or (11), Art. 103.

Rankine's formula, like all others except Euler's, while quite convenient for finding the working or the ultimate load for a given area and shape of cross-section, is not very direct for finding the dimensions of cross-section in order to carry a given load; it leads to a quadratic equation in the square of some dimension. For practical purposes, however, with standard forms of section the area required is easily found by trial.

Johnson's Parabolic Formula. Prof. J. B. Johnson adopted an empirical formula

$$p_0 = f_c - b(l/k)^2 \quad . \quad . \quad . \quad . \quad (7)$$

which, when plotted on a base-line giving values of l/k, is a parabola, f_c is the yield point in compression, and b is a constant determined so as to make the parabola meet the curve plotted with Euler's values of p_0 tangentially. For a strut absolutely freely hinged at the ends this condition makes $b = f_c^2/4\pi^2 E$, and, owing to friction, Johnson adopted the smaller values of about $f_c^2/64E$ for pin ends and $f_c^2/100E$ for flat ends. For values of l/k beyond the point of tangency with Euler's curve, Euler's values of p_0 must be adopted, and to allow for the frictional resistance to bending offered by pin or flat ends (7) of Art. 103 is modified to $16E(k/l)^2$ and $25E(k/l)^2$ respectively, these values of p_0 being based on experimental results. The form of Johnson's formula is a trifle more convenient than that of Rankine's.

Straight Line Formula. A great many experimental determinations of the ultimate strength of struts have been made under various conditions,[1] and various empirical formulae have been devised to suit the various results. The results have been most consistent, and in agreement with empirical algebraic formulae, as might be expected, when the conditions of loading and fixing have approached most nearly to the ideal, but, on the other hand, such conditions do not correspond to those for the practical strut, as used in machines and structures which deviate from the ideal in want of straightness and homogeneity of material, more or less eccentricity of the thrust, and in the conditions of freedom or fixture at the ends. The results

---

[1] See "Experimental Researches on Cast Iron Pillars," Hodgkinson, *Phil. Trans. Roy. Soc.*, 1840; "Iron Bridges," by T. C. Clark, *Proc. Inst. C.E.*, vol. liv; "Experiments on Strength of Wrought Iron Struts," J. Christie, *Trans. Am. Soc. Civ. Eng.*, 1884, vol. xiii; also extract *Proc. Inst. C.E.*, vol. lxxvii, p. 396.

H. Fidler's *Notes on Construction in Mild Steel* (Longmans); and T. C. Fidler's *Treatise on Bridge Construction.*

L*

of tests obtained for struts under more or less working conditions show great variations, and no formula, empirical or otherwise, can more than roughly predict the load at which failure will take place in a given case.   This being so, for design purposes one empirical formula is generally about as accurate as another, and the simplest is the best form to use, the constants in any case being deduced from a (short) range of values of l/k, within limits for which experimental information is available; for example, straight-line formulae of the type

$$p_0 = f - (\text{constant} \times l/k) \quad . \quad . \quad . \quad . \quad (8)$$

where p_0 is the load per unit area of cross-section and f is a constant, may be used to give the working or the breaking-stress intensities over short ranges of l/k.

For example, an American rule for the safe load on a built-up steel column with square (or flat) ends per square inch of section is 12,000 lb. for values of l/k less than 90 and above this length

$$p_0 = 17,100 - 57 \; l/k \text{ lb. per sq. in.} \quad . \quad . \quad . \quad (9)$$

which is equivalent to about

$$p_0 = 7 \cdot 5 - 0 \cdot 025 \; l/k \text{ (British) tons per sq. in.} \quad . \quad . \quad (10)$$

these giving about $\frac{1}{4}$ of the ultimate load per square inch.

Consideration of the ideal strut would suggest doubling the coefficient (57 or 0·025) for struts freely hinged at both ends, but flat-ended struts fall short of absolute fixture, and round ends or hinges of struts offer more resistance to turning than ideally freely hinged ends, and to apply an empirical experimental straight-line formula such as (9) to struts not fixed at the ends the coefficient (or l) should be multiplied by about 1·25 only.   The formula must not, of course, be used for values of l/k below that stated, or it would give too high a working stress.

Moncrieff's Formula.   An extensive analysis of experimental results was made by J. M. Moncrieff [1] and his formulae adopted as the basis of working load p_0 tons per sq. in. tables by Messrs. Redpath Brown in their Structural Steel Handbook are
For round ends

$$l/k = 100\sqrt{[\{ 21 \cdot 4/(53 \cdot 5 - 4 \cdot 4 p_0)\}\{ 10 \cdot 7/p_0 - 1 \cdot 6\}]} \quad . \quad (11)$$

For both ends fixed for all values of l/k and for both ends flat for values of l/k not exceeding 106·9

$$l/k = 200\sqrt{[\{ 21 \cdot 4/(53 \cdot 5 - 4 \cdot 4 p_0)\}\{ 10 \cdot 7/p_0 - 1 \cdot 6\}]} \quad . \quad (12)$$

and for flat-ends and values of l/k exceeding 106·9

$$l/k = 200\sqrt{(21 \cdot 4 \times 0 \cdot 4 \div 5 \cdot 6 p_0)} \quad . \quad . \quad . \quad (13)$$

British Standard Practice.   British Standard Specification No.

---

[1] *Trans. Am. Soc. Civ. Eng.*, vol. xlv, and *Engineering*, June 6th, 1902.

449, relative to structural steel in building gives a series of values of allowable (axial loading) stress intensity p_0 for different values of l/k ranging from 7·2 down to 2·0 tons per sq. in. as l/k rises from 20 to 150. These are based on a formula, illustrated in Fig. 163,

$$Ap_0 = \tfrac{1}{2}\{p_1 + (\eta + 1)p_e\} - \sqrt{[\tfrac{1}{4}\{p_1 + (\eta + 1)p_e\}^2 - p_1 p_e]} \quad . \quad (14)$$

where p_1 is the intensity of yield stress (taken as 18 tons per sq.in.) and p_e is the Eulerian load per square inch 13,000 $\pi^2/(l/k)^2$ tons per sq. in., and A is a factor taken as 2·36 and η is 0·003 l/k.

The foregoing is not an exhaustive account of all the various strut formulae in use, but the reader can compare any one with others by a diagram such as Fig. 155. A point of great uncertainty in the design of struts, and particularly of stanchions, is the condition of the ends. Whether a base and its foundation is so rigid as to be taken as " fixed," and whether a top end or cap is to be taken as " fixed," " hinged," or absolutely free, makes much difference in estimated strength, but must generally be a matter of individual judgment (see Art. 175).

Experiments always show that flexure of struts intended to be axially loaded begins at loads much below the maximum ultimately borne, this being due to eccentricity and other variations from the premises upon which Euler's and Rankine's rules depend. This leads us to consider in Art. 107 the effect of eccentric loading on a long column where the flexure is not negligible (as it is in a very short one), and where the greatest bending moment may be mainly from the increased eccentricity which results from flexure.

Example 1. A mild-steel strut hinged at both ends has a **T** section $6 \times 4 \times \tfrac{3}{8}$ in. (see B.S.T. 21, Table VI, Appendix), the area being 3·634 sq. in., and the least moment of inertia is 4·70 (in.)^4. Find, by Rankine's formula, the crippling load of the strut, which is 6 ft. long, if the ultimate crushing strength is taken at 21 tons per sq. in.

The square of the least radius of gyration is $\dfrac{4·7}{3·634} = 1·293$ (in.)^2

$$\left(\frac{l}{k}\right)^2 = \frac{72 \times 72}{1·293} = 4,000$$

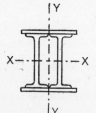

FIG. 156

Using the constant given in the text, viz. $\tfrac{1}{7500}$ for this case

$$P = \frac{3·634 \times 21}{1 + \frac{4000}{7500}} = \tfrac{15}{23} \times 3·634 \times 21 = 49·7 \text{ tons}$$

Example 2. A steel stanchion of the form shown in Fig. 156 has a cross-sectional area of 39·88 sq. in., and its least radius of gyration is 3·84 in. Both ends being fixed, and the length being 40 ft., find its crippling load, (1) by Euler's formula, (2) by Rankine's formula, (3) by the straight-line formula. (E=13,000 tons per sq. in.)

By Euler's formula

$$P = \frac{4\pi^2 \times 13,000 \times 39 \cdot 88 \times (3 \cdot 84)^2}{480 \times 480} = 1,307 \text{ tons}$$

By Rankine's formula, and the constants given

$$P = \frac{21 \times 39 \cdot 88}{1 + \dfrac{480 \times 480}{3 \cdot 84 \times 3 \cdot 84 \times 30,000}} = \frac{21 \times 39 \cdot 88}{1 \cdot 520} = 551 \text{ tons}$$

Formula (10) gives $p_0 = 7 \cdot 5 - \frac{1}{40} \times 480/3 \cdot 84 = 4 \cdot 38$ tons per sq. in., which corresponds to a working load of $39 \cdot 88 \times 4 \cdot 38 = 175$ tons, and to a crippling load of $4 \times 175 = 700$ tons.

Taking the equivalent length for hinged ends as 20 ft., $l/k = 240/3.84 = 62 \cdot 5$, and formula (11) gives $p_0 = 14 \cdot 1875$ tons per sq. in., or a crippling load of $14 \cdot 1875 \times 39 \cdot 88 = 565$ tons, agreeing closely with Rankine's formula.

Example 3. Find the necessary thickness of metal in a cast-iron column of hollow circular section, 20 ft. long, fixed at both ends, the outside diameter being 8 in., if the axial load is to be 80 tons, and the crushing load is to be 6 times this amount.

Let d be the necessary internal diameter in inches.

The sectional area is $\frac{\pi}{4}(8^2 - d^2)$, and $I = \frac{\pi}{64}(8^4 - d^4)$, hence $k^2 = \frac{1}{16}(8^2 + d^2)$.

The breaking load being 480 tons, Rankine's formula, with the constants given in Art. 105, becomes

$$480 = \frac{36 \times \frac{\pi}{4}(8^2 - d^2)}{1 + \dfrac{240 \times 240 \times 16}{6,400(8^2 + d^2)}} = \frac{9\pi(8^4 - d^4)}{208 + d^2}$$

$$d^4 + 17d^2 - 560 = 0$$

$$d^2 = 16 \cdot 65 \qquad d = 4 \cdot 08 \text{ in.}$$

Thickness of metal $= (8 - 4 \cdot 08)/2 = 1 \cdot 96$, or nearly 2 in.

106. Forms of Section for Stanchions and Built-up Struts. The theory of bending or the theory of buckling of struts (see (7), Art. 103, or (5), Art. 105) shows that for economy of material the section of a stanchion, strut, or column must have a radius of gyration large in proportion to its area. This involves a spread-out form of section, and for cast-iron columns hollow circular sections with comparatively thin walls are usual. For steel stanchions the commonest forms of cross-section are illustrated in Fig. 157; these consist of sections built up of I, angle, channel, Z, and plate sections, and for comparatively small members single I, T, channel, or angle bars are also used. (For caps and bases see Art. 175.) The moments of inertia, etc., of the built-up stanchions may be found by the rules given in Chapter III. In sections such as (c), (d), (f), (g) it is easy to so space the plates or channels that the moments of inertia about both principal axes of the compound section are equal.

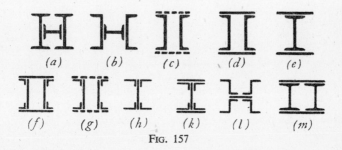

FIG. 157

Latticed Stanchions and Struts. Built-up stanchions often consist partly of open lattice work, as shown in Figs. 158 and 159, and indicated by dotted lines in the sections (c) and (g), Fig. 157. In estimating the moment of inertia of a latticed stanchion section the lattice bars are neglected. Thus in section (c), Fig. 157, if I_1 is the moment of inertia of each of the channel sections about an axis parallel to its base, A its area, d the distance apart of the centroids of the two channels, the moment of inertia about a central axis parallel to the channel basis is by Theorem 1, Art. 34.

$$2I_1 + 2A(d/2)^2 = 2I_1 + A \cdot d^2/2 \quad . \quad . \quad . \quad . \quad (1)$$

And if I_2 is the moment of inertia of each channel section about an axis perpendicular to its base the moment of inertia of the built-up section about the principal axis perpendicular to the channel bases is

$$2I_2 \quad . \quad . \quad . \quad . \quad . \quad . \quad . \quad . \quad (2)$$

The lattice bars are usually designed to withstand any shearing force to which the stanchion may be subjected. If F is the shearing force at any cross-section and θ is the angle (Fig. 158) which the lattice bars make with the axis of the column, the pull or thrust in a lattice bar with single lacing on one side only is

$$F \cosec \theta$$

and the bars must be sufficient to withstand this as a tie or a strut. With single lacing on two sides the force will be halved, and with double lacing it will be again halved. With single lacing the angle θ

(Fig. 158) is usually not less than 60°, and with double lacing (Fig. 159) not less than 45°. With regard to resistance of axial loads only it is evident that a single channel of length l' between lattice bar ends must be capable of carrying at least half the total load as a strut. Let L be the equivalent length of a column hinged at both ends and of the full latticed section, and let K be its least radius of gyration; let k be the least radius of gyration of one channel or

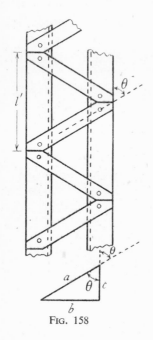

Fig. 158

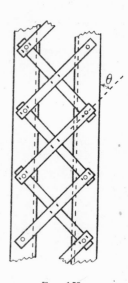

Fig. 159

other component section, then it is evident from Euler's rules that since one of the two channels carries at least half the load

$$A\left(\frac{k}{l'}\right)^2 \text{ must be at least equal to } \frac{1}{2} \cdot \frac{2AK^2}{L^2}$$

or that $\quad\quad\quad\quad k/l'$ must be at least equal to K/L

that is $\quad\quad\quad\quad l'$ must not exceed $\dfrac{k}{K} \cdot L$ . . . . . (3)

Proportions of Lattice Bars. The usual thickness of the lattice bars for single lacing is about $\frac{1}{40}$ of their length, and for double lacing about $\frac{1}{60}$ of their length, while their width usually varies from $2\frac{1}{2}$ to $1\frac{3}{4}$ in. according to the size of channel used, being not less than three times the diameter of the rivet passing through them nor less than $\frac{1}{8}$ of their length.

The use of lattice bars instead of solid plate renders all parts of a column accessible for painting.

The above rules would make the lattice bar dimensions nearly the same for any size of channels, *i.e.* for any proportions of k to l, or would make a quite arbitrary connection between the cross-section of the column and the cross-section of lattice bars used. Actually the latticing should be heavier in short than in long columns to develop the full strength of the former. A better empirical rule might perhaps be framed as follows, although an entirely rational treatment of so complex a built-up structure is quite impracticable as the distribution of stress is indefinitely known and depends upon the method of manufacture. Let f be the working unit stress for a very short column and p_0 be the working unit stress for the actual column. Then

$$f - p_0$$

may be looked upon as the allowance for flexural stress in the channels. The moment of resistance to bending may be taken as

$$M = (f - p_0)Z \quad . \quad . \quad . \quad . \quad . \quad (4)$$

in a plane parallel to the lattices where Z is the modulus of section about a central axis of the section perpendicular to the lattice planes. Then for equivalent shear due to transverse loading at the ends over a length $L/2$ from the centre to the end of a double-pinned column; since $dM/dx = F = $ constant [1]

$$F = M \div L/2 = 2(f - p_0)Z/L \quad . \quad . \quad . \quad (5)$$

and the stress in a bar of a single lattice (with lacing on both sides of the stanchion) will be as before

$$F(\operatorname{cosec} \theta)/2 = (f - p_0)Z(\operatorname{cosec} \theta)/L \quad . \quad . \quad (6)$$

For double lacing this must be halved, and for stanchions fixed at one end and entirely free to move at the other L must stand for twice the length, while for columns fixed at both ends it must stand for half the length of the column; in any case for the length of the equivalent doubly pinned strut.

For Z the product $A \times d$ may be approximately substituted where d is the distance between the centroids of the two channels and A the area of one channel section, giving the stress in (6) as

$$\frac{(f - p_0)A \cdot d \cdot \operatorname{cosec} \theta}{L} \quad \text{or} \quad \frac{(f - p_0)Al}{L} \quad . \quad . \quad (7)$$

where l is the length of a lattice bar.

The lattice bar should then be of such a section as to carry this

---

[1] British Standard Specification No. 327 requires that apart from transverse loads a value of F not less than 2·5 per cent. of the axial thrust shall be allowed for in latticed strut members of derrick cranes.

amount of thrust as a strut with pin ends, and low unit stress as there may be considerable eccentricity of loading.

Secondary Stress. Stresses in the lattice bars may arise due to the strain of the column. Thus if the column is shortened and the width remains unchanged the diagonal lattice bars are also shortened, inducing a secondary stress. Thus if c, Fig. 158, is shortened by an amount δc, since $a^2 = b^2 + c^2$, differentiating, $2a\dfrac{da}{dc} = 2c$, and hence the proportional strain $\dfrac{\delta a}{a} = \dfrac{c^2}{a^2} \times \dfrac{\delta c}{c} = \cos^2 \theta \cdot \dfrac{\delta c}{c}$, and if all parts are of steel, $\dfrac{1}{E}$ s × econdary stress $= \dfrac{p_0}{E} \times \cos^2 \theta \cdot = \dfrac{p_0}{E} \cos^2 \theta$, and

$$\text{secondary stress in lattice bars} = p_0 \times \cos^2 \theta \quad . \quad . \quad (8)$$

Since $\cos^2 60° = \frac{1}{4} = \frac{1}{2} \cos^2 45°$, both types of lattice would get an equal secondary unit stress.

Comparatively little is known as to the real distribution of stress in a latticed strut, but investigations made in America [1] on large latticed columns show (by means of strain measurements) great variations such as 40 to 50 per cent. of extreme stress from the average over the section as well as great changes of stress for small axial changes of distances which would indicate local flexure. The experiments of Talbot and Moore showed small strains of the lattice bars, but quite irregular variations in different parts of the column length. The average stress on cross-sections of the lattice bars was such as would be produced by a transverse shear on the column of from 1 to 3 per cent. of the compression load. Individual compression tests of lattice bars showed very low ultimate strengths, these being below half the yield point of the material. The tests of Howard and Buchanan showed marked elastic failure at loads below 9 tons per sq. in. of column section with complete failure below 14 tons per sq. in., on struts having a ratio l/k less than 50. Such results point to the desirability of a conservative allowance of unit stresses in built-up columns. It may be recalled that the Quebec bridge disaster resulted from the failure of a latticed member of a compression chord.

Example 1. A stanchion consists of two British standard channels 12 in. $\times 3\frac{1}{2}$ in. $\times 32 \cdot 88$ lb. per ft. (see B.S.C. 25, Table II, Appendix) placed back to back $6\frac{1}{2}$ in. apart and connected by $\frac{1}{2}$-in. plates 14 in. wide. Find the working load which is to be

---

[1] See " An Investigation of Built-up Columns under Load," by Talbot and Moore, *Engineering Bulletin*, No. 44, of Univ. of Illinois; also " Some Tests of Large Steel Columns," by J. E. Howard, in *Proc. American Soc. of Civil Engineers*, Feb., 1911; or an extract from both these papers in *Engineering News*, Vol. 65, No. 11, March 16th, 1911.

¼ that given by Rankine's rule if one end of the column is fixed and the other end hinged, the length being 30 ft.

Using the values from Table II in the Appendix without the plates, from (2), the moment of inertia about the central axis parallel to the plates is

$$(2 \times 190\cdot7) = 381\cdot4 \ (\text{in.})^4$$
and for the two plates add $\frac{1}{12} \times 14(13^3 - 12^3) = 547\cdot2 \ (\text{in.})^4$

$$\text{Total} \quad . \quad . \quad = 928\cdot6 \ (\text{in.})$$

About the central axis parallel to the channel, using (1) the moment of inertia, is

For the channels

$$(2 \times 8\cdot922) + \frac{9\cdot671}{2} \times (6\cdot5 + 2 \times 0\cdot867)^2 = 345\cdot7 \ (\text{in.})^4$$
For the plates $\frac{1}{12} \times 14^3 = 228\cdot7 \ (\text{in.})^4$

$$\text{Total} \quad . \quad . \quad = 574\cdot4 \ (\text{in.})^4$$

The total area of section is

$$2 \times 9\cdot671 + 14 = 33\cdot34 \ \text{sq. in.}$$

Hence the least radius of gyration is

$$\sqrt{(574\cdot4/33\cdot34)} = 4\cdot15 \ \text{in.}$$

The equivalent length of strut with ends freely hinged is $30/\sqrt{2}$ ft. $= 360/\sqrt{2}$ in.; hence $(l/k)^2$ in (5), Art. 105, is $\dfrac{360 \times 360}{2 \times (4\cdot15)^2} = 3{,}764$; hence from (5), Art. 105, the allowable stress is

$$\frac{\frac{1}{4} \times 21}{1 + \frac{3764}{7500}} = \frac{5\cdot25 \times 7{,}500}{11{,}264} = 3\cdot49 \ \text{tons per sq. in.}$$

and the working load is $3\cdot49 \times 33\cdot34 = 116\cdot5$ tons.

Example 2. How far apart should two 15-in. × 4-in. British Standard (see B.S.C. 27, Table II, Appendix) channel-shaped sections be placed back to back in a latticed stanchion in order that the resistance to buckling may be approximately equal in all directions.

To satisfy this condition the moments of inertia about the two principal axes of the compound section must be equal, hence from (1) and (2), using the table

$$(2 \times 14\cdot55) + \frac{12\cdot334}{2} \times d^2 = 2 \times 377 \ (\text{in.})^4$$

hence

$$d = 10\cdot83 \ \text{in.}$$

Distance apart of channels $= 10\cdot83 - 2 \times 0\cdot935 = 8\cdot96$ in.

These channels are often spaced $9\frac{1}{2}$ in. apart, and then the value about the axis parallel to the bases is somewhat greater than (2×377) (in.)[4] about the other principal axis.

Example 3. What is the maximum distance apart of the lacing bar ends in the previous example, if each channel between these points of support is to be of resistance at least equal to that of the whole stanchion, 30 ft. long, fixed at one end and hinged at the other. Equivalent length of stanchion with hinged ends is

$$30/\sqrt{2} \text{ ft.} = 21\cdot21 \text{ ft.}$$

Hence, referring to Table II, from (3) l' must not exceed $(1\cdot09/5\cdot53) \times 21\cdot21$ ft $= 4\cdot18$ ft. (actually it would be less than one-third of this length).

Example 4. Estimate a suitable width for single lattice bars (both sides of the stanchion) for the data in Example 2, if the stanchion is 30 ft. long, fixed at the base and hinged at the top, using Rankine's formula, with a factor of safety of 4. The distance of the rivet-hole centres from the outside edge of the channels is $1\cdot7375$ in.

$$k^2 = \frac{377}{12\cdot334} = 30\cdot5 \text{ (in.)}^2 \qquad\qquad 30 \text{ ft.} = 360 \text{ in.}$$

hence from (5), Art. 105

the working unit stress $p_0 = \dfrac{\frac{1}{4} \times 21}{1 + \dfrac{360 \times 360}{15,000 \times 30\cdot5}} = \dfrac{5\cdot25}{1\cdot283}$

$$= 4\cdot09 \text{ tons per sq. in.}$$

$$f - p_0 = 5\cdot25 - 4\cdot09 = 1\cdot16 \text{ tons per sq. in.}$$

The horizontal distance apart of the lines of rivet centres is $8\cdot96 + 2 \times 4 - 2 \times 1\cdot7375 = 13\cdot485$ in., and with 60° lacing $l = 13\cdot485 \times 2/\sqrt{3} = 15\cdot57$ in.; and $L = 360/\sqrt{2} = 254\cdot5$ in.

Hence from (7) the thrust in a bar may be

$$\frac{1\cdot16 \times 12\cdot334 \times 15\cdot57}{254\cdot5} = 0\cdot8754 \text{ ton.}$$

If thickness $= \frac{1}{40}$ of length, for rectangular section $(l/k)^2 = 40^2 \times 12 = 19,200$; allowable unit stress by (5), Art. $105 = \dfrac{5\cdot25}{1 + \frac{19200}{7500}} = 1\cdot474$ tons per sq. in.

$$\text{Area required} = 0\cdot8754/1\cdot474 = 0\cdot594, \text{ or say } 0\cdot6 \text{ sq. in.}$$

$$\text{Thickness} = \tfrac{1}{40} \text{ of } 15\cdot57 = \tfrac{3}{8} \text{ in. say;}$$

hence   width $= 0\cdot6 \div \tfrac{3}{8} = 1\cdot6$ in.

If we allow for secondary stress, by (8) the amount is $p_0 \times \cos^2 60° = 4\cdot09 \times \frac{1}{4} = 1\cdot02$ tons per sq. in. This, if reckoned additional to the stress due to shearing, would require a larger section, viz. $0\cdot8754/(1\cdot474 - 1\cdot02) = 1\cdot92$ sq. in. For a reasonable width of bar on this basis double lacing would be required, but probably the assumption of pin ends is too severe, and a higher stress than 1·474 tons per sq. in. may be allowed.

107. Long Columns under Eccentric Load. As Euler's formulæ are only strictly applicable to struts absolutely axially loaded, it is interesting to find what modifications follow if the line of thrust is not, even initially, along the line of the centroids of cross-sections, *i.e.* not along the central axis of the column. Such a defect from the ideal conditions may result from initial curvature of the column (lack of perfect straightness) or from eccentricity in the application of the load to the column at its end.

Initial Curvature. The stress produced by the load is not much affected by the precise *form* of curvature although dependent on the amount of deviation from straightness. Thus we may take a form of curvature which simplifies the analysis to assuming the initial form to be that of a cosine curve. With the notation of Fig. 160 let ACB be the initial form of a strut hinged at its ends A and B so that

$$y' = h_1 \cos \frac{\pi}{l} x \quad . \quad . \quad . \quad (1)$$

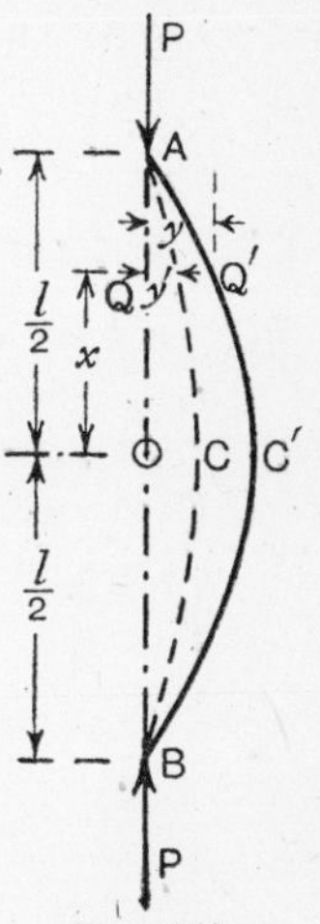

which is zero for $x = \pm \frac{1}{2} l$ and is equal to h_1 or OC at $x = 0$. Then if AC'B is the deflected shape under the thrust P, when $x = OQ$, $y = QQ'$, and the *change* in deflection due to flexure under the load is $y - y'$. Hence

$$EI \frac{d^2}{dx^2} (y - y') = M = -Py \quad . \quad . \quad . \quad (2)$$

$$\frac{d^2 y}{dx^2} + \frac{Py}{EI} = \frac{d^2 y'}{dx^2} = -\frac{\pi^2}{l^2} h_1 \cos \frac{\pi}{l} x \quad . \quad (3)$$

The solution of this equation is

$$y = \frac{\pi^2/l^2}{\pi^2/l^2 - P/EI} h_1 \cos \frac{\pi}{l} x \quad \text{or} \quad \frac{P_e}{P_e - P} h_1 \cos \frac{\pi}{l} x \quad (4)$$

FIG. 160

which agrees with Case II, Art. 103, if $h_1 = 0$, giving Euler's value $P_e = \pi^2 EI/l^2$. At $x = 0$ the maximum eccentricity of loading $OC' = a$, say, occurs and

$$y = a = \frac{P_e}{P_e - P} \cdot h_1 \quad . \quad . \quad . \quad . \quad (5)$$

Here the bending moment of P is greatest, viz. $-Pa$ and the maximum compressive stress intensity occurring on the concave side of the column is

$$p = p_0 + p_b = \frac{P}{A} + \frac{Pay_e}{Ak^2} \quad . \quad . \quad . \quad . \quad (6)$$

where y_c is the distance of the concave side from the central axis of cross-section of the column perpendicular to the plane of bending and k is the radius of gyration of the section about the same axis. And substituting the value of a from (5) the maximum compressive-stress intensity

$$p = p_0\left(1 + \frac{p_c}{p_e - p_0}\frac{h_1 y_c}{k^2}\right) \quad . \quad . \quad . \quad . \quad (7)$$

where $p_0 = P/A$ the load per unit area and $p_e = P_e/A$.

Eccentric Loading. If the column is initially straight but the line of loading of P deviates by a distance h_2 from the axis of the column as in Fig. 161

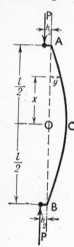

$$EI\frac{d^2y}{dx^2} = -P(y + h_2) \quad . \quad . \quad . \quad (8)$$

$$d^2y/dx^2 + Py/EI = -Ph_2/EI \quad . \quad . \quad . \quad (9)$$

The solution of this is

$$y = -h_2 + A\sin(\sqrt{P/EI}x) + B\cos(\sqrt{P/EI}x). \quad (10)$$

Since $dy/dx = 0$ for $x = 0$, $A = 0$ and putting $y = 0$ for $x = l/2$

$$0 = -h_2 + B\cos(\sqrt{P/EI}l/2) \text{ or } B = h_2\sec(\sqrt{P/EI}l/2)$$

Hence

$$y = h_2\{\sec(\sqrt{P/EI}l/2)\cos(\sqrt{P/EI}x) - 1\} \quad . \quad (11)$$

and at $x = 0$

$$y = OC = h_2\{\sec(\sqrt{P/EI}l/2) - 1\} \quad . \quad (12)$$

The total eccentricity of loading at O is

$$OC + h_2 = h_2\sec(\sqrt{P/EI}l/2) \quad . \quad . \quad (13)$$

And the maximum intensity of compressive stress is

$$p = p_0 + p_b = p_0\{1 + \frac{y_c h_2}{k^2}\sec(\sqrt{p_0/Ek^2}l/2)\} \quad . \quad . \quad (14)$$

or

$$p = p_0\{1 + \frac{y_c h_2}{k^2}\sec(\pi/2\sqrt{p_0/p_e})\} \quad . \quad . \quad . \quad (15)$$

which agrees with (1), Art. 100, for $l = 0$ for which p_e is indefinitely large.

Perry[1] pointed out that the function $\sec(\sqrt{P/EI}l/2)$ or $\sec(\pi/2\sqrt{P/P_e})$, corresponds very closely with $1\cdot2\,p_e/(p_e - p_0)$, which brings (15) into the same form as (7). In other words if the maximum deviation from straightness be taken as

$$h = h_1 + 1\cdot2h_2 \quad . \quad . \quad . \quad . \quad (16)$$

[1] "On Struts," *Engineer*, Vol. 62, p. 464, Dec. 10th, 1886.

a column initially curved and eccentrically loaded at its ends may be taken as centrally loaded at its ends with the augmented initial curvature. Thus the maximum compressive stress intensity from (7) is

$$p = p_0\left(1 + \frac{p_e}{p_e - p_0} \cdot \frac{hy_c}{k^2}\right) \quad . \quad . \quad . \quad . \quad (17)$$

which agrees with (1), Art. 100 when $l=0$. This may also be written

$$(p/p_0 - 1)(1 - p_0/p_e) = hy_0/k^2 \quad . \quad . \quad . \quad . \quad (17\text{A})$$

It may be added that variation in E is substantially equivalent to a further addition to the eccentricity h.

If the compressive stress intensity p reaches that at the limit of compressive elastic stress or the yield stress, f_c, say,

$$f_c = p_0\left(1 + \frac{p_e}{p_e - p_0}\frac{hy_c}{k^2}\right) \quad . \quad . \quad . \quad . \quad (18)$$

Re-arranging this quadratic equation in p_0,

$$p_0{}^2 - p_0\left\{f_c + p_e\left(1 + \frac{hy_c}{k^2}\right)\right\} + f_c p_e = 0 \quad . \quad . \quad . \quad (19)$$

and taking the smaller root,

$$p_0 = \tfrac{1}{2}\{f_c + (1 + hy_c/k^2)p_e\} - \tfrac{1}{2}\sqrt{[\{f_c + (1 + hy_c/k^2)p_e\}^2 - 4f_c p_e]} \quad . \quad (20)$$

or $\quad p_0 = \tfrac{1}{2}\{f_c + (1 + \eta)p_e\} - \tfrac{1}{2}\sqrt{[\{f_c + (1 + \eta)p_e\}^2 - 4f_c p_e]} \quad . \quad (21)$

where $\qquad\qquad \eta = hy_c/k^2$

Perry-Robertson Formula. This value, (21), of the average stress intensity at elastic failure has been made the basis for calculation of safe loads for steel columns in the specification of the British Standards Institution.[1] The factor η or hy_c/k^2 depends upon h the maximum deviation of the load line from the axis of the column. This in ordinary practice cannot be known. Prof. A. Robertson [2] has examined the available experimental evidence and concludes that for free-ended columns of structural materials such as mild steel, wrought iron, and timber, which show a drop of stress on yielding, $\eta = 0 \cdot 001 l/k$ represents well the general results of tests up to yield conditions and that $\eta = 0 \cdot 003 l/k$ represents the lower limit of such tests. This latter value ($\eta = 0 \cdot 003 l/k$) has been adopted in the B.S.I. specification. The working stresses in mild-steel columns in B.S.S. 449 (1937) are to be found by dividing the stress given by (21) by a factor of safety 2·36, and using the values $f_c = 18$ tons per sq. in., $p_e = 13,000 \times \pi^2 \div (l/k)^2$ tons per sq. in., and $\eta = 0 \cdot 003 l/k$.

In the foregoing it is, of course, assumed that eccentricity of load-

---

[1] British Standard Specification No. 449 (1937). This includes also limitations for the allowable slenderness ratio l/k.

[2] " The Strength of Struts," *Inst. C.E. Selected Engineering Paper*, No. 28 (1925).

ing is in a direction which would be most effective in increasing stress so that the bending produced would be in that plane in which the column has least flexural rigidity or perpendicular to the principal axis of cross-section for which k is least.

If failure should occur in tension, say in cast iron, under an eccentric load the modifications in the formulae are simple, e.g. for maximum intensity of tensile stress (15) would become

$$p = p_0 \left\{ \frac{y_t h_2}{k^2} \sec \frac{\pi}{2} \sqrt{p_0/p_e} - 1 \right\} \quad . \quad . \quad . \quad . \quad (22)$$

and (17) would become

$$p = p_0 \left(\frac{p_e}{p_e - p_0} \frac{h y_t}{k^2} - 1 \right) \quad . \quad . \quad . \quad . \quad (23)$$

For the more general cases of curvature and eccentricity for a long column corresponding to (7), of Art. 100, for short strut, (7) would become

$$p = p_0 \left(1 + \frac{p_e}{p_e - p_0} \frac{h_1 y_t}{k^2} + \frac{p_e'}{p_e' - p_0} \frac{h_1' y_t'}{(k')^2} \right). \quad . \quad . \quad (24)$$

where the accented symbols refer to values in relation to the second principal axis of cross-section.

Similarly, equation (15) would become

$$p = p_0 \left\{ 1 + \frac{y_t h_2}{k^2} \sec \left(\frac{\pi}{2} \sqrt{p_0/p_e} \right) + \frac{y_t' h_2'}{(k')^2} \sec \left(\frac{\pi}{2} \sqrt{p_0/p_e'} \right) \right\} . \quad (25)$$

It is evident from (7), or (15) or (17), that p becomes infinite for $P = \pi^2 EI/l^2$, just as in Euler's theory, where the eccentricity $h = 0$; but these equations show that where h is not zero, p approaches the ultimate compressive or tensile strengths for values of P much below Euler's critical values. The reader will find it instructive to plot the values of P and p for any given section, and for several different magnitudes of the eccentricity h, and to observe how p increases with P in each case.

Fig. 162 shows the ultimate values of p_0 for mild-steel struts of circular section and various lengths, taking $f_c = 21$ tons per sq. in. with various degrees of eccentricity. It shows that for struts about 20 diameters in length, for example, an eccentricity of $\frac{1}{100}$ of the diameter greatly decreases the load which the ideal strut would support. Also that when there is an eccentricity of $\frac{1}{10}$ of the diameter an additional eccentricity of $\frac{1}{100}$ of the diameter does not greatly reduce the strength.

It is interesting to note that for practical design purposes curves of this kind are not greatly different from those for the empirical rules of Art. 105. Nor do they differ greatly in type from the ideal case as corrected by Southwell.

Basquin [1] has dealt in considerable detail with the cases of eccentricity of loading, crookedness, and variation of elastic modulus in columns, and suggested stress estimations based upon such probable imperfections as a basis of column design.

It may be noticed from equations (15) and (17) that with increase of load P the maximum intensity of stress is increased more than proportionally, because the part due to bending increases with the increased eccentricity due to flexure as well as with the increased load. Hence the ratio of the ultimate or crippling loads to any working load will be less than the factor of safety, as understood by

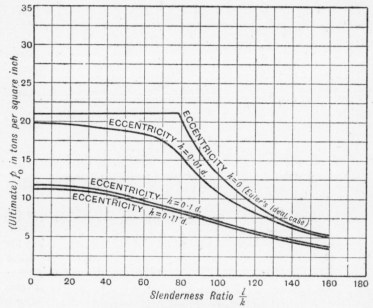

Fig. 162.—Eccentric loading of struts

the ratio of the maximum intensity of stress to the ultimate intensity of crushing stress (at the yield point, say). This point is illustrated in Examples Nos. 3 and 4 at the end of the present article.

In the case of a long tie-rod with an eccentric load, the greatest intensities of stress are at the end sections, where the eccentricity is h; in the centre it is only h sech $\{(l/2)\sqrt{P/EI}\}$.

Fig. 163 shows the failing loads per square inch and the working stress per square inch for mild steel according to the formula (21) as adopted in B.S.S. 449 and the constants given above. This does not differ widely from the curves for the various empirical formulae

[1] *Journal of the Society of Western Engineers*, vol. xviii, No. 6, June, 1913.

with a suitable choice of constants and in all cases the working stresses are tabulated for values of l/k for the purpose of column design.

Example 1. A cast-iron pillar is 8 in. external diameter, the metal being 1 in. thick, and carries a load of 20 tons. If the column is 40 ft. long and rigidly fixed at both ends, find the extreme intensities of stress in the material if the centre of the load is $1\frac{3}{4}$ in. from the centre of the column. What eccentricity would be just sufficient

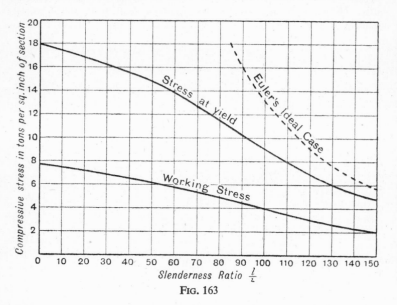

Fig. 163

to cause tension in the pillar? (E=5,000 tons per sq. in.) The corresponding problem for a very short column has been worked in Example 2, Art. 100, and these results may be used

$$p_0 = 0.909 \text{ ton per sq. in.} \qquad k^2 = \tfrac{1}{16}(8^2 + 6^2) = \tfrac{25}{4}.$$

The bending stress is increased in the ratio $\sec(\tfrac{1}{4}l\sqrt{P/EI})$ or

$$\sec \frac{l}{4}\sqrt{\frac{p_0}{Ek^2}} = \sec \frac{480}{4}\sqrt{\frac{0.909 \times 4}{5,000 \times 25}} = \sec 0.646 = \sec 37° = 1.25.$$

Hence the bending-stress intensity is

$$1.017 \times 1.25 = 1.27 \text{ ton per sq. in.}$$

The maximum compressive stress $= 1.27 + 0.909 = 2.18$ tons per sq.in.

The maximum tensile stress $= 1.27 - 0.909 = 0.36$ ton per sq. in.

of more than treble that when there is no flexure increasing the eccentricity.

If the eccentricity is just sufficient to cause tension in the pillar, its amount is

$$1 \cdot 75 \times 0 \cdot 909/1 \cdot 27 = 1 \cdot 25 \text{ in.}$$

Example 2.   A compound stanchion has the section shown in Fig. 156; its radius of gyration about YY is 3·84 in., and its breadth parallel to XX is 14 in.   The stanchion, which is to be taken as free at both ends, is 32 ft. long.   If the load per square inch of section is 4 tons, how much may the line in which the resultant force acts at the ends deviate from the axis YY without producing a greater compressive stress than 6 tons per sq. in., the resultant thrust being in the line XX?   How much would it be in a very short pillar? (E=13,000 tons per sq. in.)

Evidently from (14) the bending-stress intensity must be $6-4=2$ tons per sq. in.; hence, if h_2 is the eccentricity

$$4\frac{h_2 y_c}{k^2} \sec \{ (l/2)\sqrt{p_0/Ek^2} \} = 2$$

$$\frac{4 \cdot h_2 \cdot 14}{2 \times (3 \cdot 84)^2} \sec \frac{192}{3 \cdot 84}\sqrt{\frac{4}{13,000}} = 2$$

$$h_2(1 \cdot 897 \sec 50 \cdot 3°) = 2 \cdot 97 h_2 = 2$$

$$h_2 = 0 \cdot 675 \text{ in.}$$

For a very short pillar where the flexure is negligible this would evidently be

$$h \times 1 \cdot 897 = 2 \qquad h = 1 \cdot 055 \text{ in.}$$

the equation reducing to the form (1), Art. 100, since the secant is practically unity.

It is interesting to compare the solution by (17A)

$$(\tfrac{6}{4}-1)\left(1-\frac{10,000 \times 4}{13,000\pi^2}\right) = \frac{1 \cdot 2 \times 14}{2 \times 14 \cdot 75}h_2$$

$$h_2 = 0 \cdot 605 \text{ in.}$$

This is less than the previous result, because the factor 1·2 introduced in (16) is too great for an average stress so much below the ultimate value; without the factor the approximate method would give a value 20 per cent. higher, *i.e.* $h_2 = 0 \cdot 726$, which is too large, and errs on the wrong side for safety.

Example 3.   Find the load per square inch of section which a column of the cross-section given in Example 2 will carry with an eccentricity of $1\frac{1}{2}$ in. from XX, the column being 28 ft. long and free at both ends, the maximum compressive stress not exceeding 6 tons per sq. in.   Find also the ultimate load per square inch of section if the ultimate compressive strength is 21 tons per sq. in.   (E= 13,000 tons per sq. in.)

Using first the approximate method, (17A) gives

$$\left(\frac{6}{p_0}-1\right)\left\{1-\frac{p_0}{\pi^2\times 13,000}\left(\frac{28\times 12}{3\cdot 84}\right)^2\right\}=\frac{1\cdot 2\times 1\cdot 5}{2}\cdot\frac{14}{(3\cdot 84)^2}$$

$$(6-p_0)(1-0\cdot 059p_0)=0\cdot 858p_0$$

or, $$p_0^2-37\cdot 3p_0+102=0$$

hence $p_0=2\cdot 95$ tons per sq. in.

Testing this value in (14)

$$2\cdot 95\left(1+\tfrac{3}{2}\times\frac{14}{2\times 14\cdot 75}\ \sec\frac{168}{3\cdot 84}\sqrt{\frac{2\cdot 95}{13,000}}\right)$$

$$=2\cdot 95(1+0\cdot 715\ \sec 37\cdot 8°)=5\cdot 62\text{ tons per sq. in.}$$

instead of 6, hence 2·95 is rather too low.   Trial shows that

$$p_0=3\cdot 12\text{ tons per sq. in.}$$

satisfies (14), and is the allowable load per square inch of section.
Substituting 21 tons per sq. in. for 6 in the above work gives 8·2
tons per sq. in. of section as the crippling load.   Note that while the
factor of safety reckoned on the stress is $\frac{21}{6}=3\frac{1}{2}$, the ratio of ultimate
to working load is $8\cdot 2/3\cdot 12=2\cdot 63$.

Example 4.   A steel strut is to be of circular section, 50 in. long
and hinged at both ends.   Find the necessary diameter in order that,
if the thrust of 15 tons deviated at the ends by $\frac{1}{10}$ of the diameter
from the axis of the strut, the greatest compressive stress shall not
exceed 5 tons per sq. in.   If the yield point of the steel in compression is 20 tons per sq. in., find the crippling load of the strut.
(E=13,000 tons per sq. in.)

$$k=\frac{d}{4}\qquad A=\frac{\pi d^2}{4}\qquad h_2=\frac{d}{10}$$

Using the approximate equation (17A)

$$\left(\frac{5\pi d^2}{4\times 15}-1\right)\left(1-\frac{15\times 64\times 2,500}{\pi^2\times 13,000\times\pi d^4}\right)=1\cdot 2\times\frac{d}{10}\times\frac{d\times 16}{2d^2}=0\cdot 96$$

$$(0\cdot 2616d^2-1)\left(1-\frac{5\cdot 88}{d^4}\right)=0\cdot 96$$

$$d^6-7\cdot 5d^4-5\cdot 88d^2+22\cdot 5=0$$

a cubic equation in d^2, which by trial gives

$$d^2=7\cdot 9$$

$$d=2\cdot 81\text{ in.}$$

Testing this result by equation (14)

$$\frac{15\times 4}{\pi\times 7\cdot 9}(1+\tfrac{16}{20}\ \sec 0\cdot 484)=4\cdot 58$$

instead of 5 tons per sq. in.

By trial $d=2\cdot7$ in. nearly.

Taking this value for failure when $p=20$ tons per sq. in., (17A) gives

$$\left(\frac{20}{p_0}-1\right)\left(1-\frac{5,500p_0}{128,000}\right)=0\cdot96$$

$$p_0=8\cdot15 \text{ tons per sq. in.}$$

and by trial, from (14)

$$p_0=8\cdot43 \text{ tons per sq. in.}$$

the whole load on the strut being

$$8\cdot43 \times \tfrac{1}{4}\pi \times (2\cdot7)^2 = 48\cdot4 \text{ tons}$$

Thus the factor of safety reckoned on the greatest intensity of stress is $\frac{20}{5}=4$, but the ratio of crippling load to working load is $48\cdot4/15=3\cdot22$.

108. Struts and Tie-rods with Lateral Loads.   When a prismatic piece of material is subject to axial and lateral forces it may be looked upon as a beam with an axial thrust or pull, or as a strut or tie-rod with lateral bending forces.   A good example occurs in the case of a sloping beam acted upon by vertical forces as in the main rafters of a roof.   The stress intensity at any cross-section is, as indicated by (1), Art. 99, the algebraic sum of the bending stress, and the direct stress which the axial thrust would cause if there were no lateral forces.

In a beam which is only allowed a very limited deflection, *i.e.* which is not very long in proportion to its dimensions of cross-section, the bending stress may usually be taken as that resulting from the transverse loads only.   If, however, the beam is somewhat longer in proportion to its cross-section, the longitudinal force, which may be truly axial only at the ends, will cause a considerable bending stress due to its eccentricity elsewhere, and will play an appreciable part in increasing or decreasing the deflection produced by the lateral load, according as it is a thrust or a pull.   In this case, the bending stresses at any section are the algebraic sum of those produced by the transverse loads, and those produced by the eccentricity of the longitudinal forces.   Unless the bar is very long, or the longitudinal force is very great, a fairly close approximation to the bending moment may be found by taking the algebraic sum of that resulting from the transverse forces and that resulting from the eccentricity of the longitudinal force, on the assumption that the deflection or eccentricity is that due to the transverse loads only. The solution of a problem under these approximations has already been dealt with, the bending stress due to transverse loads being as calculated in Chapter v, the deflection being as calculated in Chapter vii, and the stresses resulting from the eccentric longitudinal force being calculated as in Art. 100. It remains to deal with those cases where the end thrust or pull materially affects the deflection, and where consequently the above approximation is not valid; this is the work of the two following articles, which give the stress intensities for members of any proportion, and indicate the circumstances under which the simpler solution of the problem will be approximately correct.

Strut with Lateral Load.[1] Let *l* be the length of a uniform strut freely hinged at each end and carrying a load *w* per unit length. Let the end thrust which passes through the centroid of the cross-section at each end be P. Take the origin O (Fig. 164) midway

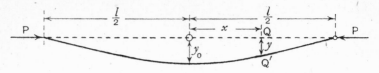

FIG. 164

between the ends, the line joining the centroids of the ends being the axis of *x*. The bending moment at Q' is $-\frac{w}{2}\left(\frac{l^2}{4}-x^2\right)$ due to the lateral load and $-P \cdot y$ due to the end thrust P. The sum is equal to $EI\frac{d^2y}{dx^2}$, where I is the (constant) moment of inertia of the cross-section about an axis through its centroid and perpendicular to the plane of flexure, or

$$EI\frac{d^2y}{dx^2}=-\frac{w}{2}\left(\frac{l^2}{4}-x^2\right)-P \cdot y \quad . \quad . \quad . \quad (1)$$

$$\frac{d^2y}{dx^2}+\frac{P}{EI} \cdot y=-\frac{w}{2EI}\left(\frac{l^2}{4}-x^2\right). \quad . \quad . \quad . \quad . \quad (2)$$

The solution of this equation under the conditions $\frac{dy}{dx}=0$ for $x=0$, and $y=0$ for $x=l/2$ is

$$y=\frac{w}{2P}x^2-\frac{wl^2}{8P}-\frac{wEI}{P^2}\left(1-\sec\frac{l}{2\sqrt{}}\sqrt{\frac{P}{EI}}\cos\sqrt{\frac{P}{EI}} \cdot x\right) \quad . \quad (3)$$

and the maximum bending moment at O is

$$-M_\wedge=P \cdot y_0+\tfrac{1}{8}wl^2=\frac{wEI}{P}\left(\sec\frac{l}{2\sqrt{}}\sqrt{\frac{P}{EI}}-1\right) \quad . \quad . \quad (4)$$

or $$-M_0=\frac{wEI}{P}\left(\sec\frac{l}{2}\sqrt{\frac{P}{P_e}}-1\right) \quad . \quad . \quad . \quad . \quad . \quad (5)$$

[1] For extensions of this subject to Continuous Beams, see *Aeroplane Structures*, by Pippard and Pritchard, Art. 90 and references therein.

where $P_e = \dfrac{\pi^2 EI}{l^2}$, Euler's limiting value for the ideal strut (Case II,

Art. 103). If $P = P_e$, M_0 and y_0 become infinite. The expansion

$$\sec \theta - 1 = \frac{\theta^2}{2!} + \frac{5\theta^4}{4!} + \frac{61\theta^6}{6!} + \frac{1385\theta^8}{8!} +, \text{etc.} \quad . \quad . \quad (6)$$

may be applied to (4), which then reduces to

$$-M_0 = \frac{wl^2}{8}\left\{1 + \frac{5\pi^2}{48}\left(\frac{P}{P_e}\right) + \frac{61\pi^4}{5,760}\left(\frac{P}{P_e}\right)^2 + \frac{277\pi^6}{258,048}\left(\frac{P}{P_e}\right)^3 +, \text{etc.}\right\} . \quad (7)$$

or

$$-M_0 = \frac{wl^2}{8} + \frac{5}{384} \cdot \frac{wl^4}{EI} \cdot P\left\{1 + \frac{61\pi^2}{600} \cdot \frac{P}{P_e} + \frac{277\pi^4}{26,880}\left(\frac{P}{P_e}\right)^2 +, \text{etc.}\right\} . \quad (8)$$

These two forms (7) and (8) show the relation of the approximate methods mentioned at the beginning of this article to the more exact method of calculating bending moment. The first term in each is the bending moment due to the lateral loads alone; the second term in (8) is the product of the axial thrust P and the deflection $\dfrac{5}{384} \cdot \dfrac{wl^4}{EI}$ (see (11), Art. 79) due to the transverse load alone. Even in the longest struts P/P_e will not exceed about $\frac{1}{5}$, and in shorter ones will be much less. The errors involved in the approximate method of calculation, which gives the first two terms in (9), are evidently then not great.

If the strut carried a lateral load W at the centre instead of the uniformly distributed load, equation (2) becomes

$$\frac{d^2y}{dx^2} + \frac{P}{EI} \cdot y = -\frac{W}{2EI}\left(\frac{l}{2} - x\right) \quad . \quad . \quad . \quad . \quad . \quad (9)$$

and

$$y_0 = \frac{W}{2P}\sqrt{\frac{EI}{P}} \tan \frac{l}{2}\sqrt{\frac{P}{EI}} - \frac{Wl}{4P} \quad . \quad . \quad . \quad (10)$$

$$-M_0 = \frac{W}{2}\sqrt{\frac{EI}{P}} \tan \frac{l}{2}\sqrt{\frac{P}{EI}} \quad . \quad . \quad . \quad . \quad (11)$$

Using the expansion

$$\tan \theta = \theta + \tfrac{1}{3}\theta^3 + \tfrac{2}{15}\theta^5 + \tfrac{17}{315}\theta^7 + \quad . \quad . \quad . \quad (12)$$

$$-M_0 = \frac{Wl}{4}\left\{1 + \frac{\pi^2}{12} \cdot \frac{P}{P_e} + \frac{\pi^4}{120}\left(\frac{P}{P_e}\right)^2 + \frac{17\pi^6}{20,160}\left(\frac{P}{P_e}\right)^2 +, \text{etc.}\right\} . \quad (13)$$

or

$$-M_0 = \frac{Wl}{4} + \frac{Wl^3}{48EI}P\left\{1 + \frac{\pi^2}{10} \cdot \frac{P}{P_e} + \frac{17\pi^4}{1,680}\left(\frac{P}{P_e}\right)^2 +, \text{etc.}\right\} . \quad . \quad (14)$$

which illustrates again the same points.

Other cases may be found in a paper in the *Philosophical Magazine*, June 1908.

The expression in brackets in (7) and (13) approximates to [1]

$$1+\frac{P}{P_e}+\left(\frac{P}{P_e}\right)^2+\left(\frac{P}{P_e}\right)^3+\left(\frac{P}{P_e}\right)^4+,\text{ etc.}=\frac{1}{1-\dfrac{P}{P_e}}\text{ or }\frac{1}{1-\dfrac{Pl^2}{10EI}}\text{ nearly (15)}$$

P/P_e being a fraction less than $\frac{1}{4}$ say, hence to find the bending stress approximately in any case for a strut hinged at both ends we simply use the maximum bending moment M, say, due to the lateral loads alone and increase it in the ratio given by (15), so that

$$M_0=\frac{M_1}{1-\dfrac{Pl^2}{10EI}}\qquad\ldots\quad\ldots\quad(16)$$

Whether the bending moment is calculated by the approximate methods of the previous article applicable to short struts, or by (5) or by (16), the maximum intensity of bending stress p_b disregarding sign, by Art. 46, is

$$p_b=\frac{M_0y_1}{I}=\frac{M_0}{Z}=\frac{M_0d}{2I}\quad\ldots\quad\ldots\quad(17)$$

where y_1 is the half-depth $d/2$ in a symmetrical section, and Z is the modulus of section. Hence, by Art. 99 (1) the maximum intensity of compressive stress

$$f_c=\frac{M_0}{Z}+p_0\quad\text{or}\quad\frac{M_0d}{2I}+p_0\quad\ldots\quad\ldots\quad(18)$$

where p_0 is the mean intensity of compressive stress on the section, viz. P/A, where A is the area of cross-section, and the bending moment is taken as positive.

And the maximum intensity of tensile stress is

$$f_t=\frac{M_0}{Z}-p_0\quad\text{or}\quad\frac{M_0d}{2I}-p_0\quad\ldots\quad\ldots\quad(19)$$

which, if negative, gives the minimum intensity of compressive stress. If the section is not symmetrical, the value of the unequal tensile and compressive bending stress intensities must be found as is Art. 46 (6).

The formula (18) affords an indirect means of calculating the dimensions of cross-section for a strut of given shape, in order that, under given axial and lateral loads, the greatest intensity of stress shall not exceed some specified amount. As the method is indirect, involving trial, the value M_1 may be used to give directly a first approximation to the dimensions, which may then be adjusted by

[1] Prof. Perry obtains this result and the succeeding one (27) for tension in a different way by substituting an approximation for the right-hand side of equations (2) and (22).

testing the values of f_c by the more accurate expression (18), where M_0 satisfies (5) or (11) or (16).

Using the approximate values (18) becomes

$$f_c = \frac{M_1 y_1}{I - \dfrac{Pl^2}{10E}} + \frac{P}{A} \quad \cdots \quad \cdots \quad (20)$$

and (19) becomes

$$f_t = \frac{M_1 y_1}{I - \dfrac{Pl^2}{10E}} - \frac{P}{A} \quad \cdots \quad \cdots \quad (21)$$

Tie-rod with Lateral Load. If the axial load P is tensile the sign of P in (2) is reversed and the equation becomes

$$\frac{d^2 y}{dx^2} - \frac{P}{EI} \cdot y = -\frac{w}{2EI}\left(\frac{l^2}{4} - x^2\right) \quad \cdots \quad \cdots \quad (22)$$

and the conditions of fixing being the same, the solution is

$$y = -\frac{w}{2P}x^2 + \frac{wl^2}{8P} - \frac{wEI}{P^2}\left(1 - \operatorname{sech}\frac{l}{2}\sqrt{\frac{P}{EI}}\cosh\sqrt{\frac{P}{EI}}x\right) \quad \cdot \quad (23)$$

and

$$-M_0 = \frac{wEI}{P}\left(1 - \operatorname{sech}\frac{l}{2}\sqrt{\frac{P}{EI}}\right) = \frac{wEI}{P}\left(1 - \operatorname{sech}\frac{\pi}{2}\sqrt{\frac{P}{P_e}}\right) \quad \cdot \quad \cdot \quad (24)$$

This when expanded gives a series identical with (7) and (8) except that the signs of successive terms are alternately positive and negative. The second term, viz. $-P \cdot \dfrac{5}{384} \cdot \dfrac{wl^4}{EI}$ gives the reduction in bending moment resulting from the eccentricity of the tension on the assumption that the deflection is that due to the transverse load only.

If the tie-rod carries only a lateral load W at the centre, (11) becomes

$$\frac{d^2 y}{dx^2} - \frac{P}{EI} \cdot y = -\frac{W}{2EI}\left(\frac{l}{2} - x\right). \quad \cdots \quad \cdots \quad (25)$$

and

$$y_0 = \frac{W}{2P}\sqrt{\frac{EI}{P}}\tanh\frac{l}{2}\sqrt{\frac{P}{EI}}$$

$$-M_0 = \frac{W}{2}\sqrt{\frac{EI}{P}}\tanh\frac{l}{2}\sqrt{\frac{P}{EI}} \quad \cdots \quad \cdots \quad (26)$$

Other cases may be found in a paper in the *Philosophical Magazine,* June 1908.

The expansion of (26), which is similar to that of (11), further illustrates the same points as the previous cases.

Proceeding as for struts, the approximation for either (24) or (26) is

$$M_0 = M_1\left\{1 - \frac{P}{P_e} + \left(\frac{P}{P_e}\right)^2 - \left(\frac{P}{P_e}\right)^3 +, \text{etc.}\right\} = \frac{M_1}{1 + \frac{P}{P_e}} \quad \text{or} \quad \frac{M_1}{1 + \frac{Pl^2}{10EI}}$$

$$\text{nearly} \quad . \quad . \quad (27)$$

and corresponding to (18) or (20), the maximum intensity of compressive stress is

$$f_c = \frac{M_0}{Z} - p_0 \quad \text{or} \quad \frac{M_1 y_1}{1 + \frac{Pl^2}{10E}} - \frac{P}{A} \text{ approximately} \quad . \quad (28)$$

and corresponding to (19) or (31), the maximum intensity of tensile stress is

$$f_t = \frac{M_0}{Z} + p_0 = \frac{M_1 y_1}{1 + \frac{Pl^2}{10E}} + \frac{P}{A} \text{ approximately} \quad . \quad . \quad (29)$$

Example. A round bar of steel 1 in. diameter and 10 ft. long has axial forces applied to the centres of each end, and being freely supported in a horizontal position carries the lateral load of its own weight (0·28 lb. per cu. in.). Find the greatest tensity of compressive and tensile stress in the bar: (*a*) under an axial thrust of 500 lb.; (*b*) under an axial pull of 500 lb.; (*c*) with no axial force. (E = 30×10^6 lb. per sq. in.)

$$w = 0·28 \times \frac{\pi}{4} = 0·22 \text{ lb. per in. length.} \quad M_1 = \frac{wl^2}{8} = 396 \text{ lb. in.}$$

$$y_1 = 0·5 \text{ in.} \qquad\qquad I = \frac{\pi}{64} = 0·04909.$$

$$\frac{Pl^2}{10E} = \frac{500 \times 120 \times 120}{10 \times 30 \times 10^6} = 0·024. \qquad p_0 = \frac{500}{0·7854} = 637 \text{ lb. per sq. in.}$$

(*a*) Maximum intensity of bending stress by (16) is approximately

$$p_b = \frac{M_0 y_1}{I} = \frac{396 \times \frac{1}{2}}{0·04909 - 0·024} = \frac{198}{0·02509} = 7,900 \text{ lb. per sq. in.}$$

Maximum compressive stress, $f_c = 7,900 + 637 = 8,537$ lb. per sq. in.

Maximum tensile stress, $f_t = 7,900 - 637 = 7,263$ lb. per sq. in.

(*b*) Maximum intensity of compressive stress by (28) is approximately

$$f_c = \frac{198}{0·04909 + 0·024} - 637 = 2,710 - 637 = 2,073 \text{ lb. per sq. in.}$$

Maximum intensity of tensile stress by (29) is approximately, similarly

$$f_t = 2,710 + 637 = 3,347 \text{ lb. per sq. in.}$$

(c) $$f_t = f_c = \frac{198}{0 \cdot 04909} = 4,030 \text{ lb. per sq. in.}$$

The values of the bending stress by the more exact rules (5) and (24) are for (a) 8,100 lb. per sq. in., and for (b) 2,666 lb. per sq. in.; they are worked out in the author's *Strength of Materials.*

109. General Case of Combined Bending and Thrust or Pull. An empirical approximate formula covering any case of combined bending and longitudinal load corresponding to (14), Art. 107, and to (20) and (29), Art. 108, for the greatest intensity of stress is

$$\text{maximum } f = \frac{M_1 y_1}{I \mp \dfrac{P l^2}{cE}} + \frac{P}{A}$$

where M_1 is maximum bending moment resulting (algebraically) from the eccentricity of P (neglecting flexure) and lateral loads, and where the negative sign is to be used when P is a thrust, and the positive sign when P is a pull. The *constant c* for a strut hinged at both ends is about 8 for eccentric loads, 10 for uniformly distributed loads, and rather higher values for concentrated loads. It may be taken as, say, 10 in all cases.

A more exact but unwieldy result might, of course, be obtained by combinations of such equations as (1), Art. 107, and (1), Art. 108. The value of *c* applicable to other forms of ends depends on the type of loading and also upon whether the maximum stress occurs at the ends or at some intermediate point.[1] When both ends of a strut are fixed, *c* may be taken as roughly about 34 for estimating the stress about the middle of its length, and as about 57 for the ends. When one end is hinged and the other is fixed, *c* may be taken as about 24 for maximum stress at any section. The other extreme stress at the section of maximum stress is found in any case by reversing the sign of P/A.

110. Reinforced Concrete under Bending and Thrust. (*a*) *Axial Loading.* Reinforced columns have longitudinal reinforcing bars parallel to the axis of the column and other structural elements have bars parallel to the direction of thrust. We consider a column so short that no question of buckling arises. (For long columns the allowable load is reduced by an empirical factor based on experiment to allow for the effect of buckling.) Thus for values of *l/k* of

---

[1] These values may be obtained by expanding the transcendental functions involved in more exact values of the bending moments or by the method illustrated between equations (8) and (9) of Art. 108, but in the latter case deflections must be measured from a line joining points of contraflexure.

M

50 to 150 a coefficient $1\cdot5-l/100k$ is employed (where k is as defined below, equation (8)).   The steel bars having the same proportional strain as the concrete take a proportion of the load, namely m times that of the same cross-sectional area, where m is the ratio E_s/E_c, as in Art. 56.   Let Fig. 165 represent the section of such a

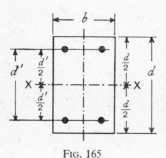

column which might also take other shapes, such as circular or octagonal. The longitudinal steel bars are generally held in place by hoops made of thinner rod encircling them or by wire surrounding them helically.   Such binding serves to resist buckling of the bars and to resist shearing of the concrete in planes inclined about 45° to the axis of the column.   Helical binding in addition may be considered in practice to add slightly to the longitudinal

Fig. 165

reinforcement.   But such an effect is small and any allowance for it must be empirical and based on tests to destruction.   For information of this kind the reader is referred to manuals on design [1] which embody references to Codes of Practice or Rules of responsible building authorities.   Let A_s be the total area of section of the steel and f_c be the intensity of stress in the concrete so that the intensity in the steel is mf_c.   Then the load or total thrust

$$P = f_c \{ bd + (m-1)A_s \} \quad . \quad . \quad . \quad . \quad (1)$$

It is to be noted that if the reinforcement is not symmetrical about both principal axes of the un-reinforced cross-section, axial loading implies loading in the line of the centre of pressure when the various parts of A_s carry stress of m times the intensity of that in the remainder $(bd-A_s)$ of the section.   Design by the Code is, however, based on the sum of the ultimate loads which could be carried by the steel (up to yield point) and by the concrete.   A working load is then taken to be the sum of these ultimate loads divided by a factor such as 3.   Thus the working load on a short column for a concrete mixture of nominally 1 cement to 2 of sand and 4 of aggregate and mild-steel reinforcement, in pounds, might be

600 × (sectional area of concrete in square inches) + 13,500 × (area of steel in square inches)

(*b*) *Under Combined Bending and Thrust.*   If the load parallel to the axis is eccentric (*i.e.* not axial) or is accompanied by a bending moment, the stress is not uniformly distributed over the section of the concrete.   If the bending stress is sufficiently large to more than

---

[1] See C. P. Manning's *Reinforced Concrete Design* (Longmans).

neutralise the compressive stress due to the longitudinal thrust P we shall have a resultant tensile stress in the steel reinforcement and an ignored tensile stress in the concrete, as in Art. 56.   Thus it is better to treat this case separately from that in which, though varying, the stress is compressive throughout the section.

Firstly, let the bending moment be sufficient to cause tension. For such a symmetrical section as in Fig. 165, this will occur when

$$\text{maximum } p_b > P/\{ bd + (m-1)A_s \} \quad . \quad . \quad . \quad . \quad (2)$$

that is when

$$\frac{\mu d}{2I_c} > P/\{ bd + (m-1)A_s \} \quad . \quad . \quad . \quad . \quad (3)$$

where μ is the bending moment in the plane of a vertical axis of the section in Fig. 165 (*i.e.* an axis perpendicular to XX) and I_c stands for $\frac{1}{12}bd^3 + (m-1)A_s \times (\frac{1}{2}d')^2$.   In this, as in $bd + (m-1)A_s$ on the right-hand side of (2) and (3), A_s is virtually increased m times to

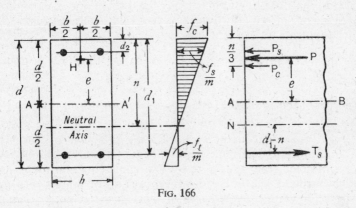

FIG. 166

allow for the fact that the steel takes m times the intensity of stress in concrete similarly placed. I_c is more fully defined later (before equation (7)).

If $\mu = Pe$ where e is the eccentricity of P from the central axis XX of the cross-section, $\frac{1}{2}\mu d/I$ becomes $\frac{1}{2}Ped/I_c$ and the condition (3) becomes

$$e > 2I_c/[d\{ bd + (m-1)A_s \}] \quad . \quad . \quad . \quad . \quad (3\text{A})$$

If this condition (3) or (3A) is fulfilled we must determine the neutral axis as in Art. 56 on the convention that the concrete carries no tension and it is wholly borne by the steel bars.

To take a more general and not necessarily symmetrical case let A_1 be the sectional area of reinforcement on the tension side (Fig. 166), and A_2 that on the compression side.   The column has an axial thrust P and a bending moment μ or an eccentric thrust P at

H distant e from the central axis AA' ($\mu = Pe$). The total thrust across a section on the concrete is P_c and on the steel section A_2 is P_s and the total pull across the lower reinforcement is T_s. These three forces exerted across a section (by the material on the other side of the section) have a resultant P. But it is convenient to take P_s as $(m-1)A_2 \times$ (concrete stress intensity at $n-d_2$ from the neutral axis) and P_c as for the unperforated section $b \times n$, with a resultant line of action at a distance $\frac{2}{3}n$ from the neutral axis. Then if f_c is the intensity of compressive stress at the top edge of the section (Fig. 166), the intensity of tensile stress in the lower steel bars is

$$f_t = mf_c \times (d_1 - n)/n \text{ and } T_s = A_1 \times f_t \quad . \quad . \quad . \quad (4)$$

$$\left.\begin{array}{l} P = P_c + P_s - T_s \text{ (see right-hand side of Fig. 166)} \\ = \frac{1}{2}bnf_c + (m-1)A_2 f_c(n-d_2)/n - mA_1 f_c(d_1-n)/n \\ \text{or} \qquad P = f_c\{\frac{1}{2}bn + (m-1)A_2(n-d_2)/n - mA_1(d_1-n)/n\} \end{array}\right\} \quad . \quad (5)$$

The (external) bending moment μ is equal to Pe and is balanced by the moments of the constituent parts of the internal resistance of which moments we can write the sum thus

$$Pe = \frac{1}{2}f_c bn(\frac{1}{2}d - \frac{1}{3}n) + (m-1)A_2 f_c . \frac{n-d_2}{n}(\frac{1}{2}d - d_2) + mA_1 f_c \frac{d_1-n}{n}(d_1 - \frac{1}{2}d)$$

or

$$\mu = Pe = f_c\{\frac{1}{2}bn(\frac{1}{2}d - \frac{1}{3}n) + (m-1)A_2(\frac{1}{2}d - d_2)(n-d_2)/n$$
$$+ mA_1(d_1 - \frac{1}{2}d)(d_1 - n)/n\} \quad . \quad . \quad . \quad (6)$$

If the remaining quantities are known, these two equations, (5) and (6), suffice to determine n and P or μ. If (5) is multiplied by e and subtracted from (6) the result is a cubic equation for n. For design purposes charts are drawn consisting of graphs relating P or P/bd for various percentages of steel in the gross cross-section bd to the values of e expressed sometimes as a fraction of d, viz. e/d. We return to this later (Fig. 168).

The case of single reinforcement such as in Fig. 80 is covered by making $A_2 = 0$ in (5) and (6).

If the tensile bending stress is not sufficient to neutralise the compressive stress due to the longitudinal thrust P, the whole section is available to resist the thrust and moment and is in a state of compressive stress. Taking the overall dimensions, we may employ the formulae (1) and (2) of Art. 100, provided we give specialised meanings to the symbols A and I (or Ak^2), though the names, area, and second moment of area should then be qualified by the prefix " equivalent." A subscript may then be added to A and I. Since the reinforcement carries m times the intensity of the stress of the concrete at the same distance from the neutral axis, its effect is equivalent to the addition of $(m-1)$ times the area of cross-section

1·3
1·2
1·1
1·0
0·9
0·8
0·7
0·6
Ratio P/bdf_c
0
0·05
0·1
0·15
0·2
Proportional eccentricity e/d

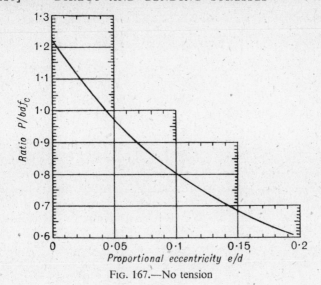

FIG. 167.—No tension

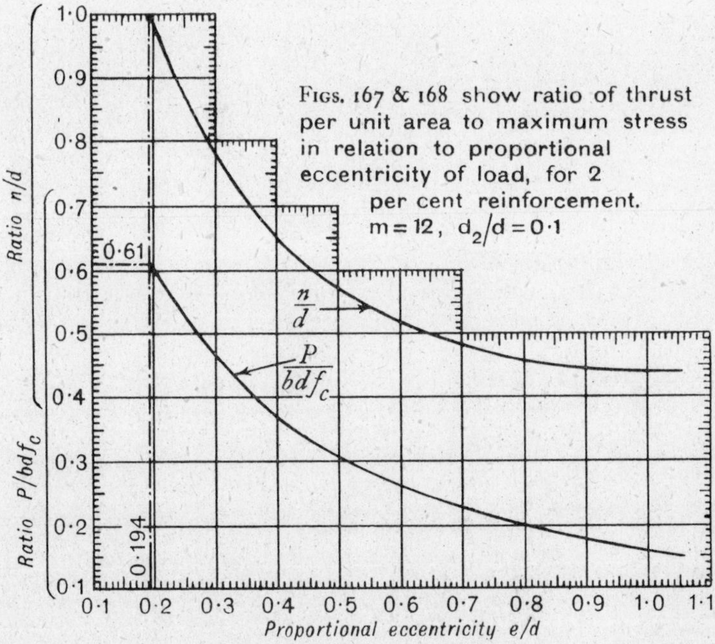

FIGS. 167 & 168 show ratio of thrust per unit area to maximum stress in relation to proportional eccentricity of load, for 2 per cent reinforcement.
m = 12, d2/d = 0·1
Ratio n/d
Ratio P/bdf_c
0·61
0·194
n/d
P/bdf_c
1·0
0·9
0·8
0·7
0·6
0·5
0·4
0·3
0·2
0·1
0·1 0·2 0·3 0·4 0·5 0·6 0·7 0·8 0·9 1·0 1·1
Proportional eccentricity e/d

FIG. 168.—With tension in steel bars

A_s to the gross concrete section bd and at the same distance from the neutral axis of bending stress as the actual steel section. Thus in standard symbols

$$\text{Equivalent sectional area} = A_e = bd + (m-1)A_s$$

Equivalent moment of inertia in terms of concrete $= I_c$, where I_c is equal to I of the gross section about n.a. of bending plus $(m-1)A_s$ $\times$ (distance of A_s from n.a.)^2, that is plus $(m-1)A_s(\tfrac{1}{2}d')^2$ in Fig. 165 or plus $(m-1)A_s(d-n)^2$ in Fig. 80 or plus $A_1(m-1)(d_1-n)^2 +$ $(m-1)A_2(n-d_2)^2$ in Fig. 82. It must be noted that in this connection the position of the n.a. of bending stress (*i.e.* the value of n) is to be calculated as for pure bending and as if the concrete bore its due proportion of tensile stress which is in fact neutralised by the longitudinal thrust. (For a column symmetrically reinforced the n.a. is the central axis of the gross cross-section.) The working out of complete formulae here in terms of the symbols would give an appearance of complexity which is unnecessary and numerical problems can be solved from the necessary data and the fundamental equations of Art. 100. If a column carries an axial load P and a bending moment μ, it is only necessary to replace by μ the product Pe when it represents a bending moment in (1) of Art. 100, *i.e.* to take $p_b = \mu y / I_c$. Thus with the specialised meanings of A and I, from (1) and (2) Art. 100 we have

$$\text{(maximum)} \; f_c = \frac{P}{A_e} + \frac{\mu y_1}{I_c} \quad \text{or} \quad \frac{P}{A_e}\left(1 + \frac{ey_1}{k^2}\right) \quad . \quad . \quad (7)$$

and

$$\text{(minimum)} \; f_c = \frac{P}{A_c} - \frac{\mu y_1}{I_c} \quad \text{or} \quad \frac{P}{A_e}\left(1 - \frac{ey_1}{k^2}\right) \quad . \quad . \quad (8)$$

where $k^2 = I_c/A_e$ (h of Art. 100 is here replaced by e in accordance with concrete practice).

The maximum deviation e not involving tension would be where $k^2 = ey_1$, and here e is the eccentricity of P reckoned from the central axis of such a symmetrical section as that in Fig. 165. For such a section let the total area of cross-section of steel be p per cent. of the gross area bd. Then

$$A_e = bd + (m-1)\frac{p}{100}bd = bd\{1 + (m-1)p/100\} \quad . \quad . \quad (9)$$

$$I_c = \tfrac{1}{12}bd^3 + (\tfrac{1}{2}d')^2(m-1)bd \times p/100 \quad . \quad . \quad . \quad (10)$$

And if we take $d' = 0.8d$, *i.e.* each steel bar in Fig. 165 is centred a distance $\tfrac{1}{10}$ of d from the top and bottom edges of the section

$$I_c = \tfrac{1}{12}bd^3 + (0.4d)^2(m-1)bdp/100 \quad . \quad . \quad (11)$$

If we write (7) in the form

$$P/A_e + Pe \times \tfrac{1}{2}d/I_c = f_c . \text{(max.)} \quad . \quad . \quad . \quad (12)$$

we can write an expression for P in terms of f_c and e for such a beam. Take $m=12$, say.   Then (12) becomes (using (9) and (11))

$$P\left[\frac{1}{bd\{1+(m-1)p/100\}}+\frac{e}{bd^2/6+2p(m-1)bd^2\times0\cdot0016}\right]=f_c$$

$$\frac{P}{bdf_c}=\frac{1}{\dfrac{1}{1+0\cdot11p}+\dfrac{e/d}{0\cdot167+0\cdot035p}}\quad\cdots\cdots\quad(13)$$

If we limit ourselves to $p=2$ (per cent.)

$$\frac{P}{bdf_c}=\frac{1}{0\cdot820+4\cdot22e/d}\quad\cdots\cdots\quad(14)$$

The values of this for various values of e/d are plotted in Fig. 167. From such a chart, drawn to a suitably large scale on squared paper, we can read off values of P/bd or of P by giving the necessary numerical values to b, d, and f_c the allowable (maximum) compressive stress intensity in the concrete.   Designers use such charts plotted with separate graphs for different percentages p or ratios r of steel.   The graphs terminate at that value of e/d at which tension in the concrete would appear.   There is here a discontinuity because conventionally tension in the concrete is ignored.   Another graph, such as Fig. 168, allowing for tension in the steel only, would be required for higher values of e/d.   The terminal value of e/d for Fig. 167 is found by equating the bending stress to the value of P/A from (12).   From (14) we can write for the critical value of the eccentricity of loading

$$4\cdot22e/d=0\cdot8197$$

$$e/d=0\cdot8197/4\cdot22=0\cdot194\quad\cdots\cdots\quad(15)$$

If this eccentricity is exceeded there will be tension across the section all taken, conventionally at least, by the steel reinforcement. Under these conditions we use equation (6) in conjunction with (5). Considering again the symmetrical section of Fig. 165 and the notation of Fig. 166 and $d_1=0\cdot9d$, $d_2=0\cdot1d$, and $A_1=A_2=\frac{1}{2}pA/100$ as before, (5) becomes for $m=12$ and $p=2$ (*i.e.* $A_1+A_2=2$ per cent. of bd).

$$P/(bd\cdot f_c)=\tfrac{1}{2}n/d+0\cdot11(1-0\cdot1d/n)-0\cdot12\{0\cdot9(d/n)-1\}\quad.\quad(16)$$

and (6) becomes

$$Pe/(bd^2f_c)=\tfrac{1}{2}(n/d)\{0\cdot5-n/(3d)\}+0\cdot044(1-0\cdot1d/n)$$
$$+0\cdot048\{0\cdot9(d/n)-1\}\quad.\quad.\quad.\quad.\quad.\quad(17)$$

And substituting any value of n/d in (16) and (17) we obtain a value of $P/(bd\cdot f_c)$ and dividing (17) by (16) a corresponding value of e/d, which together determine one point on Fig. 168.   Choosing a second value of n/d we obtain the co-ordinates of a second point.

The co-ordinates of the seven points from which the graph, Fig. 168, was drawn are given below, following the five pairs of co-ordinates of points on the graph of Fig. 167 calculated from equation (14):

e/d	0	0·05	0·10	0·15	0·194	0·286	0·454	0·648	0·713	0·845	1·046
P/bdf_c . . .	1·22	0·970	0·805	0·688	0·61	0·481	0·332	0·242	0·222	0·191	0·157
n/d					1·0	0·8	0·6	0·5	0·48	0·45	0·42

Figs. 167 and 168 are explanatory sample graphs (for $d_2/d=0\cdot1$). For design purposes, a series with differing percentages p can be used and can be drawn for different values of m.   Examples can be found in text-books on design.[1]   The conditions of design and production do not warrant great refinement in calculation.

Example 1.   A reinforced concrete structural member having a section 20 in. deep and 10 in. wide has four bars of steel 1 in. diameter placed two with their axes 2 in. from the upper face and two with their axes 2 in. from the lower face of the beam.   If the beam is subjected to a longitudinal thrust, the line of which is in the vertical central axis of the cross-section and 7 in. from the horizontal axis, find the position of the neutral axis and the greatest magnitude of the thrust if the compressive stress in the concrete is to be limited to 1,000 lb. per sq. in.   Take $m=12$.

It is evident that the criterion (3A) is satisfied for

$$A_e = 200 + 11\pi = 234\cdot6 \text{ sq. in.}$$

$$I_c = 10 \times 20^3/12 + 11\pi \times 8^2 = 6,667 + 2,212 = 8,879 \text{ (in.)}^4. \quad e = 7 \text{ in.}$$

From Art. 100

$$\text{maximum } p_b = \frac{P \times 7 \times 10}{8,879} = \frac{P}{126\cdot8}$$

$$p_0 = P/234\cdot6$$

hence since max. $p_b > p_0$ there is tension.

From (5), the total thrust when f_c reaches 1,000 lb. per sq. in. is

$$P = 1,000\{\tfrac{1}{2} . 10 . n + \tfrac{1}{2}\pi \times 11 \times \frac{n-2}{n} - \tfrac{1}{2}\pi \times 12 \times (18-n)/n\} \text{ lb.}$$

The total moment of resistance (about the n.a.) is

$$P(n-3) = 1,000\{ 10n^2/3 + 5\cdot5\pi(n-2)^2/n + 6\pi(18-n)^2/n\} \text{ lb.-in.}$$

Multiplying the first equation by $(n-3)$ and subtracting the second and multiplying by $0\cdot6n$

$$n^3 - 9n^2 + 159\cdot28n - 3,033 = 0$$

Plotting or tabulating the value of the left side of this equation

[1] For example, C. P. Manning's *Reinforced Concrete Design* (Longmans).

from $n=14$ in. downwards we get the value $n=13\cdot57$ in. And substituting for n in the value of P,

$$P=1,000(\tfrac{1}{2}\times135\cdot7+5\cdot5\pi\times11\cdot57/13\cdot57-6\pi\times4\cdot43/13\cdot57)$$
$$=1,000(67\cdot85+8\cdot58)=76,430\text{ lb.}$$

The stress in the steel on the tension side is

$$1,000\times12\times4\cdot43/13\cdot57=3,918\text{ lb. per sq. in.}$$

and on the compression side is

$$1,000\times12\times11\cdot57/13\cdot57=10,230\text{ lb. per sq. in.}$$

If, instead of taking the moment of resistance about the n.a., we had taken moments about the central horizontal axis we should have had as in equation (6)

$$P\times7=1,000\{5n(10-\tfrac{1}{3}n)+\tfrac{1}{2}\pi\times11\times(n-2)8/n+\tfrac{1}{2}\pi\times12\times(18-n)8/n\}$$

and multiplying the equation for P by 7 and subtracting and multiplying by $0\cdot6n$ we obtain

$$n^3-9n^2+159\cdot28-3,033=0$$

as before.

Example 2. For the beam in Example 1 of Art. 56 (Fig. 80), find the neutral axis of the bending stresses if there is no tension because of a longitudinal thrust: (*a*) find the maximum eccentricity of the thrust for which there is no tension in the material; (*b*) if the line of thrust is in the central vertical axis of cross-section and 8 in. from the top edge, find minimum intensity of stress in the concrete when the maximum is 1,000 lb. per sq. in., and the total thrust and find the intensity of stress in the steel. Take $m=12$.

(*a*) Let $_bf_c$ and $_bf_t$ be the extreme *bending* stress intensities *in the concrete*. Since the stress intensities are proportional to the distances from the neutral axis of *bending stress*

$$_bf_t/_bf_c=(20-n)/n$$

and bending stress intensity in steel$=_bf_c\times12\times(18-n)/n$.

And for the *bending* stresses across the section

$$\text{Total tension}=\text{Total thrust}$$
$$\pi\times11_bf_c\times(18-n)/n+10(20-n)\times\tfrac{1}{2}_bf_c\times(20-n)/n=\tfrac{1}{2}_bf_c\times10n$$
$$11(18-n)\pi+(20-n)^2\times5-5n^2=0$$
$$234\cdot56n=2,622$$
$$n=11\cdot2\text{ in.}$$

The distance of the bending axis from the central is therefore $11\cdot2-10=1\cdot2$ in.

$A_e=200+11\pi=234\cdot56$ sq. in.

$I_e=\tfrac{1}{3}\cdot10\cdot n^3+\tfrac{1}{3}\cdot10(20-n)^3+11\pi(18-n)^2=8,553$ (in.)^4

$$_bf_c=\frac{P(e+1\cdot2)\times11\cdot2}{8,553}\qquad _bf_t=\frac{P(e+1\cdot2)\times8\cdot8}{8,553}\qquad f_o\quad\text{or}\quad\frac{P}{A_e}=\frac{P}{234\cdot6}$$

M*

If $_bf_t$ just reaches the intensity of compressive stress due to the longitudinal thrust P

$$8\cdot8P(e+1\cdot2)/8{,}553 = P/234\cdot6$$
$$e+1\cdot2 = 8{,}553/(8\cdot8 \times 234\cdot6) = 4\cdot14 \text{ in.}$$
$$e = 2\cdot94 \text{ in.}$$

At this eccentricity the stress intensity is zero at the bottom edge of the section.

(b) When the thrust is 8 in. from the top edge its distance from the n.a. is $11\cdot2-8=3\cdot2$ in.

Hence from (7) or Art. 100

$$f_c(\text{max.}) = \frac{P}{234\cdot6} + \frac{P \times 3\cdot2 \times 11\cdot2}{8{,}553} = 1{,}000 \text{ lb. per sq. in.}$$

$$P\left(\frac{1}{234\cdot6} + \frac{1}{238\cdot6}\right) = 1{,}000 \text{ lb. per sq. in.}$$

hence $P = 118{,}290$ lb.

At the lower edge

$$f_c(\text{min.}) = 118{,}290\left(\frac{1}{234\cdot6} - \frac{3\cdot2 \times 8\cdot8}{8{,}553}\right) = 115 \text{ lb. per sq. in.}$$

At 2 in. above the lower edge

$$\text{Stress in steel} = 12 \times 118{,}290\left(\frac{1}{234\cdot6} - \frac{3\cdot2 \times 6\cdot8}{8553}\right) = 2{,}439 \text{ lb. per sq. in.}$$

Example 3.   Solve Example 2 if the beam has four 1-in. diameter bars centred 2 in. from the compression edge in addition to the other four.

From the symmetry n (for bending stress) $=10$ in.

$A_e = 200 + 11 \times 2\pi = 269\cdot1$ sq. in.

$I_c = 10 \times 20^3/12 + 11 \times 2\pi \times 8^2 = 11{,}090$ (in.)^4.

(a) Maximum bending stress at outer edges $P_e \times 10/11{,}090$.

Mean compressive stress $P/A_e = P/269\cdot1$.

If this just equals the maximum bending stress

$$e = \frac{11{,}090}{10 \times 269\cdot1} = 4\cdot12 \text{ in.}$$

(b) If the line of action of P is 8 in. from the top edge:

$e = 10-8 = 2$ in.

Maximum bending-stress intensity $= 2 \times P \times 10/11{,}090 = P/554\cdot5$.

Additional compressive stress $P/A = P/269\cdot1$.

Maximum compressive stress intensity

$$P\left(\frac{1}{269\cdot1} + \frac{1}{554\cdot5}\right) = 1{,}000 \text{ lb. per sq. in.}$$

$$P = 181{,}170 \text{ lb.}$$

$$f_c(\text{min.}) = 181{,}170\left(\frac{1}{269{\cdot}1} - \frac{1}{554{\cdot}5}\right) = 347 \text{ lb. per sq. in.}$$

$$\text{Compressive stress in upper steel} = 12 \times 181{,}170\left(\frac{1}{269{\cdot}1} + \frac{2 \times 8}{11{,}090}\right)$$

$$= 11{,}210 \text{ lb. per sq. in.}$$

$$\text{Compressive stress in lower steel} = 12 \times 181{,}170\left(\frac{1}{269{\cdot}1} - \frac{2 \times 8}{11{,}090}\right)$$

$$= 4{,}940 \text{ lb. per sq. in.}$$

EXAMPLES X

1. In a short cast-iron column 6 in. external and 5 in. internal diameter, the load is 12 tons, and the axis of this thrust passes $\frac{1}{2}$ in. from the centre of the section. Find the greatest and least intensities of compressive stress.

2. The axis of pull in a tie-bar 4 in. deep and $1\frac{1}{2}$ in. wide passes $\frac{1}{10}$ in. from the centre of the section and is in the centre of the depth. Find the maximum and minimum intensities of tensile stress on the bar at this section, the total pull being 24 tons.

3. The vertical pillar of a crane is of I section, the depth of section parallel to the web being 25 in., area 24 sq. in., and the moment of inertia about a central axis parallel to the flanges being 3,000 (in.)[4]. When a load of 10 tons is carried at a radius of 14 ft. horizontally from the centroid of the section of the pillar, find the maximum intensities of compressive and tensile stress in the pillar which is fixed at the base and quite free at the top.

4. If a cylindrical masonry column is 3 ft. diameter and the horizontal wind pressure is 50 lb. per foot of height, assuming perfect elasticity, to what height may the column be built without causing tension at the base if the masonry weighs 140 lb. per cu. ft.?

5. A mild-steel strut 5 ft. long has a T-shaped cross-section $6 \times 4 \times \frac{1}{2}$ in. (see B.S.T., 21 in Table VI, Appendix). Find the ultimate load for this strut, the ends of which are freely hinged, if the crushing strength is taken as 21 tons per sq. in. and the constant a of Rankine's formula $\frac{1}{7500}$.

6. Find the greatest length for which the section in Problem No. 5 may be used, with ends freely hinged, in order to carry a working load of 4 tons per sq. in. of section, the working load being one-quarter of the crippling load and the constants as before.

7. A mild-steel stanchion, the cross-sectional area of which is 53·52 sq. in., is as shown in Fig. 156, the least radius of gyration being 4·5 in. The length being 24 ft. and both ends being fixed, find the crippling load by Rankine's formula, using the constants given in Art. 105.

8. Find the ultimate load for the column in Problem No. 7, if it is fixed at one end and free at the other.

9. Find the breaking load of a cast-iron column 8 in. external and 6 in. internal diameter, 20 ft. long and fixed at each end. Use Rankine's constants.

10. Find the working load for a mild-steel strut 12 ft. long composed of two T-sections $6 \times 4 \times \frac{1}{2}$ in., the two 6-in. cross-pieces being placed back to back, the strut being fixed at both ends. Take the working load as a quarter the crippling load by Rankine's rule.

11. Find the ultimate load on a steel strut of the same cross-section as that in Problem No. 10, if the length is 8 ft. and both ends are freely hinged.

12. Find the necessary thickness of a metal in a cast-iron pillar 15 ft. long

and 9 in. external diameter, fixed at both ends, to carry a load of 50 tons, the ultimate load being six times greater.

13. Find the external diameter of a cast-iron column 20 ft. long, fixed at each end, to have a crippling load of 480 tons, the thickness of metal being 1 in.

14. A latticed stanchion is built of two standard channel sections 7 in. by 3 in. (see B.S.C. 9, Table II, Appendix) placed back to back. How far apart should they be placed in order to offer equal resistance to buckling in all directions?

15. Solve Problem No. 1 if the column is 10 ft. long, one end being fixed and the other having complete lateral freedom. (E=5,000 tons per sq. in.)

16. With the ultimate load as found by Rankine's formula in Problem No. 5, what eccentricity of load at the ends of the strut (in the direction of the least radius of gyration and towards the cross-piece of the **T**) will cause the straight homogeneous strut to reach a compressive stress of 21 tons per sq. in., assuming perfect elasticity up to this load? The distance from the centroid of the cross-section to the compression edge is 0·968 in. (E=13,000 tons per sq. in.)

17. With the eccentricity found in Problem No. 16 and a load of 16 tons per sq. in. of section, of what length may the strut be made in order that the greatest intensity of compressive stress shall not exceed 21 tons per sq. in.? What is then the least intensity of stress, the distance from the centroid of the cross-section to the tension edge being 3·032 in.?

18. Find the load which will cause an extreme compressive stress of 21 tons per sq. in. in a stanchion of the section given in Problem No. 7, 12 ft. long and freely hinged at the ends, if the depth of section in the direction of the least radius of gyration is 16 in., and the deviation of the load from the centre of the cross-section is 1 in. in the direction of the 16-in. depth. (E=13,000 tons per sq. in.)

19. What load will the column in Problem No. 1 carry if it is fixed at one end, and has complete lateral freedom at the other, if the column is 10 ft. long, the eccentricity of loading ½ in., and the greatest tensile stress 1 ton per sq. in.? What is the greatest intensity of compressive stress? (E=5,000 tons per sq. in.)

20. Find the necessary diameter of a mild-steel strut, 5 ft. long, freely hinged at each end, if it has to carry a thrust of 12 tons with a possible deviation from the axis of $\frac{1}{10}$ of the diameter, the greatest compressive stress not to exceed 6 tons per sq. in. (E=13,000 tons per sq. in.)

21. Solve Problem No. 19 if the deviation may amount to 1 in.

22. A round straight bar of steel 5 ft. long and 1 in. diameter rests in a horizontal position, the ends being freely supported. If an axial thrust of 2,000 lb. is applied to each end, find the extreme intensities of stress in the material. Weight of steel, 0·28 lb. per cu. in. (E=30×10⁶ lb. per sq. in.)

23. Find what eccentricity of the 2,000-lb. thrust in the previous problem will make the greatest intensity of compressive stress in the bar the least possible, and the magnitude of the stress intensity.

24. A reinforced concrete beam is 10 in. wide and 20 in. deep. It has three bars of steel centred 2 in. below the top face and three centred 2 in. above the bottom face. Find what longitudinal load 3 in. below the upper edge of a cross-section will produce a maximum compressive stress of 1,000 lb. per sq. in. in the concrete if *m*=12. What are the stress intensities in the steel bars?

25. Solve No. 24 if there are four bars of reinforcement in the upper row and two below.

CHAPTER XI

FRAMED STRUCTURES

111. Frames and Trusses. The name *frame* is given to a structure consisting of a number of bars fastened together by hinged joints; the separate bars are called members of the frame. Such structures are designed to carry loads mainly applied at their joints, the members being simple ties or struts although the structure as a whole may be subjected to bending.

The external forces acting on a framed structure are the loads, and the supporting forces or reactions at its points of support. In many important framed structures the centre lines of all members and of all loads and reactions lie approximately in one plane; such structures may be called plane frames. In other cases, of which we shall notice a few, the members and forces do not lie in one plane, but are more generally distributed in space; such frames may be called space frames. The most important frames are *trusses*, which act as a whole as beams; they include braced girders of bridges called bridge trusses and roof principals called *roof trusses*.

Although the name *frame* has been applied to hinge-jointed structures, it is the usual British practice to make most framed structures with riveted or welded joints. In America and elsewhere pin-jointed structures are in many cases employed, and in such cases the force or stress in members can be determined by the principles of statics with more certainty than where the more rigid riveted joints are used. It is usual, however, to estimate the stresses in structures of which the members are riveted together, or in some cases two or more members form one continuous piece, as if the bars were all freely hinged at every joint. Such a computation neglects *secondary* (*bending*) *stresses* arising from resistance to free angular movement at the joints. The secondary stresses are sometimes separately estimated (see Art. 164).

112. Perfect and Imperfect Frames. A *perfect* frame is one which has just sufficient members to keep it stable in equilibrium under any system of external forces acting at its joints without change of shape. If the frame has either more or fewer than this number it is said to be *imperfect*. If it has fewer members it is said to be *deficient* or unstable. If it has more it is said to be a *redundant* or over rigid frame. Fig. 169 represents examples of perfect plane frames; they have the property that the length of any one member may be slightly altered (as by change of temperature or error of workmanship) without inducing stress in any of the other members.

Fig. 170 represents deficient frames: while they may be stable under a certain system of loads any change in direction or magni-

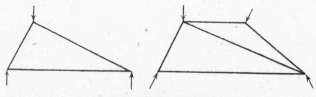

Fig. 169.—" Perfect " plane frames

tude of the applied loads may render them unstable, and change their shape except in so far as such change is resisted by rigid joints. A member joining either AB *or* CD would make the frames perfect.

Fig. 171 represents redundant frames formed by the addition of

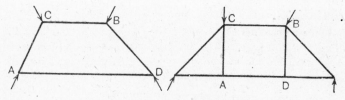

Fig. 170.—Deficient plane frames

members AB and CD to Fig. 170. Such frames are generally stressed if an alteration of length takes place in any one member due to change in its temperature or error in construction, and the frame is then said to be self-strained. The stresses in redundant frames

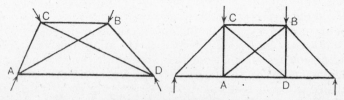

Fig. 171.—Redundant plane frames

are not calculable by the simple statical principles applicable to perfect frames; the frames are called statically indeterminate structures (see Chapter xv).

Use of Counterbraces. Such frames as those shown in Fig. 171 are frequently used; although redundant they may serve as practically perfect frames if the ties or braces AB and CD are long, because their resistance to compression (as struts) is then negligible. Thus excess of external thrust at B say, puts CD in tension, and AB out of use, while excess of thrust at C puts tension in AB while CD is idle.   Thus a structure counterbraced with flexible ties may resist the changing action of a moving load employing the braces alternately.

113. Number of Members in a Perfect Frame.   The basis of the perfect plane frame is the triangle which has three members and three joints (Fig. 169).   For every additional joint two more bars will be required in building up a more complex perfect frame which is always divisible up into triangles, hence for four joints the minimum number of members is $3+2$, for five joints $3+4$, and for n joints

$$3+2(n-3)=2n-3 \text{ members.}$$

This criterion helps to show on inspection whether a plane frame is perfect, deficient, or redundant.

Similarly the basis of the space frame is the tetrahedron, having four joints and six members; for each additional joint three additional members will be required, and for n joints the number of members will be

$$6+3(n-4)=3n-6.$$

These two formulae give the *minimum* numbers of members necessary, but do not ensure a " perfect " frame.   For members may be added where not necessary, thus making part of the frame redundant or statically indeterminate and leaving another portion deficient and capable of movement and change of shape like a mechanism.

114. Roofs and Roof Trusses.   Roofs of considerable span are supported at intervals by principals or trusses, which resist the bending resulting from the loads applied to the roof.   Fig. 172 shows five roof principals, the first of which is ABCDE, and the second A′B′C′.   The roof covering is attached to the *purlins* which transfer the load to the joints of the principals. Fig. 173 shows a number of roof trusses suitable

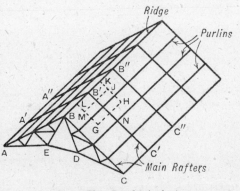

FIG. 172.—Roof principals

for various spans, and indicates to some extent the evolution of large roof trusses.   The thick lines indicate struts and the thin

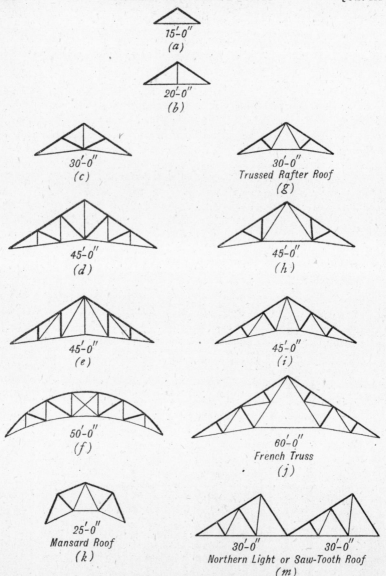

Fig. 173.—Types of roof principals or trusses

ones ties. (*a*) represents two rafters with a single tie forming a roof principal suitable for small spans; (*b*) represents the King Post truss which has a suspension rod from the apex to the cross-tie; (*c*), (*d*), and (*e*) represent suitable types of frames for larger spans; (*d*) is sometimes a timber truss, excepting the vertical ties which are steel; (*e*) represents a very common steel truss, the struts being shorter than in (*d*).   The length of main rafter between successive purlins (at joints) is usually limited to about 8 ft., which helps to determine the type of truss to be used.   The total rise of a roof with straight rafters is usually ¼ of the span, and for large spans a crescent shape such as (*f*) is sometimes adopted to obviate a high roof.

Types (*g*), (*h*), (*i*), and (*j*) may be looked upon as a different line of development for steel roofs, each main rafter being supported by its own truss, and the two trusses tied together by the main horizontal tie-bar.   The struts are short, being in many cases perpendicular to the rafters.

All these roofs may be made with the main horizontal tie-bar slightly *cambered* (*i.e.* raised above the points of support of the roof) as shown, say, $\frac{1}{40}$ of the span, or with the lower ties all in one horizontal line adjoining the two points of support.   A cambered tie admits of shorter struts.

The form (*k*) represents a Mansard roof, sometimes used when roof space is to be utilised for rooms.   (*m*) represents a very common form of roof for workshops or sheds, the short side being glazed to admit a northern light without direct sunshine.

115. Braced Girders.   A braced girder or open-webbed girder consists of tension and compression flanges to withstand the pull and thrust arising, as explained in resistance to bending moments (Chapter v), connected by bracing or web members which withstand the shearing force.   The flanges, called the upper and lower booms or chords, are often continuous, although neglecting secondary stresses, the stresses in the members are calculated as if the portions of the chords were discontinuous at the joints with the web members.   Fig. 174 shows diagrammatically the parts of a simple braced girder single-track railway bridge of the through type. When the load on a bridge is carried by the girders at the joints of the lower boom the bridge is called a *through* bridge; when at the joints of the upper chord a *deck* type.   In the former case the load passes *through* the bridge, and in the latter case *over* it.   The floor systems of bridges vary, but Fig. 174 shows a case in which the train load is carried on *rail bearers* which are supported by *cross-girders* which transfer the weight to the main girders at the joints or panel-points of the lower boom, which is divided into a number (in this case 8) of equal panels or bays.

To resist wind pressure on the side of the main girders, *wind bracing* (crossed) is placed below the track and, if head room allows, also connecting the upper booms.   If the head room is insufficient, curved or arched girders sometimes connect the top booms.   Where head room is ample, crossed braces in a vertical plane called sway bracing sometimes connect the vertical posts and assist in resisting side pressure of the wind and centrifugal force (if any) of the moving load, and in reducing distortion of the bridge due to deflection of the cross-girders or floor beams.   The end posts are also usually connected by a substantial strut called the portal strut which, particularly in the absence of upper wind bracing, transfers a considerable part of the wind load from one main girder to the other.   The portal formed by the end posts and the connecting strut is usually braced when possible.

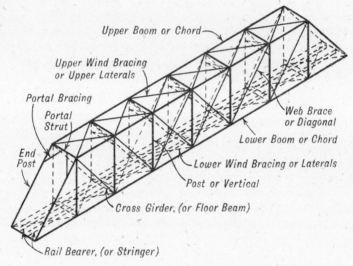

FIG. 174.—Names of parts of braced bridge girders

Chief types—(a) *Parallel type.* The commonest forms of girders with parallel chords are shown in Fig. 175; the struts are shown by thick lines and the ties by thin ones.

The **N** or Pratt type is the commonest type of braced girder for moderate spans; it is also sometimes made with end posts vertical instead of sloping as shown in the figure and in Fig. 174 (see Fig. 187).   The central bay or bays being counterbraced, the frame is, strictly speaking, redundant, but the counterbraces serving as ties only, the frame is virtually perfect.   The necessity for counterbracing near the middle of the span arises from the change in sign of the shearing force (see Art. 71 and Fig. 99) which is taken by the diagonals.

The Warren girder, the diagonals of which are inclined at 45° or 60°, also represents a fairly common form, and is a perfect frame. The Howe truss, which is fairly common in America, is used for

BRACED BRIDGE GIRDERS—PARALLEL CHORDS.

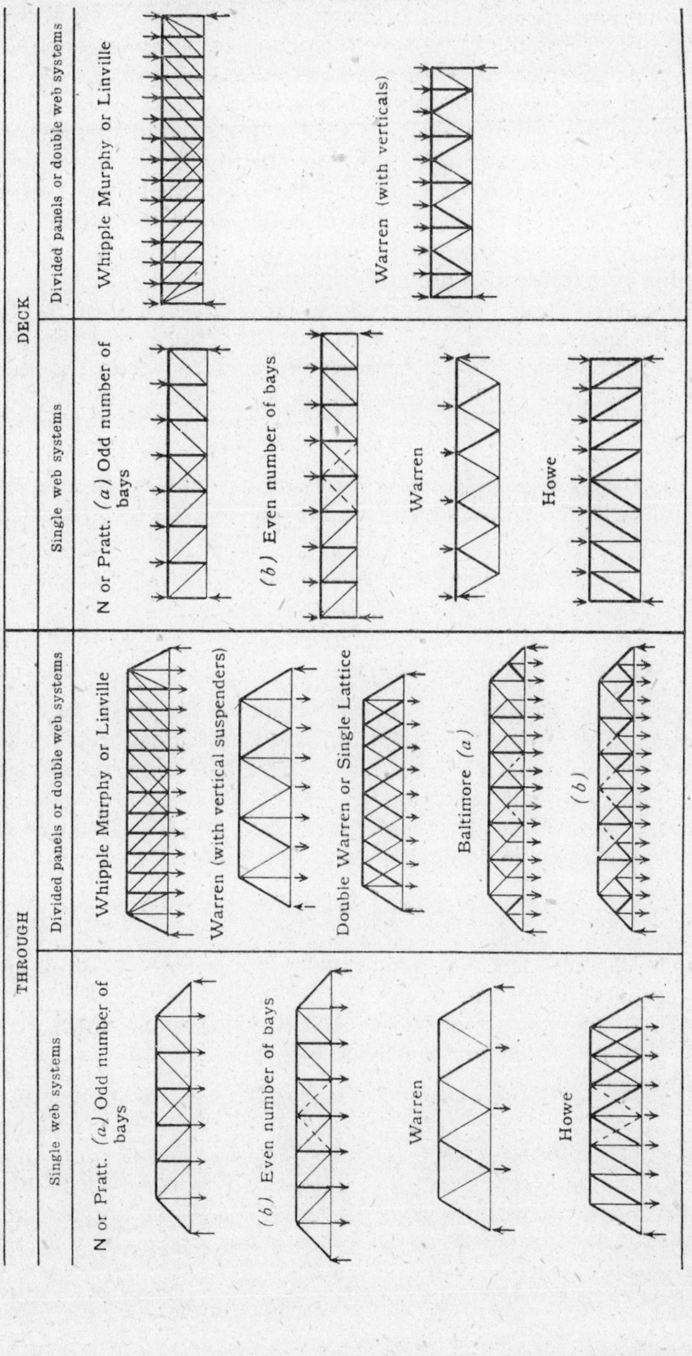

THROUGH

Single web systems

N or Pratt. (*a*) Odd number of bays

(*b*) Even number of bays

Warren

Howe

Divided panels or double web systems

Whipple Murphy or Linville

Warren (with vertical suspenders)

Double Warren or Single Lattice

Baltimore (*a*)

(*b*)

DECK

Single web systems

N or Pratt. (*a*) Odd number of bays

(*b*) Even number of bays

Warren

Howe

Divided panels or double web systems

Whipple Murphy or Linville

Warren (with verticals)

FIG. 175

combinations of steel and timber construction, the sloping struts being timber. In the **N** type, with diagonals sloping the other direction, the steel struts are vertical and as short as possible.

The shorter panels of double intersection trusses allow a shorter railbearer to be used in a large bridge with a fixed inclination of the diagonals, but require more, although slightly lighter, cross-girders. The Baltimore truss is a simple modification of the **N** type with subdivided panels and is used largely in America for long spans.   The double Warren or single-lattice girder has one redundant member. Double lattices are also used.

(b) *Curved type.*   For long spans (above, say, 180 or 200 ft.) a braced girder with a curved or broken chord becomes more economical although more expensive to construct than the parallel type.   Examples of hog-back girders, *i.e.* girders with the upper chord curved convex upwards, are shown in Figs. 179, 191, 197, and 198.

116. Dead Loads on Roofs.   The coverings may be taken as about the following weights per square foot of horizontal ground area covered:

Tiles on boarding, with steel purlins . . .	24 lb.
Slates on boarding, with steel purlins . . .	14 lb.
Corrugated iron, and steel purlins . . ; .	6 lb.
Glazed covering and purlins ·	8 lb.

In addition to this there is the weight of the truss itself to be carried.   This cannot be known accurately until it has been designed, but various formulae have been devised from existing roofs to give a preliminary estimate which may be checked after the roof is designed and if necessary the design modified accordingly.   The following such formulae are in use for pine and steel roofs: Ricker's formula [1]

$$w = \frac{s}{25} + \frac{s^2}{6,000}$$

where s=span in feet, w=weight of truss in pounds per square foot of horizontal projection of roof.   This varies from about 1 to 15 lb. per sq. ft. for spans from 20 to 200 ft.   For spans under 100 ft. roofs entirely of steel are somewhat heavier.

Howe's formula

$$w = \tfrac{3}{4}\left(1 + \frac{s}{10}\right)$$

For moderate spans inclusive dead loads some 2 to 5 lb. per sq. ft. greater than those given for coverings alone are commonly adopted.

[1] " A Study of roof Trusses," Bulletin No. 16, Univ. of Illinois, Eng. Experiment Station.

Special loads. Any load suspended from the truss must be separately allowed for in estimating the stress in the members.

Occasional loads. Snow. The allowance to be made for snow on a roof depends upon the climate. In Great Britain the usual allowance is 5 lb. per sq. ft. of horizontal projection of the roof on which snow can collect, taken in addition to dead and wind loads.

117. Wind Loads on Structures. The pressure of the wind is often one of the most important loads which exposed structures such as roofs have to bear.

Many experiments have been made to determine the pressure on surfaces resulting from wind pressure. Of these we notice particularly three series.

(1) Experiments made during the construction of the Forth Bridge [1] 1883–1890.

Pressures were recorded by gauges on small areas of 1–5 sq. ft. and also on a larger area of 300 sq. ft. The most notable fact recorded was that the maximum pressure per square foot reached on the small area was much greater than the average reached on the whole of the large area, the highest value being 41 lb. per sq. ft. on the small area and 27 lb. per sq. ft. on the large one, with average maximum values for 12 violent gales of 29·8 and 16·9 lb. respectively. The maximum values on the areas were not necessarily reached simultaneously and later experiments referred to below support the explanation that the greater pressure on the smaller area results mainly from the very localised intensity of gusts.

(2) Records made on the Forth Bridge since its erection. [2]

On 1·5 sq. ft. gauges, these experiments show the great difference of pressure at different heights above ground varying from a maximum of 65 lb. per sq. ft. at 378 ft. elevation to 20 lb. per sq. ft. at 50 ft., with average values during 15 storms (1890–1906) of 50 and 13 lb. per sq. ft. respectively.

(3) Experiments made at the National Physical Laboratory. [3]

The earlier experiments indicate a normal pressure intensity P on small circular and square surfaces a few square inches in area perpendicular to the direction of an artificial air current of

$$P = kV^2 = 0·0027 \, V^2 \text{ lb. per sq. ft.} \quad . \quad . \quad . \quad (1)$$

where V = velocity of the wind in miles per hour; other experimenters have obtained a rather higher value of the coefficient k. Various interesting results were obtained relating to pressures on

---

[1] See *Engineering*, Feb. 28th, 1890.

[2] See paper by A. Hunter, in the Transactions of the Junior Inst. of Engrs., 1906.

[3] *Proc. Inst. C.E.*, vol. clvi, " The Resistance of Plane Surfaces in a Uniform Current of Air," by T. E. Stanton; and later, " Experiments on Wind Pressure," vol. clxxi.

surfaces of different shapes, and model lattice girders on which the intensity of pressure was higher than on square plates.

It also appears that the wind pressure on flat plates consists partly of the pressure on the windward side and partly of a suction on the leeward side. On small roof models the suction on the leeward slope appeared to be of equal importance with the pressure on the windward slope.

The later experiments in the open air with wind pressure on surfaces 25 to 100 sq. ft. in area indicate a normal pressure on rectangular surfaces of about

$$P = kV^2 = 0.0032 \, V^2 \text{ lb. per sq. ft.} \quad . \quad . \quad . \quad (2)$$

with little or no difference in pressure per square foot with difference in area.

Experiments on a large model lattice girder in the open air show a pressure of

$$0.00405 \, . \, V^2 \text{ lb. per sq. ft.} \quad . \quad . \quad . \quad . \quad (3)$$

or 1·26 times as great a pressure as on a rectangular board of equal area.

The later experiments on roof slopes 56 sq. ft. in area in the open air indicate important suction effects [1] on the leeward slopes of roofs of buildings the internal pressure of which may be affected by wind, and negligible suction effects on the leeward slopes if the roof is mounted on columns through which the wind can pass freely. The normal pressure on the roof being

$$P = k \, . \, V^2 \text{ lb. per sq. ft.} \quad . \quad . \quad . \quad . \quad (4)$$

the values of k for three slopes are given as follows for the case in which internal pressure of a building may be affected by the wind (*e.g.* openings on windward side, and none on the leeward side).

	Values of k for slopes of		
	60°	45°	30°
Windward side . . .	+0·0034	+0·0028	+0·0015
Leeward side	−0·0032	—	−0·0022

The values of k for the case of a building open on both sides are the same for the windward slope and zero for the leeward slope. There is considerable advantage in being able to state the intensity of pressure on a surface, which is either perpendicular to, or oblique

---

[1] Important suction effects have also been obtained on more than half of a semi-circular roof by Albert Smith. See " Wind Loads on Buildings," in the *Journal of the Western Society of Engineers*, vol. xix, p. 369 (April, 1914). Also by H. P. Boardman, " Wind Pressure against Inclined Roofs," in the *Journal of the Western Society of Engineers*, vol. xvii, p. 285 (April 1912).

to, the direction of the wind in terms of the wind velocity, as in (2), (3), or (4), since to predetermine the probable pressure which a proposed structure will have to bear, it is only necessary to measure the maximum velocity of the wind at the site.

Actual Wind Load Allowances. A usual allowance for wind pressure perpendicular to the wind (*i.e.* on a vertical surface normal to an assumed horizontal wind) is from 30 to 50 lb. per sq. ft., according to the exposure of the situation. The value given by (3) for $V = 100$ miles per hour (about a maximum value for Great Britain) would be 40·5 lb. per sq. ft. A common allowance for bridge designs is 30 lb. per sq. ft. of train (taken at 10 sq. ft. per lineal foot) for the travelling wind load. A value often quoted for the pressure P_n normal to a roof sloop inclined at an angle α to the horizontal, in terms of the horizontal wind pressure P (neglecting leeward suction) is that given by Unwin's formula based on experiments by Hutton, viz.:

$$P_n = P \cdot \sin \alpha^{1 \cdot 84 \cos a - 1} \quad . \quad . \quad . \quad . \quad (5)$$

Another formula in common use is that of Duchemin, viz.

$$P_n = P \cdot \frac{2 \sin \alpha}{1 + \sin^2 \alpha} \quad . \quad . \quad . \quad . \quad (6)$$

The relative complication of such formulae does not appear to be justified by experimental results, and a simpler formula reasonably correct would be

$$P_n = P \cdot \alpha / 45 \quad . \quad . \quad . \quad . \quad . \quad (7)$$

for values of α up to 45° and above that slope, P_n may be taken as equal to P. This agrees with Unwin's formula for the almost standard rise of $\frac{1}{4}$ span for which $\alpha = 26° - 34'$, and $P_n = 0 \cdot 59$ P.

For roofs in inland situations codes of practice now often specify a wind load of 15 lb. per sq. ft. normal to the windward surface and a suction of 10 lb. per sq. ft. on the leeward surface acting separately and not simultaneously.

118. Dead Loads on Bridges. These consist of the weight of the steel superstructure, roadway, ballast, permanent way, etc.

Some of these items can be fairly accurately estimated before the design is complete from the known volume and density of the materials carried. The following are usual values [1]

Ballast (normally about 1 ft. deep) .	120 lb. per cu. ft.	
Concrete	140 ,,	,,
Brickwork	140 ,,	,,
Masonry	150 ,,	,,
Asphalt	136 ,,	,,
Timber	45 ,,	,,

[1] For other materials see B.S.S. No. 153, Part I (Girder Bridges).

Permanent way for single line of railway 175 lb. per ft. run (excluding ballast).

The *actual* weight of cross-girders, rail bearers, etc., should be taken into account in designing the main girders, or if a preliminary estimate is used the design should afterwards be checked by the actual values.   The weight of the main girders depends upon the type of bridge, and the actual weight should be calculated after a preliminary design; before this can be made a preliminary estimate of the dead weight of the main girders is required, and is based on the known weight of bridges of similar types.   This must be largely a matter of experience and available data of similar designs.   Various formulae have been devised to give for various types of bridges approximations to the dead weight of either the main girders, or of the whole of the steelwork including the floor.   The following may be cited:

Unwin's Formula:

$$\text{Weight of girder in tons per foot run} = w = \frac{Wr}{cs - lr} \quad . \quad (1)$$

where W = total equivalent uniformly distributed dead load in tons.

r = ratio of span to depth.

l = clear span in feet.

s = working stress in tons per square inch in the booms.

c = a constant of about 1,400 in small plate girders to about 1,800 for braced girders, or may be deduced for any type of girder from examples of known size, weight, and working stress.

Anderson's Formula (for plate girders):

$$w = W/500 \quad . \quad . \quad . \quad . \quad . \quad (2)$$

American Formulae.   These are generally attempts to approximate to all the dead load of the structure including the floor and are of the type

$$w = al + b \quad . \quad . \quad . \quad . \quad . \quad . \quad (3)$$

where a and b are constants depending on the type of bridge, and whether for single or double-track railway, on the traffic to be borne, and upon the working intensity of stress allowed.   Evidently the variables s and r in (1) must affect the value of w, and a formula such as (3) can only be used under fairly restricted values of s and r which are established practice.   Thus the values of a and b applicable to say an American bridge company's usual design would give a much smaller value of w than would correspond to the practice of say a British railway for a similar rolling load.

119. Moving Loads on Bridges.[1]   These vary greatly according to

[1] For British Standard loadings, longitudinal forces and centrifugal effects see B.S.S. No. 153, Part 3, and Appendix.

the class of traffic to be borne, and some values have been given in Arts. 69 and 70.

The wind load on a moving train is sometimes treated separately as a moving load, or allowed for by an increase in the uniformly distributed wind load on the girders.

Load due to Centrifugal Force. The lateral pressure on the rails due to the centrifugal force exerted by any part of a train if the line of rails crossing a bridge is on a curve is calculated from the formula $W \cdot v^2/gr$, where W is the weight of the portion considered, v its speed in feet per second, $g = 32 \cdot 2$ ft. per sec. per sec., and r is the radius of the curve in feet. This lateral pressure is added to the wind pressure on the loaded boom of the bridge and affects the stress in the lateral or wind bracing. The eccentricity of the centre of gravity of the train loads due to elevation of the outer rail on a curve will also cause some slight modification in the stresses produced in the structure.

Load due to Braking Forces. The (forward) horizontal forces exerted by a train on the rails when brakes are applied may amount to about one-fifth of the weight of the train distributed in the same way as the wheel loads. The most important effect will be to cause bending stress in the cross-girders which bend in a horizontal plane.

120. Incidence and Distribution of Loads on Framed Structures. A frame is designed to resist forces applied at its joints, and in framed structures means are taken to insure that the loads are applied at the joints. Thus in a roof the loads due to the covering and the wind are carried on purlins (Fig. 172) resting on the joints of the rafters and the purlins transfer the load to the joint.

The load taken at any joint, such as that between B′ and N (Fig. 172), is regarded as the load falling on the surface MGHJ extending half-way to each of the neighbouring joints B′ and N on the same principal A′B′C′ and half-way to the neighbouring principals ABC and A″B″C″. The load carried at B′ is that on a similar area extending on either side of the ridge, while that carried at C′ is on an area equal to that between two consecutive principals and extending from C′ half-way to the nearest purlin.

Again, in a through bridge (Fig. 174) the floor load carried by a cross-girder is that on the area extending half-way to each of the neighbouring cross-girders and is transferred by the cross-girders to the joint of the loaded (lower) chord of the main girder. The rolling load is transferred from the railbearers to the cross-girders, the amount borne by the latter being the reactions of the railbearers calculated by the principles of statics for a beam resting *freely* on supports at its ends (see Art. 68).

The weight of the main girders is actually a distributed load, but where there are many cross-girders and therefore many panels their weight may, like the loads, be generally divided up for convenience and with sufficient accuracy into concentrated loads at the joints; the load at each joint being that on the half-panel on either side of it and that at an end joint being the load on half an end panel. The dead load exclusive of the weight of the girder is carried by the same chord as the live load. Consequently it is often assumed that two-thirds of the total dead load comes on the loaded chord joints and one-third (due to part of the weight of the girder) comes on the joints of the unloaded chord. In large girders the proportion on each should be carefully estimated.

Where a load is applied other than at a joint (as where purlins are placed between joints) or in the case of the weight of the members of a frame, such load is divided between joints according to the principles of statics (Art. 32), but in addition to the simple stresses there is bending stress in the members carrying such loads, and this, unless negligible, must be taken into account in estimating the stresses in members of the structure (see Arts. 108 and 109).

In some cases a load is shared by two or more parts of a structure in a way which cannot very simply be calculated, the proportion borne by each depending upon the relative stiffness of the parts. Examples of such distribution are given in Arts. 148 to 154, but frequently some assumption as to the distribution greatly simplifies calculation and is sufficient for a reasonably approximate estimate of stresses. For example, if a horizontal wind load is carried by one side of the girders of the through bridge in Fig. 174, the load on the upper flange is transferred to the end supports of the bridge partly by the main girder's end posts, the upper horizontal girder or wind bracing being thereby stressed in passing some of the load to the leeward main girder. But some load on the upper boom is transferred to the lower or loaded boom by the verticals at each joint (resisting bending), and consequently the lower wind bracing may be taken to carry somewhat over half the wind load. Nevertheless it would be well to allow for the full half of the wind load being transferred from the upper to the lower flange at the ends and for the full half-wind load being carried by the upper wind bracing. Various assumptions are in use.

Examples XI

1. A roof of the type shown in Fig. 176, 28-ft. span and 7-ft. rise with principals 8 ft. apart has a covering weighing 14 lb. per sq. ft. of covered area. Find the total dead load assignable to each of the five outer joints of the principals. If in addition there is a wind exerting a pressure of 30 lb. per sq. ft. normal to the roof, find the normal wind loads assignable to each of the three outer joints on the windward side of the roof.

2. Find the total wind load per principal on the slope of a roof of 40-ft. span, 10-ft. rise, principals 10 ft. apart when the horizontal wind pressure is 56 lb. per sq. ft., using Unwin's formula or formula (7) of Art. 117

3. With the same wind pressure as in Problem No. 2, find the wind loads on each of the five joints on the windward side of a French roof truss of 50-ft. span, $12\frac{1}{2}$-ft. rise, principals 12 ft. apart.

CHAPTER XII

STRESSES IN FRAMES

121. Methods of Determining Stresses in Members of Perfect Frames. The stresses in individual members of a perfect frame which are all either struts or ties are determined by application of the principles of statics stated in Chapter III. Either graphical or algebraic methods or a combination of both may be employed, but in any case the following are the guiding principles. (1) The frame as a whole is a rigid body and the external forces (load and reactions) acting upon it form by themselves a system of forces (generally non-concurrent) in equilibrium. (2) The pulls or thrusts of the several members meeting in any joint form a system of concurrent or nearly concurrent forces in equilibrium. (3) Any portion of the structure may be taken as a rigid body held in equilibrium by the external forces acting upon it together with the forces exerted upon it, through members, by the remainder of the structure.

122. Stress Diagrams. If force polygons are drawn for the external forces on a plane frame and for each joint of the frame, the polygons can all be fitted together in a single vector figure called a stress diagram. In this vector diagram each line, taken in opposite directions, represents two forces, viz. a side in each of the two separate force polygons which go to make up the whole stress diagram.

Simple Roof Truss. An example will make this clear. Let the simple roof truss shown in Fig. 176 be acted upon by the vertical forces AB, BC, CD, at its joints as shown. The vertical reactions DE and EA may be found by the method of Art. 32, but in this case from the symmetry, DE and EA are each half of the sum of the three loads. The line *abcd* is set out to represent the loads, and its point of bisection at *e* gives the magnitude of *de* and *ea* the reactions, *abcdea* constituting the closed polygon for the external forces on the frame. The force polygon for the joint at the left-hand support may now be drawn, since only the two sides *af* and *fe* are unknown. Indicating joints by the space letters for the members or force lines radiating from it, the polygon for the joint ABGF may now be drawn, for the thrust of the member AF is equal and opposite at its two ends. The sides *fa*, *ab* are already drawn, and the polygon *fabgf* is completed by drawing through *b* a line parallel to BG, and then through *f* a line parallel to FG to meet in *g*. Proceeding in this way the whole stress diagram *abcdefghkl* may be drawn in, and includes force polygons for each joint. When the polygon for either the joint LEHK or LKCD has been drawn there remains only one side to complete the stress diagram: if the former joint is solved first the remaining side is *ld*; this may be drawn parallel to LD from say *l*, and if it passes through *d* this fact checks the accuracy of the previous drawing. The polygon for the joint DEL will have been drawn (unconsciously) in drawing the polygons for the external forces and the two neighbouring joints. In the completed figure

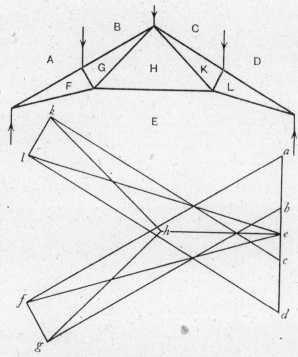

Fig. 176.—Stress diagram for simple roof truss

each line represents as previously stated two forces; thus the vector *bg* represents the thrust of the rafter BG on the joint ABGF, while the vector *gb* represents the thrust of the same rafter BG on the joint BCKHG. Or again, *he* represents the pull in the rod HE at the joint HEFG, while *eh* represents the pull of the tie-rod HE at the joint HKLE.

Reciprocal Figures. The frame or space diagram of, say, Fig. 176, and the stress or vector diagram, form reciprocal figures which have certain reciprocal properties; to each node or vertex from which lines radiate in one figure there is a corresponding closed polygon in the other bounded by sides corresponding to the radiating lines and respectively parallel to them. To each line joining two nodes in either figure there is a corresponding line in the other forming a common side to the polygons corresponding to the two nodes.

To distinguish between Ties and Struts from the Stress Diagram. Knowing the direction of, say, the force EA (upward) at the joint EAF, it is evident from Fig. 176, that the correct order of letters in the vector polygon for this joint is *eaf* (not *efa*), hence the force at this joint exerted by the rafter AF is represented by *af* (not *fa*), and is a thrust, *i.e.* the member is a strut. The correct order of sides *eaf* being *ea, af, fe* the corresponding order of the lines EA, AF, FE radiating from this joint is a *clockwise* order. When this order is clockwise for one joint it immediately follows that it must be the same for the neighbouring joints, for a thrust, *af*, must be associated with a balancing thrust, *fa*, at the next joint of the rafter. Similarly, it follows that the correct order is clockwise for *all* the joints. Hence if we wish to know whether the member HK say is a strut or a tie, we know that for the joint HKLE the force in HK is in the direction *hk* (not *kh*), and reference to the vector diagram shows that the direction *hk* is a *pull* at the joint HKLE, *i.e.* HK is a *tie*.

This characteristic order of space letters round the joints is a very convenient method of picking out the kind of stress in one member of a complicated frame. Note that it is the characteristic order of space letters round a joint that is constant in a given diagram—*not* the direction of vectors round the various polygons constituting the stress diagram.

Fig. 177 represents the stress diagram for exactly the same frame diagram and lettering as Fig. 176, but is the contra-clockwise vector diagram, *e.g.* the left-hand reaction AE is now represented by *ae* (instead of *ea*), and the force of KH at the joint HELK is represented by *kh* (instead of *hk*), which still indicates the member to be a tie.

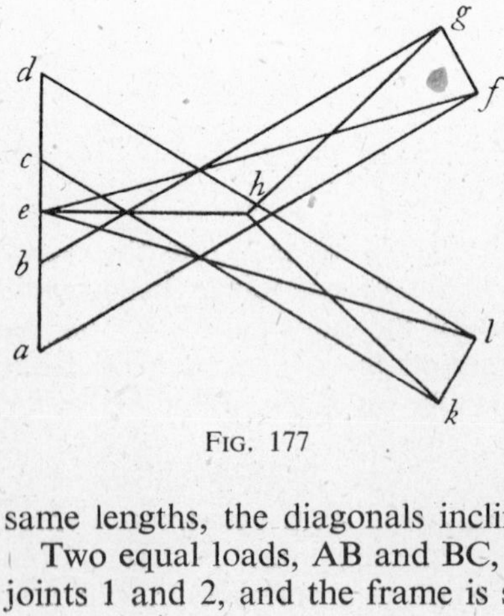

Fig. 177

Warren Girder. A second example of a simple stress diagram is shown in Fig. 178, viz. that of a Warren girder, all members generally being of the same lengths, the diagonals inclined 60° to the horizontal.

Two equal loads, AB and BC, have been supposed to act at the joints 1 and 2, and the frame is supported by vertical reactions at

3 and 4, which are found by a funicular polygon or may be very easily calculated by taking moments about the points of support. The remaining forces in the bars are found by completing the stress diagram *abc . . . klm.*

Note that the force AB at joint 1 is downward, *i.e.* in the direction *ab* in the vector diagram corresponding to a contra-clockwise order, A to B, round joint 1. This is, then, the characteristic order (contra-clockwise) for all the joints, *e.g.* to find the nature of the stress in KL, the order of letters for joint 5 is K to L (contra-clockwise), and referring to the vector diagram, the direction *k* to *l* represents a thrust of the bar KL on joint 5; the bar KL is, therefore, in compression.

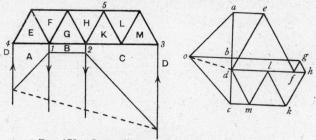

Fig. 178.—Stress diagram for simple Warren girder

Curved or Hog-back N *Girder.* Fig. 179 shows the stress diagram for a girder of the Hog-back or Curved Top Chord type, the span being divided into eight equal panels each carrying a load W. Half the load on the end panels is carried directly at the supports, and may be ignored in the reactions used for calculating the stress in the members. The following are the stresses scaled from Fig. 179 in terms of the panel loads W:

Members	AL, AY	AN, AW	AP, AU	AR, AS	AK, AZ	LM, YX	NO, WV	
Compression.	4·07W	5·6W	6·25W	6·375W	3·5W	1·375W	0·417W	

Members	HM, CX	GO, DV	FQ, ET	KL, ZY	MN, XW	OP, VU	PQ, UT	QR, TS	RS
Tension	3·88W	5·5W	6·2W	4·57W	2·13W	1·00W	0·25W	0·267W	0·583W

The members JK and BZ are not stressed.

French Roof Truss. The stress diagram of this roof truss (known in America as the Fink roof truss) involves an interesting special point such as may be met with in other structures. The vertical loads are shown in Fig. 180 as symmetrical, but the methods are the

same in any case.   When the reactions HJ and JA have been determined, the polygons for the joints JAK, KABL, KLMJ, may
successively be drawn.   On attempting to draw the vector polygon
for either of the joints BCPNML or MNRJ, it will be noticed that
more than two sides are unknown, and the plane polygon is therefore not determinate.   If a start be made to draw the stress diagram
from the other end the same difficulty is apparent.   To overcome it,
the stress in one or more members must be determined by some other

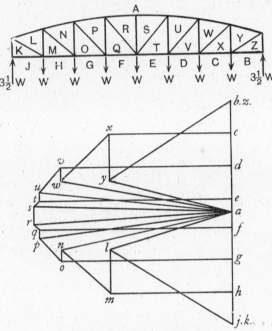

Fig. 179.—Hog-back N girder

method, and several are available, such as the method of sections
(see Art. 127).   The method adopted in Fig. 180 is known as the
method of substitution.   By it the stress in QD is determined from
the fact that the thrust in QD is not affected by the form of the
internal bracing consisting of the members QP and PN.   Hence to
find the stress in QD, replace (temporarily or in imagination) the
bars QP and PN by a single bar QY, connecting the joints marked
1 and 2, thus reducing the number of bars radiating from the joint
BCNML by one, the polygon *bcyml* may now be completed by
drawing *my* and *cy* parallel to MY and CY respectively to intersect
in *y*, and the polygon *cdqy* may then be completed by drawing *dq*
and *yq* parallel to DQ and YQ respectively to intersect in *q*.   The
stress *dq* in DQ is now known, and the previous bracing may be

replaced and the polygon *cdqb* drawn, and the whole stress diagram completed. The point *y* is not a vertex or node in the completed diagram.

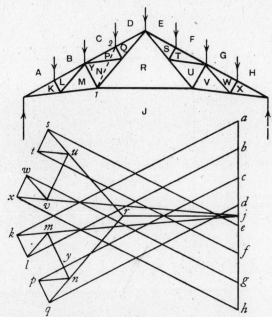

Fig. 180.—Stress diagram for French roof truss

Island Station Roof. This is shown in Fig. 181, the loads being given in tons, and is an example of a structure which is not wholly a perfect frame. The post is continuous from the base Y to the apex V. *abcdeml* is the stress diagram for the left side and *ghkon* that for the right side. The post is subjected to bending moments proportional to the ordinates shown to the right of the space diagram. The principal magnitudes of these bending moments, found by taking component forces perpendicular to the post (neglecting the effect of flexure), are

$$M_X = VX \times \text{horizontal component of } mn = \frac{15}{\sqrt{3}} \times 1·60 = 13·9 \text{ tons-ft.}$$

$M_Y = VY \times$ horizontal component of $mn - XY \times$ horizontal components of *am* and *nk*.

$\quad = (VX + XY) \times$ horizontal component of $mn - XY \times$ horizontal components of *am* and *nk*.

$\quad = M_X - XY \times$ horizontal component of $ak = 13·9 - 1·61 \times 15.$

$\quad = -10·2$ ton-ft.

where the positive sign corresponds to contra-clockwise bending moments above the section considered.

N

The point of contraflexure being distant z from X
$$13 \cdot 9 - 1 \cdot 61 z = 0, \qquad z = 8 \cdot 66 \text{ ft.}$$
which may also be found from the bending-moment diagram.

The bending moments between X and Y might be found by con-

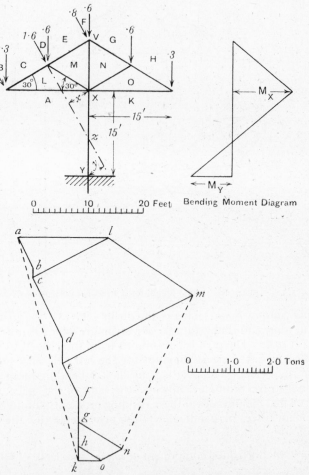

FIG. 181.—Open-stress diagram for roof on column

sidering the roof as a rigid body, the oblique forces only producing bending moment on XY. The resultant oblique force is evidently $0 \cdot 8 + 1 \cdot 6 + 0 \cdot 8 = 3 \cdot 2$ in the line CD. Then
$$M_X = 3 \cdot 2 \times x = 13 \cdot 9 \text{ ton-ft.}$$
$$M_Y = -3 \cdot 2 \times y = -10 \cdot 2 \text{ ton-ft.}$$

and the line CD cuts XY in Z, which measures 8·67 ft. from X and gives the point of inflexion.

123. Stress Diagrams for Roofs with Wind Loads. When, in addition to vertical loads, a roof is subjected to oblique forces such as wind loads distributed as explained in Art. 120, the reactions at the supports of a principal will not be vertical. The magnitude and direction of the reactions will depend partly upon the way in which the roof principal is supported. In roofs of considerable span it is not uncommon to support one end on horizontal rollers, while the other end is horizontally hinged; this admits of expansion of the principal, and also makes the supporting forces determinate, for, neglecting friction, the supporting force at the end resting on rollers, or the " free " end, must be vertical. The other reaction is known by a point in its line of action (the hinge), and therefore both reactions may be determined as explained below. Figs. 183, 184, and 184A show an example of a roof hinged at the left side, and " free " or freely supported on rollers at the right-hand side; we return to this in the next article (Art. 124).

If the maximum and minimum stresses are required it will be necessary to draw a stress diagram for the vertical loads acting alone. Sometimes the stress diagrams for the wind loads alone for either side are drawn without inclusion of the dead vertical loads and a separate diagram for the vertical loads. This plan is illustrated in the next article (Art. 124, Fig. 182).

When a roof is hinged at both sides the reactions are not really statically determinate. They are usually taken as parallel; but if the wind loads and vertical loads are combined, and the reactions taken both parallel to the resultant load, the result is not the same as if wind loads and vertical loads are drawn on separate diagrams and the reactions taken parallel to the resultant in each case. The vertical components of the reactions are the same in either case, but the horizontal components arising from the oblique wind pressures differ; it may be shown that the most probable distribution of horizontal pressure on the hinges is half the horizontal wind pressure on each hinge. However, if either of the other two methods are used the resulting stress determinations for the members is not in practical cases greatly different, and both separate and combined diagrams are in frequent use. Fig. 185 shows the stress diagram for a curved roof hinged at one side and freely supported on rollers at the other. The roof principals are spaced 12 ft. 6 in. apart, and a wind load of 40 lb. horizontally and a vertical load of 25 lb. per sq. ft. have been assumed. The vertical and wind loads have been combined by parallelograms in the space diagrams of Fig. 185. For wind from the left the resulting inclined forces AB, BC, CD, and DE have been set off in the stress diagram at *abcde* and the remaining (vertical) forces EF, FG, GH, and HJ at *efghj*. Then an indefinite vertical line *ka* has been drawn to represent the direction of the vertical reaction KA at the left-hand side; any pole *o* has been chosen and radiating lines have been drawn from *o*, to *a, b, c, d, e, f, g, h*, and *j* and the corresponding funicular polygon *starting from the fixed (or hinged) end* and finally meeting the vertical through the free end in X has been drawn. This point X has been joined to the hinge centre at the fixed end thus closing the funicular polygon and through *o*, a line *o, k* parallel to this closing side has been drawn to determine *k*, thus giving the magnitudes of the supporting forces *jk* at the hinged end and *ka* at the free end. The stress diagram is then easily completed. The diagram for the case of wind from the right has been similarly drawn.

124. Simple Roof Design. A simple example of roof design is shown in Plate I. The effective span is 40 ft. The centres of the principals are 12 ft. apart. Rise, $\frac{1}{4}$ span = 10 ft. Purlins are assumed to be over struts only so that there is no transverse load on principal rafters between their points of support. The stress diagrams (Figs. 182–184A) involve no new point, but again the funicular polygon used to determine the end supporting forces must be started from the hinge at the left-hand support.

Dead loads per square foot of sloping surface:

Slates	8·0 lb.
Slating battens .	0·6 ,,
Counter-battens .	0·5 ,,
Roofing felt . .	0·5 ,,
1-in. rough boards	2·5 ,,
Common rafters .	1·5 ,,
Fir purlins . .	1·4 ,,
Weight of truss .	2·4 ,,

Total dead load . . 17·4 lb., say, 18 lb. per sq. ft. Principal rafter lengths are 22·4 ft.

Total Dead Load per Principal = 2(22·4 ft. × 12·0 ft. × 18 lb. per sq. ft.)

= 9,677 lb. (see stress diagram for dead loads only (Fig. 182), where *ah* = 9,677 lb.).

Snow Load. = 5 lb. per sq. ft.

Snow Load per Principal = 2 × 22·4 ft. × 12 ft. × 5 lb. per sq. ft. = 2,688 lb. A separate stress diagram for this is not necessary; the stresses in column 3 of the Table of Stresses are calculated as $\frac{5}{18}$ of those in column 2.

Total Static Load. 9,677 + 2,688 = 12,365 lb., which appears as the total vertical load AH in the auxiliary diagram on the right of

Fig. 183, which shows how the load line has been obtained in the stress diagram for combined static loads and wind pressure on the fixed side.

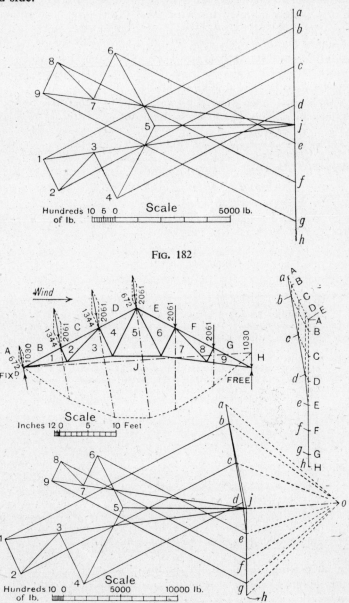

FIG. 182

FIG. 183

Wind Loading. 15 lb. per sq. ft. pressure normal to the windward surface and 10 lb. per sq. ft. suction, acting separately and not simultaneously on the leeward surface. These are values such as are now widely adopted for structures of this type in inland situations.

Total Windward Pressure $=22\cdot4$ ft. $\times 12$ ft. $\times 15$ lb. per sq. ft. $=$ 4,032 lb. used in stress diagrams Figs. 183, 184, and 184A.

Total Leeward Suction $=22\cdot4$ ft. $\times 12$ ft. $\times 10$ lb. per sq. ft. $=$ 2,688 lb. used in Figs. 184 and 184A.

A table of stresses is given. Columns 2 to 7 inclusive are figures obtained by scale from the stress diagrams.

TABLE OF STRESSES FROM STRESS DIAGRAMS, FIGS. 182, 183, 184 AND 184A

(*Compression+*, *Tension* −)

1	2	3	4	5	6	7	8	9	10
			Wind pressure		Wind suction		Minimum dead +suction	Maximum dead +snow +pressure	Stress for practical design
Member	Dead load	Snow load	on left (fixed)	on right (free)	in left (fixed)	on right (free)			
B 1	+12200	+3390	+6220	+2700	−3930	−1770	+8270	+21810	
G 9	+12200	+3390	+3410	+5400	−2180	−3580	+8620	+20990	
C 2	+11500	+3190	+6220	+2700	−3930	−1770	+7570	+20910	+21810
F 8	+11500	+3190	+3410	+5400	−2180	−3580	+7920	+20090	
D 4	+8670	+2410	+4350	+2700	−2680	−1770	+5990	+15430	
E 6	+8670	+2410	+3410	+3580	−2180	−2390	+6280	+14660	
J 1	−11030	−3060	−7160	−620	+4550	+390	−6480	−21250	
J 9	−11030	−3060	−3090	−4590	+1940	+3000	−8030	−18680	
J 3	−8810	−2450	−5200	−620	+3220	+390	−5590	−16460	−21250
J 7	−8810	−2450	−3090	−2630	+1940	+1670	−6870	−14350	
J 5	−6090	−1690	−2870	−560	+1820	+360	−4270	−10650	−10650
1–2	+1440	+400	+1340	Nil	−900	Nil	+540	+3180	+3180
8–9	+1440	+400	+1340	+1340	Nil	−900	+540	+3180	
2–3	−2230	−620	−1960	Nil	+1330	Nil	−900	−4810	−4810
7–8	−2230	−620	Nil	−1960	Nil	+1330	−900	−4810	
3–4	+2160	+600	+2020	Nil	−1340	Nil	+820	+4780	+4780
6–7	+2160	+600	Nil	+2020	Nil	−1340	+820	+4780	
4–5	−3470	−960	−2830	−130	+1720	+80	−1750	−7260	−7260
5–6	−3470	−960	−410	−2400	+250	+1570	−1900	−6830	

In calculating the maximum combinations of stresses in column 9 of the table, reduction of stress due to suction is not generally permissible, but as suction tends to reverse the nature of the stress in all members (compare columns 6 and 7 with 2) it is necessary to

Plate I.—Details of the Roof Truss shown in Figs. 182, 183, 184 & 184A.   40' 0" effective span.   Centres of Trusses, 12' 0" rise, ¼ span.

6 lbs. lead flashing on wood roll
Tilting fillet
Countess Slates (20"×10") centre nailed
1"× 2" slating battens 8½"cens
1"× 2" counter battens 12"cens
Sarking Felt
1" roof boarding
Slating is shown diagrammatically.

2 bolts zigzag
2"× 2" steel seating 6" long.
2"×11" ridge board
Ridge plates bent from 6"×⅜"flats
3/8" apex plate or crown plate
Bolts for site assembly

Notes

If timber is of high-grade Douglas Fir or Long-Leaved Pitch Pine, scantlings may be reduced thus :—
For Purlins, 5"×8" or 4"×9".   For Common Rafters, 2"×3½".

If Common Rafters are omitted and Roof Boarding is carried on 3"×7" ungraded fir purlins at 2' 6" centres (2½"×7" graded), the Principal Rafters are to be increased to 2—3½"×2½"×¼" ⌐s for resistance to tranverse bending.

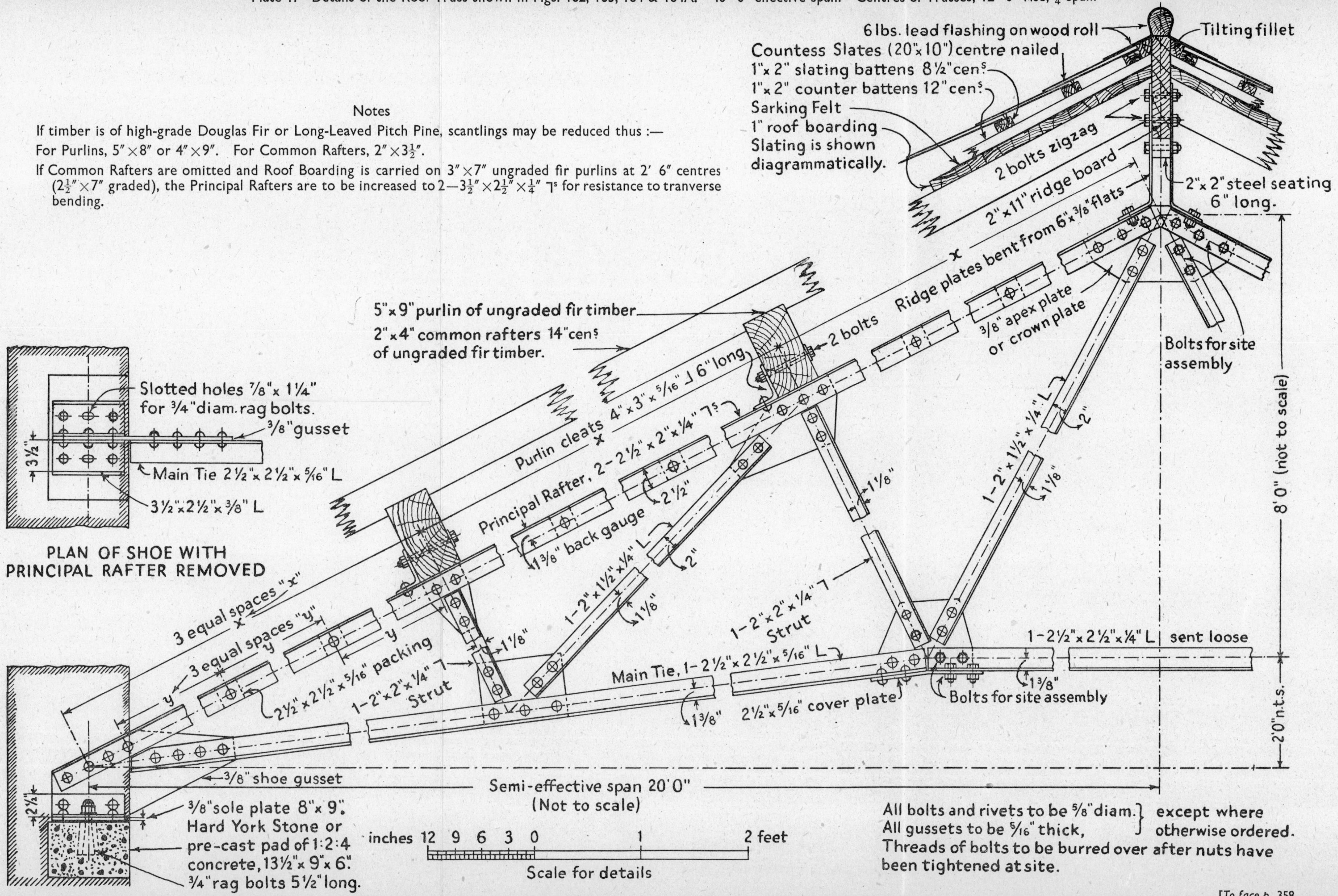

5"×9" purlin of ungraded fir timber
2"×4" common rafters 14"cens of ungraded fir timber.

Purlin cleats 4"×3"×5/16" ⌐ 6" long.
2 bolts
1—2"×1½"×¼"⌐
2"
1⅛"

8'0" (not to scale)

Slotted holes ⅞"× 1¼" for ¾"diam. rag bolts.
3/8"gusset
3½"
Main Tie 2½"×2½"×5/16" L
3½"×2½"×3/8" L

Principal Rafter, 2–2½"×2"×¼" ⌐s
1⅜" back gauge
2½"
2"
1⅛"

PLAN OF SHOE WITH PRINCIPAL RAFTER REMOVED

3 equal spaces "x"
3 equal spaces "y"
y
2½"×2½"×5/16" packing
1—2"×2"×¼"⌐ Strut
1⅛"

1—2"×1½"×¼"⌐
1⅛"
1—2"×2"×¼"⌐ Strut
1—2½"×2½"×¼"L sent loose
2"
1⅛"

Main Tie, 1–2½"×2½"×5/16" L
2½"×5/16" cover plate
1⅜"
Bolts for site assembly
1⅜"

Semi-effective span 20'0"
(Not to scale)

3/8"shoe gusset
2'0" n.t.s.

2½"
3/8"sole plate 8"× 9".
Hard York Stone or pre-cast pad of 1:2:4 concrete, 13½"× 9"× 6".
¾"rag bolts 5½"long.

inches 12 9 6 3 0   1   2 feet
Scale for details

All bolts and rivets to be ⅝"diam.} except where
All gussets to be 5/16" thick, otherwise ordered.
Threads of bolts to be burred over after nuts have been tightened at site.

[To face p. 358.

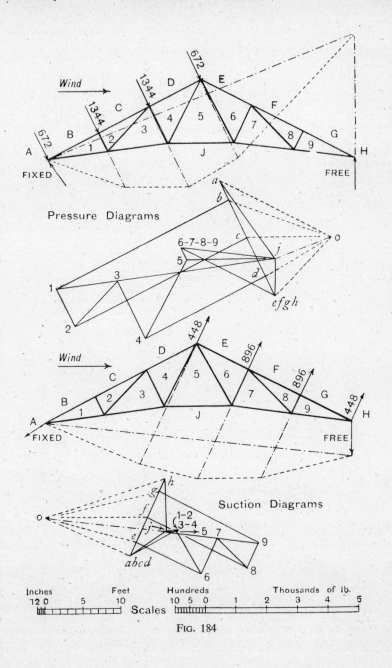

Pressure Diagrams

Suction Diagrams

| Inches | | Feet | Hundreds | | Thousands of lb. |
Scales

FIG. 184

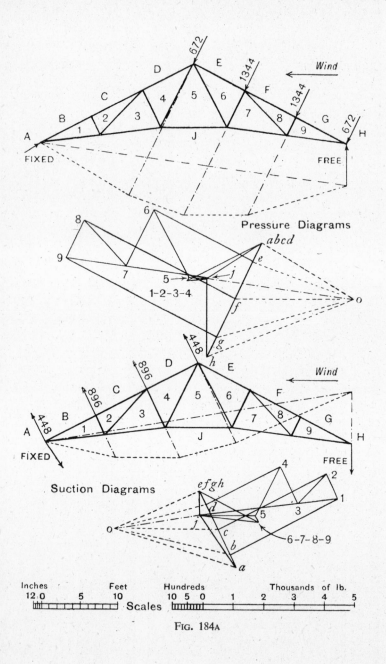

Pressure Diagrams

Suction Diagrams

Inches　　　　Feet　　　Hundreds　　　　Thousands of lb.

FIG. 184A

consider whether reversal of stress is possible, hence the necessity of column 8 giving the minimum stresses. If the stress in a member is liable to reversal the member must be capable of acting as a tie or a strut. In this example no member has to act in such a dual capacity. But it is usual for all tension members to be made of a section capable of resisting some compression in order to provide lateral rigidity and resistance to deformation during transport and hoisting. In this case the maximum stresses all arise from the incidence of dead load, snow load on both main rafters, and wind

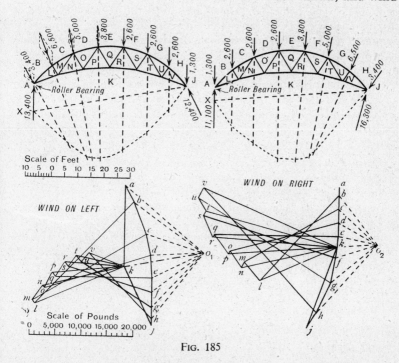

FIG. 185

pressure on the rafter having the fixed shoe so a single-stress diagram combining this loading in one operation would suffice and give the governing stresses. Such a diagram is shown in Fig. 183.

The design is simplified by making members continuous where economically practicable, *e.g.* the stress of B1 determine the section of C2 and D4 and for symmetry also E6, F8, and G9.

The table of stresses shows that in every case the proportion of the practical stress which is due to wind pressure exceeds one-third of the sum of dead and snow stresses, hence advantage can be taken of an important concession in design regulations which permits, in such cases, an increase of allowable unit working stresses to

N*

one-third beyond those recognised for static loading. Normally roof structures are much under-stressed.

Practical considerations. Tension members are often made of unequal angle sections, the longer leg being attached to the gussets and thus carrying the major portion of the stress. A conventional allowance is made (without exact calculation) by taking the tension member section as (area of attached leg, less rivet holes)+($\frac{1}{2}$ area of unattached leg). For compression members of single angles fixed by one leg a similar allowance is made, but the area of hole is not deducted. The principal rafters are preferably made of pairs of small angles with the gusset plates between them giving symmetrical connections for purlins and ensuring transverse loading in the plane of a principal axis where such loading occurs and avoiding unsymmetrical bending (see Art. 52).

Compression members in roof trusses are commonly assumed to have one end fixed and the other end hinged and the effective lengths are conventionally assumed to be 0·85 [1] of the actual unsupported length.

Working Stresses (allowing for one-third increases):

Tension, $8 \times 1\frac{1}{3} = 10\cdot67$ tons per sq. in.

Shop-driven rivets, single shear, $6 \times 1\frac{1}{3} = 8$ tons per sq. in.

Shop-driven rivets, bearing pressure, $12 \times 1\frac{1}{3} = 16$ tons per sq. in.

Black bolts for site assembly, single shear, $4 \times 1\frac{1}{3} = 5\cdot3$ tons per sq. in.

Black bolts for site assembly, bearing pressure, $8 \times 1\frac{1}{3} = 10\cdot67$ tons per sq. in.

Compression members, $1\frac{1}{3} \times$ (stress calculated by the Perry-Robertson formula (21), Art. 107).

Bolts and rivets are $\frac{5}{8}$ in. diameter, cross-sectional area = 0·3068 sq. in.

Design of Typical Members:

Member B1. Compression 21,810 lb. = 9·74 tons. Unsupported length between centre lines of shoe and strut 1–2 = 7 ft. 6 in. Effective length $l = 0\cdot85 \times 90 = 76\cdot5$ in. The smallest section for the principal rafters from practical considerations consists of two $2\frac{1}{2}$ in. $\times 2$ in. $\times \frac{1}{4}$ in. angles and their adequacy must be checked. Least radius of gyration (k) of this combination (from tables in Structural Handbooks) is 0·77 in., total cross-sectional area = 2·12 sq. in. Slenderness ratio $(l/k) = 76\cdot5/0\cdot77 = 100$ approximately. Using the symbols of Art. 107, yield stress, $f_c = 18$ tons per sq. in.; $p_e = \pi^2 \times 13{,}000/(l/k)^2 = 12\cdot83$ tons per sq. in.; $\eta = 0\cdot003 \times 100 = 0\cdot3$.

---

[1] The ideal fraction is 0·7 (see Art. 103, Case IV, Fig. 154), but the Steel Structures Research Committee recommends 0·85 as the value for the more indefinite conditions of practical design.

Factor of safety $=2\cdot36$ applied to (21) of Art. 107 gives a working stress of

$$p=[\tfrac{1}{2}(18+1\cdot3\times12\cdot83)-\tfrac{1}{2}\sqrt{(18+1\cdot3\times12\cdot83)^2-4\times18\times12\cdot83]}\div2\cdot36$$
$$=8\cdot99/2\cdot36=3\cdot81 \text{ tons per sq. in.}$$ (Fig. 163 shows it to be a little less than 4 tons per sq. in.)

Permissible total stress $=1\tfrac{1}{3}\times3\cdot81=5\cdot08$ tons per sq. in.

Actual stress $=9\cdot74$ tons $\div2\cdot12$ sq. in. $=4\cdot59$ tons per sq. in., therefore this proposed section is adequate.

Connection of B1 *to shoe gusset.* Strength of one rivet in double shear $=2\times0\cdot3068$ sq. in. $\times8$ tons per sq. in. $=4\cdot91$ tons. The thickness being less than that of two angles, bearing strength $=\tfrac{5}{8}$ in. $\times\tfrac{3}{8}$ in. $\times16$ tons per sq. in. $=3\cdot75$ tons, which, being less than the shearing strength of $4\cdot91$ tons, determines the number of rivets required, viz. $9\cdot74/3\cdot75=3$ rivets. Four rivets are adopted to give a better fixing of the long projecting gusset.

Strut 3–4. 4,780 lb. $=2\cdot14$ tons compression. Unsupported length from frame diagram (representing rivet-pitch lines) $=$ 5 ft. 2 in. Effective length $=0\cdot85\times62=52\cdot7$ in. A single angle is sufficient but the connected leg must be at least 2 in. wide for $\tfrac{5}{8}$-in. rivets. Checking the adequacy of a $2\times2\times\tfrac{1}{4}$ in. angle, $k_{min}=$ $0\cdot39$ in. (see Table V, Appendix); conventional effective area $\{2+\tfrac{1}{2}(2-\tfrac{1}{4})\}\times\tfrac{1}{4}=0\cdot719$ sq. in.; $l/k=52\cdot7/0\cdot39=135$, from which, by (21), Art. 107, or enlarged graph of Fig. 163, the stress is $2\cdot42$ tons per sq. in., giving in this case a permissible total stress intensity of $1\tfrac{1}{3}\times2\cdot42=3\cdot23$ tons per sq. in. The conventional stress intensity is only $2\cdot14$ tons/$0\cdot719$ sq. in. $=2\cdot98$ tons per sq. in., hence the section is adequate.

Connection of strut 3–4 *to gussets.* One rivet would suffice for strength but would not constitute a " fixed " end. Two bolts or rivets should be provided in each end of truss members however small the loading.

Member J1. Tension, 21,250 lb. $=9\cdot49$ tons. Checking the adequacy of one $2\tfrac{1}{2}\times2\tfrac{1}{2}\times\tfrac{5}{16}$ in. angle, held by one leg at shoe end, deducting hole $\tfrac{1}{16}$ in. larger than rivet diameter, conventional effective area $=\{(2\tfrac{1}{2}-\tfrac{11}{16})+\tfrac{1}{2}(2\tfrac{1}{2}-\tfrac{5}{16})\}\times\tfrac{5}{16}=0\cdot908$ sq. in. Minimum area required $=9\cdot49$ tons/(10$\cdot$67 tons per sq. in.) $=0\cdot89$ sq. in., hence the section of $0\cdot908$ sq. in. is adequate.

Connection of J1 *to shoe gusset.* Strength of one rivet in single shear $=0\cdot3068\times8=2\cdot454$ tons. Bearing strength of one rivet (in $\tfrac{5}{16}$ angle) $=(\tfrac{5}{8})$ in. $\times(\tfrac{5}{16})$ in. $\times16$ tons per sq. in. $=3\cdot125$ tons, which exceeds the shearing strength of $2\cdot454$ tons. Number of rivets required $=9\cdot49$ tons/$2\cdot454$ tons per rivet $=4$ rivets.

125. Statically Indeterminate Frames. Method of Superposition. The stresses in the members of a frame containing redundant members (see Arts. 112 and 113) are frequently difficult to determine and depend upon the relative stiffness of the various parts. But simple approximate methods are sometimes used; for example, a structure and its loads may be subdivided into two or more perfect frames containing some members in common, so that when the

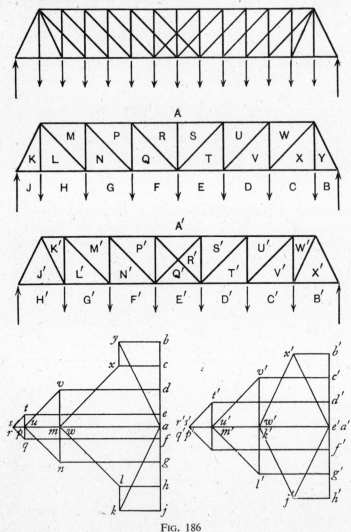

Fig. 186

perfect frames are superposed they form the actual structure. The stresses in these perfect frames having been determined, the stresses in the actual imperfect frame are found by adding algebraically the stresses in the component frames. This method, which is only a conventional approximation, is called the method of superposition, and its accuracy is tested by an example and commented upon in Art. 149. The method of superposition is illustrated in Fig. 186, which shows the stress diagrams for a double intersection N or Whipple Murphy girders equally loaded at each panel point ; the frame and forces are resolved into the parts shown by unaccented and accented letters in the frame and vector diagrams. The members AK and A'J' are identical, and the thrust in this member is found by adding *ak* and *a'j'*. Again, the pull in the bottom boom for the two central panels is found by adding the tensions *qf* (or *te*) and *q'e'*. The member J'K', on the other hand, appears in the second only, and the pull in it is *j'k'*. A second illustration is given in Fig. 149, which represents the method applied to the girder in (*a*) Fig. 220. Table B in the example at the end of Art. 150 shows how nearly correct the stresses conventionally calculated by the method of superposition are in this case; also that for symmetrical loading the results are exact.

126. Method of Resolution. When a small number (say three) of

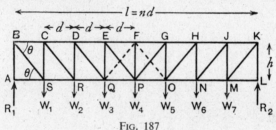

FIG. 187

members of a frame meet at a common joint, all but two of the forces being known, the others may often be found easily by simple resolution of these concurrent forces into components and application of conditions (1) and (2) of Art. 32. Taking the simple N girder in Fig. 187, as an example, the reactions R_1 and R_2 at the supports being calculated by moments, the vertical downward thrust of AB at A must just balance R_1, and the stress in AS must be zero, since there is no other horizontal force at A. Then proceeding to joint B, the vertical component of the force BS say in BS must balance the upward thrust R_1 in AB, since these are the only vertical forces at B or BS sin $\theta = R_1$, and BS $= R_1$ cosec θ (a pull at B). And the wholly horizontal force (BC) in the member BC must balance the horizontal component of the pull BS at B, or

$$BC = BS \cdot \cos \theta = R_1 \cdot \text{cosec } \theta \cdot \cos \theta = R_1 \cdot \cot \theta$$

Proceeding to joint S, resolving vertically, if SC = tension in SC
BS sin $\theta + SC = W_1$,
or $SC = W_1 - BS \sin \theta = W_1 - R_1$ (or thrust $R_1 - W_1$)

And resolving horizontally, BS cos θ=tension in SR, or SR= R_1 cot θ.

Similarly proceeding from joint to joint, the stresses in all the members of the girder may be found. A simpler method for such a frame is given in the next article.

127. Method of Sections. This method, due to Rankine, enables the stress in any member of a simple frame to be calculated without first calculating the stresses in a great number of other members. The principle of the method is that if a structure be divided by an ideal surface into two parts, the forces in the bars cut by the ideal surface, together with the external forces on either part of the divided structure, form a system of forces in equilibrium. If the external forces on either part of the structure are known, the forces in the members cut may be determined by applying to either portion of the structure the principles of Art. 32; and frequently a single equation will suffice to determine the stress in any one member; the determination may, of course, be made graphically or algebraically, according to convenience in a particular case.

Examples. (1) *French Roof Truss.* The difficulty mentioned in Art. 122 in connection with drawing the stress diagram for the French roof truss (Fig. 180) may conveniently be overcome by finding the stress in a single member by the method of sections. For example, to find the stress in one or more of the members DQ, QR, RJ in Fig. 188, take an imaginary plane of section XX. Then

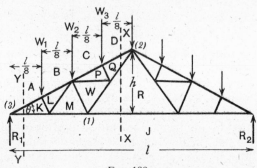

FIG. 188

the structure to the left of XX is in equilibrium under the external forces AB, BC, CD, and JA, together with the three forces exerted by DQ, QR, and RJ, which may therefore be determined by the principles of Art. 32. The most convenient method of finding the stress in one of these three members (avoiding simultaneous equations) will be to apply condition (3), Art. 32, taking clockwise moments about the intersection of the other two, *e.g.* to find the pull of RJ on joint (1), taking moments about point (2)

$$R_1 \times \tfrac{1}{2}l - W_1 \times \tfrac{3}{8}l - W_2 \times \tfrac{1}{4}l - W_3 \times \tfrac{1}{8}l - RJ \times h = 0$$

or
$$RJ = +\frac{1}{h}(\tfrac{1}{2}R_1 l - \tfrac{3}{8}W_1 l - \tfrac{1}{4}W_2 l - \tfrac{1}{8}W_3 l)$$

Similarly, the force in QR might be found by a single equation of moments about point (3), the intersection of DQ and RJ (produced). Again, if the tie KJ is horizontal, the method of sections might be very simply applied to find the stress in AK by assuming a section surface YY; for resolving vertically upwards the forces on the portion of the structure to the left of YY by (1) or (2), Art. 32

$$R_1 + AK \sin \theta = 0, \quad \text{or} \quad AK = -R_1 \operatorname{cosec} \theta$$

i.e. the force in AK thrusts downwards at point (3) with a force R_1 cosec θ. If the tie KJ were not horizontal two simultaneous equations corresponding to (1) and (2), Art. 32, with horizontal and vertical components respectively, might be employed.

(2) N *Girder*. The method of sections is particularly simple in the case of girders with parallel flanges or booms. For a diagonal member such as *ab* (Fig. 189) assume a section XX cutting the three

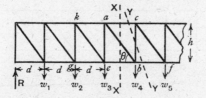

Fig. 189.—Method of sections

members *ab*, *ac*, and *be*, then taking the vertical forces on the left of the section upwards, say, *ab* being the stress in *ab*

$$R + ab \sin \theta - W_1 - W_2 - W_3 = 0$$
$$ab = (W_1 + W_2 + W_3 - R) \operatorname{cosec} \theta, \text{ or } F_3 \operatorname{cosec} \theta$$

thrust toward *a* where F_3 is the shearing force in the panel *eb* according to the sign given in Art. 42. The tension in *ab* is, of course, $-F_3 . \operatorname{cosec} \theta$, and if R is greater than $W_1 + W_2 + W_3$, *ab* is then in tension. For a vertical member such as *cb*, take a section such as YY, then resolving vertically upwards to the left of YY, if *bc* = thrust of *bc* on *b*

$$R - W_1 - W_2 - W_3 - W_4 - bc = 0$$
$$bc = R - (W_1 + W_2 + W_3 + W_4) = -F_4$$

where F_4 is the shearing force on the panel *bf*.

For a horizontal member *ka* of the top chord take a plane section through the bottom joint *e* passing just to the left of the joint *a*; then considering clockwise moments about e of forces on the part of the structure to the left of the section

$$R \times 3d - W_1 \times 2d - W_2 \times d + ka \times h = 0$$

$$ka = \frac{1}{h}(-3Rd + 2W_1d + W_2d), \quad \text{or} \quad \frac{1}{h} \cdot M_e$$

where M_e is the bending moment on the girder at e with sign according to Art. 42, and ka is the pull of the member ka on the joint k. In this case M_e is negative, and the tension in ka is negative, i.e. it is a thrust $\frac{1}{h}(3Rd - 2W_1d - W_2d)$.

The force in the lower chord is similarly found by taking a nearly vertical section through a joint of the top chord; thus by moments about k

$$R \times 2d - W_1 \cdot d - h \times ge = 0$$

$$ge = \text{pull in member } ge = (2Rd - W_1d)/h \quad \text{or} \quad -M_k/h$$

where $M_k =$ the bending moment at k with sign according to Art. 42.

The stresses in the web members are shown in Fig. 190 by drawing

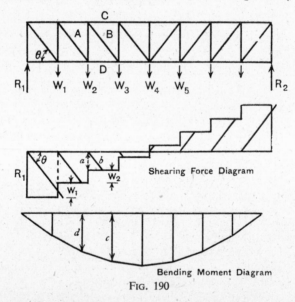

Shearing Force Diagram

Bending Moment Diagram

FIG. 190

vertical and oblique lines across the shearing-force diagram parallel to the members. The stresses in the vertical members are given by the lines vertically below the members, and those in oblique members by oblique lines crossing the space vertically below the corresponding bay. Similarly, the ordinates of the bending-moment diagram give the stresses in the upper and lower chords to a scale dependent upon the depth of the girder. Stresses in four members, A, B, C, D, are shown by the lines *a, b, c, d* respectively.

(3) *Warren Girder.* This may be similarly dealt with, by vertical sections clear of joints for all web members, and vertical sections through opposite joints for all chord members. The web members resist shearing force, and the chord members resist bending moments.

(4) N *Girder with Inclined Chords. Diagonals.* For a diagonal member such as BD (Fig. 191) take a section XX, and take moments

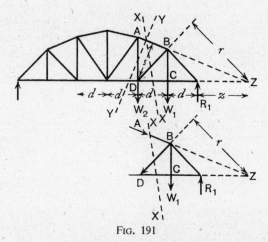

FIG. 191

of the forces on the portion to the right of XX about point Z, the intersection of two of the three members cut by XX. Let r=perpendicular distance of BD produced from Z.

$$\text{(Pull of BD at B} \times r) + W_1(d+z) - R_1 \cdot z = 0$$

$$\text{Pull in BD} = \{R_1 \cdot z - W_1(d+z)\}/r$$

Chord Members. For the thrust in AB use the same section, and take moments about D. Let s=perpendicular distance of AB from D.

$$\text{(Thrust of AB at B} \times s) + W_1 \cdot d - R_1 \times 2d = 0$$

$$\text{Thrust in AB} = (2R_1 \cdot d - W_1 \cdot d)/s = -M_D/s$$

Or, again, the horizontal component of the thrust in AB$= -M_D/AD$ from which the thrust in AB is obtained by multiplying by the secant of the inclination of AB.

The tension in DC may be found by using the section XX and considering moments about B as in the case of parallel chords, viz. Tension in DC$\times$BC$=R_1 \cdot d$; hence pull in DC$=R_1 d/BC$; or more generally $-M_B/CB$.

Verticals. For the thrust in AD the section YY may be used, taking moments about Z

{Thrust of AD at D $\times (z+2d)$}$+W_2(2d+z)+W_1(d+z)-R_1z=0$

Thrust in AD$=\{R_1 . z-W_2(2d+z)-W_1 . (d+z)\}/(z+2d)$, which may be negative.

Alternatives. As an alternative, equations of forces may be used. The vertical components of AB and BD jointly balance the shearing force in the bay ABCD; hence when the pull in BD has been determined the vertical component, and hence (multiplying by the cosecant of the inclination) the actual stress, in AB may be found.

Again, if the chord stresses in AB and DC have been determined (say, by moments about D and B), the horizontal component of the stress in BD must equal the difference of the horizontal components of the chord stresses, and the stress in BD is found from its horizontal component by multiplying by the secant of its inclination.

(5) *Parabolic Girder.* This is a particular case of the previous one, in which the vertical heights of the top chord from the lower chord are proportional to the ordinates of a symmetrical parabola, and therefore also (Art. 40, Fig. 49) to the bending moments for a uniformly distributed load on all the spans. Hence, from the previous case, the tension in the lower chord $-(M_B/BC)$ is constant throughout, and equal to the horizontal component of the thrust in the top chord for a uniform dead load of w per foot, viz. $\frac{1}{8}wl^2 \div$ central depth. For this load the stress in the diagonals will be zero, for considering such a joint as A or D (Fig. 191) the horizontal component of the diagonal stress is equal to the *difference* of the horizontal chord tensions on either side of it, which is zero. Further, considering any lower chord joint under these conditions of load, it immediately follows that the tension in the vertical member is equal to the panel load, the sole function of such members being to transfer the load to the top chord. The vertical component of the thrust of the top chord at any section then balances the shearing force.

More generally for any type of dead load similar conditions would hold if the height of the girder at every cross-section is proportional to the bending moment at that section.

(6) The Baltimore truss, Fig. 175, is a modification of the N frame suitable for long spans, and can conveniently be solved for given positions of the load by the method of sections, the treatment being almost exactly as for the N girder.

128. Stresses from Coefficients. In simple types of girders carrying uniform loads the stresses may be tabulated from general expressions for the members of any panel. The stresses in two similar members of a truss may be resolved into different coefficients (dependent only on the number of panels and position in the girder), multiplied by the same constant, and for the same number of panels, but different proportions and loadings, other constants with the same coefficients will be applicable. Taking Fig. 187 as an example, consider any panel such as DEQR. Let m be the number of panels between it and the left support, and n be the total number of panels (say, even). Let W be the load per panel, W/2 from the end panels being carried directly at each end support and W at each panel point. Then the effective reaction $R_1 = R_2 = (n-1)W/2$. The (negative) shear in panel DEQR is $\{\frac{1}{2}(n-1)-m\}$W, and by the method of sections the tensile stress in DQ is

$$\{\tfrac{1}{2}(n-1)-m\}\text{W cosec } \theta, \quad \text{or} \quad \text{W}\{\tfrac{1}{2}(n-1)-m\}\sqrt{(h^2+d^2)}/h$$

or W cosec θ multiplied by the *coefficient* $\frac{1}{2}(n-1)-m$, the coefficients for diagonals from the supports to the centre forming an arithmetical progression.

The thrust in the vertical DR to the left of the panel DEQR is equal to $\{\frac{1}{2}(n-1)-m\}$W or W multiplied by the coefficient $\frac{1}{2}(n-1)-m$. The (negative) bending moment at D is

$$\tfrac{1}{2}(n-1)\text{W} \times md - \text{W}dm(m-1)/2 = \tfrac{1}{2}\text{W}dm(n-m)$$

hence the stress in the bottom chord RQ is

$\frac{1}{2}\text{W}dm(n-m)$, or W cot θ multiplied by the coefficient $\frac{1}{2}m(n-m)$.

The (negative) bending moment at Q is

$$\tfrac{1}{2}\text{W}(n-1)(m+1)d - \text{W}dm(m+1)/2 = \text{W}d(m+1)(n-m-1)/2$$

hence the stress in the top chord DE is

$\frac{1}{2}\text{W}d(m+1)(n-m-1)/h$ or W cot θ multiplied by the coefficient $\frac{1}{2}(m+1)(n-m+1)$

the coefficients for the left-hand half of Fig. 187 in which $n=8$, for example, are:

Member of panel	Constant	Panel			
		BC $(m=0)$	CD $m=1$	DE $m=2$	EF $m=3=(\frac{1}{2}n-1)$
Left vertical . .	W	$\frac{7}{2}$	$\frac{5}{2}$	$\frac{3}{2}$	$\frac{1}{2}$
Diagonal . . .	W cosec θ	$\frac{7}{2}$	$\frac{5}{2}$	$\frac{3}{2}$	$\frac{1}{2}$
Top chord . .	W cot θ	$\frac{7}{2}$	6	$\frac{15}{2}$	8
Bottom chord .	W cot θ	0	$\frac{7}{2}$	6	$\frac{15}{2}$

When n is odd, and for other simple types of girder, the coefficients may be similarly tabulated.

129. Some Special Framed Girders.

Bollman Truss (Fig. 192). This type of girder, which is really a trussed beam (see Art. 154), carries its load at the top chord; it was most frequently used for deck bridges. The stresses, neglecting any flexural rigidity of the top chord, are easily found as follows. Thrust in $DC = W_1$. Let $_aT_1$ and $_aT_2$ be the tensions in AC and BC respectively. Then from the triangle of forces shown

$$_aT_1 = W_1 \frac{\cos \alpha_2}{\sin (\alpha_1 + \alpha_2)} \qquad _aT_2 = W_2 \frac{\cos \alpha_1}{\sin (\alpha_1 + \alpha_2)}$$

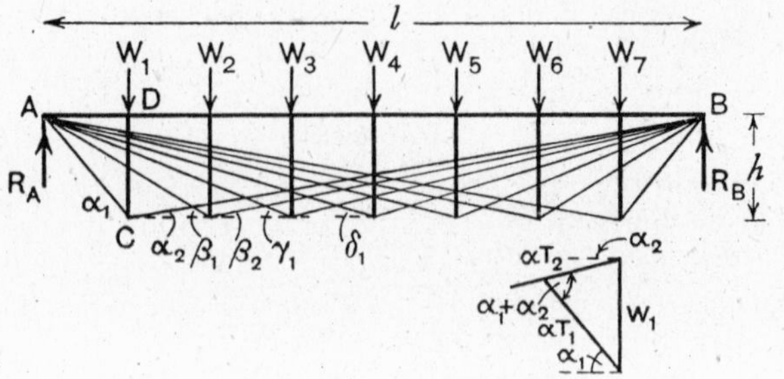

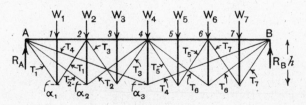

FIG. 192.—Bollman truss

and so on for all the oblique ties. Or for eight panels as in Fig. 192, reaction at A due to $W_1 = \frac{7}{8}W_1 =$ vertical component of $_aT_1$, or

$$_aT_1 \sin \alpha_1 = \tfrac{7}{8}W_1 \quad \text{and} \quad _aT_1 = \tfrac{7}{8}W_1 \operatorname{cosec} \alpha_1, \quad \text{where} \cot \alpha_1 = l/(8h)$$
$$_aT_2 = \tfrac{1}{8}W_1 \operatorname{cosec} \alpha_2 \qquad \text{where} \cot \alpha_2 = (7l)/(8h)$$

And similarly

$$_\beta T_1 = \tfrac{6}{8}W_2 \operatorname{cosec} \beta_1 \qquad \text{where} \cot \beta_1 = l/(4h)$$
$$_\beta T_2 = \tfrac{2}{8}W_2 \operatorname{cosec} \beta_2 \qquad \text{where} \cot \beta_2 = (3l)/(4h)$$

and so on.

Thrust in AB due to W_1 is $_aT_1 \cos \alpha_1$ or $_aT_2 \cos \alpha_2$; hence the total thrust in AB is

$$\tfrac{7}{8}W_1 \cot \alpha_1 + \tfrac{6}{8}W_2 \cot \beta_1 + \tfrac{5}{8}W_3 \cot \gamma_1 + \tfrac{4}{8}W_4 \cot \delta_1 + \text{etc.}$$
$$= \tfrac{7}{64}W_1 l/h + \tfrac{12}{64}W_2 l/h + \tfrac{15}{64}W_3 l/h + \tfrac{16}{64}W_4 l/h + \text{etc.}$$
$$= (7W_1 + 12W_2 + 15W_3 + 16W_4 + 15W_5 + 12W_6 + 7W_7)l/(64h)$$

FIG. 193.—Fink truss

Fink Truss (Fig. 193). This is a later form of the Bollman truss and its solution is similar. The solution is shown in Fig. 193, in which T_1 is the tension in each tie to the foot of the post under panel point number 1, and so on. Resolving at the foot of posts, 1, 3, 5, and 7, $2T_1 \sin \alpha_1 = W_1$, etc., and $T_1 = \frac{1}{2}W_1 \csc \alpha_1$, $T_3 = \frac{1}{2}W_2 \csc \alpha_1$, etc. Evidently when there are no oblique forces at the top of the posts, the thrusts in the first, third, fifth, and seventh verticals respectively are W_1, W_2, W_5, and W_7. The second post carries the vertical components of T_1 and T_3, viz. $W_1/2$ and $W_3/2$ and

Thrust in second post $= W_2 + \frac{1}{2}(W_1 + W_3)$

Thrust in fourth post

$$= W_4 + \frac{W_3 + W_5}{2} + \frac{W_2 + W_6}{2} + \frac{W_1 + W_3 + W_5 + W_7}{4}$$

$$= W_4 + \frac{1}{2}(W_2 + W_6) + \frac{3}{4}(W_3 + W_5) + \frac{1}{4}(W_1 + W_7)$$

Thrust in sixth post $= W_6 + \frac{1}{2}(W_5 + W_7)$

$T_2 = \frac{1}{2}\{ W_2 + \frac{1}{2}(W_1 + W_3) \} \csc \alpha_2$

$T_4 = \frac{1}{2}\{ W_4 + \frac{1}{2}(W_2 + W_6) + \frac{3}{4}(W_3 + W_5) + \frac{1}{4}(W_1 + W_7) \} \csc \alpha_3$

Thrust in top chord.

First two panels, $T_1 \cos \alpha_1 + T_2 \cos \alpha_2 + T_4 \cos \alpha_3$

Third and fourth panels, $T_2 \cos \alpha_2 + T_4 \cos \alpha_3 + T_3 \cos \alpha_1$

which may be reduced by writing $\cot \alpha_1 = \frac{1}{8}l/h$, $\cot \alpha_2 = \frac{1}{4}l/h$, $\cot \alpha_3 = \frac{1}{2}l/h$.

Very long Span Trusses. For very long spans the Baltimore trusses, Fig. 175 (in which the panel of the N girder is subdivided), are modified by having the top chord curved. Fig. 194 shows such

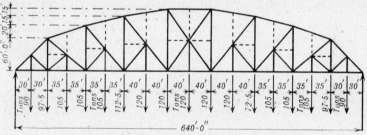

FIG. 194.—Modified Baltimore truss for long spans

a truss as is used for the centre span in the Quebec Bridge and of approximately the same dimensions. The stress diagram presents no special difficulty. The members shown dotted support other members, and are not to be considered as members of the truss.

EXAMPLES XII

1. A roof truss of the type shown in Fig. 176 has a span of 28 ft., rise 7 ft., and no camber of the tie-rods, the joints in the main rafter bisecting

its length.   For the loads given in Problem No. 1, Examples XI, find the maximum stresses in all members due to dead loads, and to wind loads separately, assuming fixed hinges at both supports.

2. If the roof principals in Problem No. 2, Examples XI, are of the types shown in (*h*), Fig. 173, but the ties have no camber, find the maximum stresses due to wind pressure when both sides have fixed hinges.

3. A French roof truss (see Fig. 180) has a span of 50 ft. and a rise of 12 ft. 6 in., and the lower ties have no camber.   Find the stresses in all members due to a dead load of 25 lb. per sq. ft. of covered area, the principals being 12 ft. apart.

4. Find the maximum stresses in the roof of Problem No. 3 when the horizontal wind pressure is 56 lb., adopting the formula (7) of Art. 117, and taking one side " free " and the other " fixed."   Assume that the wind may be from either side.

5. A Warren girder having web members all inclined 60 degrees has eight panels, the first five from the left end being loaded with 5 tons per panel uniformly distributed.   Find the stress in all members.

6. An N girder having seven panels each 6 ft. long and 8 ft. high has the first five from the left-hand end loaded with a uniformly distributed load of W per panel.   Find the stress in each member if the central bay is counter-braced by members capable of bearing tension only.

7. Find an expression for the compression in the top chord of a Bollman truss fully loaded with a load W at each panel point if there are *n* panels of height *h*, the total span being *l*.

8. Find the maximum compression in the top chord of a Fink truss having a load W at each panel point, there being eight panels and the span being *l* and the height *h*.   Find also the thrust in the central vertical post.

9. Find the chord stresses for the truss and loading shown in Fig. 194.

CHAPTER XIII

MOVING LOAD STRESSES IN FRAMES

130. Stresses due to Rolling Loads. The methods of finding stresses given in the preceding chapter are applicable to known loads on the various parts of the truss. But in order to compute the maximum stresses to which a member of a bridge will be subjected by a travelling load crossing the span, the position of the load to produce this maximum effect has to be considered. This matter has been partially dealt with in Chapter vi, but the application to framed girders will require further notice and illustration.

131. Chord Stresses. The chord stresses may be found (Art. 127) by taking moments about joints in the opposite chord, to which the stress is proportional, and the stress in the chord is a maximum when the moment about the opposite joint is a maximum. For a uniformly distributed load this occurs (see Art. 61 and end of Art. 75) when the whole span is loaded. Hence, if an equivalent uniformly distributed load is adopted the determination of chord stresses due to rolling loads is precisely similar to that for uniformly distributed dead loads.

In the case of concentrated loads arising from axle loads or from conventional train loads (Art. 70) the maxima occur when the bending moments at opposite joints reach maximum values and the corresponding positions of the load (for joints of both loaded and unloaded chords) are given in Art. 66. The calculation of maximum bending moments in such a case may be accomplished for determined positions of the load by moving the span length under the loads as in Art. 65 or by algebraic calculation. In either case the calculation is much more tedious than when an equivalent uniformly distributed load is employed.

132. Conventional Calculation of Web Stresses for Uniform Rolling Loads. We have seen that for girders with horizontal chords (Art. 127, section 2) the web member stresses are proportional to the shearing force at the member, and hence the maximum (positive or negative) stresses due to rolling loads will occur in such members when the maximum positive or negative shearing forces occur. A simple conventional method (Fig. 195) is to assume that the maximum positive shearing force at any section occurs when all panel points to the left of that section are fully loaded and those to the right are unloaded: and that maximum negative shearing force occurs when all panel points to the right are fully loaded and those to the left unloaded. This is an approximation which will be shown to be on the safe side, but is clearly an impossible condition, for no panel point can be entirely unloaded if the adjacent panel point carries the *full* panel load ($w \times d$) due to a uniformly distributed load.

Adopting such conventional loading for both horizontal and curved chord girders, maximum positive and negative stresses in web members due to a uniformly distributed rolling load can be calculated as in Art. 127, sections (2), (3), and (4). If these be added algebraically to the stress due to dead load the extreme maximum and minimum stresses are obtained.

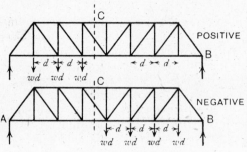

FIG. 195.—Conventional loading for extreme shearing forces and stresses in web members

Example 1. A through **N** girder of 80-ft. span has eight bays of 10 ft. each, the height throughout being 12 ft. The uniformly distributed dead load is 0·6 ton per foot run, and the rolling load is equivalent to 2 tons per ft. Find the maximum and minimum stresses in each diagonal and vertical member. All dead loads as well as live loads to be taken as at the bottom chord joints.

The panel loads are, for dead loads 6 tons, and for rolling loads 20 tons. Using the reference letters of Fig. 187 or 196, the dead load reactions (effective) are $R_1 = R_2 = \frac{42}{2} = 21$ tons. The dead load shears in the main panels, altering by the panel load of 6 tons at each lower chord joint, are:

Panel	AS	SR	RQ	QP	PO	ON	NM	ML
Dead load shear in tons	−21	−15	−9	−3	+3	+9	+15	+21

The extreme shears due to rolling load on, say, the panel RQ are for maximum positive shear, loads of 20 tons at S and R only, then $R_2 = (40 \times 1.5)/8 = 7.5$ tons = maximum positive shear. For panel QP the value is $R_2 = (60 \times 2)/8 = 15$ tons. The full values are:

Panel	AS	SR	RQ	QP	PO	ON	NM	ML
Maximum positive shear	0	+2·5	+7·5	+15	+25	+37·5	52·5	70
Maximum negative shear	−70	−52·5	−37·5	−25	−15	−7·5	−2·5	0

combining these with the dead loads shears, the extreme shears in each panel are:

Panel	AS	SR	RQ	QP	PO	ON	NM	ML
Maximum positive or negative shear .	−91	−67·5	−46·5	$\begin{Bmatrix} -28 \\ +12 \end{Bmatrix}$	$\begin{Bmatrix} +28 \\ -12 \end{Bmatrix}$	+46·5	+67·5	+91
Minimum positive or negative shear.	−21	−12·5	−1·5	—	—	+1·5	+12·5	+21

The maximum positive shear due to the rolling load and the positive shear due to dead load are shown on Fig. 196, together

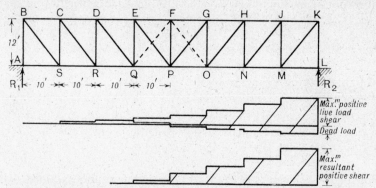

FIG. 196.—Maximum positive shearing force and web member stresses

with the resultant for half the span. The negative quantities for the other half are symmetrical.

The maximum thrusts in AB, CS, DR are 91, 67·5 and 46·5 tons respectively, that is, the shearing forces in the panels AS, SR, and RQ, while the minimum thrusts are 21, 12·5, and 1·5 tons respectively. The stress borne by EQ varies from a thrust of 28 tons to a tension of 12 tons. The stress in FP is always zero. If the dead load is so distributed that $\frac{1}{3}$ of the total comes on the joints of the top chord, 2 tons thrust will have to be added to the results for CS, DR, EQ, and FP, and 1 ton to that for AB.

The stresses in the diagonals are found by multiplying the extreme shears by cosec θ, *i.e.* by $\dfrac{BS}{AB} = \frac{1}{12}\sqrt{(144+100)} = 1·30$, giving:

Member . . .	BS	CR	DQ	EP	GP	HO	JN	KM
Maximum tension . .	118·3	88·0	60·5	36·4	36·4	60·5	88·0	118·3
Minimum tension . .	27·3	16·3	1·95	—	—	1·95	16·3	27·3
Maximum thrust . .	—	—	—	15·6	15·6	—	—	—

These are also shown by the diagonal lines parallel to the diagonal members, across the shear diagram in Fig. 196. The change from tension to thrust in EP and GP may of course be prevented by counterbracing the bays QP and PO as shown by the dotted lines (see Art. 137).

133. Exact Method for Girders with Horizontal Chords and Single Web Systems. The exact load position for and amount of the maximum shear has been dealt with fully in Art. 75, section (1). It is interesting to compare the results from the conventional loading above with the true value. Using Fig. 104, the maximum positive shearing force in any panel DC having m panels to the left of it (out of n panels total), with a rolling load w per ft. and span l ft., is by (4), Art. 75

$$\frac{w}{2} \cdot \frac{m^2}{n(n-1)} \cdot l \qquad . \quad . \quad . \quad . \quad . \quad (1)$$

According to the conventional loading above, the right-hand side would be (taking moments about A, Fig. 104)

$$m \cdot \frac{l}{n} w\left(\frac{m+1}{2} \cdot \frac{l}{n}\right) \div l = \frac{w}{2} \cdot \frac{m(m+1)}{n^2} \cdot l \quad . \quad . \quad (2)$$

For the extreme right-hand side panel at B, Fig. 104, $m = n-1$, and both (1) and (2) give

$$\tfrac{1}{2} wl(n-1)/n$$

But for smaller values of m (nearer the middle of the span) (2) gives a slightly higher value than (1), i.e. it is a trifle on the safe side. Applying both methods to such a truss as Fig. 187, where $n = 8$, we get the following maximum positive shears (with corresponding negative values), taking $wl/2 = 100$:

Panel	AS	SR	RQ	QP	PO	ON	NM	ML
$m =$	0	1	2	3	4	5	6	7
Conventional maximum +shear.	0	3·12	9·4	18·8	31·2	46·8	65·5	87·5
Actual maximum+shear	0	1·78	7·13	16·1	28·5	44·5	64·1	87·5

The difference in the results from the two methods is very small, as will be realised if the results are plotted on such shear diagrams as Fig. 196 or Fig. 104, which are too small to show the difference.

Example. Find the exact maximum stress in the member HO (Fig. 187 or 196), with the loading given in the example at the end of Art. 132.

The actual maximum positive shearing force in the panel ON, putting $m = 5$, and $n = 8$, is from (1)

$$\frac{2}{2} \cdot \frac{25 \times 80}{8 \times 7} = 35 \cdot 71 \text{ tons}$$

and adding the dead-load shear of $+9$ tons gives $44 \cdot 71$ tons (instead of $46 \cdot 5$ tons), and multiplying by cosec θ or $1 \cdot 30$ gives the maximum stress in HO

$$1 \cdot 3 \times 44 \cdot 71 = 58 \cdot 1 \text{ tons instead of } 60 \cdot 5 \text{ tons.}$$

When the shearing force has been determined, the stresses in the web members follow, as for the conventional method, viz. from Art. 127, section (2).

134. Exact Method with Curved Top Chord and Single-Web Systems. For a girder with curved top chord the stress in a web member such as BD (Fig. 197) is found as shown in Art. 127,

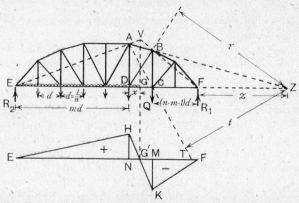

FIG. 197.—Extreme stresses in web members of girder with curved top chord

section (4), and Fig. 191.[1] To find the position of the uniform load w per ft. to give the maximum pull in BD, suppose it covers entirely all the m panels to the left of DC (Fig. 197) and extends a distance DG or x beyond D towards C, and the pull in BD is P. By moments about E

$$R_1 = \frac{w}{2l}(md+x)^2 \qquad \ldots \ldots \ldots \quad (1)$$

And the joint load Q at C, from moments about D, is

$$Q = \frac{wx^2n}{2l} = \frac{wx^2}{2d} \qquad \ldots \ldots \ldots \quad (2)$$

Then by moments about the centre Z

$$P = \frac{1}{r}[R_1 \cdot z - Q\{z+(n-m-1)d\}] \qquad \ldots \ldots \quad (3)$$

$$= \frac{w}{2rl}[z(md+x)^2 - nx^2\{z+(n-m-1)d\}] \qquad (4)$$

[1] It is assumed that the two chord members cut by the section taken for finding the stress in BD will, if produced, intersect outside the span of the girder. If they intersect inside the span, as often occurs in the braced arch (see Fig. 273, but omit central hinge), the span must be fully loaded for maximum stress in the member BD.

And for a maximum value of P, $dP/dx=0$, hence

$$x=\frac{m}{n-1+n(n-m-1)d/z}\cdot d \quad \ldots \ldots \quad (5)$$

which reduces to $ml/\{n(n-1)\}$ when z is infinite, *i.e.* for a horizontal top chord as in (2), Art. 75. Substituting this in (1) and (2), equation (3) gives P.

The distance CG from C for maximum thrust when the load extends from F to G is

$$\frac{n-m-1}{n-1-nmd/(l+z)}\cdot d$$

The position of the load for maximum stress in any vertical may similarly be found.

Alternative Method. The influence method may also be used. Considering unit load rolling over the span EF, when it has moved a distance y from E (short of D), $R_1=y/l$, and as in (3), $P=yz/(lr)$, which is proportional to y, *i.e.* the influence line EH is a straight line, such that $HN=mdz/(lr)=mz/(nr)$, similarly for the load between C and F the influence line is the line KF, such that $KM=(n-m-1)(z+nd)/(nr)$. Also it is easy to show that the rate of change as the unit load moves from D to C is proportional to x, *i.e.* the influence line is a straight line through H and K, which is the line HG'K. As in Art. 75, the stress due to a uniform load w per ft. extending from E to G' is found from the area EHG' under the influence line, viz.

$$\tfrac{1}{2}w(HN\times EG') \quad \ldots \ldots \ldots \quad (6)$$

$EG'=md+NG'$, and NG' may be found (confirming (5)), by dividing DC in the known ratio $\dfrac{HN}{KM}=\dfrac{mz}{(n-m-1)(z+nd)}$, and substituting in (6), this gives

$$\text{max. pull in DB}=\frac{w}{2}\cdot\frac{m^2}{n}\cdot\frac{z}{r}\cdot d\left\{1+\frac{1}{n-1+n(n-m-1)d/z}\right\}\cdot \quad (7)$$

Similarly, the maximum thrust in DB due to live load is

$$\frac{w}{2}\cdot\frac{(n-m-1)^2}{n}\cdot\frac{(z+nd)}{r}d\left\{1+\frac{1}{n-1-n\cdot m\cdot d/(z+l)}\right\}\cdot \quad (8)$$

Similar methods may be used to draw the influence lines for the stress in the verticals.

An alternative simple method of finding the point G' is to join AE and FB. These lines produced meet at V, and G' is the projection of V. For G' is the point at which a load would produce no stress in DB; to the left of G' a load would produce tension in DB, and to the right it would produce thrust. That no stress is produced in DB by a load under V is proved by the fact that EVB would be a bending-moment diagram for such a load, and hence $M_D \div AD = M_B \div BC$, therefore the tension in DC equals the horizontal component of the thrust in AB. Hence by the method of sections the horizontal component of the stress in DB equals zero. When the point G is determined, the stress in DB may be found by various means, such, for instance, as a stress diagram.

Graphical Construction. The maximum stress in a diagonal DB due to a rolling load may be determined graphically by dropping a perpendicular VG (Fig. 198) from V. Then Dg represents the pull in DB on the same scale that VG represents half the load on EG.

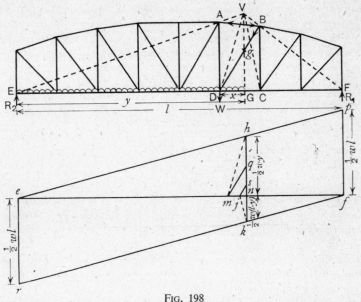

Fig. 198

Similarly, gB represents the minimum stress or maximum thrust in DB on the same scale that VG represents half the load on GF. When these stresses are required for each diagonal it is convenient to set off the diagram *pfer* with the dimensions shown for a load w per ft. Then nh represents half the load w . EG or $\frac{1}{2}w$. y, hence by drawing hm parallel to VD, and then mq parallel to DB, mq gives the maximum stress to a known scale, viz. that on which pf has been made equal to $\frac{1}{2}wl$. The correctness of the construction may be proved as follows. The load w . ED on ED may be replaced by $\frac{1}{2}w$. ED at E, and $\frac{1}{2}w$. ED at D; similarly, the part w . DG may be replaced by $\frac{1}{2}$. w . DG at D, and $\frac{1}{2}$. w . DG at G. The load at E may be ignored, and the load at G, we have just seen, causes no stress in DB.   Hence the effect in DB is that of a load $\frac{1}{2}(ED+DG)w$ $=\frac{1}{2}EG$. $w=W$, say, at D.   Let T′ be the thrust in AB, T the tension in DC, and S the tension in DB, of which h and v are horizontal and vertical components respectively.   Taking, say, a vertical section through the panel DC, the forces on the right-hand part of the structure are, firstly, T′ and S at B, and, secondly, T and R_1 meeting at F; these pairs must balance, and therefore act through B and F, hence the resultant of T′ and S is in the line VF.   Again, considering forces on the left-hand portion, there are, firstly, T′ and (downwards) W$-v$ through A; secondly, T$+h$ and R_2 through E. Since these balance, their resultants act through E and A, hence the resultant of T′ and W$-v$ are in the line VA.   Finally, taking, say, clockwise moments about V of forces on the structure to the left of the section, since the resultant of T′ and S is through V, the sum of the moments of T′ and S about V is zero, and resolving S at D.

If a is the perpendicular distance of V from AB

$$-T' . a - v . x + h . VG = 0 \quad . \quad . \quad . \quad (9)$$

and since the resultant of T′ and W$-v$ is through V

$$+T' . a - (W-v)x = 0 \quad . \quad . \quad . \quad . \quad (10)$$

hence adding (9) and (10).

W . $x = h$. VG or $\dfrac{x}{VG} = \dfrac{h}{W}$, or if VG represents W, x or DG represents h to the same scale, and consequently Dg represents S, of which h is the horizontal component to the same scale.   Similarly, gB represents the thrust in BD for a load w . GF on GF to the same scale that VG represents a load $\frac{1}{2}w$. GF.

Example 1.   Taking Fig. 197 to represent a girder 80-ft. span subjected to a uniform rolling load of 1 ton per ft., and the heights of successive verticals from either end to the centre being 0, 10, 15, 17·5, and 17·5 ft., find the maximum tension and the maximum thrust due to rolling load in the member BD by the conventional, and the exact methods when the panel DC is not counterbraced.

The lengths of z and r may conveniently be measured from a drawing to scale and used in, say, inches as measured; they may also be calculated in feet as follows.   Fall in AB$=2$·5 ft. in 10 ft. horizontally; hence the length CZ for a fall of 15 ft. $= 15 \times 10/2$·5$=$ 60 ft., and $z=40$ ft., DB$= \sqrt{(15^2+10^2)}=18$·03 ft., $r=70 \sin$ B$\hat{D}$C$=$ $70 \times 15/18$·03$=58$·2 ft.

Using the conventional method, all joints E to D having full panel loads of 10 tons, by moments about E

$$R_1 = \tfrac{10}{80}(10+20+30+40+50) = \tfrac{10}{8} \times 15 = 18 \text{·}75 \text{ tons.}$$

Hence by taking a vertical section in the panel DC, and considering the structure to the right of it, and taking moments about Z of the external forces

$$\text{Pull in BD} = \frac{1}{58 \cdot 2}(18 \cdot 75 \times 40) = 12 \cdot 87 \text{ tons.}$$

Using the exact method, $m = 5$, $n = 8$, then from (5)

$$x = \frac{5 \times 10}{7 + (8 \times 2 \times \frac{10}{40})} = \frac{50}{11} = 4 \cdot 55 \text{ ft.}; \quad EG = 54 \cdot 55 \text{ ft.}$$

$$R_1 = \tfrac{1}{2}(54 \cdot 55)^2 / 80 = 18 \cdot 6 \text{ tons}$$

$$Q = \tfrac{1}{2}(4 \cdot 55)^2 / 10 = 1 \cdot 04 \text{ tons.}$$

Hence by moments about Z

Pull in BD $= (18 \cdot 6 \times 40 - 1 \cdot 04 \times 60)/58 \cdot 2 = 11 \cdot 71$ tons, which may also be checked by (7).

It may be noted that the conventional method is more in error (although on the safe side) for curved chord girders than for the horizontal chord type (see Art. 133). The errors are greater the more inclined the chords are to the horizontal.

For maximum thrust in BD by the conventional method, joints C to F are loaded, giving $R_2 = \frac{10}{80}(10 + 20) = 3 \cdot 75$ tons. Hence by moments about Z for the structure to the left of the previous section

$$\text{Thrust in BD} = 3 \cdot 75 \times 120 / 58 \cdot 2 = 7 \cdot 74 \text{ tons.}$$

Using the exact method, $R_2 = \tfrac{1}{2}(25 \cdot 45)^2 / 80 = 4 \cdot 05$ tons.

$$\text{Load at D} = \tfrac{1}{2}(5 \cdot 45)^2 / 10 = 1 \cdot 49 \text{ tons.}$$

Hence by moments about Z, thrust in BD $= (4 \cdot 05 \times 120 - 1 \cdot 49 \times 70)/58 \cdot 2 = 6 \cdot 55$ tons, which may be checked by equation (8).

Example 2. What uniformly distributed load in the above example would be sufficient to prevent a reversal of stress in the member BD?

Let w be the uniform load per foot. Then the dead load must be just sufficient to cause a tension $7 \cdot 74$ tons in BD. Right-hand reaction $= \tfrac{1}{2}70w = 35w$. Taking moments of the dead load about Z

$$35w \times 40 - 10w \times 50 - 10w \times 60 = 7 \cdot 74 \times 58 \cdot 2 = 450$$

$$w = \tfrac{450}{300} = 1 \cdot 5 \text{ tons per ft.}$$

or more exactly, taking $6 \cdot 55$ tons thrust to be neutralised

$$35w \times 40 - 10w \times 50 - 10w \times 60 = 6 \cdot 55 \times 58 \cdot 2 = 382$$

$$w = \tfrac{382}{300} = 1 \cdot 273 \text{ tons per ft.}$$

135. Trusses with Multiple-Web Systems. In finding the maximum stresses in multiple-web trusses due to rolling loads the same principles as have been used for single-web systems are applicable. Usually the conventional loading will be sufficiently near for finding the maximum stresses in web members in accordance with the methods given in Art. 127, section (2), for fixed loads.   Thus in the Whipple-Murphy truss the method of superposition (Art. 125) may be employed to find, as in the present article, the maximum web stresses in each of two girder systems into which the Whipple-Murphy girder may be split (Fig. 186).

Again, in the Baltimore truss, Fig. 175, and Art. 127, section (2), the methods are those which have been dealt with already.   An exact solution by means of the influence line is also possible, but the conventional system of complete panel loads is sufficiently near for most purposes, and much less complicated.

136. Stress Calculations for Concentrated Loads.   The maximum stress in a web member of a truss with horizontal chords occurs when the shearing force in its panel is a maximum, and the position of the loads to give the maximum shearing force has been demonstrated in (4), Art. 67, a condition which is fulfilled when a particular wheel load passes into the panel concerned.   When the position is determined the maximum shear is easily calculated. When the top chord is curved, as in Fig. 197, the position of the load for maximum stress in BD, say, instead of being given by (3), Art. 67, viz. $W/l = W_2/d$, writing d instead of k, is given by the modified equation

$$\frac{W}{l} = \frac{W_2}{d}(1 + md/z) \quad \text{or} \quad W_2 = \frac{W/n}{1 + md/z}$$

the term md/z arising from the slope of the top chord, and being zero when z is infinite.   For examples of stress calculations in web members of curved chord girders having multiple-web systems subjected to concentrated travelling loads, see *Modern Framed Structures*, by Johnson, Bryan, and Turneaure.

137. Stresses in Counterbraces.   The reversal of live-load shear in a particular panel of a braced girder may be taken up by making the diagonal of such a section as will enable it to resist the necessary tension and thrust.   But instead of this very frequently a second diagonal capable of resisting tension only is introduced to take up the shear which would otherwise put the main diagonal in compression.   Such diagonals, shown dotted in Figs. 175, 187, 196, and 199, are called *counter-braces*.[1]   The main diagonal is that which takes tension when the girder is fully loaded, and also the dead-load tension.

The counterbracing of a panel really makes the structure statically indeterminate (see Chapter xv), and the stresses in the main diagonal and counterbrace depend upon their sections, and particularly on the initial conditions of attachment which determine the initial

---

[1] The American practice is to call this a *counter* or counter-tie, and to call a diagonal capable of taking a reversal of stress a counterbrace.

stresses which may exist due to dead load. If the main diagonal carries completely its dead-load stress when the attachment (or final adjustment) is made, any live load tending to reduce this tension will put the counterbrace in tension without first reducing the main diagonal to a state of ease or zero stress. And these conditions will be safer to assume in calculating the possible tension in a counterbrace. In some constructions the counterbrace is actually left slack during erection and then given a slight tension; in such a case it would be required to resist live-load stress plus the initial adjusting tension. Actually the stress in both counterbrace and main brace will be affected by the fact that the other one is capable of resisting considerable thrust, although nominally unable to do so. For several reasons, then, the stress calculations for counterbraced panels must be regarded as conventional in a greater degree than is true for other simpler types of girders.

The calculations of tension in the counterbraces due to the live load are made in the same way as for live-load stresses in the main braces, the other braces being ignored, and will be best illustrated by examples.

Example 1. Find the stress in the counterbrace FO, Fig. 187 or 196, with the data given in Example 1, Art. 132.

Referring to the results of the example quoted, the maximum negative live-load shear in the panel PO is 15 tons, which is assumed to be wholly borne by the counterbrace. The inclination is equal to that of the main brace, *viz.* θ where cosec $\theta = 1\cdot3$, hence the maximum tension in FO is $15 \times 1\cdot3 = 19\cdot5$ tons.

If we assume that the two diagonals jointly carry the dead-load shear (FO being slightly either shortened or bowed), but that the main brace cannot be relied upon to take thrust, the stress to be allowed for in FO calculated for the maximum negative shear of 12 tons in panel PO, given in Example 1, Art. 132, would be $12 \times 1\cdot3 = 15\cdot6$ tons, the same as the thrust in PO when the panel is not counterbraced. The actual stress would probably be between $15\cdot6$ and $19\cdot5$ tons, but depends upon initial conditions. .

Example 2. Find the maximum tension in a counterbrace AC, Fig. 197, under the conditions of Example 1, Art. 134.

The distance *t* of AC from Z is CZ·sin T$\hat{C}$Z.

$$AC = \sqrt{(17\cdot5^2 + 10^2)} = 20\cdot15$$
$$\sin A\hat{C}D = 17\cdot5/20\cdot15 = 0\cdot868,$$

hence $t = 60 \times 0\cdot868 = 52\cdot1$ ft.

When joints C to F are fully loaded, $R_2 = 3\cdot75$ as before. Omitting member BD, by moments about Z

Pull in $AC = (3\cdot75 \times 120)/52\cdot1 = 8\cdot64$ tons.

o

For a more exact value the conditions are as before, but in a counterbraced panel such a refinement is unnecessary; the result would be

$$(4\cdot05 \times 120 - 1\cdot49 \times 70)/52\cdot1 = 7\cdot33 \text{ tons.}$$

The stress in the vertical of a counterbraced panel is a minimum thrust (or maximum tension) when the counterbrace meeting its foot is in action, e.g. if AC, Fig. 197, is in tension and BD out of use, consider the joint B. The resultant of the two chord stresses at B will cause a tension in the vertical BC unless a load at B is sufficient to cause thrust. The load position to give maximum tension in BC has to be found by trial; it occurs when the chord stresses at B are as great as possible, consistent with BD remaining out and AC in action, i.e. when the load extends from F as far beyond C as to just cause BD to have zero stress in it.

138. Stress in Wind Bracing. The wind bracing or laterals of a framed girder bridge are very generally (unless head room requires arched girders) of the form shown in Figs. 174 and 199, i.e. N girders counterbraced in every panel (as the wind may blow from either side), and having as chords the chords of the main girders. In the case of open-floor bridges the cross-girders will form the struts of the wind-bracing system.

Such a girder of course forms a statically indeterminate system, and, as in the preceding article, the wind stress can only be determined in a conventional manner by arbitrary assumptions. Again, the distribution of wind load on the girders and on moving vehicles between the upper and lower wind bracing (if both are used) is arbitrary. It is usual to assume that all the moving wind load is taken on the wind bracing of the loaded chord, and this bracing (which may consist of a plated floor) is also often taken to withstand more than half the wind load on the girders. Some stress is also caused by the overturning effect of the wind increasing the downward pressure on the supports on the leeward side of a bridge and decreasing it on the windward side. Altogether the determination of wind stresses in the lateral bracing is somewhat empirical. It may also be pointed out that quite apart from wind pressure the lateral bracing will be stressed by the straining of the main girder chords to which it is attached. An estimate of such stresses may be made from the stresses in the main chords and the geometry of the consequent deformations.[1]

The conventional method of estimating the most important wind stresses is to ignore one system of triangulation, as in counterbraced panels dealt with in Art. 137, and to find the stress due to dead and

[1] See an article on " The Design of Wind Bracing " in *Engineering*, June 9th, 1911.

travelling wind loads by the method of Arts. 131 and 132.   As the diagonals are for greater stiffness made capable of resisting thrust this cannot give accurate results, but any error involved is on the side of safety.   The calculation may be shown by an example.

Example. The N or Pratt girder shown in Fig. 199 has wind bracing shown at (*b*) and (*c*).   Estimate the maximum stresses in the lower lateral bracing and in the lower chords due to a stationary wind load of 2,000 lb. per panel and a travelling wind load of 30 lb. per sq. ft. on 10 sq. ft. per lineal foot, assuming that 60 per cent.

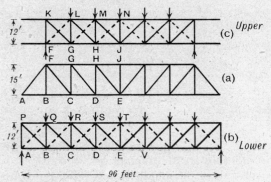

FIG. 199.—Stresses in lateral or wind bracing

of the stationary wind load and the whole of the travelling load is taken by the lower system.

$$\text{Dead load per panel} = 0.6 \times 2,000 = 1,200 \text{ lb.}$$
$$\text{Moving load per panel} = 30 \times 10 \times 12 = 3,600 \text{ lb.}$$

As the two halves are symmetrical it is only necessary to work out the stress for half the span.   The wind may blow on either side, and with the wind load on the side selected in Fig. 199 the dotted braces are assumed to go out of action.

Chord Stresses. For stationary load the reactions at the ends are $\frac{1}{2}(7 \times 1,200) = 4,200$ lb.

Denoting bending moments by M and a suffix and stresses by the letters at the ends of the members

$-M_B = 4,200 \times 12 = 50,400$ lb.-ft.,   hence $PQ = 50,400/12 = 4,200$ lb. Similarly, $QR = -M_C/12 = 86,400/12 = 7,200$ lb., $RS = -M_D/12 = 108,000/12 = 9,000$ lb., $ST = -M_E/12 = 115,200/12 = 9,600$ lb., $AB = 0$, $BC = -M_Q/12 = 4,200$ lb., $CD = -M_R/12 = 7,200$ lb., $DE = -M_S/12 = 9,000$ lb.   For the total stress due to live and dead load it is only necessary to multiply the above by $(3,600 + 1,200)/1,200 = 4$, since the maximum chord stresses occur with full load.

Web Stresses. The inclination of the braces to the chords is 45°, so from the shearing forces, falling by 1,200 lb. per panel, the dead-load stresses are, *Tensile*, PB=4,200$\sqrt{2}$=5,940 lb., QC=(4,200−1,200)$\sqrt{2}$=4,240 lb., RD=1,800$\sqrt{2}$=2,540 lb., SE=600$\sqrt{2}$=850 lb.

Compressive. AP=4,200, QB=3,000, RC=1,800, SD=600, TE=0. The maximum live-load web stresses may similarly be written from the maximum live-load shears, as in Art. 132, and are as follows:

Live-load Web Stresses.

Panel.	AB	BC	CD	DE	EV
Maximum negative shear . . .	12,600	9,450	6,750	4,500	2,700
Diagonal, and tension in lb. . .	PB 17,800	QC 13,360	RD 9,540	SE 6,360	— —
Cross-strut, and thrust in lb. . . .	AP 12,600	BQ 9,450	CR 6,750	SD 4,500	TE 2,700

The dead-load stresses may now be added to these to give the total stresses; the additions are all of quantities of like sign, as change of sign in the diagonals of the middle panels is prevented by the counter-bracing.

EXAMPLES XIII

1. The girder shown in Fig. 195 is 16 ft. high and has a panel length of 12 ft. Find the maximum and minimum stresses in the upper and lower chords due to a dead load of 0·4 ton per foot run and a travelling load of 1 ton per foot run.

2. Find the maximum and minimum stresses in the diagonals of the girder in Problem No. 1. (*a*) By the conventional loadings. (*b*) By the more exact method.

3. A through Warren girder with web members inclined at 60° has six bays in the lower (loaded) boom and five in the upper. The loads are— (1) dead loads of 3 tons at each joint of the lower boom and 1 ton at each top joint; (2) a travelling load of 1·2 ton per foot run, the bays being each 10 ft. long. Find the maximum and minimum stresses in all members.

4. A through Warren girder is the same as in Problem No. 3, but has five bays in the lower boom and four in the upper one, and is subjected to the same dead load per joint. What is the maximum travelling load per foot which will only cause a reversal of stress in two web members?

5. In a hog-back or curved top chord N girder of six bays, the heights in successive verticals, including the end posts, are 10, 12·5, 14, 14, 14, 12·5, and 10 ft., and the bays are each 10 ft. long. Find approximately the maximum stresses in the members of half the girder under a dead load of 0·3 ton per ft., and a live load of 1·2 ton per foot run.

CHAPTER XIV

SELECTED TYPICAL FRAMED STRUCTURES

139. Cantilever Bridges.   The disadvantage of continuous girders have been referred to in Art. 95.   In a cantilever bridge, although there may be several supports, the girders are separable into parts, each of which is statically determinate.

Two types of support for a bridge of three spans (and four supports) are shown in Figs. 200 and 201, which also show the bending-

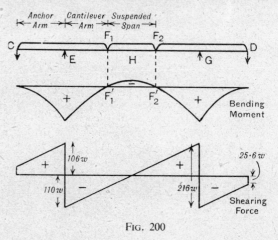

Fig. 200

moment and shearing-force diagrams for uniformly distributed dead loads.   The construction of the trusses is such as to form virtual hinges at F_1 and F_2, thus fixing the points of inflexion whatever the load.   Then for different loadings, although the shape of the bending-moment diagram will alter, the points of inflexion will remain at F_1' and F_2'.   Either type may be looked upon as a continuous beam with hinges inserted or may be regarded as an arrangement of overhung beams simply supported at two points and carrying other simple beams suspended from their ends.   Thus that in Fig. 200 consists of two beams CF_1 and DF_2, carrying the simply suspended span F_1F_2 from their overhung ends or *cantilever arms* at F_1 and F_2.   Whether the support required at C and D is upward or downward depends upon the load between E and G compared to that between C and E and between G and D; generally a downward anchorage will be required.   The type shown in Fig. 201 consists of a central beam with overhung " cantilever " ends, which carry one end of each side span, the other ends resting on the end supports or abutments.

A great advantage of the cantilever type of bridge in many cases

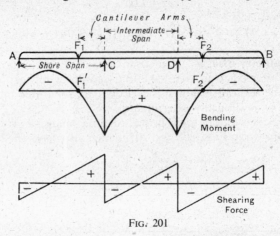

FIG. 201

arises from the fact that the side spans being erected in the ordinary manner the cantilever arms can be built outwards from the piers and the central span completed from them without the use of falsework,

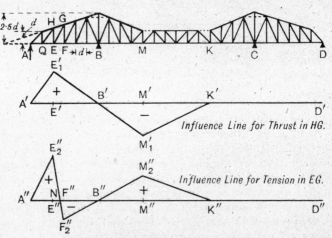

FIG. 202.—Stresses in cantilever bridge

i.e. support from below; erection stresses must be estimated and allowed for. For long spans where the dead load of the structure becomes very large the cantilever is advantageous because the dead weight is somewhat concentrated near the supports, and also because the average bending moments are smaller than for a simply supported span.

Figs. 202 and 203 show typical forms of cantilever bridges, the former being of the through and the latter of the deck type. The dotted (redundant) members which would render the structure statically indeterminate are used in erection, during which the suspended span is built out as an extension of the cantilever arms. In Fig. 203 there are two supports at the piers, but the panel between them is so lightly braced as not to transmit any shearing force, and consequently there is no change of bending moment between the two. This panel may in fact be ignored in calculating stresses and the truss may be treated as if there were a single support between the two adjoining panels. The load positions for maximum effects will have to be investigated for each type of bridge in order to find the maximum and minimum stresses due to a rolling load. It is usual to determine some form of equivalent uniformly distributed load for a cantilever bridge, but this will not be necessarily the same for the

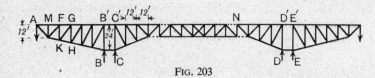

FIG. 203

cantilever portions as for a simple span. The conventional method of taking full panel loads may then be adopted, and the determination of live load stresses is illustrated in the following examples. The more exact methods of Art. 134 for web members are applicable, but the conventional method is simpler and sufficiently accurate, as exemplified in Example 4.

Influence Lines for Cantilever Bridges. The structure being statically determinate influence lines which are straight lines are easily drawn for any section and may be used to determine maximum and minimum stresses in the members. A numerical example (No. 4) illustrates this application.

Example 1. The dimensions of Fig. 200, which is symmetrical, being $CE = 80$ ft., $EF_1 = 70$ ft., $F_1F_2 = 80$ ft., determine the dimensions of the bending-moment and shearing-force diagrams for a uniform dead load of w per ft.

Since the bending-moment at F_1 is zero, and the shearing force from the span F_1F_2 at F_1 is $\frac{1}{2} \times 80w = 40w$, taking moments about C of the forces on CF_1,

$$40w \times 150 + 150w \times \tfrac{150}{2} = 80 \times R_E$$

therefore
$$R_E = 215 \cdot 6w = R_G$$
$$R_C \text{ (downwards)} = \tfrac{1}{2}(2 \times 215 \cdot 6 - 380)w = 25 \cdot 6w = R_D.$$

The shearing-force diagram can now be set out as shown in Fig. 200. $F_C = +25 \cdot 6w$, $F_E = (25 \cdot 6 + 80)w = 105 \cdot 6w$, and $105 \cdot 6w - 215 \cdot 6w = -110w$.

The shearing force at mid-span is zero and the other half of the diagram is symmetrical.

$$M_E = 25 \cdot 6w \times 80 + 80w \times 40 = 5{,}248w$$
$$M_F = 0, \quad M_H = -\tfrac{1}{8}w \times 80^2 = -800w$$

or checking from the span EC,

$$M_H = 5{,}248w - \tfrac{1}{8}w \times 220^2 = -802w$$

the maximum negative bending moment or the height of the vertex of the parabola at section H. The complete bending-moment diagram is shown in Fig. 200, the signs being according to the conventions of Art. 42.

Example 2. The bridge girders in Fig. 202, the dimensions of which are given in terms of the equal panel lengths d, are subjected to a dead-panel load of 5 tons and a travelling load of 15 tons per panel. Determine the maximum and minimum stresses in the members HG, EF, EG, and HE. Assume the dead as well as the live load to be carried on the lower chord.

For dead load only. Taking moments about A,

$$R_B = (3 \times 5 \times 10d + 10 \times 5 \times 5d)/6d = 66 \cdot \dot{6} \text{ tons}$$

Half the downward load $= 13 \times 5 = 65$ tons

hence $R_A = -1 \cdot \dot{6}$ tons, *i.e.* $1 \cdot \dot{6}$ tons downwards

which may be found directly by moments about B.

Member HG. By simple geometry, length $EH = 1 \cdot 3d$ and the perpendicular distance of the top chord from $E = 1 \cdot 245d$.

For live load on AB only (*i.e.* for maximum negative bending moment at E)

$$R_A = \tfrac{1}{2} \times 6 \times 15 - 1 \cdot \dot{6} = 43 \cdot \dot{3} \text{ tons}$$

maximum negative $M_E = 43 \cdot \dot{3} \times 2d - 2(5+15)d = 46 \cdot \dot{6}d$

and using E as a moment centre for a section

maximum thrust in $HG = 46 \cdot 6d/(1 \cdot 245d) = 37 \cdot 5$ tons.

For live load on BK only (*i.e.* for maximum positive bending moment at E),

$R_A = -(45 \times 4d + 60 \times 2d)/6d - 1 \cdot \dot{6} = 51 \cdot \dot{6}$ tons (downwards)

maximum positive $M_E = 51 \cdot \dot{6} \times 2d + 5 \times 2d = 113 \cdot \dot{3}d$
maximum pull in $HG = 113 \cdot 3d/(1 \cdot 245d) = 91$ tons

Member EF. Length $GF = 1 \cdot 6d$

maximum negative $M_G = 43 \cdot 3 \times 3d - 3(5+15)\tfrac{3}{2}d = 40d$
maximum tension in $EF = -M_G/GF = 40d/1 \cdot 6d = 25$ tons
maximum positive $M_G = 51 \cdot \dot{6} \times 3d + 3 \times 5 \times 1 \cdot 5d = 177 \cdot 5d$
maximum thrust in $EF = 177 \cdot 5d/(1 \cdot 6d) = 111$ tons.

Member EG. The stresses are found by the method of sections, taking moments about the intersection of HG and EF, the position of which by calculation or measurement to scale is $2\frac{1}{3}d$ to the left of A and $3 \cdot 68d$ from EG produced; the section taken cuts HG, EG, and EF. For minimum tension (or maximum thrust if any) in EG, using the conventional approximation of full panel loads, see Art. 132, the panel points from F to B will be loaded, and for this live load, taking moments about B,

$$R_A = 15(d + 2d + 3d)/6d - 1 \cdot \dot{6} = 13 \cdot \dot{3} \text{ tons}$$

Hence minimum tension in EG

$$= \frac{1}{3 \cdot 68d}(\tfrac{5}{2} \times 2\tfrac{1}{3}d + 5 \times 3\tfrac{1}{3}d + 5 \times 4\tfrac{1}{3}d - 13 \cdot 3 \times 2\tfrac{1}{3}d) = 3 \cdot 54 \text{ tons}$$

For maximum tension in EG the panel points Q and E and B to K will be loaded, and for this live load, taking moments about B,

$$R_A = \{(4d + 5d)15 - (4 \times 2d + 3 \times 4d)15\}/(6d) - 1 \cdot 67 \text{ tons}$$
$$= 29 \cdot 17 \text{ tons}, \text{ } i.e. \text{ } 29 \cdot 17 \text{ tons downwards.}$$

Hence the maximum tension in EG

$$= \frac{1}{3 \cdot 68d}\{(29 \cdot 17 + 2 \cdot 5) \times 2\tfrac{1}{3}d + 20 \times 3\tfrac{1}{3}d + 20 \times 4\tfrac{1}{3}d\} = 61 \cdot 6 \text{ tons.}$$

Similar calculations for the diagonal to the left of E would show a thrust as well as a tension, and the members would have to be made accordingly or the bay counterbraced.

Member HE. The section taken cuts HG, HE, and the lower chord to the left of E and moments about the same point, $2\frac{1}{3}d$ beyond A, as for EG are taken.   The minimum thrust (or maximum tension) in HE will occur when panel points from E to B are loaded. The live-load reaction from moments about B is

$$R_A = 15(d + 2d + 3d + 4d)/6d - 1 \cdot 67 = 23 \cdot 3 \text{ tons (upwards).}$$

Hence

maximum tension in HE $= (23 \cdot \dot{3} \times 2 \cdot \dot{3}d - 5 \times 3 \cdot \dot{3}d)/(4 \cdot 33d) = 8 \cdot 74 \text{ tons.}$

The maximum thrust in HE will occur when Q and all panel points from B to K are loaded.   For live load

$$R_A = \{5d \times 15 - (4 \times 2d + 3 \times 4d)15\}/(6d) - 1 \cdot 67 = -39 \cdot 17 \text{ tons.}$$

Hence

maximum thrust in HE $= (39 \cdot 17 \times 2 \cdot \dot{3}d + 20 \times 3 \cdot \dot{3}d)/(4 \cdot \dot{3}d) = 36 \cdot 5 \text{ tons.}$

The maximum tension will be slightly reduced and the maximum thrust increased if part of the dead loads are taken as applied at the top chord panel points.

Example 3.   The deck cantilever bridge girders in Fig. 203 are subject to a uniform dead load of $\frac{1}{2}$ ton per ft. and a rolling load

o*

equivalent to 2 tons per ft. Find the extreme stress in FG, HK, FK, and KG.

The main difference between this problem and the last lies in the fact that the open or lightly braced bays over the supports BC and DE can transmit no shearing force, so that $M_B = M_C$. The panel length of 12 ft. is taken as the unit of length, and the live-panel load as 24 tons, and the dead-panel load as 6 tons.

For dead load only, taking moments about B and ignoring the panel BC (*i.e.* for forces on the right hand using the point C instead of B),

$$R_A = \tfrac{1}{6}(6 \times 3 - 4 \times 2 - 3\tfrac{1}{2} \times 4)6 = -4 \text{ tons}$$

i.e. 4 tons downward. Effective reactions at C and D balance the load between them, hence

$$R_C = 7\tfrac{1}{2} \times 6 = 45 \text{ tons (upward)}$$
$$R_B = 13\tfrac{1}{2} \times 6 + 4 - 45 = 40 \text{ tons.}$$

Also FK = 1·2 units, KG = 1·562 units. KH meets the top chord produced, 4 units to the left of A and 5·37 units from KG produced. Perpendicular distance of KH from G = 1·372 units.

Member KH. The maximum tension will occur when A to B only is covered by the live load for which

$$R_A = \tfrac{1}{2} \times 6 \times 24 - 4 = 68 \text{ tons (upward)}$$
$$\text{maximum negative } M_G = 68 \times 3 - 3 \times 30 \times 1\cdot5 = 69$$
$$\text{maximum tension in KH} = 69/1\cdot372 = 50\cdot3 \text{ tons.}$$

For live load on C′ to N only

$$R_A = -\tfrac{1}{6}(4 \times 24 \times 2 + 3\tfrac{1}{2} \times 24 \times 4) - 4 = -92 \text{ tons (\textit{i.e.} downward)}$$
$$\text{maximum positive } M_G = 92 \times 3 + 3 \times 6 \times 1\cdot5 = 303$$
$$\text{maximum thrust in KH} = 303/1\cdot372 = 221 \text{ tons.}$$

Member FG. Maximum thrust will occur when A to B′ only is covered by the live load

$$\text{maximum negative } M_F = 68 \times 2 - 2 \times 30 = 76$$
$$\text{maximum thrust in FG} = -M_F/FK = 76/1\cdot2 = 63\cdot3 \text{ tons.}$$

Maximum tension will occur when live load extends from C′ to N only

$$\text{maximum positive } M_F = 92 \times 2 + 2 \times 6 = 196$$
$$\text{maximum tension in FG} = M_F/FK = 196/1\cdot2 = 163 \text{ tons}$$

Member GK. For maximum thrust in KG all panel points from G to B′ must be loaded

$$R_A = \tfrac{1}{6}(1 + 2 + 3)24 - 4 = 20 \text{ tons upward}$$
$$\text{maximum thrust} = \{(20 - 3) \times 4 - 6 \times 5 - 6 \times 6\}/5\cdot37 = 0\cdot38 \text{ ton.}$$

For maximum tension in KG all panel points from C′ to N in addition to from F to A must carry live load; then

$$R_A = \tfrac{1}{6}(4+5-4\times2-4\times3\tfrac{1}{2})24-4$$
$$= -56 \text{ tons}$$

maximum tension in

$$KG = \frac{1}{5\cdot37}\{(56+3)\times4+30\times5+30\times6\} = 105\cdot5 \text{ tons.}$$

Member KF. For minimum thrust or maximum tension, if any, the panel points G to B′ will carry live load

$$R_A = \tfrac{1}{6}(1+2\times3)24-4 = 20 \text{ tons}$$

maximum tension in $FK = \tfrac{1}{6}\{(20-3)\times4-6\times5-6\times6\} = 0\cdot33$ ton.

For maximum thrust the panel points M and F and all from C′ to N will carry live load. Then

$$R_A = \tfrac{1}{6}\{5+4-(4\times2+3\tfrac{1}{2}\times4)\}24-4 = 56 \text{ tons downward}$$

maximum thrust in $FK = \tfrac{1}{6}\{(56+3)\times4+30\times5+30\times6\} = 94\cdot3$ tons.

Example 4.   Determine the influence lines for stresses in HG and GE of Fig. 202, and hence with the travelling load given in Example 2, check the stresses in these members; use the dimensions in Example 2.

With unit load (1 ton) at E, $R_A = \tfrac{2}{3}$, $-M_E = \tfrac{2}{3}\times2d = \tfrac{4}{3}d$, hence thrust in $HG = -M_E \div 1\cdot245d = 1\cdot07$ ton. $E'E_1'$ is set off in Fig. 202 to represent $1\cdot07$ ton and (proportional) ordinates to the line $A'E_1'$ represent the stress in HG for corresponding positions of the unit load along AE. For positions beyond E there is a decrease at a uniform rate to zero at B, and at the same rate to M, hence the straight line $E'B'M_1'$. Beyond M there is again uniform increase of thrust (*i.e.* decrease of tension) in HG to zero at K, hence M_1' is joined to K′ giving the complete influence line $A'E_1'B'M_1'K'D'$, which also represents the negative moment at E if $E'E_1'$ represents $\tfrac{4}{3}d$.

If the uniform live load $w = 15/d$ tons per ft., the maximum live-load thrust in $HG = w\times$ area $AE_1'B' = \tfrac{1}{2}(15/d)\times1\cdot07\times6d = 48\cdot15$ tons.   The dead-load thrust is

$$(-1\cdot6\times2d-10\times d)/(1\cdot245d) = -10\cdot6 \text{ tons.}$$

Net maximum thrust in HG is therefore $48\cdot15-10\cdot6 = 37\cdot5$ tons, as in Example 2.

Similarly,

$$\text{live-load tension} = 48\cdot15\times\frac{\text{area } B'K'M_1}{\text{area } A'E_1'B'} = 48\cdot15\times\frac{10}{6} = 80\cdot25 \text{ tons}$$

net tension $= 80\cdot25+10\cdot6 = 91$ tons nearly, as before.

With unit load at E

$$\text{tension in } EG = (1\times4\tfrac{1}{3}d-\tfrac{2}{3}\times2\tfrac{1}{3}d)/3\cdot68d$$
$$= 0\cdot756 \text{ ton shown by } E''E_2'' \text{ (Fig. 202).}$$

With unit load at F, thrust in EG is

$(\frac{1}{2} \times 2\frac{1}{3}d)/3\cdot68d = 0\cdot317$ ton represented by $F''F_2''$ in Fig. 202.

Uniform rate of change from E to F gives $E_2''NF_2''$.   Uniform rate of change from F to M gives $F_2''B''M_2''$ through zero at B'' to $M_2''M'' = \frac{4}{3} \times 0\cdot317 = 0\cdot423$ ton tension.

Uniform rate of decrease to zero at K gives $M_2''K''$.

For maximum tension in EG the load must be on $A''N$ and $B''K''$.

$$E''N = \frac{0\cdot756}{0\cdot756 + 0\cdot317}d = 0\cdot705d, \quad A''N = 2\cdot705d$$

maximum live-load tension $= 15$ (area $A''E_2''N +$ area $B''M_2''K'')/d$

$= \frac{1}{2} . 15(0\cdot756 \times 2\cdot705 + 0\cdot423 \times 10) = 47\cdot0$ tons.

Dead-load tension $= (1\cdot6 \times 2\frac{1}{3}d + 10 \times 3\frac{1}{3}d)/3\cdot68d = 10\cdot0$ tons.

Net tension $= 47 + 10 = 57$ tons as against $61\cdot6$ tons by the approximate method of Example 2, which gives an error on the safe side.

Similarly, since $NF'' = d - 0\cdot705d = 0\cdot295d$, maximum live-load thrust $= \frac{15}{2} \times 3\cdot295 \times 0\cdot317 = 7\cdot83$ tons.   Hence the minimum tension $= 10 - 7\cdot83 = 2\cdot17$ tons against $3\cdot54$ tons in Example 2, the latter being for a minimum stress in error on the safe side.

140. Two-span or Centre-bearing Swingbridge.   Swingbridges which turn on a central pivot or its equivalent, form when closed continuous girders of two spans such as illustrated in Fig. 204.   The

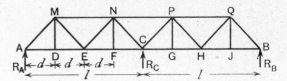

FIG. 204.—Two-span or centre-bearing swingbridge

stresses in the members under given loads may easily be calculated by the methods already given for simple spans when the reactions have been calculated.   Sometimes the ends A and B are lifted (or C depressed) when the bridge is closed, by such an estimated amount as will prevent any uplift under the live load.   It is well to estimate for a lift varying from zero to one which will make the dead load upward reactions at A and B equal to those corresponding to a continuous girder.   In the case of the latter full lift the reactions for both live and dead load are to be reckoned as for a continuous beam.

In other cases the ends A and B are secured by latches or pins capable of exerting upward or downward reactions due to various positions of the moving load, and the end reactions due to the dead load are zero.   All stresses due to dead load are the same when the bridge is closed as when it is open and may conveniently be computed separately. Each span for the dead loads may be treated as a cantilever fixed at the pivot and free at the ends. In the case of unequal spans, in order to balance the long arm about the pivot, dead load will have to be added to the short arm.

The reactions, and consequently the stresses arising from the live load, will be those for a continuous girder of two spans. The continuous girder is a particular case of a statically intermediate structure, and the reactions, etc., for continuous beams of solid section have been dealt with in Chapter VIII. The reactions for a framed girder can only be reliably computed when the sections (or the relative sections) of the various members are known, *i.e.* when the girder has been designed. The principle of finding a reaction by equating the upward deflection due to the reaction to the downward deflection at the same point due to the load is valid, but the deflections are to be found (as in Art. 152) by the methods given in Arts. 145 to 147, which differ from the methods applicable to the deflections of a solid beam of uniform section in two important respects by taking account of (1) the variable cross-section of the girder, and (2) the shearing deflection or distortion arising from the strain of the web members, which is much greater than in a solid beam. The methods applicable to a solid beam may, however, be employed as a first approximation to design the members and then checked by the methods of Art. 145. In the case of two-span trusses of usual proportions this approximate method is found to be sufficiently accurate, and checking by the more exact method does not usually involve any important redesign. A simple example will illustrate the methods. The modifications for unequal arms do not involve any difference in principle.

Example. Find the stress in DE, EM, and MN (Fig. 204) if the web members are inclined at 45°, the dead load being w_1 per ft. and the equivalent uniform live load being w_2 per ft., the dimensions being in feet.

Dead-Load Reactions. $R_A = 0$, $R_C = 2w_1 . l$, $R_B = 0$.

Live-Load Reactions. Panel load $= w_2 . d = w_2 l/4$.

To find a general formula for the reactions, approximating by assuming the condition of a solid continuous beam, let a load W be at a distance kl from A in the span AC. Following the method used in the example at the end of Art. 81, imagine the support C removed and equate the deflection at C due to W to $R_C(2l)^3/(48EI)$ (see (4), Art. 79). To find the deflection at C due to W write in (7) Art. 81, kl for b, $(2-k)l$ for a, and l for x; this gives a deflection

$$\frac{Wl^3k(3-k^2)}{12EI} = \frac{R_Cl^3}{6EI}$$

hence $\qquad\qquad R_C = \tfrac{1}{2}W . k(3-k^2)$ . . . . . (1)

And by taking moments about B

$$R_A = \tfrac{1}{4}W(4 - 5k + k^3) \quad . \quad . \quad . \quad . \quad (2)$$

and

$$R_B = -\tfrac{1}{4}Wk(1 - k^2) \quad . \quad . \quad . \quad . \quad (3)$$

Writing in succession values of k of $\tfrac{1}{4}$, $\tfrac{1}{2}$, and $\tfrac{3}{4}$ for unit load at D, E, and F, and by symmetry for J, H, and G, we get then for $W = 1$ the following values:

Unit load at	D	E	F	G	H	J	D, E, and F	G, H, and J
R_A .	0·6914	0·4063	0·1680	−0·0820	−0·0938	−0·0586	1·2657	−0·2344
R_B .	−0·0586	−0·0938	−0·0820	0·1680	0·4063	0·6914	−0·2344	1·2657

Dead-Load Stresses (by method of sections)

$$M_E = 2w_1 d \times d \quad \text{tension in MN} = M_E/d = 2w_1 d^2 \div d = 2w_1 d$$
$$M_M = \tfrac{1}{2}w_1 d^2 \quad \text{thrust in DE} = M_M/d = 0.5w_1 d$$

shear in bay DE $= \tfrac{3}{2}w_1 d$ \qquad thrust in ME $= \sqrt{2} \times \tfrac{3}{2}w_1 d = 2.121w_1 d$

Live-Load Stresses.—Member MN. Tension $= M_E \div d$. Extreme live-load stresses occur for maximum positive and negative values of M_E. Maximum tension occurs for CB fully loaded; from the Table

$$R_A = -0.2344w_2 d \quad M_E = +0.2344w_2 d \times 2d$$

maximum tension in MN $= M_E \div d = 0.4688w_2 d$

Maximum thrust occurs for AC fully loaded; [1] from the Table

maximum thrust $= -M_E \div d = 1.2657w_2 d \times 2d \div d - w_2 d = 1.5314w_2 d$

Member DE.

$$\text{Thrust} = M_M/d = M_D/d$$

maximum thrust (for CB fully loaded) $= +0.2344w_2 d$

maximum tension (for AC loaded) $= 1.2657w_2 d$

Member ME.

Maximum tension $= \sqrt{2} \times$ maximum negative shear in DE

maximum thrust $= \sqrt{2} \times$ maximum positive shearing force in DE

For maximum thrust G, H, J, and D must be loaded, and employing conventional full panel loads

$$R_A = -0.2344w_2 d + 0.6914w_2 d = +0.4570w_2 d$$

maximum thrust $= (w_2 d - 0.4570w_2 d)\sqrt{2} = 0.768w_2 d$

maximum tension (E and F loaded) $= \sqrt{2}(0.4063 + 0.1680)w_2 d$
$$= 0.813w_2 \, . \, d.$$

---

[1] Note that for more than five panels per span for the negative M at points near the central support (C) one or more panel points near the end support (A) may be unloaded, and for maximum positive M these points will be loaded (if the live load may be broken up).

Total Stresses.   Adding the dead-load stresses algebraically to the extreme live-load stresses we get:

Member	Maximum tension	Maximum thrust
MN	$d(0\cdot4688w_2+2w_1)$	$d(1\cdot5314w_2-2w_1)$
DE	$d(1\cdot2657w_2-0\cdot5w_1)$	$d(0\cdot2344w_2+0\cdot5w_1)$
ME	$d(0\cdot813w_2-2\cdot121w_1)$	$d(0\cdot768w_2+2\cdot121w_1)$

Influence Lines for these Cases.   From the fact that (1), (2), and (3) are higher than the first degree in k, it is evident that the influence lines for reaction, shear, and bending moment will be curved; consequently the influence line method is much less simple than for statically determinate girders, and is not here given.

141. Rim-bearing Swingbridge.   Swingbridges which turn on a ring of rollers form a more or less " continuous " girder over three spans, the central span being approximately the diameter of the roller track.   A simplified type is shown in Fig. 205.   The determination

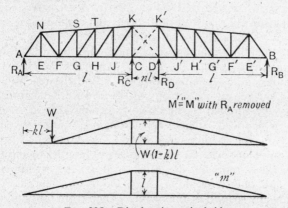

Fig. 205.—Rim-bearing swingbridge

of stresses in such a structure does not involve any fresh point of importance after the reactions have been found.

Continuous Truss.   If the girder in the central span CD (Fig. 205) is rigidly braced by very substantial web members the truss may be regarded as continuous.   The dead loads and stresses may be treated as in the previous article if the free ends are simply latched when the bridge is closed.   The live-load reactions may be found by assuming the girder to act as a solid beam, as in Chapter VIII, but the limitations to the accuracy in such a case are considerable; the neglected effects of the distortion of the web members of the relatively short central span are really considerable, and the live-load reactions found on such assumptions involve negative values at the central supports greater than the positive dead-load values. It has been shown [1] by a numerical example that for a very short central span with simple bracing the more exact methods of Art. 152 give very different values. The method of finding the live-load reactions for any panel load, and hence for any combination of panel loads, is to take a single-load distant, say, kl from A, and (by Wilson's method, Art. 92) find R_C and R_D in terms of k by equating to zero the deflections at C and D produced jointly by the load, and by R_C and R_D using the formulae (7) and (10) of Art. 81. The reactions R_B and R_A are then found by simple statics. Tabulating reaction coefficients, as in the previous article for values of k corresponding to each panel point, will give the reactions for any position of the moving load.

Partially Continuous Truss. It is a common practice to make the central diagonal bracing very light, and quite inadequate to carry shear stresses which would arise from partial live loading. Such a construction may be regarded as only partially continuous. The shear stress in the span CD (Fig. 205) is nearly zero, and consequently the statical relations of the load and reactions are simplified. On account of the only partial continuity at C and D, the ordinary relations of bending-moment slope and deflection are not applicable throughout the length of the beam. Applying the theory of solid beams under the assumed conditions to find the reaction R_A, say, due to a load W distant kl from A, the upward deflection at A due to R_A may be equated to the downward deflection at A, due to W when R_A is removed. These deflections may most conveniently be calculated by the strain-energy method of Art. 96. The separate bending moments over the three ranges of length are shown on the simple bending-moment diagrams in Fig. 205, from which the ordinates M' due to W alone, or m due to unit load at A, may be written for any section of the beam. Then from (16) and (17), Art. 96, assuming a constant section throughout

$$R_A \times \int m^2 dx = \int M' m dx \quad \ldots \ldots \quad (1)$$

Splitting these integrals into the three ranges over which they are continuous, and using convenient origins

$$\int M' m dx = W \int_{kl}^{l} (x-kl)x dx + W(l-kl)l \times nl + W \int_{0}^{l} (1-k)x^2 dx$$

$$= \frac{Wl^3}{6} \{4 - 5k + k^3 + 6n(1-k)\} \quad \ldots \ldots \quad (2)$$

---

[1] *Modern Framed Structures*, by Johnson, Bryan, and Turneaure, Part II.

And $\int m^2dx = \int_0^l x^2dx + l^2 \times nl + \int_0^l x^2dx = \tfrac{1}{3}l^3(2+3n)$ . . . (3)

Hence $R_A = \int M'mdx \div \int m^2dx = W(1-k)\left\{1 - \dfrac{k(1+k)}{2(2+3n)}\right\}$. (4)

And since the shearing force in CD is zero

$$R_C = W - R_A = W\left\{k + \dfrac{k(1-k^2)}{2(2+3n)}\right\} \quad . . . \quad (5)$$

And from moments about A and since $R_B = -R_D$

$$R_B = -R_D = Wk - R_C = -W\dfrac{k(1-k^2)}{2(2+3n)} \quad . . . \quad (6)$$

It may be noted that as n approaches zero the end reactions approach the values given in (2) and (3), Art. 140, for a two-span truss.

Example.   Take the panel length in Fig. 205 to be 15 ft.   NE = CD = 20 ft.   KC = 25 ft.   Live load 3,000 lb. per ft.   Dead load 1,000 lb. per ft.   Find the extreme stresses in ST, TG, and GH.

$$n = \frac{20}{6 \times 15} = \tfrac{2}{9}$$

hence for unit load on various panel points, kl from A (4) gives

$$R_A = (1-k)\{1 - \tfrac{3}{16}k(1+k)\}$$

and (6) gives

$$R_B = -\tfrac{3}{16}k(1-k^2)$$

which gives R_A for loads on the right-hand span; and taking successive values of $\tfrac{1}{6}$, $\tfrac{2}{6}$, $\tfrac{3}{6}$, $\tfrac{4}{6}$, and $\tfrac{5}{6}$ for k, we get the following coefficients for the reaction at A.

Unit load at .	E	F	G	H	J	J'	H'	G'	F'	E'	EFGH and J	E'F'G'H' and J'
End reaction R_A	0·804	0·612	0·430	0·264	0·119	−0·0477	−0·0695	−0·0703	−0·0556	−0·0304	2·229	−0·2735

Calculated dimensions SG = 22 ft., perpendicular distance of ST from G = 21·7 ft., TH = 23 ft., ST meets HG 20 panel lengths to the left of E, *i.e.* $19 \times 15 = 285$ ft. to the left of A; distance of this moment centre from GT produced = 276·8 ft.

Live-Load Stresses.   Taking unit panel loads and then multiplying by 45,000 lb., and assuming full panel loads for maximum stresses
Member GT.   Maximum thrust for H and J loaded

$$R_A = 0·264 + 0·119 = 0·383$$

By moments about the intersection of ST and GH

thrust $= 45,000(0·383 \times 285)/276·8 = 17,700$ lb.

Maximum tension for E, F, G, and D to B loaded

$$R_A = 0.804 + 0.612 + 0.430 - 0.2735 = 1.5725$$

tension $= (300 + 315 + 330 - 285 \times 1.5725)45,000/276.8 = 80,900$ lb.

Member ST.   Maximum thrust, for A to C loaded

$$R_A = 2.229, \quad -M_G = (2.229 \times 3 - 2 - 1)15 \times 45,000$$
$$\text{thrust} = -M_G/21.7 = (3.687 \times 15 \times 45,000)/21.7 = 114,500 \text{ lb.}$$

Maximum tension, for D to B loaded

$$R_A = -0.2735$$
$$M_G = 0.2735 \times 3 \times 15 \times 45,000$$
$$\text{tension} = (0.2735 \times 45 \times 45,000)/21.7 = 25,500 \text{ lb.}$$

Member GH.   Maximum tension, for A to C loaded

$$-M_T = (2.229 \times 4 - 3 - 2 - 1)15 \times 45,000$$
$$\text{tension} = -M_T/23 = (2.916 \times 15 \times 45,000)/23 = 85,600 \text{ lb.}$$

Maximum thrust, for D to B loaded

$$M_T = 0.2735 \times 4 \times 15 \times 45,000$$
$$\text{thrust} = 1.094 \times 15 \times 45,000/23 = 32,100 \text{ lb.}$$

Dead-Load Stresses.   Take the loads as being all on the lower chords and the ends as not lifted when closed, then the dead-load stresses are as for a cantilever.   Half a panel load is taken at A. Full panel load $= 15,000$ lb.

Member GT.   Tension $= (\frac{1}{2} \times 285 + 300 + 315 + 330)15,000/276.8$
$$= 59,000 \text{ lb.}$$

Member ST.   Tension $= M_G/21.7 = (45 \times \frac{1}{2} + 30 + 15)15,000/21.7$
$$= 46,600 \text{ lb.}$$

Member GH.   Thrust $= M_F/23 = (60 \times \frac{1}{2} + 45 + 30 + 15)15,000/23$
$$= 78,300 \text{ lb.}$$

Total Extreme Stresses.
Member GT—

> Maximum tension $= 80,900 + 59,000 = 139,900$ lb.
> Minimum tension $= 59,000 - 17,700 = 41,300$ lb.

Member ST—

> Maximum thrust $= 114,500 - 46,600 = 67,900$ lb.
> Maximum tension $= 25,500 + 46,600 = 72,100$ lb.

Member GH—

> Maximum tension $= 85,600 - 78,300 = 7,300$ lb.
> Maximum thrust $= 78,300 + 32,100 = 110,400$ lb.

142. Stresses in Braced Piers.   Fig. 206 represents a type of braced pier often used to support railway viaducts; a height of only two panels is shown, but more may be used. The panels are counterbraced by long diagonals which may be regarded as offering a negligible resistance to thrust, and the tensile stresses in any diagonals due to any cause may be safely computed as if the other diagonal intersecting it were absent, thus making the structure statically determinate. The stresses arise from the vertical loads carried by the pier, from the weight of the pier itself, and from horizontal wind pressure on the viaduct, the train, and the pier (the latter being taken as if applied at panel points), and occasionally from the centrifugal force of a train in the case of bridges built on curves. In Fig. 206 the horizontal loads are represented by P_1, P_2, and P_3. The stresses resulting from vertical and horizontal loads may conveniently be found separately.

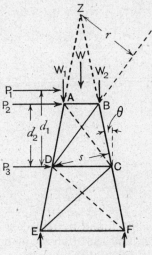

FIG. 206.—Stresses in a braced pier

Vertical Loads. The total top load W may be divided by the simple principles of statics into parts W_1 and W_2 at A and B. If W is symmetrically placed, W_1 and W_2 are equal, and the stresses in the braces AC and BD are both zero, while those in AD and BC are each $\frac{1}{2}$W secant θ and that in AB is $\frac{1}{2}$W tan θ. If W is eccentrically placed towards A so that W_1 is greater than W_2, the additional stress may be found by taking a downward force $W_1 - \frac{1}{2}$W at A and an upward force $\frac{1}{2}$W$ - W_2$ at B, and drawing a stress diagram after removing the member AC.

In any case the stresses may conveniently be determined by the method of sections, *e.g.* if W is eccentric by an amount *e* towards A, taking a horizontal section through the top panel for member BD and using the moment centre Z

$$\text{tension BD} = W \cdot e/r \quad \ldots \ldots \quad (1)$$

And using the moment centre D

$$\text{thrust BC} = (\text{moment of W about D})/s \quad \ldots \quad (2)$$

Horizontal Loads. The stresses for horizontal loads are simply those for a braced cantilever; using the same methods

$$\text{thrust BC} = (P_1 \cdot d_1 + P_2 \cdot d_2)/s$$
$$\text{tension BD} = (\text{moments of } P_1 \text{ and } P_2 \text{ about Z})/r$$

143. Space Frames. The polygon of forces is not limited to the case of coplanar forces but is applicable to general cases of concurrent forces in space by means of solid geometry. The stress diagram for structures not in one plane can be drawn and used by means of a plan and elevation, but for some simple structures a simple resolution of forces often reduces the problem to that of a plane frame.

Shear Legs. For example, in the shear legs BD and BC (Fig. 207)

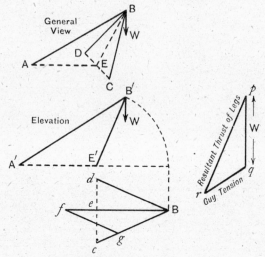

FIG. 207.—Stresses in shear legs

stayed by the guy-rope AB and carrying the load W the stresses are readily found by replacing the two legs by an imaginary single or resultant leg BE in the plane of AB and W, which carries the result-ant thrust of the two legs. The length of BE is found by setting off, $ed=ED$, $ec=EC$, and striking arcs from d and c with radii BD and CB respectively to intersect in B, then $eB=EB=E'B'$. A plane

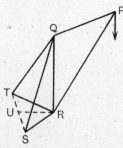

FIG. 208.—Derrick crane

triangle of forces pqr for the plane AEB from the elevation gives this resultant thrust of the two legs and the tension in the guy-rope AB. It only remains to resolve the resultant thrust pr (which is in the plane BDC of the legs) along BD and BC. The length Bf is set off equal to pr and then fg is drawn parallel to dB, then gf repre-sents the thrust in DB and Bg represents the thrust in BC.

Derrick Crane. Fig. 208 shows a com-mon derrick crane in which the vertical post QR is braced by two ties TQ and SQ, the pull in which is

resisted at their feet by the thrust of RS and RT together with the
dead weights placed at S and T to balance the load W. The
stress in the tie-rod QP and jib PR are found by the triangle of
forces or by moments, but for the remainder of the structure the
simplest plan is to replace QT and SQ by a single intermediate tie
in the planes of QPR and TQS, the pull in which gives the resultant
of the tensions in TQ and SQ. This resultant in the plane TQS may
then be resolved into its components along QT and QS. The jib

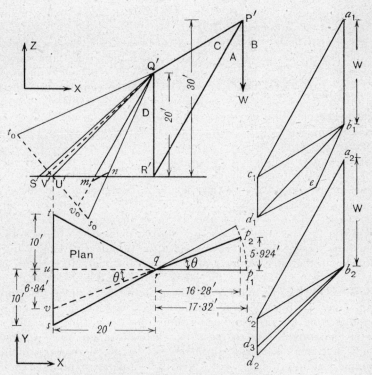

FIG. 209.—Stresses in derrick crane

and tie may turn horizontally about RQ; so long as their common
plane produced does not go outside the angle between the planes
RQS and QTR no thrust will be imposed upon QS or QT.

Fig. 209 with letters corresponding to Fig. 208 shows the determination of the stresses for the central position, for the extreme
position, and for an intermediate position. The plan shows the
distance st between the feet and the elevation U'Q' gives the length
of UQ, while the triangle $Q't_0s_0$ gives the real shape of the triangle
QTS by making $U't_0 = ut$ and $U's_0 = us$. The stress diagram

$a_1b_1c_1d_1$ is drawn for the central position, b_1d_1 being the pull in QU; this is resolved into components for the legs by drawing b_1e parallel to $Q's_0$ and ed_1 parallel to $Q't_0$. For the position in which the vertical plane of P'Q'R' is inclined θ to the central plane the stress diagram $a_2b_2c_2d_2$ is similarly drawn. The tensions in the legs are found by making $s_0v_0 = sv$ and $Q'm = b_2d_2$ and drawing mn parallel to t_0Q'. Then $Q'n$ represents the tension in QS and mn that in QT. For the extreme position when PQ, PR, and QS are in the same vertical plane, $a_2b_2c_2d_3$ is the stress diagram, b_2d_3 parallel to S'Q' is the tension in QS, and QT is not stressed. If θ is further increased QT suffers a thrust.

Braced Crane. Fig. 210 shows a braced crane the members of which lie in various planes. The joints in the space frame may be named for reference by the capital letters A, B, C, D, etc., not shown in Fig. 210, where these joints are denoted in the elevation of the frame by a', b', c', d', etc., and in the plan of the frame by a, b, c, d, etc. The plan and elevation of the stress diagram are shown, corresponding lines in the space diagram being denoted by the same figure.

Starting with the vector force polygon for joint A. The line 0 is drawn downwards in elevation to represent 8 tons, and then lines 3, 1, and 2 are drawn, the line 1 being placed in the only possible position symmetrical with respect to line 0. 0, 3, 1, 2 give the order and direction of the forces at the crane head, A. The polygon for the joint D, where 1, 4, 5, and 6 meet, is next drawn; the lines 4 and 5 being drawn in elevation of indefinite length, line 6 follows in the only symmetrical position, and the plan is projected, its sides being parallel to the plans of the members. It is always possible by the methods of solid geometry to complete the force polygon for a point if three sides are unknown in length but known in direction, the problem being simply to draw a line parallel to a given straight line to meet two given straight lines which is fully determinate unless all three lines lie in one plane. In this simple example the process is greatly facilitated by the symmetry of the frame. Any but the most symmetrical order of the lines in the stress diagram may involve duplication of certain sides in plan or elevation; in this case the (point) elevation of vector 7 is duplicated in elevation. · The member 12 is not stressed by the load; it is required for lateral stability to resist side forces such as wind. The feet of braces 10 and 11 being omitted, and any force in 10, 11, and 12 being treated as a reaction at the upper joint, the remainder of the structure is a perfect frame having five joints and nine members in agreement with the formula $3n-6$ given in Art. 113.

Note that in general neither plan nor elevation of the stress diagram show the true lengths of the space vectors.   To scale off the forces in the members the true lengths of the vectors are required. These are given by the hypotenuses of right-angled triangles, the

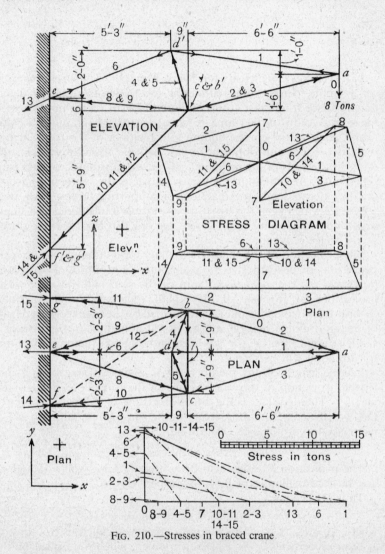

FIG. 210.—Stresses in braced crane

bases of which are equal to plans of the respective vectors and the heights equal to the difference in heights of the ends of the respective vectors measured from the elevation.   Thus the true length of the vectors are shown at the foot of Fig. 210 by the sloping lines which are the hypotenuses of triangles right angled at O.   The forces in the members, scaled from Fig. 210, are as follows:

Member or reaction	1	2–3	4–5	6	7	8–9	10–11	12	13
Force (in tons) .	21·9 T	11·5 C	6·4 C	20·0 T	6·2 T	1·4 C	11·1 C	—	17·6 T

144. Tension Coefficients for Space Frames.   The stress diagram for a simple, perfect, non-redundant and therefore statically determinate space frame is a group of closed (space) vector polygons for the several joints of the frame.   As in the stress diagram for a plane frame, each vector corresponding to a member of the frame represents two equal and opposite forces, namely, those exerted on the joints at the ends of the member.   If these opposite vectors are cancelled out there remain in the vector polygons the vectors representing the external loads and reactions or supporting forces.   All these are forces which keep the structure as a whole (considered as a single rigid body) in equilibrium.   These vectors also must form a closed vector space polygon.

The projection of the space-stress diagram on three mutually perpendicular planes will give, on each plane, a group of closed plane polygons, *i.e.* the *geometrical* sum of the sides will be zero.   The projections of any one of these plane polygons on the axes of co-ordinates lying in its plane (and formed by the intersections of two of the co-ordinate planes) will be closed polygons in the form of a single straight line, *i.e.* the *algebraic* sum of such vector projections for any joint will be zero.

Let the length of any member AB in a space frame be L_{AB} and let the projection of this on OX, one of the three co-ordinate axes, be l_{AB}.   Then l_{AB}/L_{AB} is the direction cosine of AB with respect to OX.   If the corresponding vector in the space-stress diagram is T_{AB} its projection on the axis OX will be

$$T_{AB} \times l_{AB}/L_{AB} \quad . \quad . \quad . \quad . \quad . \quad . \quad (1)$$

The projection l_{AB} may also be written $x_B - x_A$, where x_B and x_A are the x-co-ordinates of B and A respectively.

Thus (1) becomes

$$(x_B - x_A)T_{AB}/L_{AB} \text{ or } t_{AB}(x_B - x_A)$$

where $t_{AB} = T_{AB}/L_{AB}$.   This quantity t has been called by Southwell [1] a tension coefficient.   It is a factor which, when multiplied by the length of the member, gives the tension or pull in the member (+ if tension and − if a thrust or force of compression).

[1] See " Primary Stress-Determination in Space Frames," by R. V. Southwell, *ngineering*, Feb. 6th, 1920.

The fact that the projection on the axis OX of the closed space vector polygon for a joint A, say, is a closed circuit, or the algebraic sum of the projection of the sides of the polygon on OX is zero, may be written

$$t_{AB}(x_B - x_A) + t_{AC}(x_C - x_A) + \ldots + X_A = 0 \quad . \quad (2)$$

where X_A is the projection on OX of the resultant external force (if any) on the joint A (or the x-component of such force). For the successive terms $t_{AB}(x_B - x_A)$, etc., are the projections of the sides of a closed vector space polygon.

Similarly, for projection on OY

$$t_{AB}(y_B - y_A) + t_{AC}(y_C - y_A) + \ldots + Y_A = 0 \quad . \quad (3)$$

and on OZ

$$t_{AB}(z_B - z_A) + t_{AC}(z_C - z_A) + \ldots Z_A = 0 \quad . \quad (4)$$

where Y_A and Z_A are the projections of the resultant external force on joint A on OY and OZ respectively or the y and z components of such force.

The simultaneous equations (2), (3), and (4) relate to the joint A and three similar equations may be written for each joint of the space frame and the equations more than suffice for finding the tension coefficients of each member of the frame if all the external forces are known.

In order to find the force in each member it is only necessary to multiply the tension coefficient by the length L of the member. The true length of the member is equal to the square root of the sum of the squares of its three orthogonal projections, *e.g.*

$$L_{AB} = \sqrt{\{(x_B - x_A)^2 + (y_B - y_A)^2 + (z_B - z_A)^2\}} \quad . \quad (5)$$

Southwell, in the paper previously referred to, pointed out that these equations provide an analytical method of finding the stresses in members without drawing, since the co-ordinates x, y, and z may generally be measured off from a working drawing of a plan and two elevations.

If the equations of the type (2) are added the terms relative to members of the frame will cancel out in pairs and leave

$$X_A + X_B + X_C + \text{ etc. } = 0 \quad . \quad . \quad . \quad . \quad (6)$$

And corresponding to the directions OY and OZ

$$Y_A + Y_B + Y_C + \text{ etc. } = 0 \quad . \quad . \quad . \quad . \quad (7)$$

$$Z_A + Z_B + Z_C + \text{ etc. } = 0 \quad . \quad . \quad . \quad . \quad (8)$$

These three equations represent the closure of the space vector polygon of external forces. These three equations together with three expressing zero moment of the external forces about axes perpendicular to each of the three co-ordinate planes, *e.g.*

$$(y_A X_A - x_A Y_A) + (y_B X_B - x_B Y_B) + \text{etc.} = 0 \quad . \quad (9)$$

give sufficient equations to determine the external supporting forces. For six conditions suffice for equilibrium, *viz.* that the sum of the components in each of three independent directions shall be zero and that the moments about three mutually perpendicular axes shall be zero.

For n joints, $3n$ equations such as (2), (3), and (4) can be written thus, providing for the determination of the tension in $3n-6$ members (see Art. 113) and six conditions relative to supporting forces, *viz.* (6), (7), (8), and (9) with two similar equations.

In actual numerical work it is not necessary to measure separately the co-ordinates x_A, x_B, etc. The differences $x_B - x_A$, etc., and $y_B - y_A$ can be measured directly from a plan and $z_B - z_A$, etc., from an elevation. But it is important to get correct signs and for this purpose it is desirable to mark on the plan and elevation of the frame the positive directions of x, y, and z, as shown in the following example. It is often not necessary then to specify or locate the origin of co-ordinates since we are concerned only with differences of co-ordinates in equations of the type (2), (3), (4), which suffice for many problems. An example will demonstrate the simplicity of the method.

Example 1. Find the forces in the members of the braced crane frame (Fig. 210) from the dimensions of the plan and elevation. The joints are referred to by capital letters, their plans by corresponding small italic letters and their elevations by accented small italic letters.

Joint A. $x_B - x_A = -6.5$ ft.; $x_C - x_A = -6.5$ ft.; $x_D - x_A = -7.25$ ft. For direction x, equation (2) becomes

$$-6.5t_{AB} - 6.5t_{AC} - 7.25t_{AD} = 0 \quad . \quad . \quad . \quad (10)$$

Also

$$y_B - y_A = +1.75 \text{ ft.}; \quad y_C - y_A = -1.75 \text{ ft.}; \quad y_D - y_A = 0$$

For direction y equation (3) becomes

$$1.75t_{AB} - 1.75t_{AC} + 0 = 0 \quad . \quad . \quad . \quad . \quad (11)$$

hence $t_{AB} = t_{AC}$ and substituting in (10)

$$t_{AB} = t_{AC} = -t_{AD} \times 7.25/13$$

Again, $z_B - z_A = -1.5$ ft.; $z_C - z_A = -1.5$ ft.; $z_D - z_A = +1$ ft. For direction z

$$-1.5t_{AB} - 1.5t_{AC} + t_{AD} - 8 = 0 \quad . \quad . \quad . \quad (12)$$

Substituting for t_{AB} and t_{AC} the value $-t_{AD} \times 7.25/13$

$$t_{AD}(1 + 3 \times 7.25/13) = 8$$
$$t_{AD} = 2.9928 \text{ ton/ft.}$$
$$t_{AB} = t_{AC} = -1.66906 \text{ ton/ft.}$$

$L_{AD} = \sqrt{(7.25^2 + 1)} = 7.3186$ ft. $L_{AB} = L_{AC}\sqrt{(6.5^2 + 1.75^2 + 1.5^2)} = 6.8966$ ft.

$T_{AD} = 2 \cdot 9928 \times 7 \cdot 3186 = 21 \cdot 90$ tons.

$T_{AB} = T_{AC} = 1 \cdot 6690 \times 6 \cdot 8966 = -11 \cdot 51$ tons or $11 \cdot 51$ tons compression.

The equations for joints A, D, and C are tabulated. From the symmetry the results for the remaining joints follow.

Joint	Direction	Equations		Solutions
A	x	$-6 \cdot 5t_{AB} - 6 \cdot 5t_{AC} - 7 \cdot 25t_{AD}$	$= 0$	$t_{AD} = +2 \cdot 9928$
	y	$1 \cdot 75t_{AB} - 1 \cdot 75t_{AC}$	$= 0$	$t_{AB} = -1 \cdot 66906$
	z	$-1 \cdot 5t_{AB} - 1 \cdot 5t_{AC} + t_{AD} - 8$	$= 0$	$t_{AC} = -1 \cdot 66906$
D	x	$7 \cdot 25t_{AD} + 0 \cdot 75t_{BD} + 0 \cdot 75t_{CP} - 5 \cdot 25t_{DE}$	$= 0$	$t_{CD} = t_{BD} = -2 \cdot 0208$
	y	$0 + 1 \cdot 75t_{BD} - 1 \cdot 75t_{CD} + 0$	$= 0$	$t_{DE} = +3 \cdot \dot{5}\dot{5}$
	z	$-t_{AD} - 2 \cdot 5t_{BD} - 2 \cdot 5t_{CD} + 0$	$= 0$	
C	x	$6 \cdot 5t_{AC} + 0 - 0 \cdot 75t_{CD} - 6t_{CE} - 6t_{CF}$	$= 0$	$t_{CE}(=t_{BE}) = -0 \cdot 2223$
	y	$1 \cdot 75t_{AC} + 3 \cdot 5t_{CB} + 1 \cdot 75t_{CD} + 1 \cdot 75t_{CE}$		
		$-0 \cdot 5t_{CF}$	$= 0$	$t_{CF}(=t_{BG}) = -1 \cdot 3333$
	z	$1 \cdot 5t_{AC} + 0 + 2 \cdot 5t_{AD} + 0 \cdot 5t_{CE} - 5 \cdot 75t_{CF}$	$= 0$	$t_{CB} = +1 \cdot 7656$

The lengths of the remaining members, from (5), are:

$L_{DE} = \sqrt{(5 \cdot 25^2 + 2^2)} = 5 \cdot 618$ ft.; $L_{BD} = L_{CD} = \sqrt{(2 \cdot 5^2 + 0 \cdot 75^2 + 1 \cdot 75^2)} = 3 \cdot 1424$ ft.

$L_{BE} = L_{CE} = \sqrt{(6^2 + 1 \cdot 75^2 + 0 \cdot 5^2)} = 6 \cdot 270$ ft.; $L_{CB} = 3 \cdot 25$ ft.

$L_{BG} = L_{CF} = \sqrt{(6^2 + 0 \cdot 5^2 + 5 \cdot 75^2)} = 8 \cdot 3254$ ft.

Multiplying the tension coefficients from the Table above by the corresponding lengths we get the force in each member as follows:

Member	1 AD	2 3 AB–AC	4 5 BD–CD	6 DE	7 CB	8 CE–BE	10–11 CF–BG
t in ton/ft.	$2 \cdot 9928$	$-1 \cdot 6691$	$-2 \cdot 0208$	$3 \cdot \dot{5}\dot{5}$	$1 \cdot 7656$	$-0 \cdot 2223$	$-1 \cdot 333$
L in ft.	$7 \cdot 3186$	$6 \cdot 8966$	$3 \cdot 1424$	$5 \cdot 618$	$3 \cdot 5$	$6 \cdot 270$	$8 \cdot 3254$
Force in tons	$21 \cdot 90$ T	$11 \cdot 51$ C	$6 \cdot 35$ C	$19 \cdot 97$ T	$6 \cdot 18$ T	$1 \cdot 39$ C	$11 \cdot 10$ C

Corresponding results have been obtained graphically in Art. 143. We may check the external supporting force or reaction 13 at E by taking moments about a point midway between F and G (in the central vertical plane of the frame). This gives 8 tons $\times$ 150 in./ $68 \cdot 25$ in. $= 17 \cdot 58$ tons.

Example 2. Find the stresses in the members of the derrick crane (Fig. 208) if QR = 20 ft.; UR = 20 ft.; TS = 20 ft.; $\theta = 20°$; W = 1,000 lb.; vertical height of P above R = 30 ft.

From the geometry of the figure evidently QP is inclined 30° to the horizontal and RP 60° to the horizontal. The length of rp_2 the horizon projection of QP and RP $= qp_2 = 10\sqrt{3} = 17 \cdot 32$ ft.

$RP = \sqrt{(30^2 + 17\cdot32)^2} = 20\sqrt{3} = 34\cdot64$ ft.; $QS = QT = \sqrt{(10^2 + 20^2 + 20^2)} = 30$ ft.

Projection of qp_2 in direction $x = 17\cdot32\cos 20° = 16\cdot28$ ft.

Projection of qp_2 in direction $y = 17\cdot32\sin 20° = 5\cdot924$ ft.

Joint P. PQR is a plane frame and only two equations are necessary.

In direction x $\qquad -16\cdot28t_{PQ} - 16\cdot28t_{PR} = 0$.

In direction z $\qquad -10t_{PQ} - 30t_{PR} - 1,000 = 0$.

From which $\qquad\qquad t_{PQ} = -t_{PR} = 50$ lb.

The equations and solutions for Q, S, T, and R follow, the reactions R_S, R_T, and R_R being included.

Joint	Direction	Equations		Solutions
Q	x	$-20t_{QS} - 20t_{QT} + 16\cdot28t_{QP}$	$=0$	$t_{QS} = 35\cdot15$
	y	$-10t_{QS} + 10t_{QT} + 5\cdot92t_{PQ}$	$=0$	$t_{QT} = 5\cdot5$
	z	$10t_{PQ} - 20t_{QS} - 20t_{QT} - 20t_{QR}$	$=0$	$t_{QR} = -15\cdot65$
S	x	$20t_{SR} + 20t_{SQ}$	$=0$	$t_{SR} = -t_{QS} = -35\cdot15$
	z	$20t_{SQ} + R_S$	$=0$	$R_S = -703$ lb. (down)
T	x	$20t_{QT} + 20t_{RT}$	$=0$	$t_{RT} = -t_{QT} = -5\cdot5$
	z	$20t_{QT} + R_T$	$=0$	$R_T = -110$ lb. (down)
R	z	$30t_{PR} + 20t_{QR} + R_R$	$=0$	$R_R = 1813$ lb. (up)

Multiplying the coefficients by the lengths of the members we get

Member	PQ	PR	QR	QS	QT	RS	RT
Force in lb.	1,000 T	1,732 C	313 C	1,054 T	165 T	788 C	123 C

Check on external forces:

Downward, $1,000 + 703 + 110 = 1,813$ lb.; Upward, $P_R = 1,813$ lb.

EXAMPLES XIV

1. The dimensions of a cantilever bridge, such as Fig. 201, being $AF_1 = 100$ ft., $F_1C = 50$ ft. $= F_2D$, $F_1F_2 = 200$ ft., $F_2B = 100$ ft., draw the bending-moment diagram and state the bending moment midway between A and F_1, at C, and midway between C and D, when the whole length carries a uniformly distributed load w per ft.

2. Determine the extreme stresses in the top chord of the fourth bay from the end support of the anchor arm in Fig. 202 if the dead-panel load is 5 tons and the live load is 15 tons per panel.

3. Which bays of the left anchor arm in Fig. 202 require counterbracing with the loads given in Problem No. 2? Find the maximum and minimum tension in the diagonal of the fourth bay from the end support.

4. Which bays in the left anchor arm of Fig. 203 require counterbracing

for a rolling load of 2 tons per foot run if the dead load is $\frac{1}{2}$ ton per ft. and the diagonals are designed as ties only?

5. Find the maximum and minimum stresses in the diagonal of the fourth bay from the end support of the anchor arm of Fig. 203 with the loads given in Problem No. 4.

6. Find the maximum and minimum stresses in GH in Fig. 203 with the loads given in Problem No. 4.

7. Find the extreme stresses in the upper (loaded) chord of the fourth bay from the end support in the anchor arm of Fig. 203, the loads being as given in Problem No. 4.

8. Find approximately the extreme stresses in the member EN (inclined 45°) of the centre bearing swingbridge, Fig. 204, the ends of which are simply supported when the bridge is closed, the dead load being $\frac{1}{2}$ ton per ft. and the live load 1·5 ton per ft. and the panel length being 15 ft.

9. Find the extreme stresses in the diagonal of the bay HJ, Fig. 205, with the loads and dimensions in the example at the end of Art. 139.

10. Find the thrust in each shear leg and in the guy-rope for equal legs placed with their feet 10 ft. apart, the line joining them being 30 ft. from the foot of the guy-rope on the same ground level. The guy-rope from the ground to the head measures 50 ft., and 15 tons is suspended from the head with an overhang of 15 ft. from the base.

11. Solve Problem No. 10 if the load hangs from a snatch block, one end of the chain going to the head and the other alongside the guy-rope.

12. A derrick crane, Fig. 208, has the following dimensions, QR=20 ft., UR=20 ft., TS=20 ft., the jib PR is inclined at 60° and the tie QP at 30°. A load of 1,000 lb. hangs from the crane head. Find graphically the stresses in the members, (*a*) for the central position, (*b*) when the jib and tie lie in a plane inclined 20° to the central plane, (*c*) when the jib and tie lie in the plane RSQ. What is the minimum balance weight required at S in the last case?

13. A tripod is made up of poles AB, AC, and AD, each 9 ft. long, their feet forming a triangle BCD on horizontal ground such that BC=8 ft., CD=7 ft., BD=9 ft. Find the thrust in each leg when 3,000 lb. hangs from A.

CHAPTER XV

DEFLECTION AND INDETERMINATE FRAMES

145. Deflection of Perfect Frames. When the various members of a perfect frame are subject to pull or thrust, strains of the individual members take place, causing rotation of the members about their pins and resulting in deflections at various parts of the structure. These deflections depend upon the strains of the members (which depend upon the loads and dimensions of the members) and also upon the geometrical form of the structure. The total deflection of a given point may depend upon the strains of all the members, and the effects of the several strains in producing deflection are separable.

Notation. (Applicable to any perfect frame and illustrated in Figs. 211, 212, 213, and 214.) Denoting members by numbers 1, 2, 3, 4, etc., let P_1, P_2, P_3, P_4, etc., be the pulls in those members respectively due to any given system of loads. Let e_1, e_2, e_3, etc., be their respective stiffnesses or total pulls required per linear unit of stretch so that $e_1 = EA_1/l_1$, where $A_1 = $(constant) area of cross-section and $l_1 = $length of members No. (1) and $E = $Young's Modulus for the material, and let k_1, k_2, k_3, k_4, etc., be the respective pulls (positive or negative) produced in the respective members by a unit pull at a particular joint C in any specified direction in which the deflection Δ of that joint is required. Consider the effect of the stretch (positive or negative) of the member, (1), say (Figs. 211 to 214), if a force of 1 lb. alone is applied in the specified direction at the joint C (all other members being supposed quite rigid or non-elastic). Let d_1 be the deflection produced in that direction at C. Then the work done $\frac{1}{2} \times 1 \times d_1$ by the force of 1 lb. is equal to the internal strain energy of member (1) since the other strains are zero. The strain energy, Art. 28 of (1) is half the product of the pull k_1 and the stretch k_1/e_1, hence

$$\tfrac{1}{2} \times 1 \times d_1 = \tfrac{1}{2} \cdot k_1 \cdot k_1/e_1$$

or $\quad d_1 = k_1 \times k_1/e_1$ or k_1 times the stretch of member (1) . (1)

This is a geometrical relation, and it is evident that if a member (1) were to stretch any amount, x say, from any cause, the consequent deflection of C would be $k_1 x$.

An important principle is thus established connecting the stretch (positive or negative) of any member and the consequent deflection of any joint in the structure, viz., *if unit pull at any joint in any specified direction would cause a pull k in any member, the deflection of that joint in the given direction due to any stretch of the member is k times the stretch of the member.* In other words, k is the ratio of the resulting deflection at C to the stretch of member.

If any member, (1), say, sustains a pull P_1 (positive or negative) its stretch is P_1/e_1, and the consequent part of the deflection at C is

$$\delta_1 = k_1 \cdot P_1/e_1 \quad . \quad . \quad . \quad . \quad . \quad (2)$$

Hence, allowing for all the members of the structure

$$\Delta = \delta_1 + \delta_2 + \delta_3 + \text{etc.} = k_1 \cdot P_1/e_1 + k_2 \cdot P_2/e_2 + k_3 \cdot P_3/e_3 + \text{etc} \quad (3)$$

or $\qquad \Delta = \Sigma(Pk/e) \quad \text{or} \quad \Sigma\{Pkl/(AE)\} \quad \text{or} \quad \Sigma(pkl/E). \quad . \quad (4)$

where $p = P/A$ is the unit stress in the member. The portions of Δ resulting from the strains of different members of the structure are obviously separable, *e.g.* the deflection of a girder resulting from the elasticity of the web members may be separated from the deflection resulting from the strains of the chord members.

If the deflection in the direction of the load is required at a joint carrying a load W which is the sole load on the structure

$P = kW$ and (4) becomes $\Delta = W\,\Sigma(k^2/e) \quad \text{or} \quad W\,\Sigma\{k^2l/(AE)\} \quad . \quad (5)$

Temperature Deflection. If any member extends due to increase of $t°$ in temperature its total stretch (see Art. 27) is $\alpha \cdot t \cdot l$, where α is the coefficient of expansion; the consequent deflection in the specified direction is k times this, viz.

$$k \cdot \alpha \cdot t \cdot l \quad . \quad . \quad . \quad . \quad . \quad . \quad (6)$$

and the deflection due to change of temperature of several members will be

$$\Delta = \Sigma(k\alpha t l) \quad . \quad . \quad . \quad . \quad . \quad . \quad (7)$$

Reckoned on the whole of a structure this may frequently be zero for the particular direction required.

Example 1. Two pin-jointed rods AC and BC are hinged to a rigid ceiling at points A and B 10 ft. apart. The piece AC is 8 ft. long and forms a right angle with BC; A, B, and C being in the same vertical plane. Find the elastic deflection of C vertically and horizontally when a load of 5 tons is suspended from that point, each rod being

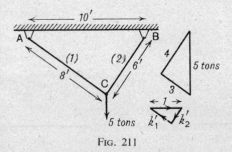

Fig. 211

1 sq. in. in cross-sectional area and E = 12,000 tons per sq. in.

The frame and stress diagrams (triangles) are sketched in Fig. 211.

Vertical Deflection. From the upper triangle of forces

for AC, $P_1 = 3$ tons, and $k_1 = \frac{3}{5}$

for BC, $P_2 = 4$ tons, and $k_2 = \frac{4}{5}$

$$e_1 = A_1 E / l_1 = 1 \times 12{,}000 / (8 \times 12) = 125 \text{ tons per inch}$$
deflection

$$e_2 = 166{\cdot}7 \text{ tons per inch.}$$

Hence from (4)

$$\Delta = \Sigma(Pk/e) = (3 \times \tfrac{3}{5} \times \tfrac{1}{125} + 4 \times \tfrac{4}{5} \times \tfrac{6}{1000}) = (72 + 96)/5{,}000$$
$$= 0{\cdot}0336 \text{ in.}$$

Horizontal Deflection. From the lower triangle (which is similar to ABC), for unit pull to the right at C, $k_1' = \frac{4}{5}$, $k_2' = -\frac{3}{5}$ (the negative sign following from the fact that a pull to the right causes *thrust* in BC). Then from (4)

$$\Delta = (3 \times \tfrac{4}{5} \times \tfrac{1}{125} - 4 \times \tfrac{3}{5} \times \tfrac{6}{1000}) = (96 - 72)/5{,}000 = 0{\cdot}0048 \text{ in.}$$

The resultant deflection might be found by compounding by vector rules these two perpendicular component deflections.

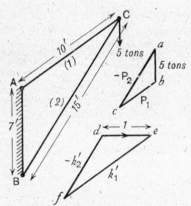

FIG. 212.—Deflection of jib crane

Example 2. The jib of a crane is 15 ft. long and is attached to a rigid support 7 ft. vertically below the end of the tie-rod, which is 10 ft. long. If the jib and tie have uniform cross-sectional areas of 8 and 3 sq. in. respectively, find the elastic vertical and horizontal deflections of the crane head when a load of 5 tons is suspended from it. Take E for both as 13,000 tons per sq. in.

The frame diagram and triangles of forces for 5 tons vertically and unit force horizontally at C are shown in Fig. 212.

Vertical Deflection. From the triangle of forces *abc*, which is similar to ABC,

$P_1 = 5 \times \frac{10}{7} = \frac{50}{7}$ tons. $p_1 = P_1/A_1 = 50/(7 \times 3) = 50/21$ tons per sq. in.

$P_2 = -5 \times \frac{15}{7} = -\frac{75}{7}$ tons (a thrust). $\qquad p_2 = P_2/A_2 = -75/(7 \times 8)$
$$= -75/56$$

Writing unity instead of 5 and $k_1 = \frac{10}{7}$, $k_2 = -\frac{15}{7}$. Hence from (4)

$$\Delta = \Sigma(pkl)/E = \tfrac{1}{13000}(\tfrac{50}{21} \times \tfrac{10}{7} \times 120 + \tfrac{75}{56} \times \tfrac{15}{7} \times \tfrac{180}{1}) = 0{\cdot}0712 \text{ in.}$$

Horizontal Deflection. In the triangle *def* the angle $\hat{dfe} = A\hat{C}B$, and $\cos ACB = \dfrac{100 + 225 - 49}{2 \times 10 \times 15} = \tfrac{23}{25}$, therefore $\sin \hat{dfe} = \dfrac{4\sqrt{6}}{25}$.

Also $\sin \ \widehat{def} = -\cos \ \widehat{CAB} = \dfrac{225-100-49}{2\times10\times7} = \tfrac{19}{35},$ and $\sin \ \widehat{fde}$

$= \cos \ \widehat{ABC} = \dfrac{49+225-100}{2\times7\times15} = \tfrac{29}{35}.$

Hence $k_1' = \tfrac{29}{35} \times \dfrac{25}{4\sqrt6} = 2\cdot115.$ $k_2' = -\tfrac{19}{35} \times \dfrac{25}{4\sqrt6} = -1\cdot383.$

$\varDelta = \Sigma(pk'l)/E = \tfrac{1}{13000}(\tfrac{50}{21} \times 2\cdot115 \times 120 + \tfrac{75}{56} \times 1\cdot383 \times 180)$
$= 0\cdot0720$ in.

Example 3. The cantilever shown in Fig. 213 carries various loads at its joints, and the sections of the members are so proportioned that the unit stress in each tie-rod is 5 tons per sq. in. and in each strut is 2 tons per sq. in. The length of each member is 5 ft., except EB, which is 2·5 ft. Estimate the vertical deflections of the points C and D taking E = 12,500 tons per sq. in.

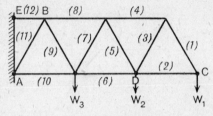

Fig. 213.—Deflection of braced cantilever

Deflection at C. The values of k for the various members are very simply found by the method of sections; the various parts of the products $\Sigma(pkl)$ are tabulated below in inch units.

Member	p	k	$\tfrac{1}{12}pkl \times \sqrt3$
1	+5	$+2/\sqrt3$	50
2	−2	$-1/\sqrt3$	10
3	−2	$-2/\sqrt3$	20
4	+5	$+2/\sqrt3$	50
5	+5	$+2/\sqrt3$	50
6	−2	$-3/\sqrt3$	30
7	−2	$-2/\sqrt3$	20
8	+5	$+4/\sqrt3$	100
9	+5	$+2/\sqrt3$	50
10	−2	$-5/\sqrt3$	50
11	−2	$-2/\sqrt3$	20
12	+5	$+6/\sqrt3$	75
	Total . .	$\sqrt3 \ \Sigma(pkl)/12 =$	525

Or $\Sigma(pkl) = 12 \times 525/\sqrt3,$ hence $\varDelta = \dfrac{1}{E} \ \Sigma(pkl) = \dfrac{12 \times 525}{12,500 \times \sqrt3} = 0\cdot291$ in.

Deflection at D. For members 1, 2, 3, and 4, $k = 0$.

P

Member	5	6	7	8	9	10	11	12
p	+5	−2	−2	+5	+5	−2	−2	+5
k	$+2/\sqrt{3}$	$-1/\sqrt{3}$	$-2/\sqrt{3}$	$+2/\sqrt{3}$	$+2/\sqrt{3}$	$-3/\sqrt{3}$	$-2/\sqrt{3}$	$+4/\sqrt{3}$
$\frac{\sqrt{3}}{12}pkl$	50	10	20	50	50	30	20	50

$$\frac{\sqrt{3}}{12}\,\Sigma(pkl)=280, \text{ hence } \varDelta=\frac{12\times280}{12{,}500\times\sqrt{3}}=0\cdot155 \text{ in.}$$

Example 4. A Pratt truss (Fig. 214) has 6 bays each 6 ft. long and 8 ft. high. Taking the stress in each tie as 5 tons per sq. in. and in each vertical strut as 2 tons per sq. in. and in the end post and top chord as 3 tons per sq. in., estimate the elastic deflection midway between the supports, taking E=12,500 tons per sq. in.

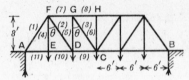

FIG. 214.—Deflection of Pratt girder

If θ=inclination of the diagonals to the vertical, $\tan\theta=\frac{6}{8}=\frac{3}{4}$, $\sec\theta=\frac{5}{4}$. Taking half the structure and reference numbers given in Fig. 214, and finding the values of k for deflection at C by the method of sections, we get

Member	k	p	$\frac{1}{12}l$	$\frac{1}{12}pkl$
1	$-\frac{5}{8}$	−3	10	18·75
2	$\frac{5}{8}$	+5	10	31·25
3	$\frac{5}{8}$	+5	10	31·25
4	0	+5	8	0
5	$-\frac{1}{2}$	−2	8	8·0
7	$-\frac{3}{4}$	−3	6	13·5
8	$-\frac{9}{8}$	−3	6	20·25
9	$\frac{3}{4}$	+5	6	22·5
10	$\frac{3}{8}$	+5	6	11·25
11	$\frac{3}{8}$	+5	6	11·25

Total . . . . 168·00

For other half . . . . . 168·00

For the structure . . . . 336·00

For member (6) $k=0$, hence there is no further addition, and $\Sigma(pkl)=12\times336=4{,}032$, and $\varDelta=\Sigma(pkl)/E=4{,}032/12{,}500=0\cdot323$ in.

A glance at the last column of the above Table shows how large a proportion of the total deflection results from strain of the web members. A fraction $2\times31\cdot25/336=0\cdot186$ of the whole deflection results from stretch of the members (2) and (3) alone or twice this fraction from the four diagonal ties.

If it were desired to find the deflection of the joint D, say under the same loading, new values of k would have to be calculated which will not be symmetrical for the two halves of the girder. The value for the member (3) will be negative, which with a positive value of p will give a negative product, *i.e.* the effect of the stretching of this member is to diminish the deflection at D.

Example 5. Find the deflection of point C in Fig. 214 if there is a load of 10 tons at each joint of the lower chord, the sectional areas of the members being as given in the following Table.

The values of k and l are as given in Example 4. The values of P are readily calculated by the method of sections.

Member	P(tons)	k	$l/12$=(ft.)	A=sq. in.	$\frac{1}{12}Pkl/A$	Stretch $=Pl/(AE)$(in.)
1	−31·25	−$\frac{5}{8}$	10	10	19·5	−0·0300
2	+18·75	+$\frac{5}{8}$	10	3	39·1	+0·0600
3	+ 6·25	+$\frac{5}{8}$	10	2	19·5	+0·0300
4	+10·0	0	8	2	0	+0·0384
5	− 5·0	−$\frac{1}{2}$	8	1·5	13·3	−0·0256
7	−30·0	−$\frac{3}{4}$	6	10	13·5	−0·01728
8	−33·75	−$\frac{9}{8}$	6	10	22·8	−0·01945
9	+30·0	+$\frac{3}{4}$	6	5	27·0	+0·03458
10	+18·75	−$\frac{3}{8}$	6	4	10·5	+0·0270
11	+18·75	+$\frac{3}{8}$	6	4	10·5	+0·0270

Total　.　.　.　175·7

For the whole structure since P=0 and k=0 for member 6
$\frac{1}{12}\Sigma(Pkl/A)=175\cdot7\times2=351\cdot4$, hence $\varDelta=12\times351\cdot4/12{,}500=0\cdot337$ in.

The last column of the Table refers to the graphical solution given in Art. 147.

Example 6. Find the central vertical deflection for the structure of Example 5 due to the upper chord and end posts rising 10° F. above the remainder of the girder. Coefficient of expansion 0·0000062 per degree F.

Using the previous figure and expansion of each heated member by 0·0000062 of its length, we get

Member	Expansion in inches $=0\cdot0000062\times l$	k	$k\alpha tl$ in.
1	0·00744	−$\frac{5}{8}$	−0·00465
7	0·004464	−$\frac{3}{4}$	−0·00335
8	0·004464	−$\frac{9}{8}$	−0·00502

$\Sigma(k\alpha tl)=-0\cdot01302$

and allowing for the whole structure the deflection is $-2 \times 0{\cdot}013$ $= -0{\cdot}026$ in., *i.e.* $0{\cdot}026$ in. *upwards*.

146. Deflection from the Principle of Work. The formulæ of the previous article were based upon a simple geometrical principle which was established from an application of the equation of external work to internal work or strain energy of a member of the structure.   They may be based directly upon this principle of work; for, using the notation of Art. 145, the total strain energy of member (1) is

$$\tfrac{1}{2}P_1 \times P_1/e_1$$

Of this, the work due to a force of 1 lb. in the specified direction is

$$\tfrac{1}{2}P_1(k_1/e_1)$$

Hence,

$$\tfrac{1}{2} \times 1 \times \varDelta = \tfrac{1}{2}\Sigma(Pk/e), \quad \text{or} \quad \varDelta = \Sigma(Pk/e), \quad \text{or} \quad \Sigma\{Pkl/(AE)\},$$
$$\text{or} \quad \Sigma(pkl/E) \quad . \quad . \quad . \quad . \quad . \quad . \quad (1)$$

Maxwell's Reciprocal Deflection Theorem for Frames. The relation (1) of Art. 145 may be restated for a load W say, instead of unit load, at C.   Using the frame shown in Fig. 213, let $_5k_C$ be the tension in member 5 per unit of load at C.   It will be convenient first to regard all other members as incapable of strain.   Then if the vertical movement of C due to the stretching of member 5 is δ_C, from equation (1) of Art. 145

$$\left.\begin{aligned} W \cdot \delta_C &= P_5 \times \text{stretch of member 5} \\ &= P_5 \times P_5/e_5 \end{aligned}\right\} \quad . \quad . \quad . \quad (2)$$

and $P_5 = W \times {}_5k_C$, hence (2) becomes

$$W \cdot \delta_C = P_5 \times W \times {}_5k_C \quad . \quad . \quad . \quad . \quad (3)$$

Both (2) and (3) may be stated as

$$W \times W\text{'s vertical movement} = \text{Force in } 5 \times \text{stretch in } 5. \quad (4)$$

or

$$W/P_5 = \frac{P_5}{e_5}\bigg/\delta_C \quad \text{or} \quad \frac{W \cdot {}_5k_C}{e_5}\bigg/\delta_C \quad . \quad . \quad . \quad (5)$$

i.e the force ratio is the inverse of the movement ratio (sometimes called the velocity ratio).   It is evident that (4) and (5) correspond to the relations of the load and effort in a frictionless machine. Also that they would hold for any other joint such as D.   Thus

$$\delta_C = {}_5k_C \times \text{stretch of } 5 \quad . \quad . \quad . \quad . \quad (6)$$

or

$$\delta_C = {}_5k_C \times P_5/e_5 \quad . \quad . \quad . \quad . \quad . \quad (7)$$

and $_5k_C$ is the ratio of the deflection of C to the stretch of 5 as well as the ratio of force in 5 to the vertical force at C.

Similarly,

or
$$\left.\begin{array}{l}\delta_D = {}_5k_D \times P_5/e_5 \\ \delta_D = {}_5k_D \times W \times {}_5k_C/e\end{array}\right\} \quad \ldots \quad \ldots \quad (8)$$

Now a vertical load of W at D would induce a force ${}_5k_D \times W$ and a stretch ${}_5k_D \times W/e_5$ in member 5, and this would produce at C a deflection ${}_5k_C$ times this length of stretch.

$$\text{Deflection at } C = {}_5k_C \times {}_5k_D \times W/e_5 \quad \ldots \quad (9)$$

which is the same as (8). Thus the deflection at C due to W at D is equal to the deflection at D due to W at C.

The deflections at D and C are here vertical, but the vertical direction is not essential to the argument which will hold for any direction provided the deflection and load at C are estimated in the same direction, and the deflection and load at D are taken in the same direction but not necessarily in the direction adopted for C. The deflection above estimated relates to those resulting from member 5 only, but the same arguments hold for the stretch or shortening of any member of the frame and therefore for the total straining effects. Hence, finally, the deflection at D in any direction, due to a load in any direction at C, is equal to the deflection at C (in the direction in which the load at C was applied) due to a load at D equal in magnitude to that applied at C and in the direction in which the deflection at D was estimated for the loading at C. This is one form of the statement of Maxwell's theorem (see also Art. 96) when applied to a perfect frame. It is very useful in the solution of problems and is also valid if a force is replaced by a torque or moment.

147. Geometrical Method of Determining Deflections. Williott-Mohr Diagrams. It is easy to obtain the movement of one point of a perfect frame relative to another point by calculating the amount of stretching or shortening of the members of the frame. A simple example will illustrate the method, and for this purpose the problem given in Example 2, Art. 145, Fig. 212, may be chosen.

The unit stress in the tie-rod was $\frac{50}{21}$ tons per sq. in., hence the stretch is

$$\frac{50}{21} \times \frac{120}{13,000} = 0.0220 \text{ in.}$$

The unit stress in the jib was $\frac{75}{56}$ tons per sq. in., hence the shortening is

$$\frac{75}{56} \times \frac{15 \times 12}{13,000} = 0.01854 \text{ in.}$$

If we take the jib (Fig. 215) as shortened to BC_2 and the tie-rod as extended to AC_1, then by striking arcs from centres A and B with radii AC_1 and BC_2 respectively the intersection gives C' the new position of C, and the vertical and horizontal projections of CC'

give the vertical and horizontal deflections of C. But the alterations of length CC_1 and CC_2 are too small to be shown on the same diagram as ABC. For very small changes in length the angles $C\hat{C}_1C'$ and $C\hat{C}_2C'$ are right angles. We therefore set off the figure $CC_1C'C_2$ only, to a very much larger scale, as shown at $Pc_1c'c_2$, in which Pc' gives the actual deflection of C, while Pn gives the vertical and nc' the horizontal deflection. Such a diagram is called a *Williott Diagram*.

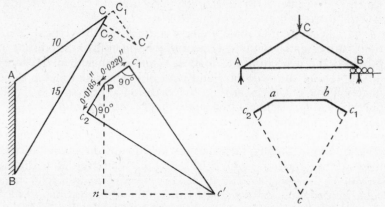

FIG. 215.—Graphical determination of a deflection of a jib crane

FIG. 216.—Graphical determination of roof deflections

The principle is further exemplified with suitable notation for the diagram in Fig. 216, a simple triangular roof truss ABC, in which A is hinged to a fixed point and B is free to slide horizontally; $ab=$ stretch of AB, $ac_2=$ compression of AC, $bc_1=$ compression of BC. Then b and c give the new position of B and C. The deflection ac of C may be split into horizontal and vertical components by projection.

Example. Find the deflection of point C (Fig. 214) under the loads in Example 5, Art. 145.

Member	CH	HG	GC	CD	GD	FG	FD	ED	FE	AF	AE
Stretch Pl/AE .	0	−0·01945	0·03	0·03458	−0·0256	−0·01728	0·06	0·0266	0·0384	−0·03	0·0266
Shown in Fig. 217 by the line	$ch(=0)$	hg_1	cg_2	cd_1	gd_2	gf_1	df_2	de_1	fe_2	fa_2	ea_1

The extensions $Pl/(AE)$ are calculated from the stresses and sectional areas given in the above Table of the example quoted, and are set off to scale in Fig. 217, starting from point C, which may be taken as fixed.

The vertical deflection of A *above* C equals the vertical projection of the line *ca*. If A and B remain at the same level this also gives the deflection of C below AB. The vertical deflections of E and D are given by the projections of *ae* and *ad*.

In case of unsymmetrical loading, if HC is supposed to remain fixed the upward deflections of A and B can be found. A small rotation about C, the amount of which can easily be cal- culated, will then bring A and B into a horizontal line. The correction of the de- flections of other points can easily be estimated to allow for this rotation.

Williott-Mohr Diagram. The Williott diagram gives the displacements of the joints of a frame relative to some point and direction, *e.g.* in Fig. 217 relative to C and CH, which are regarded as fixed in position and direction re- spectively. In other cases we may easily make a choice of a direction which does not in fact remain fixed. A neat form of correction due to Mohr may be explained by a simple example. Fig. 218 shows a short Warren girder with the end A hinged and the other end B supported on rollers which ensures a verti- cal upward supporting force at B and permits free hori- zontal movement there. Thus, the displacement at B is in a known (horizontal) direction. The loading is very far from symmetry and

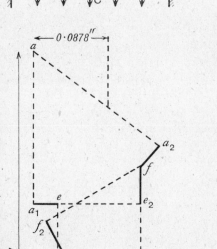

FIG. 217.—Graphical method for deflection of a Pratt truss. Williott Diagram

consists of a single load of 18 tons at C. The Williott diagram is drawn starting at *a* for the fixed hinge A and proceeding to D, the direction AD being taken as fixed. In other words the displace- ments are taken relative to AD. In order to get simple figures for the purpose of illustration, take the areas of cross-section of all compression members as $2\sqrt{3}$ sq. in. and of all ties as $\sqrt{3}$ sq. in.

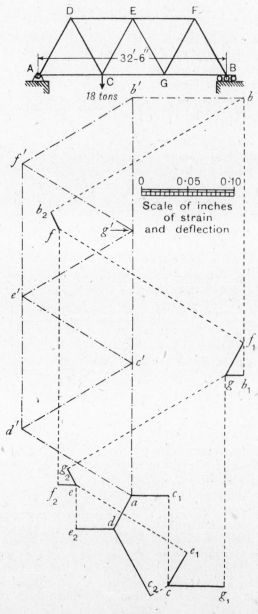

FIG. 218

The forces transmitted in the members are readily found by resolution and moments, using the method of sections and taking as a unit of length half the length of the (equal) members. Using a + sign for tension and extension of length and a − sign for thrust and shortening, we have

$$\text{extension} = +Pl/(AE) = pl/E$$

where P is the force in a member, A its area of section, *l* its length and $p = P/A$ the intensity of stress in the member. The values of P and *p* are tabulated below; the last two columns are included to check the result.

Member	$P \times \sqrt{3}$ (tons)	p in ton/sq. in. $= \text{extension} \times E/l$	$k_C \times 3\sqrt{3}$	$pk_C \times 3\sqrt{3}$
AD	−24	−4	−4	16
DC	+24	+8	+4	32
EC	+12	+4	+2	8
EG	−12	−2	−2	4
GF	+12	+4	+2	8
FB	−12	−2	−2	4
AC	+12	+4	+2	8
CG	+18	+6	+3	18
GB	+6	+2	+1	2
DE	−24	−4	−4	16
EF	−12	−2	−2	4
				$3\sqrt{3}\,\Sigma(pk_C) = 120$

The extensions are *l*/E times the figures given in the third column of the Table, where E is in tons per square inch and the extensions are in inches if *l* is in inches, *e.g.* if *l* = 130 in. and E = 13,000 tons per sq. in. the extensions are 130/13,000 or 0·01 times the figures given in column 3.

The Williott diagram is drawn as before, starting with the line *ad*, the points *c*, *e*, *g*, *f*, and *b* are determined as in Fig. 217, and the displacements are relative to AD. Thus B has a considerable vertical displacement and would appear to be above its actual position, resting on its rollers. A small clockwise rotation of the frame ABFD about the hinge A would restore B to its position on the level of A, and this must give it a vertical downward displacement equal to the height of *b* above *a*. If *bb'* is drawn horizontally to meet a vertical line from *a* in *b'*, the vectorial displacement of B, namely *ab*, is to be reduced by a vertical component *ab'*, leaving *b'b* as the actual displacement of B (vectorially *bb'* = *ab* − *ab'*). Similarly, the vectorial displacements of all other joints with respect to *a*, need appropriate vector diminution (or addition with opposite sign). Now in a rotation of the frame about A, all points (such as the joints or nodes of the frame) have displacements perpendicular to the lines

P*

joining them to A and proportional to the lengths of these lines. It ɛ a well-known geometrical proposition that if vectors proportional to such lines are drawn from a common point and perpendicular to the lines, their extremities remote from the common point will lie on a figure similar to that of the frame.[1]

On *ab'* the figure *ac'g'b'f'e'd'* is drawn similar to ACGBFED. This may be called the Mohr diagram.   Then the actual displacement of any point such as G is given by the vector *ag* minus the vector *ag'*, this difference being equal to *g'g*. (Vectorially, $ag-ag' = ag+g'a=g'a+ag=g'g$.)   Thus the actual displacement of any point is given by the vector measured from the point (with accented letter) on the Mohr diagram to the corresponding point (with unaccented letter) on the Williott diagram and the combination of the two diagrams is sometimes called the Williott-Mohr diagram.

The correctness of Fig. 218 may readily be checked by calculation, *e.g.* the *vertical* displacement of C by (1) of Art. 146.   From the last column of the Table

$$\Sigma(pk_C)=40/\sqrt{3}=23\cdot1 \quad \text{or} \quad \delta_C=23\cdot1\times0\cdot01=0\cdot23 \text{ in.}$$

This corresponds very closely with the vertical component of the vector *c'c* on Fig. 218.

Also the horizontal displacement of B may easily be calculated. Unit horizontal force at B would induce unit force in AC, CG, and GB and zero force in all other members.   Hence k_B for each of AC, CG, and GB is unity; and the values of *p* for these three members are 4, 6, and 2 tons per sq. in. respectively.   Hence $\Sigma(pk_B)=12$ and the horizontal displacement of B is $12\times0\cdot01=0\cdot12$ in., which corresponds very closely with the vector *b'b* in Fig. 218.

148. Statically Indeterminate Structures.   When a framed structure has more members (see Art. 113) than are required for a perfect frame, the distribution of internal stress depends upon the relative stiffness of the various members.   The methods of finding the stress in frames having one or more redundant members are based upon the same principles as those applicable to the closely analogous problems of statically indeterminate systems already dealt with, such as the weight supported by two or more forces (Example 2, Art. 9) and the continuous beam resting on more than two supports (Art. 79 and Chapter VIII).   There are three ways of approaching a solution to such problems, and they may be called: (1) The Method of Deformations; (2) The Principle of Minimum Strain Energy; (3) The Principle of Work.   The three ways lead of course to the same results.   Before proceeding to the general methods, it may be well to illustrate the principles by a simple example.

---

[1] The reader may be familiar with the *velocity image* where rotation is about an instantaneous centre.   In this statical example the element of time is absent and a *displacement image* replaces a velocity image.

Example 1.   A weight W is held in equilibrium by two vertical elastic supports *a* and *b*, either struts or ties (such as two parallel wires).   The elastic stiffness or force per unit of deformation of the first is e_a and that of the second is e_b.   Find the proportion of the load borne by each support.

Let F be the load carried by the first support *a*.

(1) *Method of Deformation*.   Equating the deformation or alteration in length of the two supports

$$\frac{F}{e_a} = \frac{W-F}{e_b} \qquad \qquad (1)$$

This is an example of the more general case in Art. 21, a simple equation for F giving $F = W \frac{e_a}{e_a + e_b}$.

(2) *Principle of Minimum Strain Energy*.   The strain energy U (Art. 28)

$$= \tfrac{1}{2}\left\{ F \times \frac{F}{e_a} + (W-F)\frac{W-F}{e_b} \right\}$$

And if F is such as to make U a minimum,

$$\frac{dU}{dF} = \frac{F}{e_a} - \frac{W-F}{e_b} = 0 \qquad \qquad (2)$$

which is evidently identical with (1).

(3) *Principle of Work*.

strain energy (U) = external work

$$\tfrac{1}{2}\left\{ \frac{F^2}{e_a} + \frac{(W-F)^2}{e_b} \right\} = \tfrac{1}{2}W \times \frac{F}{e_a}$$

which when simplified reduces to equation (1).

Example 2.   In Chapter VII the loads on props partially supporting beams were calculated by the method of deformations, *i.e.* by equating the upward deflection caused by the prop to the downward deflection caused by the load minus the deflection of the prop (if any).   The reader will find it instructive to solve for himself the same problems by writing U the strain energy in terms of the prop reaction P (by the method given in Art. 96) and then applying the Principle of Minimum Strain Energy and the Principle of Work.

Example 3.   If a vertical bar DC hinged to C and to the ceiling is added to the system in Example 1, Art. 145, find the stress in each bar, all three being 1 sq. in. in section.

The system is shown in Fig. 219, the tension in DC being shown as forces F at D and C.   The stress in member (1) due to the combined action of the 5-tons load and the tension F is $P_1 = \tfrac{3}{5}(5-F)$, and in member (2) is $P_2 = \frac{4}{5}(5-F)$, hence the vertical deflection of C or stretch of DC in inches is

$$\Delta = \frac{1}{E}\Sigma\left(\frac{Pkl}{A}\right) = \frac{1}{E}\{\tfrac{3}{5}(5-F)\tfrac{3}{5} \times 96 + \tfrac{4}{5}(5-F)\tfrac{4}{5} \times 72\} = \frac{288 \times 7}{25E}(5-F)$$

But the length $DC = 8 \times 6/10 = 4 \cdot 8$ ft. $= 57 \cdot 6$ in., and the stretch of DC is therefore $57 \cdot 6F/(1 \times E)$ in. Hence equating this to the deflection of C

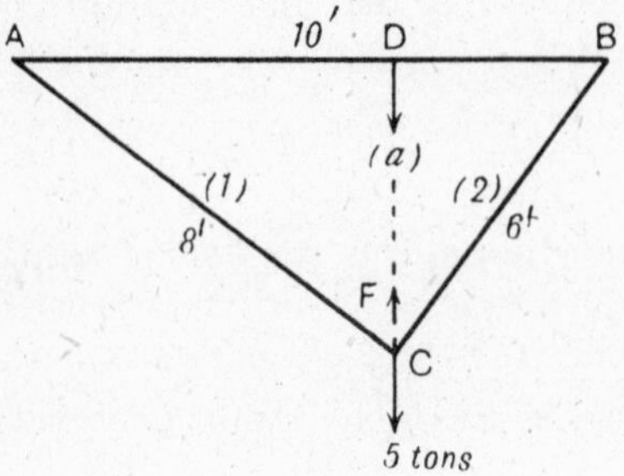

$$57 \cdot 6F = \frac{288 \times 7}{25}(5-F) \text{ and } F =$$

$\frac{35}{12} = 2\frac{11}{12}$ tons

$$5 - F = 2\tfrac{1}{12} \text{ tons}$$

The tension in AC, $P_1 = \tfrac{3}{5} \times \tfrac{25}{12} = 1 \cdot 25$ ton

The tension in BC, $P_2 = \tfrac{4}{5} \times \tfrac{25}{12} = 1 \cdot 6$ ton.

The deflection of C would

FIG. 219.—Simple statically indeterminate frame

evidently be $\frac{25}{12} \div 5$ times, or $\frac{5}{12}$ of that found in Example 1, Art. 145.

149. Method of Deformations applied to Redundant Frame Members. *Notation.* Let the unknown tensile stresses in any superfluous members a, b, c, etc., be F_a, F_b, F_c, etc. The number of redundant members is the number in excess of $2n-3$ (see Art. 113), and the choice as to which are considered redundant is largely arbitrary.

The tensile stress in any member, number (1) say, is made up of a number of terms, being

$$P_1 = R_1 + {}_ak_1F_a + {}_bk_1F_b + {}_ck_1F_c +, \text{ etc.} \quad . \quad . \quad . \quad (1)$$

and in member (2) being

$$P_2 = R_2 + {}_ak_2F_a + {}_bk_2F_b + {}_ck_2F_c +, \text{ etc.} \quad . \quad . \quad . \quad (2)$$

where R_1, R_2, R_3, etc., are the tensile stresses in the members arising from the loads alone with the redundant members removed, and the terms k. F_a, F_b, F_c, etc., are the tensions arising from the forces exerted by the various redundant members each acting alone with all the other redundant members removed. Let e_1, e_2, e_3, etc., be the tensile stiffnesses of the respective members. The tensions P_1, P_2, P_3, etc., may be found in terms of the known external loads and the unknown forces F_a, F_b, F_c, etc., by the ordinary rules dealt with in Chapter XII, either graphically or algebraically. The constants ${}_ak_1$, ${}_bk_1$, ${}_ck_1$, etc. (which may be positive or negative) are, as already used in Art. 145, numerically equal to the stress in pounds, produced in member (1) by pairs of forces of 1 lb. each pulling inwards at the pins at the ends of the redundant members a, b, c, etc., respectively. (Note that the suffix denotes the member and the prefix indicates the particular redundant member supposed replaced by inward forces at its ends.)

Single Redundant Member. If there is but one redundant member, a, say, in a frame (Fig. 219 may be referred to in order to fix the ideas), the deflection of one end towards the other (taken as fixed) is by Art. 145 (4)

$$\varDelta = \Sigma(P \cdot {}_a k/e) = P_1 \cdot {}_a k_1/e_1 + P_2 \cdot {}_a k_2/e_2 + P_3 \cdot {}_a k_3/e_3 +, \text{ etc. .} \quad (3)$$

$$\varDelta = \frac{{}_a k_1}{e_1}(R_1 + {}_a k_1 \cdot F_a) + \frac{{}_a k_2}{e_2}(R_2 + {}_a k_2 F_a) + \frac{{}_a k_3}{e_3}(R_3 + {}_a k_3 \cdot F_a) +, \text{ etc.}$$

or

$$\varDelta = \Sigma({}_a k \cdot R/e) + F_a \Sigma({}_a k^2/e) \quad . \quad . \quad . \quad . \quad (4)$$

which represents the compression or *shortening* of member a. But due to the tension F_a the member a *extends* by an amount of F_a/e_a, where e_a is the stiffness of member a, or $\varDelta = -F_a/e_a$, hence

$$-\frac{F_a}{e_a} = \Sigma({}_a k \cdot R/e) + F_a \Sigma({}_a k^2/e) \quad . \quad . \quad . \quad (5)$$

a simple equation for F_a, from which

$$F_a = -\frac{\Sigma({}_a k \cdot R/e)}{1/e_a + \Sigma({}_a k^2/e)} \quad . \quad . \quad . \quad . \quad (6)$$

the summations excluding the member a. In this case where there is only one redundant member the prefix a to the constants k may be omitted. Also the first term of the denominator may be omitted if the member a is included in the summation of the second term, ${}_a k_a$ being unity.

Any Number of Redundant Members. For any number, n, say, of redundant members a, b, c, etc., the equation arising from the deformation of the member a is

$$\varDelta = \Sigma(Pk/e) = -F_a/e_a \quad . \quad . \quad . \quad . \quad . \quad (7)$$

or written more fully

$$-F_a/e_a = {}_a k_1(R_1 + {}_a k_1 \cdot F_a + {}_b k_1 \cdot F_b + {}_c k_1 \cdot F_c +, \text{ etc.})/e_1$$
$$+ {}_a k_2(R_2 + {}_a k_2 F_a + {}_b k_2 \cdot F_b +, \text{ etc.})/e_2$$
$$+ {}_a k_3(R_3 + {}_a k_3 \cdot F_a + {}_b k_3 F_b + {}_c k_3 \cdot F_c +, \text{ etc.})/e_3 \quad . \quad . \quad (8)$$

There are altogether n similar simultaneous simple equations, one for each redundant member and each containing the n unknown quantities F_a, F_b, F_c, etc., and from these equations each may be found. It may be noted that the solution of the case involving several redundant members is closely analogous to Wilson's solution (Art. 92) for continuous supported beams while that for a single redundant member corresponds to the case of a beam with a single prop.

Example. The crossed lattice girder shown in Fig. 220 is loaded as shown; the diagonals are inclined at 45°. The ratios of length to areas of cross-section in inch units is 20 for each diagonal number, 6 for each top-chord member, 8 for each lower-boom member and 10 for the two vertical members. Determine the stresses in all the members.

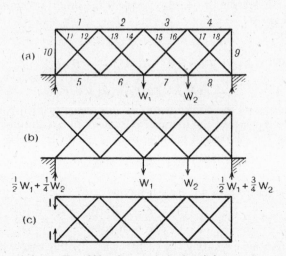

FIG. 220.—Stresses in lattice girder

Select member 10 as the redundant one. For the diagonals $e = EA/l = E/20$, or $1/e = 20/E$. For lower-boom members $1/e = 8/E$. For top-chord members $1/e = 6/E$. For verticals $1/e = 10/E$.

Then from (6), since E is the same in each term,

$$F_{10} = -\frac{\Sigma(_{10}k \cdot R/e)}{(1/e_{10}) + \Sigma(_{10}k^2/e)} = -\frac{\Sigma(_{10}k \cdot R \cdot l/A)}{(l_{10}/A_{10}) + \Sigma(_{10}k^2 \cdot l/A)}$$

The values of R are readily found by the method of sections from inspection of (b), Fig. 220, with member 10 removed and those of k from (c), Fig. 220, and are tabulated on page 431.

In the last column of Table A the resulting stresses are given. From the symmetry, the coefficients for a load W_3 on the remaining lower-chord joint may be obtained and the stresses for this case have been entered in Table B. The coefficients of W_2 in, say, members 1, 12, and 5, give the coefficients of W_3 in 4, 18, and 8 respectively. For comparison the stresses according to the conventional method of superposition (see Art. 125) are shown in Table B with loads on each lower-chord joint. These are readily obtained by splitting the girder into two systems shown in Fig. 221 and adding algebraically the stresses in the members (2, 3, 6, 7), forming a part of each.

TABLE A

Member	R	$10k$	$\dfrac{l}{A}$	$\dfrac{10kRl}{A}$	$\dfrac{10k^2l}{A}$	$P = R - k \times 0\cdot\dot2\dot6 W_2$
1	0	$+1$	6	0	6	$-0\cdot\dot2\dot6 W_2$
2	$-W_1-\tfrac{1}{2}W_2$	-1	6	$6W_1-3W_2$	6	$-W_1-0\cdot237W_2$
3	$-W_1-\tfrac{1}{2}W_2$	$+1$	6	$-6W_1-3W_2$	6	$-W_1-0\cdot762W_2$
4	$-W_2$	-1	6	$+6W_2$	6	$-0\cdot\dot7\dot3 W_2$
5	$\tfrac{1}{2}W_1+\tfrac{1}{4}W_2$	$+1$	8	$4W_1+2W_2$	8	$0\cdot5W_1-0\cdot01\dot2\dot6W_2$
6	$\tfrac{1}{2}W_1+\tfrac{1}{4}W_2$	-1	8	$-4W_1-2W_2$	8	$0\cdot5W_1+0\cdot51\dot2\dot6W_2$
7	$\tfrac{1}{2}W_1+\tfrac{3}{4}W_2$	$+1$	8	$4W_1+6W_2$	8	$0\cdot5W_1+0\cdot48\dot7\dot3W_2$
8	$\tfrac{1}{2}W_1-\tfrac{1}{4}W_2$	-1	8	$-4W_1+2W_2$	8	$0\cdot5W_1+0\cdot01\dot2\dot6W_2$
9	$-W_2$	-1	10	$+10W_2$	10	$-0\cdot\dot7\dot3W_2$
11	0	$-\sqrt2$	20	0	40	$+0\cdot3714W_2$
12	$-\dfrac{\sqrt2}{2}W_1-\dfrac{\sqrt2}{4}W_2$	$-\sqrt2$	20	$20W_1+10W_2$	40	$-0\cdot7071W_1+0\cdot0179W_2$
13	$\dfrac{\sqrt2}{2}W_1+\dfrac{\sqrt2}{4}W_2$	$+\sqrt2$	20	$20W_1+10W_2$	40	$0\cdot7071W_1-0\cdot0179W_1$
14	0	$+\sqrt2$	20	0	40	$-0\cdot3714W_2$
15	0	$-\sqrt2$	20	0	40	$+0\cdot3714W_2$
16	$\dfrac{\sqrt2}{2}W_1-\dfrac{\sqrt2}{4}W_2$	$-\sqrt2$	20	$-20W_1+10W_2$	40	$0\cdot7071W_1+0\cdot0179W_2$
17	$-\dfrac{\sqrt2}{2}W_1+\dfrac{\sqrt2}{4}W_2$	$+\sqrt2$	20	$-20W_1+10W_2$	40	$-0\cdot7071W_1-0\cdot0179W_2$
18	$\sqrt2W_2$	$+\sqrt2$	20	$+40W_2$	40	$+1\cdot0428W_2$

Totals are . . . $104W_2$ 386   and $\dfrac{l_{10}}{A_{10}}=10$

$$F_{10}=-\frac{104W_2}{396}=-0\cdot\dot2\dot6W_2$$

TABLE B

Member	Calculated stress	Conventional stress by method of superposition
1	$-0\cdot\dot2\dot6W_2-0\cdot\dot7\dot3W_3$	$-0\cdot25W_2-0\cdot75W_3$
2	$-W_1-0\cdot237W_2-0\cdot762W_3$	$-W_1-0\cdot25W_2-0\cdot75W_3$
3	$-W_1-0\cdot762W_2-0\cdot267W_3$	$-W_1-0\cdot75W_2-0\cdot25W_3$
4	$-0\cdot\dot7\dot3W_2-0\cdot\dot2\dot6W_3$	$-0\cdot75W_2-0\cdot25W_3$
5	$0\cdot5W_1-0\cdot01\dot2\dot6W_2+0\cdot01\dot2\dot6W_3$	$0\cdot5W_1$
6	$0\cdot5W_1+0\cdot51\dot2\dot6W_2+0\cdot48\dot7\dot3W_3$	$0\cdot5W_1+0\cdot5W_2+0\cdot5W_3$
7	$0\cdot5W_1+0\cdot48\dot7\dot3W_2+0\cdot51\dot2\dot6W_3$	$0\cdot5W_1+0\cdot5W_2+0\cdot5W_3$
8	$0\cdot5W_1+0\cdot01\dot2\dot6W_2-0\cdot01\dot2\dot6W_3$	$0\cdot5W_1$
9	$-0\cdot\dot7\dot3W_2-0\cdot\dot2\dot6W_3$	$-0\cdot75W_2-0\cdot25W_3$
10	$-0\cdot\dot2\dot6W_2-0\cdot\dot7\dot3W_2$	$-0\cdot25W_2-0\cdot75W_3$
11	$+0\cdot3714W_2+1\cdot0428W_3$	$+0\cdot3535W_2+1\cdot0607W_3$
12	$-0\cdot7071W_1+0\cdot0179W_2-0\cdot0179W_3$	$-0\cdot7071W_1$
13	$0\cdot7071W_1-0\cdot0179W_2+0\cdot0179W_3$	$0\cdot7071W_1$
14	$-0\cdot3714W_2+0\cdot3714W_3$	$-0\cdot3535W_2+0\cdot3535W_3$
15	$0\cdot3714W_2-0\cdot3714W_3$	$+0\cdot3535W_2-0\cdot3535W_3$
16	$0\cdot7071W_1+0\cdot0179W_2-0\cdot0179W_3$	$0\cdot7071W_1$
17	$-0\cdot7071W_1-0\cdot0179W_2+0\cdot0179W_3$	$-0\cdot7071W_1$
18	$1\cdot0428W_2+0\cdot3714W_3$	$1\cdot0607W_2+0\cdot3535W_3$

A comparison of the results shows firstly that if the structure is symmetrically loaded, *i.e.* if $W_3 = W_2$, the simple conventional method gives exactly correct results; and, secondly, that if the loading is not symmetrical the results are still nearly correct.

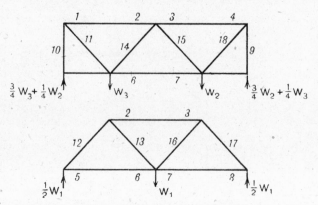

FIG. 221.—Stresses by superposition

150. Other Methods for Redundant Members.[1]

The equations of the previous article may also be derived by the Principle of Minimum Strain Energy and by the Principle of Work, the methods being briefly as follows, using the notation of Art. 149.

Principle of Minimum Strain Energy. Let U = total resilience of the frame.

u_1, u_2, u_3, . . . u_a, u_b, u_c, etc., be the resilience of members indicated by the suffixes, so that

$$U = u_1 + u_2 + u_3 + \text{etc.} + u_a + u_b + u_c + \text{etc.}$$

$$u_1 = \tfrac{1}{2}P_1 \times \frac{P_1}{e_1} = \tfrac{1}{2}\frac{P_1^2}{e_1}$$

where P_1 has the value (1), Art. 149. Differentiating (partially) with respect to F_a

$$\frac{du_1}{dF_a} = \tfrac{1}{2} \cdot \frac{2P_1}{e_1} \cdot \frac{dP_1}{dF_a} = \frac{P_1}{e_1} \cdot \frac{dP_1}{dF_a} = \frac{P_1}{e_1} \times {}_a k_1$$

$$= \frac{{}_a k_1}{e_1}(R_1 + {}_a k_1 . F_a + {}_b k_1 . F_b + {}_c k_1 . F_c + \text{etc.})$$

[1] See "Statically Indeterminate Structures," etc., by H. M. Martin, reprinted from *Engineering*. "Statically Indeterminate and Non-articulated Structures," by F. C. Lea, *Engineering*, March 17th, 24th, and 31st, 1922. "Reciprocal Load Deflection Relationships for Structures," by C. E. Larard, *Engineering*, Sept. 7th and 14th, 1923. "The Principle of Virtual Velocities," etc., by E. H. Lamb, *I.C.E. Selected Engineering Paper* No. 10, 1923. *Strain Energy Methods of Stress Analysis*, by A. J. S. Pippard (Longmans).

Similarly, $\dfrac{du_2}{dF_a}=\dfrac{_ak_2}{e_2}(R_2+_ak_2\,.\,F_a+_bk_2\,.\,F_b+_ck_2\,.\,F_c+\text{etc.})$

Also　　$\dfrac{du_a}{dF_a}=\dfrac{F_a}{e_a}$　　$\dfrac{du_b}{dF_a}=0$　　$\dfrac{du_c}{dF_a}=0$

Hence, if F_a is such that U is a minimum, $\dfrac{dU}{dF_a}=0$ and

$$0=\frac{dU}{dF_a}=\frac{du_1}{dF_a}+\frac{du_2}{dF_a}+\frac{du_3}{dF_a},\ \text{etc.}+\frac{du_a}{dF_a}+\frac{du_b}{dF_b}+\text{etc.}$$

which with the above values for the terms on the right-hand side gives equation (8), Art. 149, and for *n* redundant members there are *n* such equations.

Principle of Work. By the principle of work, if a redundant member *a* be replaced by opposite pulls F_a at its ends the algebraic sum of the work done by these forces and the strain energy in the structure is zero. Hence

$$\tfrac{1}{2}F_a\times\frac{F_a}{e_a}+\tfrac{1}{2}P_1\times\frac{_ak_1\,.\,F_a}{e_1}+\tfrac{1}{2}P_2\frac{_ak_2\,.\,F_a}{e_2}+\text{etc.}=0$$

And dividing each term by $\tfrac{1}{2}F_a$ gives

$$\frac{F_a}{e_a}+\frac{P_1\,.\,_ak_1}{e_1}+\frac{P_2\,.\,_ak_2}{e_2}+\text{etc.}=0$$

and when the values such as (1), Art. 149, are substituted for P_1, P_2 etc., this also gives equation (8), Art. 149.

Distribution and Relaxation. The methods of Moment Distribution and Relaxation (see Art. 94 and references therein) have been applied to pin-jointed redundant frames, but the successive approximation is tedious if a good degree of approximation is to be attained.

151. Stress due to Errors or Changes in Length. If a frame having a redundant member has one member made too short or shortened by a fall in temperature that member will exert inward pulls at its ends and the frame will be *self-strained*. With the notation of Art. 149, suppose member *a* is an amount *x* too short. Then when the member *a* is forced into its place the approach of its end connections toward one another, plus the stretch of the member, is equal to *x*, or

$\Delta+F^a/e_a=x$, and since R$=0$, from (4), Art. 149, $\Delta=F_a\Sigma(_ak^2/e)$

hence　　　　　　$F_a=\dfrac{x}{1/e_a+\Sigma(_ak^2/e)}$　$\cdot$　$\cdot$　$\cdot$　$\cdot$　$\cdot$　$\cdot$　(1)

Example. Six bars, each 1 sq. in. in section, are to form a square of 30-in. sides with two diagonals, pin-jointed at the corners. If one side-bar is the last to be added and is too short by 0·01 in., find the

stress in all the bars if the short bar is forced into its position.
$E = 30,000,000$ lb. per sq. in.

For each 30-in. side-bar $e = EA/l = 1,000,000$ lb. per in. deflection
and $k = +1$.

For each $30\sqrt{2}''$ diagonal $e = 1,000,000/\sqrt{2}$ lb. per in. deflection,
$k = -\sqrt{2}$, hence from (1) the tension in the bar is

$$F = \cfrac{0 \cdot 01}{\cfrac{1}{10^6} + \cfrac{1}{10^6}(1+1+1+2\sqrt{2}+2\sqrt{2})} = \frac{10,000}{4+4\sqrt{2}} = 1,036 \text{ lb.}$$

The other sides of the square have the same tension, and the
diagonals have each a thrust $1,036\sqrt{2} = 1,465$ lb.

152. Continuous Framed Girders. The principles used for finding
the stresses in redundant members of frames are also applicable to
finding the value of a redundant supporting force such as a prop to a
framed girder. For example, the reaction R_C at C in Fig. 204 may be
found by finding the deflection of C as if the supporting force R_C
were absent, and equating it to the upward deflection of a force R_C
at C. Similarly, if Fig. 205 represents a continuous girder the reactions at C and D may be found from two simultaneous equations,
the dimensions of all the members being known. If the panel
KK′DC is unbraced the stresses in this structure may best be found
by treating KK′ and CD as redundant members and replacing them
by four equal forces at their ends; the structure then falls into two
simply supported trusses.

Example. The ratios of length to uniform cross-sectional area in
inch units being as given in the Table following, find the reactions in
Fig. 204 when unit loads are carried at each of the joints D, E, F.

Firstly, assume the support at C to be removed. Then $R_A = 2\frac{1}{4}$,
$R_B = \frac{3}{4}$, hence by the method of sections find the values of the stress P
in each bar as tabulated below. Then take unit downward force at
C and find the values of k as tabulated. Multiply the terms P, k,
and l/A and find the sum $\Sigma(Pkl/A)$ which by (4), Art. 145, is E
times the deflection at C. Next calculate k^2l/A for each member
and find the sum $\Sigma(k^2l/A)$, which by (5), Art. 145, is E times the
deflection for unit force at C. Then

$$R_C \times \Sigma(k^2l/A) = \Sigma(Pkl/A)$$

and
$$R_C = \Sigma(Pkl/A) \div \Sigma(k^2l/A)$$

$R_C = \frac{471}{237} = 1 \cdot 9873$,   hence by moments $R_B = -\frac{1}{8}(4 \times 1 \cdot 9873 - 6)$
$= -0 \cdot 2437$. $R_A = 3 \cdot 2437 - 1 \cdot 9873 = 1 \cdot 2564$.

A reference to the Table of Reactions in the example of Art. 140
gives the approximate results as $R_A = 1 \cdot 2657$, $R_B = -0 \cdot 2344$, thus
justifying the approximation involved of using for this case the rules
applicable to a solid continuous girder.

Member	l/A	P	k	Pkl/A positive terms	Pkl/A negative terms	k^2l/A
AM	30	$-2.25\sqrt{2}$	$-0.5\sqrt{2}$	67·50		15·0
ME	20	$+1.25\sqrt{2}$	$+0.5\sqrt{2}$	25·00		10·0
EN	15	$-0.25\sqrt{2}$	$-0.5\sqrt{2}$	3·75		7·5
NC	10	$-0.75\sqrt{2}$	$+0.5\sqrt{2}$	—	-7.50	5·0
CP	10	$+0.75\sqrt{2}$	$+0.5\sqrt{2}$	7·50		5·0
PH	15	$-0.75\sqrt{2}$	$-0.5\sqrt{2}$	11·25		7·5
HQ	20	$+0.75\sqrt{2}$	$+0.5\sqrt{2}$	15·00		10·0
QB	30	$-0.75\sqrt{2}$	$-0.5\sqrt{2}$	22·50		15·0
MD	—	1	0	0		—
NF	—	1	0	0		—
PG	—	0	0	0		—
QJ	—	0	0	0		—
AD	12	$+2.25$	$+0.5$	13·50		3·0
DE	12	$+2.25$	$+0.5$	13·50		3·0
EF	10	$+3.75$	$+1.5$	56·25		22·5
FC	10	$+3.75$	$+1.5$	56·25		22·5
CG	10	$+2.25$	$+1.5$	33·75		22·5
GH	10	$+2.25$	$+1.5$	33·75		22·5
HJ	12	$+0.75$	$+0.5$	4·50		3·0
JB	12	$+0.75$	$+0.5$	4·50		3·0
QP	10	-1.5	-1	15·00		10·0
PN	10	-3.0	-2	60·00		40·0
NM	10	-3.5	-1	35·00		10·0

$$\begin{array}{ll} 478{\cdot}50 & \Sigma(k^2l/A)=237{\cdot}0 \\ -7{\cdot}50 & \end{array}$$

$$\Sigma(Pkl/A) = 471{\cdot}00$$

153. Simple Principles applicable to Indeterminate Structures.

The analogy between quite different cases of statically indeterminate stresses may have been noticed, and for convenience a general rule may be stated. Suppose that two elements, a and b, jointly or " in parallel," resist a load, and in consequence exert upon each other a force F, tending to deform a and restore b, say; let x_0 be the deflection of b, say, due to the load if a were removed. Let the stiffnesses or forces per foot of elastic deflection, in the direction of F of a and b, be e_a and e_b respectively. Let $1/e_a$ and $1/e_b$ be called their respective " elasticities." Then the actual deflection

$$F/e_a = x_0 - F/e_b \quad \ldots \ldots \quad (1)$$

hence

$$F = \frac{x_0}{(1/e_a)+(1/e_b)} \quad \ldots \ldots \quad (2)$$

or action of a on $b = \dfrac{\text{strain for } b \text{ acting alone}}{\text{sum of the elasticities}} \quad . \quad (3)$

and if the load can be reduced to a force W in the direction of F,

$$x_0 = \frac{W}{e_b} \text{ and } F = \frac{e_a}{e_a+e_b}W \text{ and } W-F = \frac{e_b}{e_a+e_b}W \quad . \quad (4)$$

which are the same results as in Art. 148, but not limited to struts or ties or to any one type of elastic constraint. Putting equation (4) in words, the two elements a and b divide the load W in proportion to their stiffnesses. This has already been stated with different symbols in (4) of Art. 21. The actual deflection is

$$\delta = \frac{W}{\text{total stiffness}} = \frac{W}{e_a + e_b} \quad \ldots \ldots \quad (5)$$

Examples. We have had examples in Art. 80 for the uniformly loaded rigidly propped cantilever in which a represents the prop and b the cantilever.

$$F = P, \quad x_0 = \tfrac{1}{8} \cdot \frac{wl^4}{EI}, \quad \frac{1}{e_b} = \frac{l^3}{3EI}, \quad e_a = e, \quad P = \tfrac{3}{8}wl, \text{ if } e_a = \infty$$

Also in the uniformly loaded beam (b) on elastic end supports and a central elastic prop (a) in Art. 79, $e_a = e$ and $\dfrac{1}{e_b} = \dfrac{1}{2e} + \dfrac{l^3}{48EI}$, while $x_0 = \dfrac{5}{384} \cdot \dfrac{wl^4}{EI}$, and $P = \tfrac{5}{8}wl$, when $e_a = \infty$.

In the present chapter the important formula (7), Art. 149, is but another example of the same principle, for $-\Sigma(_a k \cdot R/e) = x_0$, and $\Sigma(_a k^2/e) = 1/e_b$, where b represents the frame with the member a removed, and $\Sigma(_a k^2/e)$ is the deflection per unit of force.

If two elements a and b resist a force " in series " so that each bears the whole force, the elasticity $1/e$ of the two is the sum of the elasticities

or
$$1/e = (1/e_a) + (1/e_b) \quad \ldots \ldots \quad (6)$$

or the stiffness
$$e = e_a e_b / (e_a + e_b) \quad \ldots \ldots \quad (7)$$

which is evidently less than either e_a or e_b.

EXAMPLES XV

1. Two pin-jointed rods AC and BC in the same vertical plane are hinged to a rigid support at A and B, 8 ft. apart in the same horizontal line. Find the vertical and horizontal deflections of C when a load of 7 tons hangs from that point if AC and BC are inclined 30° and 45° respectively to the horizontal (ACB being an obtuse angle) and the sectional areas are 1·5 and 2 sq. in. respectively. E = 12,500 tons per sq. in.

2. An N girder of four bays has vertical posts at its ends and carries 16 tons at each joint of the lower chord. The bays are each 6 ft. long and 8 ft. high. Taking the tensile stress in the diagonals and the bottom chord at 5 tons per sq. in. and the compressive stress in the verticals and top chord as 2½ tons per sq. in., find the central deflection if E = 12,500 tons per sq. in.

3. A Warren girder made up of members of equal lengths has four bays in the lower boom and three in the upper boom, and rests on supports which are 24 ft. apart. If, under a central load the stresses in the ties are 6 tons per sq. in., and in the struts 3 tons per sq. in., estimate the central elastic deflection, taking E = 12,500 tons per sq. in.

4. If the point C in Problem No. 1 is joined to a fixed point D midway between A and B by a bar DC 1 sq. in. in cross-section, find the pull in each bar if 10 tons is suspended from the point C.

5. A frame consisting of six bars each 1 sq. in. in section and hinged together to form a square of 20-in. side with two diagonals is suspended from one corner. The opposite corner supports a load of 1,000 lb. Find the stress in each bar.

6. The diagram (Fig. 221A) represents a freely jointed frame supported at its ends and carrying a load W as shown. Find the stress in the two diagonal members meeting at the loaded joint if the ratio of length to area of cross-section is the same for every member.

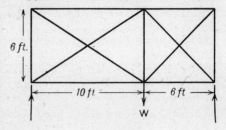

FIG. 221A

7. If one of the diagonals of the steel frame in Problem No. 5 is heated 40° F. above the remaining bars find the resulting stresses in the sides and diagonals of the frame.

8. If the girder of Problem No. 2 under the same loading were propped at the centre to the same level as the ends, find the reaction on the central prop. What would the reaction be for a continuous solid girder of uniform section with the load (*a*) uniformly distributed at $16 \div 6$ or $2\frac{2}{3}$ tons per ft. directly applied, (*b*) concentrated as 16 tons at panel points with 8 tons carried directly at each end support?

SOME INDETERMINATE COMBINATIONS

154. Trussed Beams. Trussed beams consisting of a combination of beams with ties and struts form an important structural element. The distribution of stress cannot be determined by the ordinary principles of statics, but may be determined by those given in Chapter xv.

The simplest form of a trussed beam is shown in Fig. 222. AB is

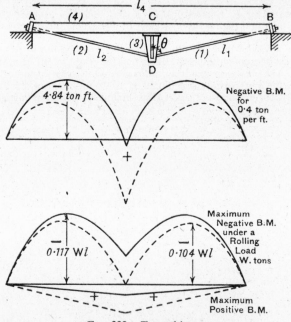

Fig. 222.—Trussed beam

a continuous beam; CD is a strut braced to the beam ends A and B by tie-rods AD and DB. The stresses in the various members are of course dependent upon the initial stresses due to tightening up the rods, and are liable to alteration by change of temperature. The stresses due to loads carried on AB may be conveniently found by the methods of Art. 153, but if the proportions are such that the

[1] Arts. 155–163, inclusive, may be omitted on a first reading of the subject.

deformation of the bracing is negligible compared to the bending deflections of the beam, the stresses in the beam and reactions at C are practically those for a continuous beam AB rigidly propped at C to the level of AB, and this has been dealt with in Chapters VII and VIII.[1]   The example at the end of the article with proportions usual in practice shows how much in error such treatment may be in some cases.

Allowing for the elasticity of the ties and strut, let e_1 and e_2 be the stiffnesses (EA/l) of the ties, e_3 that of the strut, and e_4 that of the beam in axial thrust.   Then unit downward pressure of the beam on the strut brings a tension $\frac{1}{2}$ sec θ in each tie, and an axial thrust $\frac{1}{2}$ tan θ in the beam where θ is the angle CDB=angle CDA.   And unit stretch of the tie allows a vertical deflection $\frac{1}{2}$ sec θ of D, while unit compression of the beam allows a vertical deflection $\frac{1}{2}$ tan θ of D.   Hence remembering that if 1 ton vertically at D produces a tension k in any member then the deflection of D per unit stretch of that member is k, the elasticity (vertically) of the truss system $1/e_a$, plus that of the beam $1/e_b$ is

$$\frac{1}{e_a}+\frac{1}{e_b}=\frac{1}{e_3}+\frac{(\frac{1}{2}\sec\theta)^2}{e_1}+\frac{(\frac{1}{2}\sec\theta)^2}{e_2}+\frac{(\frac{1}{2}\tan\theta)^2}{e_4}+\frac{l_4{}^3}{48\text{EI}}=\frac{1}{e}\text{ say }. \quad (1)$$

where usually $e_1=e_2$, and hence

$$\frac{1}{e}=\frac{1}{e_3}+\frac{l_1{}^2}{2l_3{}^2e_1}+\frac{1}{16}\cdot\frac{l_4{}^2}{l_1{}^2e_4}+\frac{l_4{}^3}{48\text{E}_4\text{I}_4} \quad \ldots \ldots \text{ (1A)}$$

or $\qquad \dfrac{1}{e}=\dfrac{l_3}{\text{A}_3\text{E}_3}+\dfrac{l_1{}^3}{2l_3{}^2\text{E}_1\text{A}_1}+\dfrac{1}{16}\cdot\dfrac{l_4{}^3}{l_1{}^2\text{A}_4\text{E}_4}+\dfrac{l_4{}^3}{48\text{E}_4\text{I}_4}$. (1B)

Hence if δ_c is the central deflection which the load would cause in the beam if simply supported at A and B, the thrust F in the post CD, by (2), Art. 153, is

$$\text{F}=\delta_c\div 1/e=e\cdot\delta_c \quad \ldots \ldots \quad (2)$$

The calculation of δ_c for any load is dealt with in Chapter VII, Art. 79, and when F is known the resulting bending moment on AB for F and the load is easily calculated, and hence the bending stresses may be found.

The pull in the tie-rods is $\frac{1}{2}$F sec θ which induces a thrust $\frac{1}{2}$F tan θ, which may be taken as uniformly distributed in the beam, AB to be added to the bending stresses, the increment of bending stress due to the thrust acting on the deflected beam being neglected.   If e_1, e_2, and e_3 are great compared to 48EI/l^3, the stiffness of the beam (1) becomes e=48EI/l^3, and then (2) reduces to F=48EIδ_c/l^3, the

---

[1] Solutions of this kind for several types of trussed beams are given in a paper on " Trussed Beams," by G. Higgins of Melbourne University. *Proceedings Australian Association for Advancement of Science.* 1910.

reaction of a rigid prop at the centre of a continuous beam of two equal spans.

Example 1. A trussed timber beam 20 ft. long is square in section 9×9 in., and has a central cast-iron strut 2 ft. long, and 24 sq. in. in sectional area; the wrought-iron tie-rods which are each 10·2 ft. long are 1 in. diameter. Take E for wrought iron as 12,000 tons per sq. in., for cast iron 6,000 tons per sq. in., and for timber as 600 tons per sq. in. Find the thrust in the strut, the pull in the tie-rods, the maximum bending moment in the beam and the extreme stresses, when the beam carries a uniformly distributed load of 0·4 ton per ft.

The elasticity in inches per ton of load at C for the several elements are

$$\text{for strut } \frac{24}{6,000 \times 24} = 0.00016$$

$$\text{for two ties } \frac{2 \times 10 \cdot 2 \times 12}{12,000 \times 0.7854} \times \tfrac{1}{4} \times (10 \cdot 2/2)^2 = 0.169$$

$$\text{for beam in compression } \frac{240}{600 \times 81} \times (10/2)^2 \times \tfrac{1}{4} = 0.0308$$

$$\text{for bending } \frac{(240)^3 \times 12}{48 \times 600 \times 9^4} = 0.8780$$

or the total elasticity

$$1/e = 0.0002 + 0.169 + 0.0308 + 0.8780 = 1.0780 \text{ in. per ton}$$

which is considerably in excess of the value (0·878) for flexure alone, the difference being mainly in the ties. The deflection at C for the unbraced beam is

$$\tfrac{5}{384} \cdot \frac{Wl^3}{EI} = \frac{5 \times 8 \times 240^3 \times 12}{384 \times 600 \times 9^4} = 4.39 \text{ in.}$$

hence the thrust in the strut C from (2) is

$$4.39 \div 1.078 = 4.07 \text{ tons}$$

instead of 4·39/0·878 or $\tfrac{5}{8}$ of $8 = 5$ tons if the flexibility of the beam alone were allowed for.

The pull in each tie-rod is $4.07 \times \tfrac{1}{2} \times 10 \cdot 2/2 = 10.38$ tons.

The thrust in the beam is

$$\tfrac{1}{2} \times 4.07 \times \tfrac{10}{2} = 10.175 \text{ tons, or } 10.175/81 = 0.1255 \text{ ton per sq. in.}$$

The bending moment at x ft. from the end is

$$-\tfrac{1}{2}(8 - 4.07)x + \tfrac{1}{2} \times 0.4x^2 \text{ ton-ft.}$$

which is represented by a parabola which may easily be plotted. The maximum negative bending moment occurs with zero shearing force at x ft. from the end where

$$x = \tfrac{1}{2}(8 - 4.07)/0.4 = 4.9125 \text{ ft.}$$

The maximum negative bending moment is

$$-1{\cdot}965 \times 4{\cdot}9125 + \tfrac{1}{2} \times 0{\cdot}4 \times (4{\cdot}9125)^2 = -4{\cdot}84 \text{ ton-ft.}$$

The bending moment at the post is

$$4 \times 5 - 1{\cdot}965 \times 10 = +0{\cdot}35 \text{ ton-ft.}$$

the thrust at the post (4·07) being just greater than that required (4 tons) to change the sign of the bending moment; there are points of inflexion just on either side of the centre, viz. at $2 \times 4{\cdot}9125$ =9·825 ft. from the ends. The curves of bending moment are shown in Fig. 222.

The modulus of section is

$$81 \times 9/6 = 121{\cdot}5 \text{ (in.)}$$

hence the extreme bending stress is

$$4{\cdot}84 \times 12/121{\cdot}5 = 0{\cdot}478 \text{ ton per sq. in.}$$

the maximum compressive stress is

$$0{\cdot}478 + 0{\cdot}126 = 0{\cdot}604 \text{ ton per sq. in.}$$

and the maximum tensile stress is

$$0{\cdot}478 - 0{\cdot}126 = 0{\cdot}352 \text{ ton per sq. in.}$$

The vertical end reactions are each 4 tons, made up of $\tfrac{1}{2}(8 - 4{\cdot}07)$ =1·965 tons from the beam, and $\tfrac{1}{2} \times 4{\cdot}07 = 2{\cdot}035$ tons from the tie-rods. If the elasticity of the bracing were neglected the maximum negative bending moment would have been

$$-\tfrac{9}{512} \times \frac{0{\cdot}4 \times 400}{1} = -2{\cdot}81 \text{ ton-ft.}$$

while the maximum positive bending moment (at the post) would have been

$$\tfrac{1}{32} \times \frac{0{\cdot}4 \times 400}{1} = +5 \text{ ton-ft.}$$

The curve for this assumption is shown dotted for comparison in Fig. 222. On the other hand, the stresses in the bracing would be exaggerated by the supposition that the bracing was perfectly rigid.

An empirical rule [1] for estimating the maximum bending stress is to take the beam as if separated into two parts at C. This would give a maximum bending moment

$$= -\tfrac{1}{8} \times 0{\cdot}4 \times 100 = -5 \text{ ton-ft.}$$

which seems to be justified by the result $-4{\cdot}84$, for this more elaborate calculation in an example with typical proportions.

Example 2.   If the beam in Example 1 is traversed by a concentrated load W tons, find the position and amount of the maximum bending moment.

[1] See *Notes on Building Construction*, Part IV, Chapter XI (Longmans).

If the load is a distance nl from the near end of the beam, length l, say, supposed simply supported at its ends, the central deflection, writing $b=nl$, $a=(1-n)l$, and $x=\frac{1}{2}l$ in (7), Art. 81, is

$$\delta_C = \frac{Wl^3 n(3-4n^2)}{48EI}$$

Hence from (2), using the previous value 1·078

$$F = \frac{1}{1·078} \cdot \frac{Wn(3-4n^2) \times 240^3 \times 12}{48 \times 600 \times 9^4} = 0·814n(3-4n^2)W$$

The upward reaction on the beam at the near end is $W(1-n)-\frac{1}{2}F$, and the bending moment under the load (which exceeds in magnitude that at the centre) is $-nl$ times this or

$$M = -Wln\{1-n-0·407n(3-4n^2)\} = -Wln(1-2·221n+1·628n^3)$$

This is plotted on the lower part of Fig. 222. The maximum value for any position, found by writing $dM/dx=0$, is about $M = -0·1175Wl$, for a value of n, a trifle under 0·25. The maximum positive bending moments occur at the centre, and elsewhere, when the reaction on the far end of the beam (from the load) is a downward maximum value. Even at the centre of the beam the greatest maximum positive bending moment only amounts to 0·0156Wl, falling off uniformly to zero at the ends.

The maximum negative and positive bending moment curves for the rigidly propped beam are shown dotted, and may be obtained by using 0·878 in place of 1·078 above, or

$$F=n(3-4n^2)W, \qquad M=-Wln(1-2·5+2n^3)$$

the greatest values being about

$$-0·1038Wl \text{ under the load for } n=0·216,$$
$$\text{and } +0·048Wl \text{ at C for } n=0·289$$

The empirical calculation taking the beam as discontinuous at C gives the maximum bending moment at $\frac{1}{4}l$ as

$$-\tfrac{1}{4}W \times \tfrac{1}{2}l = -0·125Wl$$

a fair estimate on the safe side.

155. Simple Braced Shed Frames and Portals. An important type of statically indeterminate building frame containing continuous members resisting flexure and others acting as ties and struts only is introduced by the simple framework shown in Fig. 223. Members AB and CD are similar and represent vertical stanchions hinged at each end and their caps connected by a cross-beam, knee braces inclined θ to the horizontal connecting K to G and E to F. The sole load is a horizontal force W, such as a wind load, applied at B.

Reactions. By taking moments about A and D, of the forces on the whole structure, it is evident that the vertical component V of the reactions at D and A are equal and opposite as shown and of magnitude WL/l.   The horizontal components H_1 and H_2 are such that $H_1+H_2=W$, but their magnitudes depend upon the compressibility of the cross-beam in the direction of its length.   If R_1 and R_2 are the resultant reactions they must meet at some point X in the line of action of W, and X will be a point of inflexion of the beam BC, for the resultant force on the structure either side of X passes through X and has therefore zero moment about X. By taking a section through the hinge C cutting EF, and moments about C of forces on the structure to the right of the section, if T' is the thrust in EF,

$$T' \cdot CF \cos \theta = L \cdot H_1 \quad \text{or} \quad T'=H_1\frac{L}{L-h} \sec \theta. \quad . \quad (1)$$

And similarly if T is the tension in KG,

$$T=H_2 \cdot \frac{L}{L-h} \sec \theta . \quad . \quad . \quad . \quad . \quad (2)$$

And if $t'=$ tension in EC, by moments about D of the forces on the stanchion CD,

$$t' \cdot L=T' \cos \theta \cdot h, \text{ hence } t'=H_1 \cdot \frac{h}{L-h} \quad . \quad . \quad (3)$$

and similarly if

$$t=\text{thrust in BG}, \ t-W=H_2\frac{h}{L-h} \cdot \quad . \quad . \quad . \quad (4)$$

hence the transverse or bending forces on the stanchions are as shown at (*b*) and (*c*), Fig. 223, and it is evident that the forces being

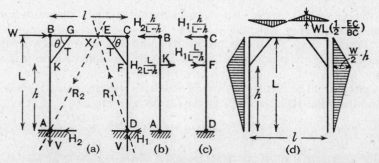

FIG. 223.—Simple braced rectangular frame, hinged at caps and bases

proportional to H_2 and H_1 respectively the type of deflection is the same in each case.   Hence the deflections of B and C are proportional to H_2 and H_1 respectively, and if we treat the compressibility from B to C as negligible compared to the flexibility of the stanchions the deflections are equal and

$$H_1 = H_2 = \tfrac{1}{2}W \quad . \quad . \quad . \quad . \quad . \quad (5)$$

The point of inflexion X is then midway between B and C. Further, if we know the dimensions of the members and express all the forces in terms of say H_1 (writing $H_2 = W - H_1$), using the principle of deformations (Art. 148), we can find H_1 in terms of W by equating say the deflection of AB at B to the deflection of CD at C plus the compression of BC. This principle will be applicable to the cases which follow, whether B is united to C by some form of bracing or by a roof, and also to the case of stanchions fixed at their bases, for the fixing couples will then be proportional to H_1 and H_2. For stanchions of different lengths or moments of inertia (I) the principle of deformation may be applied to find H_1 and H_2.

Stresses in Members. Assuming a rigid connection of B to C, from (5), (1) and (2), we get

$$T = T' = \tfrac{1}{2}W\frac{L}{L-h}\sec\theta \quad . \quad . \quad . \quad . \quad (6)$$

and from (3) and (4)

$$t - W = t' = \tfrac{1}{2}W\frac{h}{L-h} \text{ and } t = \tfrac{1}{2}W\frac{2L-h}{L-h} \quad . \quad . \quad . \quad (7)$$

And from a vertical section through GE

the thrust in $GE = H_1 = \tfrac{1}{2}W$ . . . . . (8)

which is accompanied by a bending moment which at a distance x from C is equal to $H_1L - Vx = WL(\tfrac{1}{2} - x/l)$. The shearing force from B to G is $V - T\sin\theta = WL\left(\dfrac{1}{l} - \dfrac{1}{2BG}\right)$ which is negative, and from G to E is $V = W \cdot L/l$. The bending-moment diagrams are shown at (*d*), Fig. 223.

Flexible Braces. If the braces KG and EF are of such small section (or I) in proportion to their lengths that they will not carry any appreciable thrust the brace on the leeward side (EF) may be neglected. The structure is now statically determinate, $H_2 = W$, and the brace KG carries twice the former tension, *i.e.*

$$T = W\frac{L}{L-h}\sec\theta \quad . \quad . \quad . \quad . \quad (9)$$

The reaction R_2 then passes through C, while $R_1 = V$ along DC. The bending moment at $G = -V \times GC = -WL/l \cdot GC$ and at K is Wh.

156. Columns fixed at Bases. The effect of fixed ends to the column at the bases in the foregoing and other types of portal bracing may easily be seen if we find the point of inflexion I of the column, for above this the structure is under precisely the same condition as that with hinged bases in Art. 155. The point I may be found as follows: Let P, Fig. 224, be the horizontal component of say the tension in the brace KG on say the windward stanchion of (*a*), Fig. 223, but supposed fixed at the base. Then the transverse forces are as shown in Fig. 224. And taking the bracing B

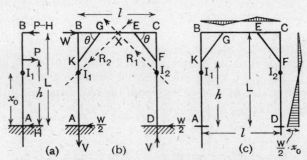

FIG. 224.—Simple braced rectangular frame fixed at bases

to C as rigid we assume that B and K deflect equally, an assumption which overcomes the indeterminate condition arising from the fixture of the stanchion ends. The deflection of K may be written from (2), Art. 80, and the general expression of which (2) is a particular value, while the deflection of B may be written from (2) and (5) of Art. 80. Equating these deflections

$$\frac{Ph^3}{3EI}-\frac{(P-H)h^2}{2EI}(L-\tfrac{1}{3}h)=\frac{Ph^3}{3EI}+\frac{Ph^2(L-h)}{2EI}-\frac{(P-H)L^3}{3EI} \quad . \quad (1)$$

From which

$$P=\frac{H}{2}\cdot\frac{2L^2+2Lh-h^2}{(L-h)(L+2h)} \quad \text{and} \quad P-H=\frac{H}{2}\cdot\frac{3h^2}{(L-h)(L+2h)} \cdot \quad (2)$$

Then at a distance x from A the bending moment

$$M_x=P(h-x)-(P-H)(L-x)$$

and substituting the above values of P and P−H, M_x vanishes for

$$x=x_0=\frac{h}{2}\cdot\frac{2L+h}{L+2h} \quad \cdots \cdots \quad (3)$$

This is always greater than $\tfrac{1}{2}h$, or KI_1 is always less than $\tfrac{1}{2}h$. By symmetry $DI_2=AI_1=x_0$. It is usual to take $x_0=\tfrac{1}{2}h$, which is on the safe side for calculating stresses in the bracing. When the points of inflexion I_1 and I_2 have been determined it is only necessary to write $L-x_0$ for L and $h-x_0$ for h in the formulae (6) and (7) of Art. 155 to obtain the stresses in the members. The bending-moment diagrams are shown in Fig. 224 (*c*). There is the same algebraic change of bending moment between F and D as for the hinged posts, viz. from $\frac{1}{2}W(h-x_0)$ at F to $\frac{1}{2}Wx_0$ of opposite sign at D. The bending moment at E is $W\left(\frac{1}{2}-\frac{EC}{BC}\right)(L-x_0)$. The vertical components of the reactions are $W(L-x_0)/l$.

157. Other Forms. Fig. 225 shows a special case of bracing, such as Fig. 223, where the braces meet at X, the point of inflexion midway between B and C. Considering forces on the part to the right of say a vertical section through X, the only external force is R_1 which passes through X, hence since the force in TY is the only one not passing through X, the stress in TY=0. It follows that the stresses in TB and CY are zero, and the remaining stresses follow from the formulae in Art. 155. From the half-structure shown to the right of Fig. 225 it is evident that the stresses in XC may be

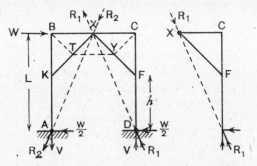

FIG. 225.—Simple braced portal, hinged at bases

found by a triangle of forces for the point X, XC having no bending stress CF will have no thrust, but will have a shearing force equal to the tension in CX. Also the vertical component of the stress in FX is equal to V.

If the stanchions are fixed in direction at their lower ends it is only necessary to calculate the position of the points of contraflexure as for I_1 and I_2 in Art. 156, and use these points in place of A and D.

Graphical Solution. A simple method of finding the stress in the internal bracings of portals for which the author is indebted to Ketchum's " Steel Mill Buildings " is illustrated in Fig. 226. The bracing DEFGK at (*a*) unites the stanchions 1, 2, and 3, 4, which at (*b*) are replaced, 1, 2, by pin-ended members Aα, αB, αβ, Bβ, and 3, 4 by γC, γδ, δC, δA, the lengths of βα and γδ being immaterial. The stress diagram (*c*) can be drawn starting from, say, joint ABα, after putting in *abc* for the external forces so that *bc*=W. The dotted portion relates to imaginary members and may be dispensed with, leaving only the portion drawn in continuous lines; the points

γ, δ symmetrical with βα have not been added, as they are not necessary to the work.   The portion relating to bracing members which
are struts or ties only needs no comment, but with regard to the
stanchions the portion 1, 5 withstands the force *ab*, viz. the vertical
projection (which is *af*) as a thrust and a transverse shearing force
equal to the horizontal projection of *ab* (*i.e.* to the length *bf*); the
portion 5, 2 carries the force *bd*, which represents zero thrust and a

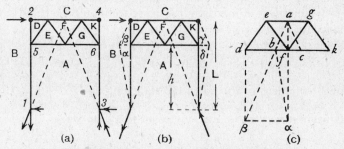

FIG. 226.—Braced portal; graphical solution

shearing force *bd*.   The method is applicable to the form shown in
Fig. 225 and to other simple forms.   In case the stanchions are
"fixed" in direction at their bases it is only necessary to calculate
the positions of the points of inflexion by (3), Art. 156, and to use
these points as the feet of hinged stanchions.

158. Stanchions with Cross-Beam.   (*a*) *Bases hinged.*   If the

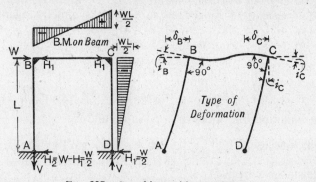

FIG. 227.—Stanchions with cross-beam

bracing in Art. 155 and Fig. 223 is replaced by a horizontal beam
rigidly connected to the stanchion caps, the solution of the stresses
depends upon the fact that the beam ends bend through the same
angles (i_B and i_C) as the stanchion ends.   Thus is Fig. 227, since each
stanchion is acted upon by a transverse force (H) and a couple (HL)
at the top, the deflections are of similar type, and if we neglect the

compressibility of the beam BC, since the deflections of B and C are equal, the two horizontal reactions are equal, *i.e.* $H_1 = W - H_1 = \frac{1}{2}W$.

By symmetry the slopes are equal at B and C, *i.e.* $i_B = i_C$, and from (12), Art. 88, and using suffixes B and C instead of A and B, since for the beam $M_C = H_1 . L$ or $\frac{1}{2}WL$,

$$i_C = \frac{H_1 L l}{6EI_b} \quad . \quad . \quad . \quad . \quad . \quad . \quad (1)$$

where I_b = moment of inertia of the cross-section of the beam.

Hence for $\delta_C = {}_4\delta_B$ we have

$$\delta_C = \frac{H_1 L^3}{3EI} + i_C L = \frac{H_1 L^3}{3EI} + \frac{H_1 L^2 l}{6EI_b} = \frac{WL^3}{6EI}\left(1 + \frac{1}{2\alpha}\right) . \quad . \quad (2)$$

where I = moment of inertia of the stanchion and $\dfrac{I_b}{l} \div \dfrac{I}{L} = \alpha$. If the cross-beam is very stiff, *i.e.* if α is great, this becomes.

$$\delta_C = \delta_B = \frac{WL^3}{6EI} \quad . \quad . \quad . \quad . \quad . \quad . \quad (3)$$

The bending-moment diagrams for the beam and one stanchion are shown in Fig. 227.

If the stanchions are of different lengths L_1 and L_2 or sections (I), the values of H_1 and H_2 may be found by equating δ_C and δ_B found as in (2), but the values of i_C and i_B will not be equal; they may be found from (12), Art. 88, by writing $M_C = H_1 . L_1$, $M_B = -H_2 . L_2$.

(*b*) *Bases fixed in Direction.* If A and D, Fig. 227, are fixed in direction instead of hinged as shown, by symmetry again $H_1 = H_2 = \frac{1}{2}W$, and for the beam $M_B = -M_C$, $M_D = M_A$, $M_C = H_1 . L - M_D = \frac{1}{2}WL - M_D$, hence from (12), Art. 88

$$E . I_b . i_C = \tfrac{1}{6}(\tfrac{1}{2}WL - M_D)l \quad . \quad . \quad . \quad . \quad (4)$$

and by integration or from (1), Art. 82

$$E . I . i_C = M_D . L - \tfrac{1}{2}HL^2 = M_D . L - \tfrac{1}{4}WL^2 \quad . \quad . \quad (5)$$

hence, equating the values of i_C from (4) and (5)

$$M_D = M_A = \tfrac{1}{2}WL . \frac{3\alpha + 1}{6\alpha + 1}, \quad M_C = -M_B = \tfrac{1}{2}WL\left(\frac{3\alpha}{6\alpha + 1}\right) . \quad (6)$$

At a distance x from D

$$M = M_D - \tfrac{1}{2}Wx \quad . \quad . \quad . \quad . \quad . \quad (7)$$

which vanishes for

$$x_0 = M_D \div \tfrac{1}{2}W = L(3\alpha + 1) \div (6\alpha + 1) \quad . \quad . \quad . \quad (8)$$

The bending moment on the stanchion will vary uniformly from M_D at D to $M_D - \frac{1}{2}WL$ at C, passing through zero at the point of inflexion x_0 from D. On CB it will vary uniformly from $\frac{1}{2}WL - M_D$ at C to the same value with opposite sign at B. The reader may as an exercise sketch the bending-moment diagrams and deformed shape of the structure, which above the points of inflexion will be similar to that in Fig. 227.

If α is great, *i.e.* the flexibility of the cross-beam is negligible in comparison with that of the stanchions, (8) becomes $x_0 = \frac{1}{2}L$, and the bending moments at A, B, C, and D are each of magnitude $\frac{1}{4}WL$.

If α is small $M_D = \frac{1}{2}WL$, $M_C = 0$, the case of hinges at the caps. If we write $L - x_0$ in this case in place of L in the previous one, the moments at the tops of the stanchions may be found; also the vertical reactions (equal and opposite) found by moments about the points of inflexion will be

$$\frac{W}{l}(L - x_0) = \frac{WL}{l} \cdot \frac{3\alpha}{6\alpha + 1}$$

159. Effect of Distributed Side Loads.[1] In Arts. 155–158 the side loads were supposed taken at the ends of the windward stanchion. They may more frequently be more or less distributed along its length. To examine the effect of this, suppose the total load W uniformly distributed along the length of the windward stanchion.

Stiff Cross-Girder: Hinged Bases. Fig. 228 represents the same structure as Fig. 227 with a uniformly distributed load W on AB, but with a stiff girder, *i.e.* $\frac{I_b}{l} \div \frac{I}{L}$ or α is great.

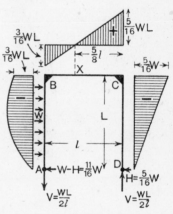

FIG. 228.—Effect of distributed load

From (2), Art. 80, the deflection at $C = \frac{HL^3}{3EI}$, and from (7) and (2), Art. 80, the deflection at $B = \frac{(W - H)L^3}{3EI} - \frac{WL^3}{8EI}$, and equating these two we find

$$H = \tfrac{5}{16}W, \qquad W - H = \tfrac{11}{16}W \quad . \quad . \quad . \quad . \quad (1)$$

The bending moments throughout the structure are then simply found, and are indicated by diagrams in Fig. 228.

Flexible Cross-Girder: Hinged Bases. In this case, still using

[1] A solution of this problem and that of Art. 162 by the principle of minimum flexural elastic strain energy is given by C. E. Larard in *Phil. Mag.*, vol. xi, May, 1931, p. 1104. Comprehensive solutions to such problems are to be found in *Univ. of Illinois Engineering Experiment Station Bulletin No.* 108 (1918), " Analysis of Statically Indeterminate Structures," by Wilson, Richart and Weiss.

Q

Fig. 228 from (12), Art. 88, with altered suffixes, writing for the beam

$$M_C = HL \text{ and } M_B = \tfrac{1}{2}WL - (W-H)L = L(H - \tfrac{1}{2}W)$$

we find

$$i_B = Ll(W - 3H) \div 6EI_b, \quad i_C = Ll(6H - W) \div 12EI_b \quad . \quad . \quad (2)$$

Then writing deflection at $C = \dfrac{HL^3}{3EI} + Li_C$ . . . . . . (3)

Deflection at $B = \dfrac{(W-H)L^3}{3EI} - \dfrac{WL^3}{8EI} + Li_B$. (4)

and equating these deflections we find, putting as before $\dfrac{I_b L}{Il} = \alpha$

$$H = \frac{W}{8} \cdot \frac{5\alpha + 6}{(2\alpha + 3)} \quad . \quad . \quad . \quad . \quad . \quad (5)$$

which approaches the value (1) when α is great, *i.e.* when the top girder is stiff, and approaches $\tfrac{1}{4}W$ when the stanchions are very stiff compared to the cross-girder.

In equating the deflections at B and C we have neglected any shortening of the cross-girder which transmits a thrust H. It is negligible in comparison with the bending deflection of the stanchions.

These results can alternatively be found from the theorem of Minimum Strain Energy (Art. 96). Ignoring any strain energy but that of flexure the total may be written as the sum of that in DC, CB, and BA, or

$$\left. \begin{aligned} U &= U_{DC} + U_{CB} + U_{BA} \\ &= \frac{1}{2EI} \int_0^L M^2 \cdot dx + \frac{1}{2EI_b} \int_0^l M^2 dx + \frac{1}{2EI} \int_0^L M^2 dx \end{aligned} \right\} \quad . \quad (1\text{A})$$

Partially differentiating with respect to H

$$EI \frac{\partial U}{\partial H} = \int_0^L M \frac{\partial M}{\partial H} dx + \frac{L}{\alpha l} \int_0^l M \frac{\partial M}{\partial H} dx + \int_0^L M \frac{\partial M}{\partial H} dx \quad . \quad (2\text{A})$$

which by (22) of Art. 96 is equal to zero since there is no deflection at D where the external force H is applied. Taking x from D (upward), from C (leftward), and from B (downward) in the three ranges we have

D to C $M = Hx; \quad \partial M / \partial H = x$

C to B $M = HL - \tfrac{1}{2}WxL/l; \quad \partial M / \partial H = L$

B to A $M = H(L-x) - \tfrac{1}{2}WL + \tfrac{1}{2}Wx^2/L; \quad \partial M / \partial H = L - x.$

Inserting these values in (2A) and equating to zero

$$H\int_0^L x^2dx+L^3\int_0^l \{H-\tfrac{1}{2}W(x/l)\}/(\alpha l)dx+\int_0^L [H(L-x)^2$$
$$-\tfrac{1}{2}WL(L-x)+W(Lx^2-x^3)/2L]dx=0 \quad . \quad (3\text{A})$$

$$\tfrac{1}{3}HL^3+(L^2/\alpha l)\{HLl-\tfrac{1}{4}WLl\}+\tfrac{1}{3}HL^3$$
$$-\tfrac{1}{4}WL^3+\tfrac{1}{2}W(\tfrac{1}{3}-\tfrac{1}{4})L^3=0 \quad . \quad . \quad . \quad (4\text{A})$$

From which

$$H=\tfrac{1}{8}W(5\alpha+6)/(2\alpha+3) \quad . \quad . \quad . \quad (5\text{A})$$

as in (5).   This method does not appear to offer any advantage over that of equating deflections.   It may be used as an alternative in this and the following cases.

Stiff   Cross-Girder: " Fixed "   Bases (Fig. 229).   Since DC

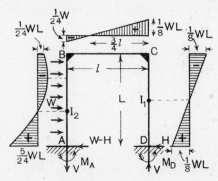

FIG. 229

remains vertical at D and C, from (1) and (2), Art. 80 (or from (1), Art. 82), $M_D=\tfrac{1}{2}HL$, hence I_1D the distance from D to the point of inflexion $=\tfrac{1}{2}L$.   And similarly $M_A=\tfrac{1}{8}WL-\tfrac{1}{2}HL$.

The deflection at C from (2) and (11), Art. 80, is

$$\frac{HL^3}{3EI}-\frac{M_DL^2}{2EI}=\frac{HL^3}{12EI} \quad . \quad . \quad . \quad . \quad (6)$$

And the deflection at B is

$$\frac{(W-H)L^3}{3EI}-\frac{M_AL^2}{2EI}-\frac{WL^3}{8EI} \quad . \quad . \quad . \quad . \quad (7)$$

And equating (6) to (7)

$$H=\tfrac{1}{4}W, \quad W-H=\tfrac{3}{4}W \quad . \quad . \quad . \quad . \quad (8)$$

At x from A
$$M=M_A+\tfrac{1}{2}\frac{W}{L} \cdot x^2-\tfrac{3}{4}Wx$$

which vanishes for
$$I_2 \cdot A=x=0.368L \quad . \quad . \quad . \quad . \quad (9)$$

The bending-moment diagrams are shown in Fig. 229.

Flexible Cross-Girder: " Fixed " Bases. Taking M_A and M_D or M_B and M_C as unknown quantities in addition to H, we can state the end slopes i_C and i_B for the stanchions from Art. 80 or Art. 82. The same slopes can also be deduced from (12), Art. 88, and equated to the previous values, thus eliminating i_C and i_B. A third relation is obtained by equating the deflections of B and C and solving; we then obtain

$$H = W(2\alpha + 3) \div 8(\alpha + 2) \quad . \quad . \quad . \quad . \quad (10)$$

If α is great this reduces to $\frac{1}{4}W$ in agreement with (8), while if α is small $H = \frac{3}{16}$. W, the value for a beam hinged at B and C, as is shown by equating cap deflections $\dfrac{HL^3}{3EI}$ to $\dfrac{WL^3}{8EI} - \dfrac{HL^3}{3EI}$. Thus for all relative stiffnesses of the stanchions and beams H will lie between $\frac{1}{4}W$ and $\frac{3}{16}W$. The general expressions for M_A and M_D obtained as described are

$$M_A = \frac{WL}{24} \cdot \frac{30\alpha^2 + 73\alpha + 15}{(1 + 6\alpha)(\alpha + 2)} \quad . \quad . \quad . \quad . \quad (11)$$

$$M_D = \frac{WL}{24} \cdot \frac{18\alpha^2 + 35\alpha + 9}{(1 + 6\alpha)(\alpha + 2)} \cdot \quad . \quad . \quad . \quad . \quad (12) .$$

Also $V = W\{\alpha/(6\alpha + 1)\}\{L/l\}$

When α is great M_D becomes $\frac{1}{8}WL$ and M_A becomes $\frac{5}{24}WL$ in accordance with the previous case and Fig. 229. The types of bending-moment diagrams will be as in Fig. 229, but the proportions will depend upon the relative stiffnesses of the parts.

If the Minimum Strain Energy method is used as an alternative we state M for each range and equate to zero each of the partial differential coefficients of U with respect to H, V, and either M_A or M_D. Or we can choose H, and either M_A or M_D, together with either M_B or M_C, solving three simultaneous equations such as $\partial U/\partial H = 0$, $\partial U/\partial V = 0$, and $\partial U/\partial M_A = 0$.

The foregoing results with those of the previous articles are summarised for comparison in the Table opposite.

Partial Distribution. When the total load is transferred to the windward stanchion at a number of isolated points, as when a side-wind load on the wall or sheeting is carried by rails attached to the stanchions, the results will be intermediate between those of the first five lines of the Table taking $W = \frac{1}{2}$ total load, and those of the last five lines taking W for the whole load. For example, taking the structure in the last line of the Table, if the load is carried at the base, the top, and a point midway between, the total load W would be divided (see Art. 120) into $\frac{1}{4}W$ at the top, $\frac{1}{4}W$ at

TABLE OF BENDING MOMENTS AND REACTIONS ON STANCHIONS CONNECTED BY CAP BEAMS AND SUBJECT TO A SIDE LOAD W

Side load W	Condition of stanchion bases	Cap beam	M_A	M_D	M_B	M_C	H
Concentrated at B.	Fixed	Stiff	$\frac{1}{4}WL$	$\frac{1}{4}WL$	$-\frac{1}{4}WL$	$-\frac{1}{4}WL$	$\frac{1}{2}W$
	Fixed	Flexible	$\frac{1}{2}WL\cdot\frac{3\alpha+1}{6\alpha+1}$	$\frac{1}{2}WL\cdot\frac{3\alpha+1}{6\alpha+1}$	$-\frac{1}{2}WL\cdot\frac{3\alpha}{6\alpha+1}$	$-\frac{1}{2}WL\cdot\frac{3\alpha}{6\alpha+1}$	$\frac{1}{2}W$
	Hinged	Stiff	0	0	$-\frac{1}{2}WL$	$-\frac{1}{2}WL$	$\frac{1}{2}W$
	Hinged	Flexible	0	0	$-\frac{1}{2}WL$	$-\frac{1}{2}WL$	$\frac{1}{2}W$
	Fixed	Hinged	$\frac{1}{2}WL$	$\frac{1}{2}WL$	0	0	$\frac{1}{2}W$
Distributed uniformly along AB.	Fixed	Stiff	$\frac{5}{24}WL$	$\frac{1}{8}WL$	$-\frac{1}{24}WL$	$-\frac{1}{8}WL$	$\frac{1}{4}W$
	Fixed	Flexible	$\frac{WL}{24}\cdot\frac{30\alpha^2+73\alpha+15}{(1+6\alpha)(2+\alpha)}$	$\frac{WL}{24}\cdot\frac{18\alpha^2+35\alpha+9}{(1+6\alpha)(2+\alpha)}$	$-\frac{WL}{24}\cdot\frac{\alpha(6\alpha+23)}{(1+6\alpha)(2+\alpha)}$	$-\frac{WL}{24}\cdot\frac{\alpha(18\alpha+25)}{(1+6\alpha)(2+\alpha)}$	$W\cdot\frac{2\alpha+3}{8(\alpha+2)}$
	Hinged	Stiff	0	0	$-\frac{3}{16}WL$	$-\frac{5}{16}WL$	$\frac{5}{16}W$
	Hinged	Flexible	0	0	$-\frac{3}{8}WL\cdot\frac{\alpha+2}{2\alpha+3}$	$-\frac{WL}{8}\cdot\frac{5\alpha+6}{2\alpha+3}$	$\frac{W}{8}\cdot\frac{5\alpha+6}{2\alpha+3}$
	Fixed	Hinged	$\frac{5}{16}WL$	$\frac{3}{16}WL$	0	0	$\frac{3}{16}W$

The cases for stiff-cap beams are derived from the cases for flexible beams by taking the limit for $\alpha=\infty$, and those for hinged-cap beams by writing $\alpha=0$, but these cases may be solved independently more easily than the general cases. The points A, B, C, D are those indicated in Figs. 227–229. H is the horizontal reaction on the leeward stanchion; $\alpha=I_b L/Il$. In the case of a wind load P, say, write $W=\frac{1}{2}P$ in the first five cases, and $W=P$ in the last five cases. The signs of the bending moments on the beam at C are opposite to those on the stanchion at C.

the base, and $\frac{1}{2}$W half-way along the stanchion. Hence, equating the deflections of the stanchion tops, using Art. 80

$$\frac{1}{3} \cdot \frac{HL^3}{EI} = \frac{W}{4} \cdot \frac{L^3}{3EI} + \frac{W}{2} \cdot \left(\frac{L}{2}\right)^3 \frac{1}{3EI} + \frac{W}{2}\left(\frac{L}{2}\right)\frac{1}{2EI} - \frac{1}{3} \cdot \frac{HL^3}{EI}$$

hence $H = \frac{13}{64}W$, whereas for uniform distribution we had $H = \frac{3}{16}W$. Thus for a single intermediate wall support the value of H falls from $\frac{16}{64}W$ to $\frac{13}{64}W$ where the limit for a large number of rails is only $\frac{12}{64}W$. For several concentrated horizontal forces F_1, F_2, F_3, etc., on the windward stanchion at distances n_1L, n_2L, n_3L, etc., from the base we should have, from Art. 80

$$\frac{1}{3} \cdot \frac{HL^3}{EI} = \frac{L^3}{3EI} \Sigma(Fn^3) + \frac{L^3}{2EI} \Sigma\{ Fn^2(1-n)\} - \frac{HL^3}{3EI}$$

or $H = \frac{1}{2}\Sigma(Fn^3) + \frac{3}{4}\Sigma\{ Fn^2(1-n)\}$

of which the above is a particular case in which $F_1 = \frac{1}{4}W$, $n_1 = 1$, $F_2 = \frac{1}{2}W$, $n_2 = \frac{1}{2}$. Similar rules may be framed for the other types of support, but the extreme cases of concentration at the two ends and complete distribution will be sufficient guide for estimation of H in any case.

Stiff Open Bracing: Hinged Bases. The effect of uniform distribution of the load on the structure of the type shown in Figs. 223 to 226 may be briefly noticed. Using the notation of Figs. 223, 225, and 226, we assume that BC is a braced girder so stiff as to resist flexure so that points B and K remain in the same vertical, and likewise C and F, although the portions BK and CF, bend. This enables the slopes at K and F to be written in terms of H and W, where H is the horizontal reaction on the leeward side. Then equating the deflections of K and F say, *i.e.* neglecting the strains in the bracing in comparison with flexure, we find

$$H = \frac{W}{16} \cdot \frac{L^2 + 5Lh - h^2}{Lh} \quad \ldots \ldots \quad (13)$$

The transverse pull of the bracing at the foot of the knee bracing (point K, Fig. 223) on the windward stanchion is found by moments about the hinged top, and is $(\frac{1}{2}W - H)\dfrac{L}{L-h}$, and subtracting this from H gives the thrust at the top. The transverse forces on the leeward stanchion are as in Fig. 223 (*c*), writing H for H_1. If h approaches L, H approaches its lowest value, which is $\frac{5}{16}W$, in agreement with (1).

Stiff Open Bracing: "Fixed" Bases. By similar methods for uniformly distributed loads, using Art. 80 for the transverse forces on the stanchions, taking H the horizontal reaction on the leeward stanchion and P' the horizontal pull of the foot of the bracing on the windward stanchion as unknown quantities, and equating all the deflections at B, K, C, and F, we find

$$H = \frac{W}{8} \cdot \frac{3L^3 + 7L^2h - 5Lh^2 + h^3}{Lh(4L - h)} \quad \ldots \quad (14)$$

which of course approaches the value $H = \frac{1}{4}W$ in agreement with (8) when h approaches L.

$$P' = -\frac{W}{16} \cdot \frac{6L^5 - 4L^4h - 17L^3h^2 + 15L^2h^3 - 7Lh^4 + h^5}{Lh(L + 2h)(4L - h)(L - h)} \quad (15)$$

The thrust of the foot of the bracing on the leeward stanchion will be as given by P in (2) Art. 166, the value (14) being used for H, which gives

$$P = \frac{W}{16} \frac{(3L^3 + 7L^2h - 5Lh^2 + h^3)(2L^2 + 2Lh - h^2)}{Lh(4L - h)(L - h)(L + 2h)} \quad (16)$$

With H, P, and P' known, all the other stresses in the bracings and stanchions are easily determined. Perhaps the best method for the bracing would be to find the point of inflexion and then use the graphical solution given in Art. 157.

The assumption of a rigid bracing in comparison with the flexibility of the stanchions would of course only be reasonable for moderately large values of h compared to L. For ordinary values of h/L, H is much less than $\frac{1}{2}W$, *i.e.* the windward stanchion carries much more than half the load.

In some open structures there may be equal distributed loads W on *each* stanchion. In such cases by symmetry $H = W$; hence the horizontal force P at K (Figs. 223 to 225) is equal to the horizontal force $P - H$ at B; hence, for Fig. 224

$$P = \frac{W}{8} \frac{(3L^3 + 3L^2h - 3Lh^2 + h^3)}{(L - h)(L + 2h)L} \quad \ldots \quad (17)$$

and

$$x_0 = L - \sqrt{\frac{(3L^3 + 3L^2h - 3Lh^2 + h^3)}{4(L + 2h)}} \quad \ldots \quad (18)$$

In all such cases the effects upon each stanchion may be found by adding the effects for the windward and leeward stanchions in the cases where W acts on only one stanchion. Thus the result (17) may be found by adding (15) and (16).

The foregoing results in symbols cover many cases of rigid frames. To extend them to unsymmetrical cases would be laborious and take much space. An example will sufficiently illustrate how to deal with such cases by the principles already used.

Example. Open Rectangular Frame. If the stanchion CD in Fig. 228 were twice as long as AB (*i.e.* CD = 2L), BC = l = AB = L,

and EI constant throughout the frame, find the component supporting forces at A and D.

$$M_C=2HL; \qquad M_B=L(H-\tfrac{1}{2}W)$$

Proceeding as at (2), (3), (4), and (5), from (12) of Art. 88

$$i_B=-l(2M_B+M_C)/(6EI)=Ll(W-4H)/(6EI)$$
$$i_C=l(M_B+2M_C)/(6EI)=Ll(5H-\tfrac{1}{2}W)/(6EI)$$

Deflection at $C=2Li_C+8HL^3/(3EI)=L^2l(10H-W)/(6EI)+$
$$8L^3/(3EI)$$

Deflection at $B=Li_B+(W-H)L^3/(3EI)-WL^3/(8EI)$
$$=L^2l(W-4H)/(6EI)+WL^3/(3EI)-WL^3/(8EI)-$$
$$HL^3/(3EI)$$

Putting $l=L$, and equating the deflections at B and C we find at D,
$H=\frac{13}{128}W$; at A, $W-H=\frac{115}{128}W$.

Taking moments about A, $W\times\tfrac{1}{2}L+\frac{13}{128}WL-V_DL=0$; $V_D=\frac{77}{128}W$ (upward).

Taking moments about D to check, $W\times1\cdot5L-\frac{115}{128}WL-V_AL=0$; $V_A=\frac{77}{128}W$ (downward).

160. Wind Stresses in more Complex Structures. The methods
of Arts 158 and 159 may be applied to the analysis of the stresses in
more complex frames, but where more members are introduced the

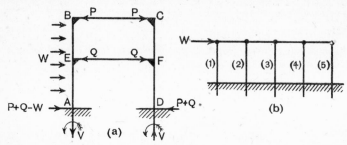

Fig. 230

solution becomes more complex and practically too difficult. An
example will suffice to illustrate the application to more complex
forms, which by different combinations of hinged and rigid attachments might be greatly extended. Fig. 230 (a) represents two
stanchions AB and CD fixed in direction at their bases A and D,
and connected by two cross-beams BC and EF rigidly attached to
the stanchions. Suppose a horizontal load W either concentrated
or distributed to act on AB. Let P and Q represent the thrust
(positive or negative) in BC and EF respectively. Then selecting as
unknown quantities P, Q, and the bending moments at B, C, F, and
E, we can form six equations to find these unknown quantities as

follows: i_B and i_E for the stanchion may be written from Art. 80. Assuming rigid connections, these may be equated to i_B and i_E for the beam written from (13), Art. 88. Two similar equations may be written for C and F, and finally two more may be formed by equating the deflection at B to that at C, and the deflection at E to that at F, all the four deflections being written from Art. 80.

Steel building frames of several stories are too complex for exact calculation, and the connections do not warrant the assumption of rigid joints, and various empirical approximations have to be used. Fig. 230 (*b*) represents say $(n-1)$ portals, consisting of n stanchions connected by beams across their caps. If F is the transverse horizontal force taken by any stanchion, then its deflection is $FL^3/(3EI)$, which must be the same for each if the load W is concentrated at the windward stanchion cap; hence for equal lengths F/I must be the same for each and the sum of the thrusts F balances W; hence for the mth stanchion

$$F = \frac{WI_m}{I_1 + I_2 + I_3 + \ldots + I_n} \quad \ldots \quad (1)$$

where the suffixes denote the various stanchions. If all the stanchions are similar, $F = 1/nW$. If the stanchions are not all equal in length I/L^3 will replace I in all the terms of (1).

If the load W is distributed uniformly over the outer stanchion and all the stanchions are similar, the remaining stanchions all take a horizontal thrust H, and equating the deflections of the windward and any other stanchion

$$\frac{WL^3}{8EI} - \frac{(n-1)HL^3}{3EI} = \frac{HL^3}{3EI} \quad \text{hence } H = \frac{3}{8n} . W \quad . \quad . \quad (2)$$

or $\tfrac{3}{4} . W/2n$, *i.e.* $\tfrac{3}{4}$ of the load which would be borne by the stanchions if $\tfrac{1}{2}W$ is transferred to the windward stanchion cap.

If the load W is uniformly distributed, let H be the thrust in the first beam, then

$$\frac{WL^3}{8EI_1} - \frac{HL^3}{3EI_1} = \frac{HL^3}{3E(I_2 + I_3 + I_4 + \ldots + I_n)} \quad . \quad . \quad (3)$$

Hence

$$H = \tfrac{3}{8}W . \frac{I_2 + I_3 + I_4 + \ldots + I_n}{I_1 + I_2 + I_3 + \ldots + I_n} \quad \text{or} \quad \tfrac{3}{8}W \Sigma_n^2(I) \div \Sigma_n^1(I) . \quad (4)$$

the horizontal force taken by any, say the mth, stanchion from (1) being

$$F = H \times I_m \div \Sigma_n^2(I) = \tfrac{3}{8}WI_m \div \Sigma_n^1(I) \quad . \quad . \quad . \quad (5)$$

which gives the value (2) in the case of similar stanchions. Here again for stanchions of unequal lengths I will be replaced by I/L^3.

Q*

161. Applications to Steel Buildings. In applying the analysis in the foregoing articles to the estimation of wind stresses in the stanchions and roofs of steel buildings, it is difficult to know how far any particular condition of fixture or rigidity will be realised. For the purpose of design some rough estimate is made upon the safest assumption, but without a thorough understanding of the problem it is dangerous to make simple assumptions which, while being on the side of safety for one element of the structure, may be quite unsafe for another. Thus the assumption that the roof is rigid to compression between its supports is on the safe side for the estimation of the leeward stanchion stresses (which are often greater than those on the windward stanchion); it is on the wrong side for estimation of the windward stanchion bending moments; for to take the other extreme, if the roof offers little resistance to horizontal compression, lacking other connections, the windward stanchion will carry nearly the whole wind load. Again, the condition of " fixed " direction at the base of a stanchion depends upon anchorage or fastening at the foot (see Art. 175), and upon an absolutely rigid foundation; probably it is never *fully* attained. This fact is equivalent to a lowering of the point of inflexion and consequent increase of the bending moment at the foot of a kneebrace (see (*c*), Fig. 224), or at the rigid cap connection (see Fig. 229); but to assume it would be to presume a diminished moment at the base (see (*c*), Fig. 224) and might be unsafe. Thus to assume in Fig. 224 that I_2 is lowered to half-way between F and D (a common recommendation) is for the purpose of computing the maximum moment on the stanchion to assume the most favourable possible conditions, *i.e.* to make the *least* safe assumption. To assume the base hinged (I_2 lowered to D) is the safest assumption (see Fig. 223, (*d*)), but may be unnecessarily wasteful in material.

Roof attached to Stanchion Caps only. If there is nothing amounting to a kneebrace the maximum bending moment on the stanchions due to wind load, assuming a stiff roof, will be given by the Table in Art. 159, half the horizontal roof load being assumed to be taken at the end of each stanchion and the transverse loads on the windward stanchion according to circumstances. The most severe condition is the hinged base and rigid top, the maximum value occurring at the top of the leeward stanchion $M_C = -L \times (\frac{1}{2}$ horizontal roof load $+\frac{5}{16}$ wall load). The stresses in the roof bracing may be determined as in Arts. 122, 123, and 127. The effect of the wind load on the walls is to bring a thrust H horizontally (transmitted to the leeward stanchion) upon the roof; the effect of this is evidently opposite to that of the normal wind and the vertical loads upon the roof, *i.e.* it will reduce the wind and dead-load stresses. Unless the conditions were such as to cause a possible reversal of stress in the ties this effect would generally be neglected. If taken into account with the wind load the *least* value of H should be chosen as external horizontal thrusts at B and C. There will be of course, with rigid attachments, some bending moment on the main rafters.

Kneebraced Roof. The wind stresses on the kneebraces may be estimated as explained in Arts. 155 and 156, taking the horizontal component of the wind load as divided between the two stanchions. In addition, there are the stresses similarly determined from the distributed wind load on the stanchions by using the values of H, P', and P given by (13), (14), and (15) in Art. 159. It will generally be nearly correct to assume that half the horizontal wind force on the roof is concentrated at the top of the windward stanchion, and to apportion the side load as explained in Art. 120 at the top of the stanchion and the foot of the kneebrace. The vertical components of the reactions at the feet or at the tops of the stanchions are easily calculated by moments after the points of inflexion have been determined. When the stress in a kneebrace has been calculated it is easy to draw the complete stress diagram, remembering that the stress in the stanchion may be split into a vertical thrust and a horizontal shearing force.

Graphical Method. The method given in Art. 157 may be applied for finding the wind stresses in a kneebraced roof if the stanchion bases are assumed to be hinged or if the points of inflexion are calculated or assumed. Thus if the loads in Fig. 231 are known the external-force diagram 1234567 may be set out. The reactions 7, 18, and 18, 1 at the base of the stanchions may be found in various ways subject to the condition that their horizontal components are equal, *e.g.* one vertical component may be calculated by moments about the hinged base of the other stanchion. Then the addition of the fictitious dotted members 1—27, 27—26 and 2—26, etc., enables the complete stress diagram to be drawn and the stresses in the internal bracing to be found. The lower stress diagram in Fig. 231 represents the case of flexible braces so that the stress in 18–10 is zero, that in 18–25 being thereby greatly increased. Member 7–18 the leeward stanchion of course then exerts only a vertical force 7–18 at its cap.

Fig. 232 shows the process for the same roof and loads when the stanchions are " fixed " at their bases, the points of inflexion being found by (3), Art. 156, or assumed to be half way between the base and the foot of the kneebrace.

In Fig. 231 the reactions are determined graphically by setting off the resultant wind pressure at QS to intersect the frame centre line at P, joining P to A, meeting a vertical through Q in N; then a horizontal projection of N on the centre line gives T such that,

for stiff braces, TQ gives the reaction (7–18) at D and ST (18–1)
that at A. For flexible braces, SN gives the reaction, (18–1), at A
and NQ that, (7–18), at D. By resolving QS into vertical and
horizontal components at P, the proof of the construction will

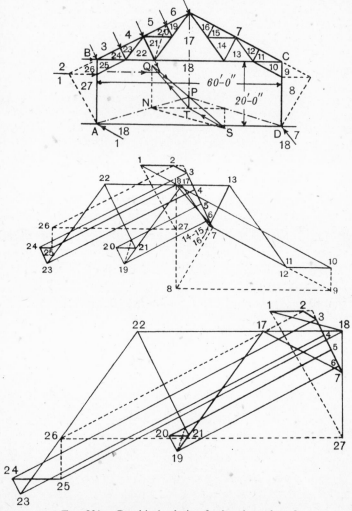

FIG. 231.—Graphical solution for kneebraced roof

become obvious, for the former gives equal components at A and D,
and the latter gives the equal horizontal plus equal and opposite
vertical components or reactions directed through the hinges
toward P.

Example 1.   A French roof truss of 60-ft. span, 15 ft. rise, and no camber of the ties (Fig. 231), is attached to stanchions 20 ft. high and braced as shown, the kneebraces meeting the stanchions 4·75 ft. below the caps, and the principals are 10 ft. apart.   Find the wind

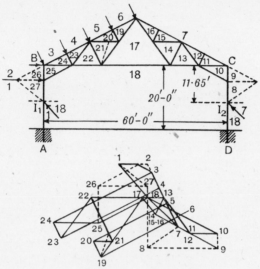

FIG. 232.—Case of " fixed " bases

stresses in the kneebraces and remaining members, and the maximum bending moment in the leeward stanchion, with a horizontal wind pressure estimated at 50 lb. per sq. ft.

Wind pressure normal to the slope ((7), Art. 117) is $50 \times 26·5/45 = 29·41$ lb. per sq. ft.

Wind load per node.

$$= \tfrac{1}{4} \times \frac{30 \times \sqrt{5} \times 10}{2} \times 29·4 = 2{,}475 \text{ lb.} = 1·10 \text{ ton, say}$$

Horizontal pressure on wall at eaves

$$= \frac{4·75}{2} \times 10 \times 50 = 1{,}187 \text{ lb.} = 0·53 \text{ ton.}$$

Horizontal pressure on wall at foot of brace
$$= 10 \times 10 \times 50 = 5{,}000 \text{ lb.} = 2·24 \text{ tons.}$$

By moments about A, vertical reaction at D

$$= \frac{1}{60} \left\{ (4·48 \times 10) + \left(4·40 \times \frac{2}{\sqrt{5}} \times 15 \right) + \left(4·40 \times \frac{1}{\sqrt{5}} \times 27·5 \right) \right\}$$
$$= 2·632 \text{ tons.}$$

Hence the point 18 is determined after 1, 2, 3, 4, 5, 6, 7, have been set off in Fig. 231, for it lies 2·632 tons above the point 7 and half-way horizontally to 1, and the remainder of the diagram is drawn as shown. To check the kneebrace stresses, the distance of the brace 18–25 from B is measured or calculated as 4·28 ft. Omitting the force carried directly at A, total horizontal force $=(4\cdot40/\sqrt{5})+0\cdot53+2\cdot24=4\cdot74$ tons, and taking half this or 2·37 tons as horizontal reaction at A and D, by a section through B and moments about B, tension in the windward brace (18–25)

$$=(2\cdot37\times20-2\cdot24\times4\cdot75)/4\cdot28=8\cdot6 \text{ tons.}$$

And similarly by moments about C, thrust in the leeward brace (18–10)

$$=2\cdot37\times20/4\cdot28=11\cdot1 \text{ tons.}$$

Checking the centre tie 17–18, by moments about the vertex, of forces on the right-hand half of the roof, the tension in the tie is

$$(2\cdot632\times30-2\cdot37\times35)/15=-0\cdot27 \text{ ton}$$

i.e. 0·27 ton thrust as in the diagram. This result is partly due of course to the flexibility of the standards, diminishing the effect of the normal wind pressure on the slope which produces tension; for wind stresses in the roof bracing it would be safer to assume rigid supports. Actually the structure is indeterminate, and computations taking account of the elasticity of the roof truss and stanchions would give an intermediate result. The maximum bending moment on the leeward stanchion is $2\cdot37\times15\cdot25=36\cdot1$ ton-ft.

We may briefly examine the effect of complete distribution (uniform) of the horizontal wind pressure. In (13), Art. 159, we have $h=15\cdot25$ ft., $L=20$ ft., for the horizontal wind pressure $W=4\cdot48$ tons, hence $H=0\cdot56\times4\cdot48=2\cdot51$ tons; adding half the horizontal roof pressure $\frac{1}{2}\times4\cdot40/\sqrt{5}$, *i.e.* 0·99 ton gives a leeward reaction of $2\cdot51+0\cdot99=3\cdot5$ tons instead of 2·37 tons. The maximum bending moment on the leeward stanchion will be proportionally increased to $3\cdot5\times15\cdot25=53\cdot5$ ton-ft., and the thrust in the leeward kneebrace would be

$$3\cdot5\times20/4\cdot28=16\cdot3 \text{ tons or nearly 50 per cent. greater.}$$

The tension in the windward kneebrace will be reduced by distribution of the pressure to

$$\{(4\cdot48-2\cdot51+0\cdot99)\times20-(4\cdot48\times10)\}/4\cdot28=3\cdot4 \text{ tons.}$$

With flexible braces incapable of taking thrust this would be

$$\{(4\cdot48+4\cdot40/\sqrt{5})20-4\cdot48\times10\}/4\cdot28=19\cdot7 \text{ tons.}$$

Example 2. Find the stresses in Example 1 if the stanchions are fixed in direction at their bases.

For an approximate graphical solution it is assumed that the heights of the points of inflexion are in both stanchions given by (3), Art. 156, viz.

$$(15 \cdot 25/2) \times (40 + 15 \cdot 25)/50 \cdot 5 = 8 \cdot 35 \text{ ft.} = A \cdot I_1 \text{ (on Fig. 232).}$$

Pressure at eaves $= 0 \cdot 53$ ton as before.

Pressure at foot of kneebrace $= 10 \times \frac{1}{2}(20 - 8 \cdot 35)50 = 2,915$ lb. $= 1 \cdot 3$ ton.

By moments about I_1 the vertical leeward reaction is

$$\frac{1}{60}\left\{\left(2 \cdot 6 \times \frac{11 \cdot 65}{2}\right) + \left(4 \cdot 40 \times \frac{2}{\sqrt{5}} \times 15\right) + \left(4 \cdot 40 \times \frac{1}{\sqrt{5}} \times 19 \cdot 15\right)\right\}$$

$$= 1 \cdot 86 \text{ tons}$$

from which the point 18 is found, allowing half the effective horizontal forces, *i.e.* loads above the level $I_1 I_2$ in each reaction, viz.

$$\tfrac{1}{2}(1 \cdot 3 + 0 \cdot 53 + 4 \cdot 40/\sqrt{5}) = 1 \cdot 9 \text{ ton.}$$

Checking the thrust in the leeward kneebrace 18–10, by moments about the cap, thrust

$$= (11 \cdot 65 \times 1 \cdot 9)/4 \cdot 28 = 5 \cdot 3 \text{ tons.}$$

Examining the effect of uniform distribution of the load on the stanchion from (14), Art. 159, the horizontal wind load transmitted to the leeward stanchion base is $0 \cdot 2935 \times 4 \cdot 48 = 1 \cdot 315$ ton, and adding half the horizontal roof pressure gives $1 \cdot 315 + 0 \cdot 99 = 2 \cdot 305$ tons. Hence from (1) and (2), Art. 156, the height of I_2 is as before, $8 \cdot 35$ ft., and the thrust in the leeward kneebrace is proportionally increased to

$$(11 \cdot 65 \times 2 \cdot 305)/4 \cdot 28 = 6 \cdot 28 \text{ tons.}$$

The height of I_2 is slightly modified by considering the load as distributed.

162. Vertical Loads on Rectangular Frames.[1]

The bending stresses in a stanchion due to vertical loads on horizontal cross-beams can be found by the same principles as were used in Arts. 158 and 159. The maximum stresses may be estimated in accordance with Art. 109, combining all the bending moments and the total thrust. Sometimes the bending stresses in stanchions are so great that the direct thrust may not be of very great importance.

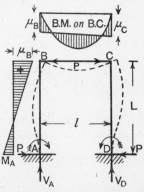

FIG. 233.—Vertical load on rectangular frame

Stanchions with Caps connected by Cross-Beam. Bases " Fixed" (Fig. 233).   Let the load on the

[1] See footnote to Art. 159.

horizontal beam BC of length l rigidly attached to the stanchion caps B and C be such that it would give a bending-moment diagram of area A with centroid distant $\bar{x}$ from B (see Art. 82, section (c)) if BC were freely supported at its ends. Let μ stand for the positive bending moment on the beam, then the clockwise couples applied to the left- and right-hand stanchions are μ_B and $-\mu_C$ respectively. Neglecting the longitudinal compressibility of the beam, the horizontal deflections of B and C are equal, or if P=thrust in the beam and I=moment of inertia of the stanchion section, from Art. 80

$$\frac{\mu_B L^2}{2EI} - \frac{PL^3}{3EI} = -\frac{\mu_C L^2}{2EI} + \frac{PL^3}{3EI} \quad \dots \quad (1)$$

hence

$$\mu_B + \mu_C = \tfrac{3}{4}PL \quad \dots \dots \quad (2)$$

Also

$$i_B = \frac{\mu_B L}{EI} - \frac{PL^2}{2EI} \quad i_C = -\frac{\mu_C L}{EI} + \frac{PL^2}{2EI} \quad \dots \quad (3)$$

$$i_B - i_C = (\mu_B + \mu_C)\frac{L}{EI} - \frac{PL^2}{EI} \quad \dots \dots \quad (4)$$

But if I_b=moment of inertia of the beam section from (13A), Art. 88

$$i_B - i_C = -\frac{A}{EI_b} - (\mu_B + \mu_C)\frac{l}{2EI_b} \quad \dots \quad (5)$$

and equating (4) and (5)

$$P = -\frac{A}{Ll} \cdot \frac{3}{\alpha+2} \quad \dots \dots \quad (6)$$

where α is the ratio $\dfrac{I_b}{l}$ to $\dfrac{I}{L}$ or $\dfrac{I_b L}{Il}$. Hence from (3) above, and (13), Art. 88

$$\mu_B = -\frac{A}{l}\left\{\frac{8+15\alpha-6(\alpha+2)\bar{x}/l}{(6\alpha+1)(\alpha+2)}\right\} \quad \dots \quad (7)$$

$$\mu_C = -\frac{A}{l}\left\{\frac{6(\alpha+2)(\bar{x}/l)-4+9\alpha}{(6\alpha+1)(\alpha+2)}\right\} \quad \dots \quad (8)$$

The bending-moment diagrams are shown in Fig. 233.

If α is small, i.e. the stanchions are very rigid compared to the beam, putting $\alpha=0$, these reduce to the values (6) and (7) of Art. 88 for the built-in beam. If the loading is symmetrical

$$\bar{x}=\tfrac{1}{2}l, \quad \mu_B = \mu_C = -\frac{2A}{l(\alpha+2)} \quad \dots \dots \quad (9)$$

$M_A = \mu_B - PL$, which is equal to $\tfrac{1}{2}\mu_B$ for symmetrical loading, the point of inflexion being $\tfrac{1}{3}L$ from A as in (10), Art. 90 (with $n=1$), to which the stanchion reduces for symmetrical loading.

Alternatively, the foregoing results can be obtained by the method of Minimum Strain Energy (as in Art. 159). The expressions for M in each of the ranges AB, BC, and CD are written down and from them the total (flexural) strain energy U is obtained. If, say, P, V_D, and M_A (or μ_B) are chosen as independent variables the three simultaneous equations $\partial U/\partial P = 0$, $\partial U/\partial V_D = 0$, and $\partial U/\partial M_A = 0$ may be solved for P, V_D, and M_A and then μ_B, μ_C, M_D and V_D may be found by equations of moments.

Hinged Bases. Using the letters of Fig. 233, in this case $\mu_A = \mu_D = 0$, $\mu_B = PL = \mu_C$; the deflections at B and C are

$$L \cdot i_B - \frac{PL^3}{3EI} \quad \text{and} \quad L \cdot i_C + \frac{PL^3}{3EI} \quad . \quad . \quad . \quad (10)$$

hence

$$i_B - i_C = \frac{2PL^2}{3EI} \quad . \quad . \quad . \quad . \quad (11)$$

and equating this to (5) gives $P = -\dfrac{A}{lL} \cdot \dfrac{3}{3+2\alpha} \quad . \quad . \quad . \quad (12)$

and

$$\mu_B = \mu_C = -\frac{A}{l} \cdot \frac{3}{3+2\alpha} \quad . \quad . \quad . \quad (13)$$

This might alternatively be solved by integrating equation (2) Art. 78, for each stanchion under the conditions that the deflections are zero at the bases, and equal at the caps, and that the slopes at the caps are given by equation (3) when $\mu_B = \mu_C = PL$. These five conditions determine the four constants of integration and give an equation to find P.

Example 1.   On the same structure a load W at nl from the left-hand stanchion (B).

From (23) and (24) of Art. 88

$$A = -\tfrac{1}{2}Wl^2 n(1-n); \quad \bar{x}/l = \tfrac{1}{3}(1+n)$$

Substituting these values in (7)

$$\mu_B = \tfrac{1}{2}Wln(1-n)\{4+13\alpha-2n(\alpha+2)\}/\{(6\alpha+1)(\alpha+2)\}$$

$$M_A = \mu_B - PL = \mu_B + (A/l)\{3/(\alpha+2)\}$$

$$= \tfrac{1}{2}Wln(1-n)\left\{\frac{1-5\alpha-2n(\alpha+2)}{(6\alpha+1)(\alpha+2)}\right\}$$

Also, taking moments about C

$$\mu_C = \mu_B + W(1-n) - V_A l$$

$$V_A l = W(1-n) + \mu_B - \mu_C$$

Hence substituting for μ_B and μ_C

$$V_A = W(1-n)\left\{1 + \frac{n(1-2n)}{6\alpha+1}\right\}$$

Similarly

$$V_D = Wn \left\{ 1 - \frac{(1-n)(1-2n)}{6\alpha+1} \right\}$$

$$P = \frac{1}{L} \left\{ \frac{3}{2} \frac{Wln(1-n)}{\alpha+2} \right\} = \frac{3}{2} W \frac{l}{L} \frac{n(1-n)}{\alpha+2}$$

For example, if $n = \frac{1}{4}$ and $\alpha = 1$

$$\mu_B = 0\cdot0692Wl. \qquad \mu_C = 0\cdot0558Wl.$$

The bending moment under the load is $\frac{3}{16}Wl - \mu_C - \frac{3}{4}(\mu_B - \mu_C)$
$= 0\cdot1216Wl$.

If $\alpha = 0$ (*i.e.* very stiff stanchions), $\mu_B = \frac{9}{64}Wl$, $\mu_C = \frac{3}{64}Wl$, as in Example 1, Art. 88.

Symmetrical Frames and Loading. If the portal frame and its loading are both symmetrical about a central vertical axis the bending moments at the joints of the frame and bases of the stanchions would be the same as those in a continuous straight beam formed by rotating the vertical stanchions into line with the horizontal cross-beam. Thus if in Fig. 233 there is a total load W uniformly spread on the beam BC and say $(I_bL)/(Il) = \alpha = 1$ (say $L = l$ and $I_b = I$), then

$$A = -\tfrac{2}{3}Wl^2/8 = -Wl^2/12$$

Hence from (9)

$$\mu_B = \mu_C = +Wl/18$$

and from (12)

$$P = Wl/(12L)$$

$$M_A = \mu_B - PL = Wl/18 - Wl/12 = -Wl/36$$

If ABCD be taken as a straight continuous beam, from the Theorem of Three Moments (6), of Art. 91,

$$M_A + 4M_B + M_C = \tfrac{1}{4}wl^2 = \tfrac{1}{4}Wl$$

and since by symmetry $M_C = M_B$

$$M_A + 5M_B = \tfrac{1}{4}Wl$$

From (7), Art. 91, M_A being fixed in direction

$$2M_A + M_B = 0 \text{ (since there is no load on AB).}$$

Hence $M_B = Wl/18$; $M_A = -Wl/36$ as for the portal above.

Unsymmetrical Cases. Side sway. The foregoing simplification from a portal to a straight beam will only hold good if B and C (Fig. 233) remain fixed in position, *i.e.* if there is no *sway* or movement of the frame to the right or left, as there is when the portal itself or the loading is unsymmetrical. If there is side sway, it is still possible to employ the methods applicable to continuous beams but an important correction is required. This will be explained by means of a simple example. In Fig. 233, let the vertical load on the beam be W at $\frac{1}{4}l$ from B (*i.e.* let $n = \frac{1}{4}$ in Example 1 above) and let the lengths of the beam and stanchions be equal ($l=L$) and let $I_b=I$. Thus $\alpha=1$.

Then treating ABCD as a straight continuous beam and using the symbols of Art. 92, $l_1=l_2=l_3=l$

$$A_1=A_3=0; \quad 6A_2\bar{x}_2/l=+\tfrac{1}{4}\times\tfrac{3}{4}\times\tfrac{7}{4}Wl^2=\tfrac{21}{64}Wl^2$$

From (4) Art. 92

$$M_A l+2M_B\times 2l+M_C\,.\,l=+\tfrac{21}{64}Wl^2$$
$$M_B l+4M_C l+M_D l=\tfrac{15}{64}Wl^2$$

Also from (4A), Art. 92

$$2M_A+M_B=0 \quad \text{hence } M_A=-\tfrac{1}{2}M_B$$
$$2M_D+M_C=0 \quad \text{hence } M_D=-\tfrac{1}{2}M_C$$

Substituting these in the previous equations

$$M_B=\tfrac{13}{160}Wl; \quad M_A=-\tfrac{13}{320}Wl; \quad M_C=\tfrac{7}{160}Wl; \quad M_D=-\tfrac{7}{320}Wl$$

These are the bending moments for a straight beam and also for the portal frame if it were supported by a horizontal force, at the level of the cross-beam, just sufficient to prevent side sway of the frame (to the right). Let H be this necessary force, say at C, from right to left to maintain B and C in position. Consider the stanchion AB while each end is held in the line AB and let H_1 be the horizontal reaction of the ground (left to right) at A. The moment of external forces on the stanchion at B is

$$M_B=M_A+H_1L \quad \text{hence } H_1=(M_B-M_A)/L$$

Similarly $\quad M_C=M_D+H_2L$ and $H_2=(M_C-M_D)/L$

where H_2 is the horizontal reaction of the ground, *right to left*, at D.

Since the total horizontal force on the portal frame is zero

$$H+H_2-H_1=0 \quad \text{or} \quad H=H_1-H_2=(M_B-M_A)/L-(M_C-M_D)/L$$
$$H=(\tfrac{13}{160}+\tfrac{13}{320})W-(\tfrac{7}{160}+\tfrac{7}{320})W$$
$$=\frac{39-21}{320}W=\frac{9}{160}W$$

If H be balanced or neutralised by a *sway* force of equal magnitude, left to right in the line BC, we shall have no resultant force on the structure and it only remains to calculate the effects of this force and to add them to those found by the Theorem of Three Moments. The effects of such a force have been investigated in Art. 158 and if we write the above value of H in place of W we can refer to the Table in Art. 159. The sway force H will produce at B a bending moment $-\tfrac{1}{2}HL\times 3\alpha/(6\alpha+1)=-\tfrac{1}{2}\times\tfrac{9}{160}Wl\times\tfrac{3}{7}=-\tfrac{27}{2240}Wl$ and at C a bending moment $+\tfrac{27}{2240}Wl$. Hence, finally,

B.M. at B$=(\tfrac{13}{160}-\tfrac{27}{2240})Wl=\tfrac{155}{2240}Wl=0{\cdot}0692Wl$

B.M. at C$=(\tfrac{7}{160}+\tfrac{27}{2240})Wl=\tfrac{125}{2240}Wl=0{\cdot}0558Wl$

These are the values previously found by the direct method in Example 1 above.

The method of moment distribution may be used both in finding the moments on the structure in its locked or unswayed position and then in determining the effects of the sway force to be added.

If the stanchions are of unequal length or unequal section, the slope and deflection method used to obtain the results (6), (7), and (8) will lead to more complicated symbolic expressions. These may be found in the references quoted but the method of moment distribution may be used when numerical data are given. Detailed examples may be found in books on moment distribution.[1]

163. More Complex Rectangular Frames. More complex structures such as shown in Fig. 234 may be solved by the principles of the previous article, but the unknown quantities and equations to find them become more numerous. We may briefly indicate the methods for Fig. 234 and similar structures with rigidly attached cross-beams BC and KF.

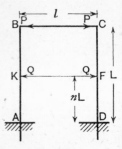

FIG. 234

Case I. A and D " fixed," B and C free except for rigid attachment to the girder. Unknown quantities, moments μ_B, μ_C, μ_K, and μ_F, and thrusts P and Q; i_B for stanchion (see Art. 80)$=i_B$ for beam BC (see Art. 88). Three similar equations for points K, C, and F. Deflections at K and B=deflections at F and C (see Art. 80 for the values).

In case of symmetry, only the equations of slopes at B and K together with deflections at B and K equated to zero are required. There is no side sway.

In this case the equations reduce to

$$\mu_B = -\frac{A_1}{l} - \frac{2\alpha_1(1-n)}{4-n}(\mu_B - \tfrac{1}{2}n\mu_K)$$

$$\mu_K = -\frac{A_2}{l} - \frac{2\alpha_2(1-n)}{4-n}(\mu_K - \tfrac{1}{2}\mu_B)$$

where A_2 and α_2 refer to the bending-moment diagram, and ratio $I_b L/Il$ for the girder KF.

Example. If $\alpha_1 = 1 = \alpha_2$ and $n = \tfrac{1}{2}$ with a central load W on the girder BC only

$$\mu_B = \tfrac{112}{1148}Wl. \qquad \mu_K = \tfrac{126}{1148}Wl.$$

With a central load on the girder KF only

$$\mu_B = \tfrac{7}{1148}Wl. \qquad \mu_K = \tfrac{126}{1148}Wl.$$

[1] *Structural Analysis* by W. F. Cassie (Longmans). " Notes on Some Modern Methods of Structural Analysis," by F. Simpson (*Assoc. of Engng. and Shipbuilding Draughtsmen* : pamphlet).

Case II.   A and D hinged, B and C as before.   The horizontal reactions being P and Q, and equation of moments about B and C gives μ_B and μ_C in terms of the four unknown quantities μ_K, μ_F, P, and Q.   Then equating the deflections at B and C and at K and F as found from i_B and i_C for the girder BC, (13), Art. 88, and again from i_K and i_F for the girder KF, give the equations required.   For symmetrical loading it is only necessary to write the deflections at B and K equal to zero.   There is no sidesway.   In this case the equations reduce to

$$\mu_B = -\frac{A_1}{l} - \frac{(1-n)\alpha_1}{6}\{(3+n)\mu_B - 2n\mu_K\}$$

$$\mu_K = -\frac{A_2}{l} - \frac{n(1-n)\alpha_2}{3}(2\mu_K - \mu_B)$$

Example.   If $\alpha_1 = \alpha_2 = 1$ and $n = \frac{1}{2}$, for a central load W on BC only

$$\mu_B = \tfrac{7}{36}WL. \qquad\qquad \mu_K = \tfrac{1}{72}WL.$$

For a central load W on KF only

$$\mu_B = \tfrac{1}{72}WL \qquad\qquad \mu_K = \tfrac{31}{144}WL$$

Other Cases.   A, B, C, and D all fixed vertically, A, B, C, and D all hinged, A and D fixed vertically, B and C hinged, all form interesting cases with possible applications, and may be worked out on similar lines to those given.

In frames consisting of two stanchions with several equally spaced cross-girders symmetrically loaded, points of inflexion in the stanchions would fall approximately midway between the girders, and a single storey would reduce to the case of A, B, C, D all hinged and $n = \frac{1}{2}$, where L is the distance between successive girders.   If only a single cross-girder of the series were loaded, the length L might be taken as twice the distance between successive cross-girders.

164. Secondary Stresses.[1]   Stresses calculated upon the supposition that frame joints are frictionless pins the axes of which are situated exactly at the intersection of all the elastic lines of the members meeting in each joint, may be called primary stresses, and are first approximations to the stresses in the members of a frame.   Actual frames differ materially from ideal conditions (1) in having either riveted joints, or pin joints which are far from frictionless; (2) in having members the elastic lines of which at some particular joints do not meet in a point, the members being thereby subjected to eccentric pulls or thrusts.   Frames with riveted joints are really statically indeterminate, but second approximations to the stresses

---

[1] For a much fuller treatment of secondary stresses see *Secondary Stresses in Bridge Trusses*, by C. R. Grimme.

in such frames may be calculated after the primary stresses, and the sections are known by estimating approximately the *secondary stresses, i.e.* the stresses produced by deviations from the above ideal conditions. Rigidity of the joints will also considerably modify the deflections (see Art. 145) calculated on the assumption of frictionless joints. Any full treatment of the computation of secondary stresses is necessarily lengthy and beyond the scope of this volume, but secondary stresses have received much attention, and an elementary insight into the principles involved in their estimation may be instructive.

Stresses arising from Rigidity of the Joints. This is perhaps the most important type of secondary stress. If we assume that, instead of being free to turn at their ends, frame members are rigidly held in the same *relative* angular positions at the joints although the joints may have small angular movement due to the strain of the frame, we can estimate the fixing couples at the ends of the members, and hence the secondary bending stresses resulting from the lack of free angular movement.

Thus, for example, a triangular frame ABC (Fig. 235) supports a vertical load at A, the joints A, B, and C being rigid. To simplify the problem, suppose BC is infinitely stiff or that B and C are rigidly fixed to rigid supports. Let $AB=c$, $BC=a$, $AC=b$, and let the primary unit tensile stresses in b and c as found by simple statics be p_b and p_c respectively, so that the extension of b and c are

$$\delta b = b \times \frac{p_b}{E}, \quad \delta c = c \times \frac{p_c}{E}$$

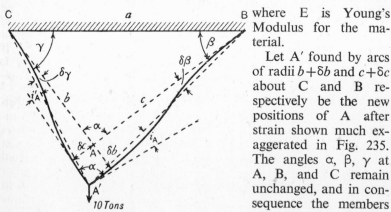

FIG. 235

where E is Young's Modulus for the material.

Let A′ found by arcs of radii $b+\delta b$ and $c+\delta c$ about C and B respectively be the new positions of A after strain shown much exaggerated in Fig. 235. The angles α, β, γ at A, B, and C remain unchanged, and in consequence the members are bent, the tangents to the members at A′, B, and C being inclined to the sides of the triangle A′BC. Let $\alpha+\delta\alpha$, $\beta+\delta\beta$, and $\gamma+\delta\gamma$ be the angles at A′, B, and C of the triangle A′BC. Then, knowing δb and δc, the total increases, $\delta\alpha$, $\delta\beta$, and $\delta\gamma$ are easily calculated geometrically from a diagram or by differentiation of the relation

$$\cos\beta = (a^2 + c^2 - b^2) \div 2ac \quad \ldots \quad (1)$$

For if only b varies, differentiating with respect to b

$$-\sin\beta(\delta\beta/db) = -b/ac$$

hence partially

$$\delta\beta = \frac{b\delta b}{ac\sin\beta} = \frac{\delta b}{b} \cdot \frac{\sin\beta}{\sin\alpha\sin\gamma} = \frac{p_b}{E}(\cot\alpha + \cot\gamma) \quad . \quad (2)$$

And if c varies alone, differentiating (1) with respect to c

$$-\sin\beta\frac{d\beta}{dc} = \frac{c^2 - a^2 + b^2}{2ac^2} = \frac{b}{ac}\cos\alpha$$

hence partially

$$\delta\beta = -\frac{\delta c}{c}\cot\alpha = -\frac{p_c}{E}\cot\alpha \quad \ldots \quad (3)$$

And from (2) and (3) the total variation is

$$\delta\beta = \{p_b(\cot\alpha + \cot\gamma) - p_c\cot\alpha\}/E \quad \ldots \quad (4)$$

a similar value holding for $\delta\gamma$

$$\delta\gamma = \{p_c(\cot\alpha + \cot\beta) - p_b\cot\alpha\}/E \quad \ldots \quad (5)$$

while from (3), with the necessary modification for α

$$\delta\alpha = -(p_c\cot\beta + p_b\cot\gamma)/E \quad \ldots \quad (6)$$

If a varies, the modifications in (4), (5), and (6) are easily made, *e.g.*

$$\delta\alpha = \{(p_a - p_c)\cot\beta + (p_a - p_b)\cot\gamma\}/E$$

similar values holding for $\delta\beta$ and $\delta\gamma$.

We may now write the angle which the strained member makes with the line joining its ends, following as far as possible the convention of signs in Art. 78; thus in Fig. 235

$$i_B = +\delta\beta \; , \quad . \; (7) \qquad i_C = -\delta\gamma \; . \quad . \; (8) \qquad i_A' = +\delta\alpha + i_A \; . \quad . \; (9)$$

i_A being unknown.

Then if M with suffixes stands for bending moments at the joints, from (10) and (11), Art. 88 (putting A=0)

$$M_B = 2(2i_B + i_A)EI/c \qquad M_C = -2(i'_A + 2i_C)EI/b \quad . \quad . \quad (10)$$

$$M_A = -2(i_B + 2i_A)EI/c = 2(2i'_A + i_C)EI/b \quad \ldots \quad (11)$$

which gives four equations to find the four unknown quantities, M_A M_B, M_C, and i_A. Reducing (11) by substituting the values (9), we get

$$i_A = (-b\delta\beta + c\delta\gamma - 2c\delta\alpha) \div 2(b+c) \quad . \quad . \quad (12)$$

$$i_A = (-b\delta\beta + c\delta\gamma + 2b\delta\alpha) \div 2(b+c) \quad . \quad . \quad (13)$$

Whether secondary stresses of this amount will exist in pin-connected frames depends upon whether the friction moment exerted by the pin is capable of withstanding the moments calculated above for the various joints.

Example. Take $a=5$ ft., $b=3$ ft., $c=4$ ft. Load $=10$ tons, sections of AB and AC rectangular 2×1 in., the shorter side being perpendicular to the figure.

From a simple triangle of forces, as in Fig. 211, the primary unit stresses are $p_b = \frac{8}{2} = 4$ tons per sq. in., $p_c = \frac{6}{2} = 3$ tons per sq. in.

And from the triangle ABC, which is right-angled at A

$$\cot \alpha = 0 \qquad \cot \beta = \tfrac{4}{3} \qquad \cot \gamma = \tfrac{3}{4}$$

Substituting in (4)

$$\delta\beta = (4 \times \tfrac{3}{4} - 3 \times 0)/E = 3/E$$

and from (5)

$$\delta\gamma = (3 \times \tfrac{4}{3} - 4 \times 0)/E = 4/E$$

and from (6)

$$\delta\alpha = -(3 \times \tfrac{4}{3} + 4 \times \tfrac{3}{4})/E = -7/E$$

Hence from (7), (8), (12), and (13)

$$i_B = 3/E \qquad i_C = -4/E \qquad i_A = 9/2E \qquad i_A' = -5/2E$$

And from (10), since $I = \frac{1}{12} \times 8 = \frac{2}{3}$

$$M_B = \tfrac{2}{48}(6 + \tfrac{9}{2})I = \tfrac{21}{48} \times \tfrac{2}{3} = \tfrac{7}{24} \text{ ton-in.}$$
$$M_A = -\tfrac{2}{48}(3 + 9)I = -\tfrac{1}{3} \text{ ton-in.}$$
$$M_C = \tfrac{2}{36}(\tfrac{5}{2} + 8)I = \tfrac{7}{18} \text{ ton-in.}$$

Hence, since f the tensile secondary bending stress per square inch on the fibres $= M \div Z$, where $Z = \frac{1}{6} \times 4 = \frac{2}{3}$

at B $f = \tfrac{7}{24} \times \tfrac{3}{2} = \tfrac{7}{16} = 0\cdot4375$ ton per sq. in.

at C $f = \tfrac{7}{18} \times \tfrac{3}{2} = \tfrac{7}{12} = 0\cdot583$,,   ,,

at A $f = -\tfrac{1}{3} \times \tfrac{3}{2} = -\tfrac{1}{2} = -0\cdot50$,,   ,,

If instead of being 2×1 in. the member had been $4 \times \frac{1}{2}$ in., these bending stresses would have been twice the above values, for I and consequently M would have been four times greater, and Z being doubled f would have been doubled. The more slender the members, *i.e.* the smaller the ratio of breadth in the plane of bending to the length, the smaller the secondary stresses due to rigid joints.

Stresses arising from Eccentric Connections. Fig. 236 illustrates a case of secondary stress arising from non-concurrency of the centre lines of members at a joint. Let the axes of the two slender diagonals intersect at a distance h from the axis of a substantial upper boom of a girder. Then, if F is the resultant of the pull and the thrust in the two diagonals, the action is equivalent to a change of direct stress F in the boom together with a moment F . h divided

equally between the two adjacent panel lengths of the upper boom
and ther efore exerting a bending stress such as arises from a bending
moment $\frac{1}{2}Fh$.   Such stresses may reduce or may augment these due
to rigid joints, and may be estimated separately, neglecting the
rigidity of the joints.   Actually the eccentricity will modify the
angles at the joints and affect the secondary stress, but we assume
in Fig. 236 that the boom section is so great compared to that of the
web members that it withstands practically all the bending moment,
which is equivalent to taking the case of web members freely
jointed to the boom.   If the web members are to be taken into
account, we should divide the total amount Fh among the members

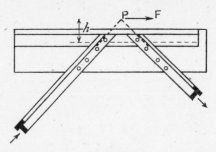

Fig. 236

meeting at the joint in their ratio of their values of I/l, where I
represents the moment of inertia of their cross-sectional areas, and
l their lengths, taking the conditions of end fixture the same for
each.

    There is very frequently a secondary stress of this kind in light
members, such as angles in which the line of rivet centres does not
coincide with the elastic line or " gravity axis " of the member, *e.g.*
the angles in their attachments in Plate I.

    Experimental determinations of the extreme stresses in tie-bars
eccentrically loaded by the pull of plates to which their ends were
riveted, were made by C. Batho.[1]   The position of the line of
resultant pull at a given section was found by strain measurements
at several points on the section, which established the fact that the
stress varied uniformly, *i.e.* according to linear law.   The maximum
unit stress was then found (1) from the linear distribution over the
section, (2) by calculation according to (4) of Art. 100, from the
estimated position of the centre of loading.   The two values were
in close agreement, and were in many cases more than twice the
mean intensity of stress on the section.

[1] " The Distribution of Stress in Certain Tension Members," *Trans. Canadian
Soc. of Civil Engineers*, vol. xxvi, p. 224, April, 1912.   See also " The Effect of the
End Connections on the Distribution of Stress in Certain Tension Members."
Journal of the Franklin Institute, August, 1915.

EXAMPLES XVI

1. A trussed purlin, 18-ft. span, is made of a British Standard Tee 4 × 4 × ⅜ in. with centre steel strut 1 in. diameter and 12 in. long.   The tie-rods are 1 in. diameter round steel; estimate the uniform load per foot length if the unit stress in the Tee is to be limited to 6 tons per sq. in.   What is then the unit stress in the ties and in the strut?

2. Estimate the maximum bending moment on the stanchions of a shed carrying a roof, due to a wind pressure which is 40 lb. per sq. ft. on the wall and 24 lb. normal to the roof.   Length of stanchions 15 ft., rise 8 ft., span 32 ft., distance between principals 20 ft.   The roof is hinged to the stanchions, which are firmly anchored at their bases.   The distributed horizontal wind load is carried directly by the stanchion.

3. Solve Problem No. 2 if the wind load on the walls is transferred to the stanchions at the cap and the base, and an intermediate point midway between the cap and the base.

4. Two vertical steel posts 15 ft. apart and 15 ft. long made of 5 × 3 in. British Standard beam sections (see Appendix, Table I) are hinged at their bases, and their caps are connected by a beam of the same section rigidly attached to each.   If this beam carries a central vertical load of 1 ton, estimate the maximum bending moment on the beam and on the posts.

5. Estimate the deflection of the beam in Problem No. 4.   E = 12,500 tons per sq. in.

6. Solve Problem No. 4 if the bases of the posts are firmly fixed.

7. Solve Problem No. 5 if the bases of the posts are firmly fixed.

8. Find the maximum bending moment on each of the posts and the beam in Problem No. 6 if the load of 1 ton is placed 3 ft. 9 in. from one post.

9. Find the deflection of the posts from the vertical in Problem No. 8. E = 12,500 tons per sq. in.

CHAPTER XVII

FRAME MEMBERS AND STRUCTURAL CONNECTIONS

165. Determination of Sectional Areas. Chapters XII to XVI are mainly devoted to the determination of the gross pull or thrust in the members of frames. When this pull or thrust has been determined the area is found by dividing this total force by the working unit stress. Any corrections for bending due to the weight of members between their ends or other secondary stresses [1] must then be made. The working stress under various conditions of loading causing fluctuations may be fixed by a specification. Some idea of its usual values and its variation with circumstances has been given in Chapter II, but we are now in a position to understand more fully the significance of the various methods of allowing for fluctuation in the load, and Art. 31 may with advantage be again referred to, and further illustrated. The simplest method is to use an equivalent dead load (see (2), Art. 31) equal to the maximum load plus k times the variation of load, whether k is unity or some other factor, such as those given in Art. 31. In this case a working unit stress independent of variation with fluctuation of the load is then employed.

If a member is subjected to both tension and compression the area necessary as a tie and as a strut should be calculated, and the greater value used.

Example 1. Find the sectional areas required for the member CR, Fig. 187, with the loads given in the example at the end of Art. 132, the unit stress being 7·5 tons per sq. in. (*a*) Using the dynamic stress formula. (*b*) Using an impact coefficient of (range of load) ÷ (maximum load).

(*a*) From the example quoted, maximum tension = 88 tons

$$\text{Range} = 88 \cdot 0 - 16 \cdot 3 = 71 \cdot 7 \text{ tons}$$
$$\text{Equivalent dead-load stress} = 159 \cdot 7 \text{ tons}$$
$$\text{Area required} = 159 \cdot 7 / 7 \cdot 5 = 21 \cdot 3 \text{ sq. in.}$$

Which may be provided by say 4 angles $6 \times 4 \times \frac{5}{8}$ in. placed back to back in pairs as in the girder of Plate II.

(*b*) Impact allowance $= 71 \cdot 7 / 88 \times 71 \cdot 7 = 58 \cdot 4$ tons

$$\text{Equivalent load} = 88 + 58 \cdot 4 = 146 \cdot 4 \text{ tons}$$
$$\text{Area required} = 146 \cdot 4 / 7 \cdot 5 = 19 \cdot 5 \text{ sq. in.}$$

[1] See Arts. 164 and 174.

Example 2. Find the sectional area required for the member EP, Fig. 196, with loads as in the example of Art. 132. Unit stress 7·5 tons per sq. in. in tension, $7·5 - 0·025l/k$ in compression. Take (*a*) Dynamic method or impact coefficient unity. (*b*) Impact coefficient = range of load ÷ maximum load.

(*a*) Range of load = $36·5 + 15·6 = 52·1$ tons
    Equivalent dead tensile load = $36·5 + 52·1 = 88·6$ tons
    Area required $88·6/7·5 = 11·8$ sq. in.
    Equivalent dead-load thrust $15·6 + 52·1 = 67·7$ tons.

Assuming that l/k will be about 80 (never exceeding 100), the working unit stress is

$$7·5 - 80 \times 0·025 = 5·5 \text{ tons per sq. in.}$$
    Area required $67·7/5·5 = 12·3$ sq. in.

Thus the section will probably be determined for the thrust. When the member section has been settled, and l/k is definitely known, a check is required to ascertain whether the unit stress is within the required limit $7·5 - 0·025l/k$.

(*b*) Equivalent dead tensile load = $36·5 + (52·1)^2/36·5 = 110·9$ tons
    Area required $110·9/7·5 = 14·8$ sq. in.
    Equivalent dead load thrust = $15·6 + 74·4 = 90$ tons.

Probable area required $90/5·5 = 16·4$ sq. in., the thrust again deciding the area.

This example also illustrates the fact that the design from the above impact coefficient will in the case of reversed stresses give a larger area than the use of the impact factor unity, *i.e.* than the dynamic method.

166. Riveted and Pin-jointed Frames. In Great Britain riveted girders for bridge work are used in almost all cases to the exclusion of pin-jointed frames. In America pin-jointed bridge girders have been much in favour for all comparatively short spans for a variety of reasons, such as cheapness, facility of rapid erection with little work at the site, and limitation of the secondary bending stresses (see Arts. 164 and 174) in the chord members. Recently, however, riveted trusses have been employed more freely; this may be accounted for by many reasons, such as means of handling larger completed pieces, and use of shorter spans owing to diminished cost of piers. Frequently some riveted web members are used in bridge trusses containing pin-connected eyebar members; such eyebars may sometimes be used to avoid the difficulty of a splice in a very large section.

167. Form of Sections for Members. The forms of section most suitable for the different members of a frame are necessarily determined largely by experience, and the types and ranges of section

available.   Practical design of structures involves not only a knowledge of structures, but of methods of manufacture and erection and
of costs, matters of prime importance which are outside the scope of
this volume.   A small selection of important types of braced girder
members is, however, given to illustrate many of the points already
dealt with in the previous chapters.   Typical examples of pin and
riveted connections for roofs have been given in connection with
Plate I, Chapter XII.

Boom Sections.   Fig. 237 shows typical sections for booms,
(*a*) being applicable to rather small girders, (*b*) and (*c*) with many
modifications to larger ones.   The side plates and angles of (*b*) are
often replaced by channel sections, as in the girder of Plate II shown
in section in Fig. 244.   As shown at (*c*), Fig. 237, latticed channels
are also used.   The top chord is usually closed by plates as at (*b*),
while the bottom chord is generally latticed, or quite open to prevent the accumulation of water, being stiffened by transverse dia-

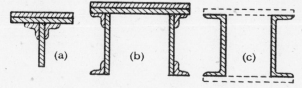

FIG. 237.—Typical boom sections

phragm plates at intervals, attached by angles to the side of the
vertical channels or plates.   The minimum depth of a boom section
is often limited to $\frac{1}{20}$ of a panel length.

Web Member Sections.   The ties are usually flats or angles in
riveted trusses, while in pin-connected frames they are eyebars (see
Art. 174).   The struts are of very varied design, including several of
those shown in Fig. 167.   The attachment of web members to the
booms is sometimes direct, but more frequently by means of gusset
plates as in Plate II.

168. Riveted Joints.   Figs. 238 to 239 inclusive show the commonest forms of riveted joints.   Lap joints are seldom used in
structural steel frames, as they obviously involve eccentricity of the
stress in the members.   Fig. 242 shows four ways in which rupture
may take place, the illustration being drawn from a single riveted
lap joint: (*a*) shows shear of the rivet, in this case exposed to single
shear, *i.e.* shear across one section only, (*b*) illustrates tearing of the
plate, (*c*) crushing of the plate (or the rivet) due to too great a
bearing pressure, while (*d*) shows bursting of the plate due to too
small an overlap, which is easily avoided.

It should be recognized at the outset in dealing with riveted joints that the distribution of shearing stress over the cross-section of a rivet is not known, nor is the distribution among a group always uniform, and that any quoted stress refers to the average over the whole area. A similar remark refers to the direct stress in the plates between rivet holes, and the resistance of the remaining plate is reduced by making the rivet holes. Another factor in the resistance of riveted joints is the frictional resistance of the parts to relative movement. This always strengthens the joint, but is never taken into account. It makes the stress calculations in an additional degree conventional.[1] It is often specified that rivet holes shall be drilled, or punched so much below the required diameter, and then

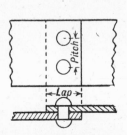
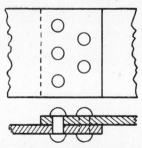

FIG. 238.—Single-riveted lap joint   FIG. 239.—Double-riveted lap joint

drilled out. The argument in favour of punching is that the increased cost of drilling if put into extra metal in the members more than makes good any loss of strength resulting from punching, except in very long spans where dead load becomes increasingly prominent.

Single and Double Shear. In Figs. 238 and 239, and the single-cover butt joint of Fig. 240, the rivets are in single shear, *i.e.* the stress per rivet on either side of the joint is resisted only by one section of a rivet, while in Fig. 241 and in the double-cover butt joint of Fig. 240 the rivets are in double shear, *i.e.* the pull or thrust per rivet on either side of the joint is resisted by two sections. It is usual to allow in cases of double shear a total stress of from 1·5 times to twice that allowed for single shear, specifications varying upon the allowed ratio; 1·75 may be taken as a usual value.

Resistance of a Riveted Joint. (*a*) *To Tearing*

$$b \cdot t \cdot f_t \quad . \quad . \quad . \quad . \quad . \quad . \quad (1)$$

where f_t = working tensile stress in a perforated plate, t = thickness

---

[1] Very interesting attempts have been made by Prof. Cyril Batho to find theoretically, by the methods applicable to statically indeterminate structures, and experimentally by extensometer measurements on the plates, the portions of the total load borne by different members of a group of rivets. See " The Partition of the Load in Riveted Joints," in the *Journal of the Franklin Institute*, Nov., 1916.

of plate, and b=available resisting breadth of plate, *i.e.* the whole breadth minus the diameter of each rivet hole which is effective in reducing the tearing resistance. It is usual to take the diameter of the hole as $\frac{1}{16}$ in. greater than that of the rivet before driving.

(*b*) *To Shearing.* In single shear

$$0.7854nd^2f_s \quad . \quad . \quad . \quad . \quad . \quad . \quad (2)$$

where n=number of rivets on each side of the joint, d=diameter of rivets, f_s=working unit stress in shear allowed in rivets.

In double shear—conventionally taken to be about

$$0.7854 \times 1.75nd^2f_s \quad . \quad . \quad . \quad . \quad (3)$$

It is usual to add a proportion, say 10 to 25 per cent., of rivet area for all rivets driven during erection called " field " rivets.

(*c*) *To Crushing.*

$$n \cdot d \cdot tf_b \quad . \quad . \quad . \quad . \quad . \quad . \quad (4)$$

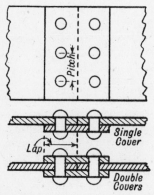

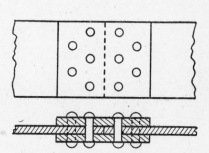

FIG. 240.—Single-riveted butt joint   FIG. 241.—Double-riveted butt joint

where f_b=the allowable unit stress for bearing reckoned on the longitudinal or axial section of the rivet. The stress f_b is usually taken as $2f_s$. The ratio of f_t to f_s is often specified for riveted joints, and may be taken as about 1·2 to 1·4.[1]

The number of rivets required in a given case of direct pull or thrust may be found by equating the smaller of the two resistances, to crushing (4), or shearing (2) or (3), to the resistance (1) to tearing. With the above values a double-covered butt joint will be weaker in shearing so long as $0.7854 \times 1.75d$ is less than $2t$, *i.e.* so long as

d is less than 1·46t, or t is greater than 0·685d.

Usual dead-load values for f_t for mild steel are 6 to 7·5 tons per sq. in., and for f_s 4·5 to 5·5 tons per sq. in.

---

[1] Lower apparent values are deduced from tests to destruction of riveted joints in which the rivet resistance is augmented by friction.

Size of Rivets.   There is no invariable rule as to the size of rivets for structural work.   The diameters vary from $\frac{5}{8}$ in. to $1\frac{1}{8}$ in. according to the thickness of plate and convenience.   The rule $d = 1 \cdot 2\sqrt{t}$ may be taken as some indication of a suitable diameter, but this may be considerably varied to suit circumstances such as a convenient pitch.

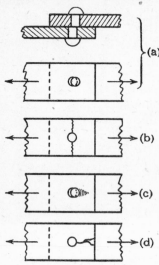

FIG. 242.—Possible failures of lap joints

Limits of Pitch.   Three-inch pitch or possibly three times the rivet diameters is about the minimum space into which $\frac{7}{8}$-in. rivets can conveniently be placed.   And to avoid opening or bulging of the plates a maximum of about sixteen times the thickness of the thinnest plate in the joint is frequently specified for tension and compression, with limits sometimes of 8 in. and 6 in. for these stresses respectively.

169. Grouping of Rivets.   The tearing resistance of the plates of a joint containing a given number of rivets depends upon the arrangement of the rivets.   For example, in Fig. 243 the form (*a*) reduces the effective breadth of the plate to the whole breadth, minus three rivet-hole diameters. The form (*b*) is stronger and only makes a reduction of two holes in the breadth, while (*c*) is the strongest form and only reduces the strength to the extent of one hole.   For before the plates can pull asunder at a section through rivets 2 and 3 the rivet 1 must be sheared, and this generally offers a resistance at least equal to the tensile resistance of the corresponding breadth of plate.[1]   Similarly, fracture of the plate across the diameters of rivets 4, 5, and 6 is resisted by the rivets 1, 2, and 3. The cover plates, on the other hand, are not so assisted, and their

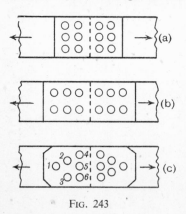

FIG. 243

combined thickness must be such that after perforation their area exposed to tension is at least equal to that of the plate section through

[1] Except in the case of a thick plate with relatively thin rivets.

the rivet hole 1. Their combined thickness generally exceeds that of the plates by 50 per cent.

Example 1. Arrange a suitable double-covered butt joint to splice a $\frac{5}{8}$-in. tie-plate 10 in. wide. Use $\frac{7}{8}$-in. rivets.

Taking the tensile load at 7·5 tons per sq. in., equivalent tensile dead load, allowing one rivet hole $\frac{15}{16}$-in. diameter is

$$(10 - \tfrac{15}{16}) \times \tfrac{5}{8} \times 7\cdot5 = 42\cdot5 \text{ tons.}$$

Stress per $\frac{7}{8}$-in. rivet in double shear, say

$$5 \times 1\cdot75 \times 0\cdot7854 \times (\tfrac{7}{8})^2 = 5\cdot26 \text{ tons.}$$

Number of rivets required $= 42\cdot5 \div 5\cdot26 = 8\cdot1$, say 9 rivets. The joint is shown in Fig. 244.

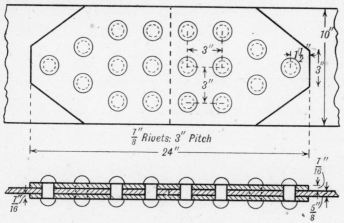

$\frac{7}{8}$" Rivets; 3" Pitch

FIG. 244.—Double-covered butt splice for the plate

Example 2. The member CR (Fig. 187) is subject to an equivalent dead load of 159·7 tons as in Example 1, Art. 165. Allowing 7·5 tons per sq. in. in tension, and 5·5 tons per sq. in. in shear stress in $\frac{7}{8}$-in. rivets, arrange the section and joints to the booms.

Net area required $159\cdot7 \div 7\cdot5 = 21\cdot3$ sq. in.

Using four standard unequal angles $6 \times 4 \times \frac{5}{8}$ in., Table IV, Appendix, gives with one rivet hole in each a net area of $4(5\cdot86 - \frac{15}{16} \times \frac{5}{8}) = 21\cdot12$ sq. in. If $6 \times 4 \times \frac{11}{16}$ in. angles are used there will be a margin above the specification. Using two angles attached to each side of the boom, each joint must withstand $159\cdot7 \div 2 = 79\cdot9$ tons. In single shear the resistance of each rivet is $(\frac{7}{8})^2 \times 0\cdot7854 \times 5\cdot5 = 3\cdot31$ tons.

Number required if in single shear $79\cdot9 \div 3\cdot31 = 24\cdot1$, say 25.

Resistance in bearing per rivet, say $\frac{7}{8} \times \frac{5}{8} \times 11 = 6\cdot01$ tons. Number required $79\cdot9 \div 6\cdot01 = $ say 14 or with $\frac{11}{16}$-in. angles, say 13. The

R

details of a joint are shown in Plate II, member S3, which is of somewhat similar strength to this calculation, having at the upper joint
passing through the gusset plate twelve rivets in double shear and two
in single shear.   But the allowable tension in the member for bear-
ing stress in this joint would be only $\frac{1}{2} \times 14 \times \frac{7}{8} \times 11 = 67 \cdot 4$ tons, the
gusset-plate being $\frac{1}{2}$ in. thick; $\frac{5}{8}$-in. plates would allow the full
79·9 tons.

170. Oblique Attachments.   The centroid of the cross-sectional
areas of a group of rivets should so far as possible lie on the centre
line or gravity axis of the member which the group attaches to
another member.   Otherwise the resistance of the rivets will exert
an eccentric force on the member, thereby subjecting it to bending,
as in Art. 100.   Fig. 245 shows at (a) an undesirable arrangement;

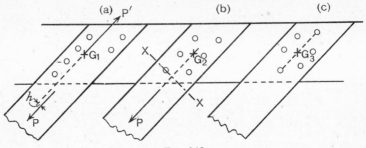

Fig. 245

assuming that all the rivets resist equally, the members are jointly
subjected to a moment $Ph = P' \cdot h$ when the pull passes at a distance
h from the centroid G_1 of the group of rivets.   (See also Art. 164.)
The grouping shown at (b) is frequently adopted as being the only
possible plan to get in the necessary rivets, but across the section XX,
which is reduced by one rivet hole, the pull is not through the centroid of the section of the member, and bending stress accordingly
arises.   The symmetrical form of grouping (about the centre line
of the sloping member) shown at (c) will obviate bending stresses,
except such as arise due to rigidity of the joint, as explained in Art.
164.

171. Flange or Boom Splices.   In making a splice in a boom
consisting of several pieces it is desirable while making the joint in
each piece to come under one set of covers, to arrange that no two
pieces lying next to each other should have their joints at the same
section.   A typical boom joint is shown in Fig. 246 (which represents the joint in the top chord of the girder shown in Plate II, but
is placed on Plate IV).   The channels and the intermediate $\frac{1}{2}$-in.
flange-plate make joint at the same section, but joints of the $\frac{3}{4}$-in.
mainplate and the outer $\frac{5}{16}$-in. plate lie on either side of this section.

172. Torsional Resistance of Rivet Groups. It frequently happens that the attachment of one member of a structure to another by a group of rivets is subjected to a direct pull or thrust, and in addition to a moment in the plane of the rivet cross-sections. In other words, the resultant force transmitted does not pass through the centroid of the rivet cross-sectional areas, but is eccentric. Examples occur in members of a riveted truss the joints of which being rigid cannot turn as if on frictionless pins, and are subject to moments which cause secondary stresses (Art. 164). More obvious cases occur in the attachment of a bracket to a stanchion or in the attachment of a cross-beam to the stanchions or to beams at its ends.

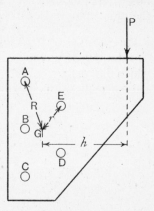

FIG. 247.—Eccentric thrust on group of rivets

Take Fig. 247 to represent a bracket attached to some support by, say, five rivets, A, B, C, D, and E, the centre of gravity or centroid of their cross-sectional areas being at G, two-fifths of the distance between the two centre lines from B. Let h be the eccentricity of a load P from G. Then the rivets jointly resist (1) a direct force P, and (2) a moment Ph. The exact distribution of these actions among the rivets cannot be calculated with any great certainty for many reasons, such as the inexactness of fitting and filling the holes. Taking probable conditions with good fitting, each rivet will exert on the bracket (1) a force equal to one-fifth P and parallel to the direction of P, (2) a force perpendicular to the line joining its centre to G and proportional to the distance from G, the sum of the moments of such forces being equal to and balancing the torsional moment Ph. Let R be the distance from G to the centre of the most distant rivet A, and let F be the force exerted by the rivet A in consequence of the moment Ph or M. Then the force exerted by any rivet such as E, say distant r from G, is

$$F \times r/R \quad . \quad . \quad . \quad . \quad . \quad . \quad (1)$$

and the total moment $M = F \Sigma(r^2)/R$ for all the rivets, hence

$$F = MR \div \Sigma(r^2) \quad . \quad . \quad . \quad . \quad (2)$$

while the force exerted by any rivet E is

$$M \cdot r \div \Sigma(r^2) \quad . \quad . \quad . \quad . \quad . \quad (3)$$

in such a direction as to oppose the moment $M = Ph$ of P, *i.e.* so as to have, as in Fig. 247, a contra-clockwise moment about G. The total force exerted by any rivet such as E is found by adding geometrically the above force (3) to the force one-fifth P opposing P. This addition may be made graphically or by trigonometrical calculation.

More generally, the forces acting on any rivet of n in a group will be $1/n$ of P and M . $r \div \Sigma(r^2)$.

Approximation for a Large Group. The process of finding $\Sigma(r^2)$ for a large group will be tedious. It may be taken as nk^2 where k is the radius of gyration of the circumscribing area about an axis through the centroid G and perpendicular to the cross-section of the group, the area being extended by half a pitch beyond the centre lines in each direction, *e.g.* for nine rows of rivets, 3-in. pitch, with nine rivets in each row. The true value of $\Sigma(r^2)$ (taking the sum of the squares of the distances from two perpendicular axes) is

$$2 \times 2 \times 9(12^2 + 9^2 + 6^2 + 3^2) = 9,720.$$

For the area 27×27 in., $k^2 = \frac{1}{6} \times 27^2 = 121 \cdot 5$, $nk^2 = 81 \times 121 \cdot 5 = 9,841$, which differs from 9,720 by just over 1 per cent.

Example 1.   Fig. 248 shows one of a pair of angle cleats $6 \times 3\frac{1}{2} \times \frac{3}{8}$

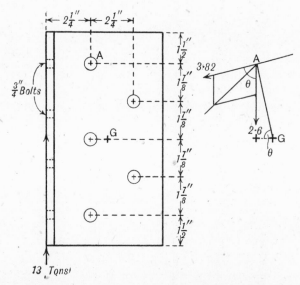

Fig. 248.—Maximum stress in rivets of angle-cleat connection.

in. by which each end of the webs of an I beam carrying a uniformly distributed load of 26 tons is attached by bolts to supports at its ends. Find the maximum stress taken by any of the five rivets attaching the two cleats to either side of the beam.

Assuming a purely vertical reaction of 13 tons (half the load) at the back of the angle,[1] exerted by the bolts, the eccentricity is $2\frac{1}{4}+\frac{2}{5}\times2\frac{1}{4}=3\cdot15$ in., hence the moment is $13\times3\cdot15=40\cdot95$ ton-in. Any term r^2 in $\Sigma(r^2)$ may be estimated by the sum of the squares of horizontal and vertical components, hence taking these component values,

$$\Sigma(r^2)=\{3\times(0\cdot9)^2\}+\{2\times(1\cdot35)^2\}+\{2\times(3\tfrac{3}{4})^2\}+\{2\times(1\tfrac{7}{8})^2\}$$
$$=41\cdot25 \text{ sq. in.}$$

Distance R of rivet A from G (the centroid)$=\sqrt{(3\cdot75^2+0\cdot9^2)}=3\cdot855$ in. Hence from the relation (2) the resistance of rivet A to torsion about G is

$$40\cdot95\times3\cdot855\div41\cdot25=3\cdot82 \text{ tons}$$

which is inclined θ to the vertical where

$$\tan\theta=\frac{3\cdot75}{0\cdot9}=4\cdot16, \text{ } i.e. \text{ } \theta=76\cdot5^\circ.$$

In addition the rivet exerts on the two cleats a vertical downward force $13\div5=2\cdot6$ tons. Hence the resultant force exerted by the rivets on the pair of cleats, found graphically or as follows, is

$$\sqrt{(3\cdot82^2+2\cdot6^2+2\times3\cdot82\times2\cdot6\times\cos 76\cdot5^\circ)}=5\cdot10 \text{ tons}$$

which even taken in double shear is a full allowance for a $\frac{3}{4}$-in. rivet, and is a high rate of bearing pressure in passing through a $\frac{1}{2}$-in. web, viz. $4\cdot87\div(\frac{1}{2}\times\frac{3}{4})=13$ tons per sq. in.

If the resulting force for the remaining rivets be similarly determined and a polygon of forces be drawn, the resultant will be found to be 13 tons vertically downwards, and if by a funicular polygon its position be determined it will be found to act in the same straight line as the 13 tons upward force at the back of the cleat, thus checking the calculations.

Example 2. One hundred $\frac{7}{8}$-in. rivets arranged in the form of a square at 3-in. pitch, in directions parallel to the sides of the square, resist a moment of 2,000 ton-in. Find the load on the four rivets at the corners of the square.

Distance R to the corners$=13\cdot5\times\sqrt{2}=19\cdot1$ in.

For a circumscribing square

$$\text{length of side}=27+3=30 \text{ in.,} \quad k^2=\tfrac{1}{6}\times30^2=150$$

hence $\Sigma(r^2)$ is 100×150 approximately $=15,000$

and from (2) $$F=\frac{2,000\times19\cdot1}{15,000}=2\cdot55 \text{ tons}$$

---

[1] Generally, there will be a considerable clockwise moment exerted on the angle cleat by the supports, consisting of a thrust at the bottom and tension in the upper bolts; this will reduce the moment exerted on the rivets and the resisting moment exerted by them. Unless there is sufficient play in the connection or the supports to allow the end tilt given by (6) and (7), Art. 82, there would be a large contra-clockwise moment exerted by the cleats on the rivets.

more accurately $\Sigma(r^2) = 2 \times 2 \times 10 \times 9(4 \cdot 5^2 + 3 \cdot 5^2 + 2 \cdot 5^2 + 1 \cdot 5^2 + 0 \cdot 5^2) = 14,850$

and $$F = \frac{2,000 \times 19 \cdot 1}{14,850} = 2 \cdot 57 \text{ tons}$$

173. Design for N or Pratt Girder.   Plate II shows the elevation of half of a riveted **N** or Pratt truss, forming one of the main girders of a double-track railway bridge for which the Author is indebted to Sir Wm. Arrol and Co., Ltd.   Part of the cross-section is shown in Fig. 249.   Actually, as shown on the plan, the bridge forms a skew span, the angle of skew being 42°, but the design corresponds fairly closely to that for a square span.   (Of the nine panel points in the girder only two will be appreciably affected by the angle of skew, viz. the two nearest the abutments at the *acute* end of the span.   The loads on these points will be diminished because the cross-girders there do not traverse the full breadth and in consequence do not carry the full load.)   The cross-section and enlarged elevation of the splice of the top chord are shown in Fig. 246 on Plate IV.

The dimensions on the drawing give the reader many examples in design.   As a basis of calculation the following data may be used. Effective span, 92 ft. 1 in.   Effective height, 11 ft. 6 in.   Panel length, 9 ft. $2\frac{1}{2}$ in.   Dead load, 0·6 ton per foot per main girder; equivalent moving load per girder, 1·5 ton per foot plus 23 tons concentrated in the most influential position.   For chord members, replacing the concentrated load by twice the amount uniformly distributed, we may take $1 \cdot 5 + \frac{46}{92} = 2$ tons per foot run.   Equivalent dead-load stress on any member = max. stress + $\dfrac{\text{(range of stress)}^2}{\text{max. stress}}$, which is equivalent to using an impact factor (see Art. 31) equal to range of load ÷ max. load.   On loads so increased for dynamical contingencies, unit stress of 9 tons per sq. in. in tension, $9 - 0 \cdot 03l/k$ in thrust, and 7 tons per sq. in. shear in rivets with 14 tons bearing stress may be used.   These really correspond to much lower working unit stresses reckoned on the maximum load, *e.g.* for chord members the stress is increased in the ratio $2 \cdot 6 + 2^2/2 \cdot 6$ to $2 \cdot 6$, *i.e.* 4·14 to 2·6, hence the tensile allowance reckoned on the maximum loads is $9 \times 2 \cdot 6/4 \cdot 14 = 5 \cdot 65$ tons per sq. in.

The rivets attaching a web member to a gusset-plate have to carry the whole pull or thrust in that member, but the rivets attaching a gusset-plate to a continuous chord at a joint have only to carry the increment of chord stress at that joint, *i.e.* the resultant force exerted by the web members meeting at that point.

174. Pin-joints. *Eye-bars.*   Such joints were formerly very common in roofs but are now generally replaced by riveted joints. In America pin-joints have largely been used in bridges, the tie

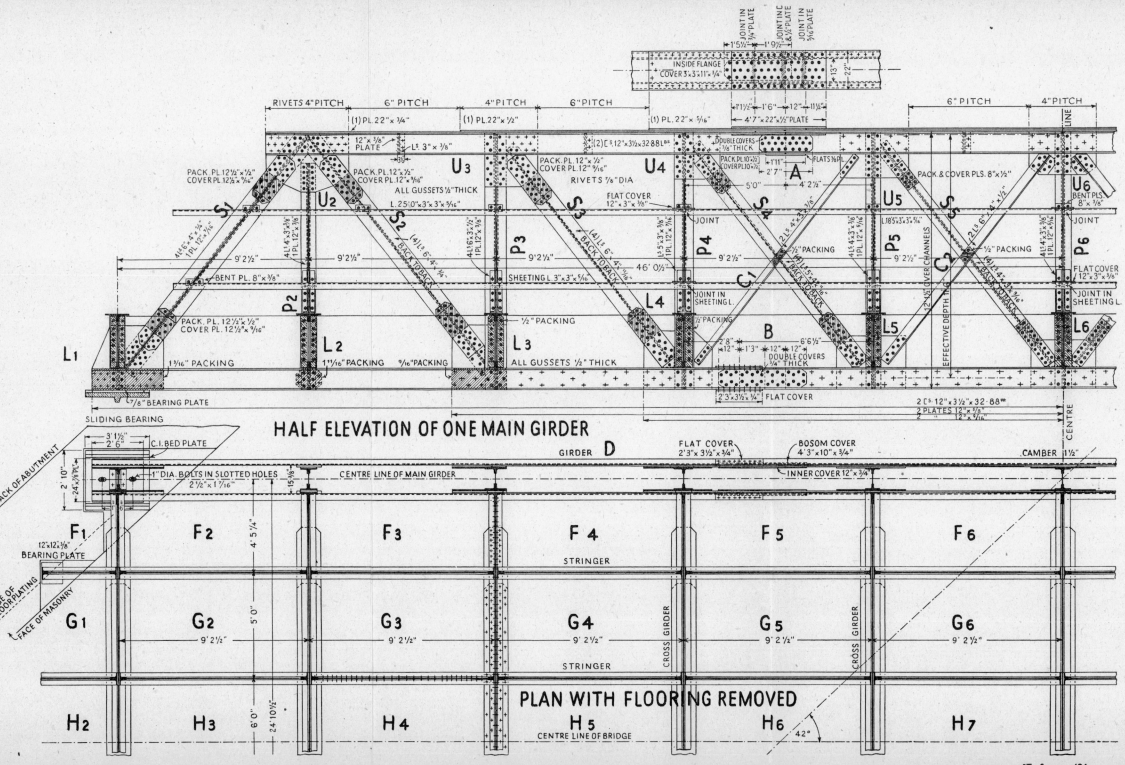

Plate II.—Design for N or Pratt Girder Bridge.

HALF ELEVATION OF ONE MAIN GIRDER

PLAN WITH FLOORING REMOVED

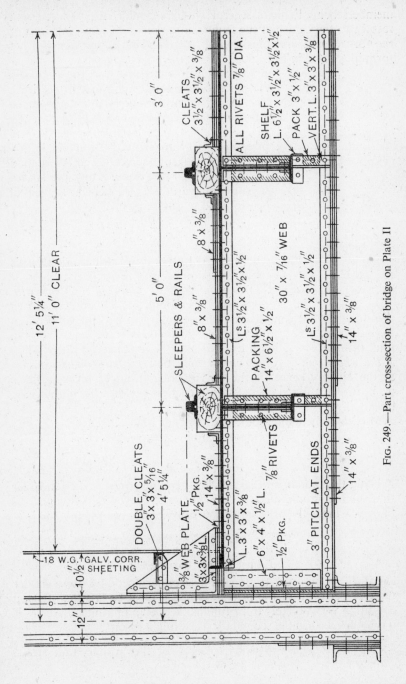

Fig. 249.—Part cross-section of bridge on Plate II

members being made of several eye-bars symmetrically placed with respect to the centre of the length of the pins. The proportions of the forged ends and pin-holes in eye-bars vary somewhat, but the form illustrated in Fig. 250, in which the hole diameter $d=\frac{3}{4}h$, where

h is the depth of flat bar and the thickness $t=\frac{1}{6}h$ represents about the usual proportions. The head is always made large enough to be stronger than the parallel bar. When the pin is a slack fit in the eye-bar holes the bearing pressure is very unevenly distributed; in any case the bearing pressure allowed is less than on rivets, being often about 8 tons per sq. in. If the ends are not thickened, for equal bearing and tensile resistance

$$f_t \cdot h \cdot t = d \cdot t \cdot f_b$$

hence $$d/h = f_t/f_b$$

where f_t and f_b are the working unit stresses for tension and bearing respectively.

FIG. 250.—Eye-bar end

Maximum Bending Stress in Eye-bars with Pin-joints. Pin-joints are sometimes said to eliminate any serious degree of secondary stress due to bending from lack of free turning movement at the joints. Let P be the total primary stress in an eye-bar of a pin-connected frame. Then *if the whole pull* P *comes on the pin*, the total frictional resistance at the circumference of the pin before movement takes place is $\mu \cdot P$, where μ is the coefficient of friction between the pin and the hole.

Maximum bending moment at the ends $M = \mu \cdot P \cdot \frac{1}{2}d$

Maximum bending stress $= \frac{1}{2}\mu P \cdot d \div Z$

$$= \frac{1}{2}\mu P d \div \frac{1}{6}th^2 = \frac{3\mu P d}{th^2}$$

Z being the modulus of section for bending stress. Then in order that the bar should move round the pin to prevent a bending stress of, say, n times the primary unit stress (where n is a fraction)

$$\frac{3\mu P d}{th^2} \text{ must be less than } \frac{nP}{th}$$

μ must be less than $\frac{1}{3}nh/d$

e.g. if $d=\frac{3}{4}h$, in order to prevent a secondary bending stress greater than 10 per cent. of the primary stress μ must be less than 0·04, a condition very unlikely to be fulfilled in such a pin-joint. Again, if μ is so low as 0·25 the secondary stress might reach

$$3 \times 0.25 \times P \times 0.75h \div th^2 = \frac{9}{16}\frac{P}{th}, \text{ i.e. } \frac{9}{16} \text{ of the primary unit stress,}$$

before it is relieved by movement about the pin. It may be noted that in a pin-joint in a continuous chord the pin does not bear the whole chord stress but only the increment at the joint, which makes movement possible with lower bending stresses than for discontinuous eye-bars supposed above.

Stresses in the Pins. In addition to the bearing and shearing stresses (the latter being usually low) in the pins, the bending stresses are important. The bending moments on a pin result from forces not all in one plane nor all parallel. The maximum bending moment may be found by resolving the forces exerted by each member hinged at the pin into two perpendicular components, say horizontal and vertical. The component bending moments in two perpendicular planes may then be calculated as in Chapter IV, the component values along the pin axis being proportional to the ordinates of a polygonal diagram such as Fig. 54. The actual bending moment at any section will in general lie in some intermediate plane, and if at any section M_h = the bending moment in a horizontal axial plane and M_v = the bending moment in the vertical axial plane, the resultant bending moment is $M = \sqrt{(M_h{}^2 + M_v{}^2)}$; the maximum bending moment will occur at the point of application of one of the forces, *i.e.* in the plane of the axis of some member hinged to the pin, and the place of its occurrence may be found by inspection. The varying bending moment along the pin axis may be conceived as represented by the radial ordinates of a winding surface, the generators of which are radial straight lines through the axis of the pin and perpendicular to it. The projections of such a surface on two planes through the pin axis give the diagrams of component bending moments in the respective planes.

175. Beam and Stanchion Connections. The attachments of the ends of an I beam to a stanchion are usually made by " cleats," *i.e.* pieces of angle section riveted to the beam and bolted to the stanchion. The supporting force which such a cleated connection may safely exert is measured by the shearing value of the bolts in single shear, the bearing and the shearing value of the rivets (in double shear), and the smallest of these three values taken. In estimating the shearing and bearing values of the rivets it is to be borne in mind that they are liable to some moment about the centroid of the group in addition to the direct force of the end reaction, in other words to an eccentric force. At an extreme estimate such a moment might be taken as the product of the end reaction into the distance of the centroid from the back of the web cleats; the effect of such eccentricity was estimated in Example 1, Art. 172, where it was pointed out that the action of the moment will to some unknown extent be neutralised by the moment exerted by the bolted attachment of the cleats to the stanchion.

R*

The question may suggest itself as to whether such beam connections do to any considerable extent correspond to the assumed end conditions of a " built in " beam.[1]   A rough numerical estimate will show that the moment value of the rivets would be quite inadequate to take the end moments involved, and that the conditions must approximate to those of a beam simply supported at its ends. Before such conditions can obtain, some local yielding must take place.   If, for example, the central deflection of the beam is say 0·001 of its length the average slope is 0·002, and the end tilt must be of the order of 0·004 of a radian.   To accommodate this, *if the rivets are tight fits in the holes* considerable local strain must occur, which may be distributed over the upper bolts in tension, the rivets in shear, and the rivets and rivet holes in bearing, particularly in the web.   When once the end slope has been accommodated by slackness or by straining, the rivet stresses may be looked upon as not exceeding the values indicated in Example 1, Art. 172.   But in any case the conditions are indefinite, and the computations of stress in these connections must be regarded as to a considerable extent conventional.

So far as it goes, the experimental evidence shows that riveted connections may transmit moments sufficient to restrain the ends of cross-beams considerably and to subject stanchions to correspondingly large moments.   Such facts greatly complicate the problem of design, particularly if a connection cannot be relied upon to behave like an experimental one which is nominally similar.

Anchorage of Stanchions.   Stanchions "fixed" at the base must have holding-down bolts as well as riveted base connections capable of withstanding bending moments such as arise from wind and other horizontal loads calculated in Art. 156 and elsewhere in Chapter XVI.   Let T be the total tension in the bolts on the " windward " side of a stanchion base, let a be the distance of the bolts on the leeward and windward sides from the centre line of the column base.   Let the straining actions at the base be reduced to an axial thrust V and a bending moment M.   Then the axial thrust assists the anchorage bolts to resist the bending moment and, taking moments about the leeward bolts,

$$T.2a + V.a = M, \quad \text{or} \quad T = \tfrac{1}{2}\left(\frac{M}{a} - V\right)$$

Pressure between Sole-plate and Foundation.   The unit pressure may be assumed to vary uniformly and consequently, from Art. 100, if A is the area of sole-plate the greatest intensity at the leeward edge

---

[1] See Second Report of Steel Structures Research Committee, H.M.S.O. (1934). Also the Final Report (1936).   The Committee's recommendations are embodied in British Standard Specification 449, which may be modified in the light of further researches.

will be

$$P = \frac{V}{A} + \frac{My_1}{I}$$

where y_1 is half the width of the sole-plate from the leeward to the windward edge and I is a principal moment of inertia of the sole-plate area.

Stress in Sole-plate. The overhang of the sole-plate beyond the attachment angles must be limited so that treated as a cantilever with a load varying as above the extreme stress on the face of the plate is within a working value.

EXAMPLES XVII

In Problems No. 1 to No. 5 inclusive, as in Art. 173, take the dead load 0·6 ton per foot run, live load 1·5 ton per ft., together with 23 tons concentrated in any position. Impact load=(range of load)²/maximum load. Unit stress 9 tons per sq. in. in tension, 9–0·03l/k tons per sq. in. in compression.   Rivet shear stress 7 tons per sq. in., bearing stress 14 tons per sq. in.

1. Find suitable sections for the booms at the centre of the span of the girder in Plate II.

2. Find suitable sections for the booms 20 ft. from the centre of the span of the girder in Plate II.

3. Design the diagonals S2, S3, S4, and S5 in Plate II.

4. Design the verticals P3 and P6, Plate II.

5. How many $\frac{7}{8}$-in. rivets are required to attach the gusset-plate at the foot of the vertical P3 to the lower boom?

6. A beam is attached to end supports by the web cleats only, shown in Fig. 251. Assuming that a reaction of 14 tons acts at the back of the cleats, find the maximum force on any rivet in the web cleats.

7. Twenty-five rivets arranged in the form of a square have a pitch of 3 in. in each direction. What is the greatest stress on any rivet if the group resists a pull of 50 tons parallel to the side of the square and a moment of 100 ton-in.

8. Solve the previous problem if the resultant pull is parallel to a diagonal of the square.

CHAPTER XVIII

PLATE GIRDERS AND BRIDGES

176. Types and Proportions. The moment of resistance to bending of plate girder sections has been referred to and illustrated in Art. 50, which the reader may revise with advantage before proceeding with the present chapter. The shear stress has been dealt with in Art. 53 and the principal stresses in Art. 54.

In the main, the flanges of a plate girder resist the bending moment and the web resists the shearing force; for a girder simply supported at its ends the bending moment to be resisted will be greatest about the centre of the span and the shearing force greatest at the ends. The plate girder represents a practical approximation to a beam of uniform strength, for its maximum moment of resistance with a full working unit stress allowance at any section is roughly proportional to the maximum bending moment which the girder has to carry. In some cases also the web section is varied, being greatest towards the ends where the shearing force is greatest. The variation in moment of resistance to bending is accomplished in two distinct ways, viz. (1) in parallel flange girders (Plates III and IV) by varying the section of the flanges, (2) in curved-flange girders (Fig. 251) by

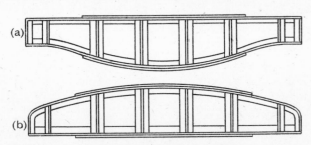

(a)

(b)

Fig. 251.—Curved-flange girders

varying the height or distance between the flanges. Of the latter kind (Fig. 251) there are two types, (*a*) the fish-bellied girder with curved bottom flange loaded on the straight top flange such as is used in large travelling cranes and (*b*) the hog-back girder with curved upper flange loaded on the straight bottom flange as used occasionally in bridges. The parallel flange type is the simplest and most economical to construct and is the commonest type. The curved types may in some cases save material and be lighter, and in some cases are used for the sake of appearance.

Plate girder bridges are used for spans of from 20 to 80 ft. and their use tends to extend to larger spans of 100 ft. and more.

The proportions vary considerably, but a depth of from $\frac{1}{12}$ to $\frac{1}{10}$ of the span is about the usual average with single webs, the proportion being somewhat greater in short girders and less in long ones, and in girders having two web plates. The breadth of flanges varies greatly in different classes of work. The flange-plates should not overlap the angles by more than say 4 in. unless there are stiffeners at short intervals, otherwise there may be local buckling of the compression flange under thrust. For this reason flanges seldom exceed 20 or 22 in. in breadth even in very deep girders and they are frequently not more than 18 in. For small spans a width equal to about a third of the depth may be taken as an average proportion.

177. Curtailment of Flange-Plates —Flange Splices.

In order to reduce the moment of resistance of a parallel-flanged girder in proportion to the bending moment, the several plates which with the angles constitute the central and maximum flange section need not all be carried throughout the whole span. It is only necessary to carry any plate so far that the moment of resistance of the remainder of the section is not less than the bending moment to be resisted. A simple way of finding where the plates may be curtailed is shown in Fig. 252; BEFHD represents the bending-moment diagram

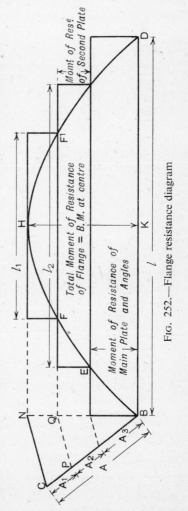

FIG. 252.—Flange resistance diagram

drawn to scale. Then if A_1, A_2, A_3, are the respective areas of section of say the top plate, second plate, and main plate including the angles, etc., the maximum bending moment and moment of resistance HK may be proportionally divided as shown into the moment of resistance of the several parts of the flange by the well-known construction of setting off lengths along BC proportional to A_3, A_2, A_1. If $A_1 + A_2 + A_3$ exceeds the total area A required at the centre to give the moment of resistance HK the point C joined to N must be such that BC represents the smaller quantity A where

$$f \times A \times d = \text{maximum bending moment},$$

or
$$A = \frac{\text{maximum bending moment}}{f \times d} \quad . \quad . \quad . \quad (1)$$

d being the effective depth of girder.

The length of the top plate necessary to keep the moment of resistance up to the amount of the bending moment is found by drawing PQ parallel to CN and a horizontal line through Q meeting the bending-moment diagram in F and F^1. Then FF^1 gives the length of top plate required, neglecting the connection to the remainder of the flange. The actual length of plate used often exceeds FF^1 (empirically) by a length at each end sufficient to contain such a number of rivets that their resistance shall be equal to the total working stress attributable to the plate, generally some three or four times the length of the rivet pitch.

The length of second and other plates is similarly determined. Examples are given in the designs in Arts. 181 and 182.

The results may of course be calculated, for the length of any plate is obtained by equating the working moment of resistance of the flange sectional area below it to an expression for bending moment in terms of a variable distance x along the girder, and solving for x.

Uniformly Distributed Load. Let w = load per inch run, l_1 = length of top plate, l = span, f = working unit stress due to bending in the flanges, then from the parabolic bending-moment diagram

$$\frac{w}{2}\{(l/2)^2 - (l_1/2)^2\} = f \times d \times (A_2 + A_3) \quad . \quad . \quad . \quad (2)$$

from which l_1 may easily be found.

Or more simply

$$\frac{l_1}{l} = \sqrt{\frac{\{A - (A_2 + A_3)\}}{A}} \quad . \quad . \quad . \quad . \quad (3)$$

and if $A_1 + A_2 + A_3 = A$ exactly (which is seldom the case in practice)

$$l_1 = l\sqrt{(A_1/A)} \quad . \quad . \quad . \quad . \quad . \quad (4)$$

In these formulae safety in approximate values of d lies in taking a *high* value; thus for the outer plate the reduction in moment of resistance is $A - (A_2 + A_3)$ multiplied by a quantity rather greater than the effective depth for the whole flange: the plate should not be curtailed before the sections at which the bending moment is similarly reduced.

In the case of girders of variable depth, such as those in Fig. 251, equation (2) holds good, d being a variable quantity. For the graphical method the ordinates of the bending-moment diagram may be all multiplied by the inverse ratio of the girder depths to that at the central or other section and the depths then taken as constant and equal to that at the chosen section.

Equivalent Uniformly Distributed Loads. When equivalent uniformly distributed loads have been determined applicable to centre sections only (see Art. 69), a different value and usually a higher one will have to be employed in constructing the flange diagram. The parabola so used would be that which would completely circumscribe the actual maximum bending-moment diagram. In order to give the plate lengths directly, without additions to allow for riveting, a still higher table of equivalent loads is sometimes used; an example is given in Art. 182 in which the load (56·5 tons) is about 8 per cent. greater than for the design of the central section.

Flange Splice. The splice of a flange should not generally be at or very near the section of greatest bending moment in the girder. It is made in a similar way to that in Fig. 242 and not more than one member constituting the flange is broken at one place.

178. Web Stresses and Stiffeners.[1] The magnitude and direction of the stresses in the web of a girder of I section have been dealt with in Art. 54. In plate girders of ordinary proportions the deep web alone is quite inadequate to resist buckling under the influence of the principal compressive stress arising mainly from the shear stress. It is therefore reinforced at intervals not usually exceeding the depth of web by stiffeners as shown in Plates III and IV. The spacing of the stiffeners depends upon the intensity of shear stress allowable in the web. The buckling resistance of the web subject to compressive and tensile stresses at right angles has sometimes been compared to that of a strut, so that if d=unsupported length of web plate between consecutive stiffeners and t=thickness of web, the line of thrust being taken as inclined 45° to the vertical stiffeners, applying Rankine's formula (5), Art. 105, and putting

$$l = \sqrt{2} \cdot d, \quad k^2 = \tfrac{1}{12}t^2, \quad a = 1/30{,}000$$

maximum allowable compressive stress=max. allowable web shear stress=

$$\frac{\text{maximum allowable compressive stress}}{1 + \tfrac{1}{1250} \cdot d^2/t^2} \quad . \quad . \quad (1)$$

which, if d and t are known, gives a rule for checking the web stress, or, if t and the actual unit shear stress in the web are known, gives a rule for finding a suitable value of d. Thus if the allowable shear

[1] For working rules and stress allowed see B.S.S. No. 153, Part 3 (1937 revision).

stress is half the tensile unit stress

$$(d/t)^2 = 1{,}250, \quad d = 35t \quad . \quad . \quad . \quad . \quad (2)$$

An American rule with a different constant is

$$\text{shear unit stress} = \frac{\text{maximum compressive unit stress}}{1 + \frac{1}{1500} \cdot (d/t)^2} \quad . \quad (3)$$

where d is the pitch of the stiffeners and therefore exceeds the length of unsupported plate by, say, 4 to 6 in.

This, like Rankine's formula for struts, might be reduced to the approximate form of, say,

$$\text{shear stress} = \text{max. direct stress} \times (1 - 0{\cdot}0125d/t) \quad . \quad (4)$$

If $d = 40 \cdot t$, these rules limit the shear to about half the direct stress.

Common requirements of specifications for plate girders are that stiffeners shall not be further apart than the depth of the web if the distance between the flange angles exceeds say 50 or 60 times the thickness of the web, with a further limitation to about 5 ft. whatever the depth of web. The maximum web shear stress is sometimes specified not to exceed half the allowable tensile unit stress; this clause is made with due regard to that for stiffener spacing and vice versa.

Another function of stiffeners is to transmit the concentrated loads at the ends or at the cross-girders to the web of a main girder. Hence, stiffeners are required at every point of application of a concentrated load. These stiffeners at load points and their rivets are required by some specifications to be capable of carrying the whole load applied by them, while by others they are required to be capable of carrying (as a strut) say two-thirds of the vertical shear on the girder at their point of attachment and the whole shear in the case of the end stiffeners, the length of strut being taken as two-thirds or three-quarters of the web length between flange angles.

The stiffeners at points of concentrated loading and at web joints are often made of two angle sections, and a gusset-plate, bent over so as to support both flanges and the web, such stiffeners being used in pairs on opposite sides of the web. In other cases either Tee or angle section stiffeners are used either bent over knee shape as shown in Plates III and IV and (a), Fig. 253, when the breadth of flange allows, or as in (b) and (c), Fig. 253, bearing tightly against the flange angles, the vertical legs of which they clear either by having packing plates (American " fillers ") behind them (c), or by being " joggled " or " crimped " near their ends (b).

Stiffeners are generally placed on both sides of the web, and where cross-girders are used the inside stiffener is turned over and riveted to the top flange, as shown in Plate IV.

In box-plate girders, stiffening diaphragms are often placed inside, attached by angles to each web plate.

For so complex a structure as a plate girder there can be no very exact theory as to the distribution of web stress, and the above rules relating to spacing must be regarded as largely empirical. Further, the pitch of stiffeners selected will frequently be influenced by the position of cross-girders and web splices.

Some idea of the effect of different sectional areas and spacings of stiffeners may be obtained from experiments carried to the point at which the web buckles into wave form; such experiments have been made by Lilly,[1] who, regarding the stiffeners as analogous to the struts in a braced truss (see Fig. 187, say), deduced under certain assumptions a rule of the type (3).

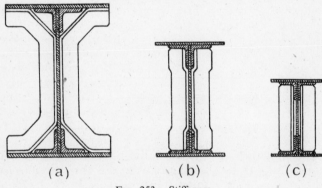

(a)　　　(b)　　　(c)

Fig. 253.—Stiffeners

179. Pitch of Rivets Uniting Flanges to Web. The rivets attaching the flange angles to the web have to transmit the longitudinal shear between the web and the flanges. Let p be the pitch of the rivets and let R be the working resistance of one rivet. Neglecting any variation in intensity of the shear stress in the web and adopting the approximation mentioned in Art. 53, the intensity of shear stress, horizontally and vertically, is

$$q = F/(th) \quad \ldots \ldots \ldots \quad (1)$$

where t = thickness, and h = depth of web, and F = gross shearing force on the section. In a distance p horizontally the total horizontal shearing force to be resisted is $q \cdot p \cdot t$, hence

$$qpt = R \text{ and } p = R/qt = Rh/F \quad \ldots \ldots \quad (2)$$

These relations are often stated in the form horizontal force per inch length $R/p = qt = F/h$. They might also be obtained by taking

---

[1] *Engineering*, Feb. 1st, 1907.

moments about a point P (Fig. 254) of the forces on a section of the web of length p, remembering that the only important force on the web is the shearing force F.   But actually a small part of the longitudinal tension and compression is carried by the web, hence the moment about P to be balanced by R is less than that of F, and B.S.S. No. 153 permits that horizontal shear per inch length (F/h) to be reduced in the ratio of the flange section area to the sum of the flange section area plus $\frac{1}{8}$ of the web section area.   The expression above for the pitch p shows that in a girder of constant depth h the pitch may be made greater where the variable shearing force F is smaller; for example, towards the middle of the span of a girder carrying a distributed load. Often a pitch suitable for the section of a maximum shearing force is used throughout for convenience instead of a variable pitch. The working resistance R of a single rivet may be its resistance to shearing or its resistance to crushing across a diameter.

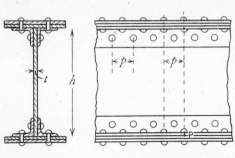

FIG. 254

For attaching the angles to the flange-plates twice as many rivets will be necessary if the shearing resistance is the criterion, for the rivets are in single shear; this will require the same pitch p as before on either side of the web, there being then twice as many rivets as are used for attaching the angles to the web.   If, however, resistance to crushing is the criterion throughout, a pitch $2p$ might be used to attach the angles to the flange.

If the above rule indicates an inconveniently small pitch, larger angles with double (zigzag or staggered) riveting, a thicker web, or larger rivets must be used.

180. Web Splices.   The number of splices in a web depends upon the maximum length of plate of given width obtainable, and also upon conditions of manufacture and erection, great lengths of broad plate being difficult to handle in making and in transport.

The commonest form of web splice is a double-covered riveted butt joint, as shown in Plates III and IV.   The number of rivets provided is sufficient to carry the shearing force at the splice, the value of each rivet being measured by its resistance in double shear or in bearing whichever may be the least.

When some one-sixth or one-eighth of the web section is for moment of resistance computation included in the flange area, *i.e.*

the web is relied upon to take a share in the moment of resistance, the web splice is calculated to resist the bending moment as well as the shear. But whether the web is assumed to resist any bending moment or not it will almost certainly carry some fraction, the upper limit of which may be taken as one-sixth of the web section divided by the total flange area, inclusive of one-sixth of the web ($f \times$ one-sixth area $\times d = \frac{1}{6}ftd^2$). Or if A=flange area, including one-sixth td where t=thickness and d=depth of web, and M=bending moment at the section, the limit of moment carried by the web may be taken as

$$\frac{td}{6A} \cdot M$$

The bending moment carried by the web is resisted by the rivets of the web splice, which are thereby stressed in the manner explained and estimated in Art. 172 in addition to the vertical shearing force which they carry. In British practice it is usual to neglect the stresses in the web-splice rivets resulting from the bending moment carried by the web; in consequence the rivets probably carry a rather higher stress than that computed, unless the joint is relieved by slight movements corresponding to the bending strains in a seamless web, throwing absolutely the whole bending moment on the flanges. But as in Plates III and IV the web splices are almost invariably made under web stiffeners, the rivets being ample in number all take their share of the resistance offered by the joint. Such a joint, from experience and from theoretical computation so far as it may reasonably be attempted in such a complex structure, is entirely satisfactory. In America web splices estimated to carry bending moment have sometimes been constructed with six plates— two pairs with their lengths horizontal (one plate being in contact with each of the four flange angles), and the third pair with their lengths vertical and filling the space between the other two pairs: the joint covers forming an I shape on each side of the web. The object of such a joint is to place the rivets advantageously (*i.e.* far from the centroid of the group) to resist bending moment without being thereby highly stressed. Another plan is to use a single pair of vertical plates, but to space the rivets closer together near the flanges and further apart near the centre of the depth of the web.

Such joints may, apart from extra constructional cost, be advantageous if made where the bending moment is great and the shearing force insignificant, but if a web has also to resist considerable vertical shearing force a concentration of rivets near the flanges may cause an unnecessary concentration of stress in that part of the web which is already (see Fig. 102) most heavily stressed. A uniform distribution of rivets corresponds most closely to the distribution of material in the web and will tend least to disturbance or secondary stress in the web. If the joint has to withstand bending moment and shearing force the rivets should of course be sufficient for both purposes. It is well to recall the fact that all calculations on riveted joints are conventional for various reasons, including the neglect of friction, which is always present to a great but unknown extent.

181. Plate Girder Deck Bridge. The various points in the four preceding articles are illustrated in the numerical computations for the design of the girders shown in Plate III.   The deck type is one of the most economical, but requires a sufficient available depth for the girders.

Data.   To carry a single line of railway. Construction depth, 5 ft. 8 in. (*i.e.* overall from rail level to underside of bridge superstructure).   Effective span, 40 ft.   Depth over angles, 4 ft.   Equivalent uniformly distributed load 2·4 tons per ft.=96 tons for bending moment, with 15 per cent. more for shear.   Working unit stresses, 7·5 tons per sq. in. tension; 5 tons per sq. in. shearing; 10 tons per sq. in bearing; all reckoned for dead loads.   Variable-load unit stress by dynamic formula (Art. 31) or the equivalent rule of adding to the maximum stress, impact stress equal to the range of stress (impact coefficient of unity).   Allowable dead-load stress in the web $\dfrac{6}{1+d^2/(1,600t^2)}$ tons per sq. in. but not exceeding 3 tons per sq. in., where d=unsupported distance between stiffeners, which are not to be spaced further apart than the depth of the web.   No section to be less than $\tfrac{3}{8}$ in. thick.

Dead Load.   Ballast, permanent way, steel
  flooring, bracing, etc. (see tabular estimate below) . . . .   12·25 tons per girder
Assumed weight of girder, checked after
  design (see below) . . . .   7·25 ,,

Total . . .   19·5 tons.

Live Load.   Per girder 96/2=48 tons.
Girder Flanges.   Equivalent dead load (taken uniformly distributed)

$$48+48+19\cdot5=115\cdot5 \text{ tons.}$$

$$\text{Central bending moment}=\frac{115\cdot5\times40}{8}=577\cdot5 \text{ ton-ft.}$$

$$=6{,}930 \text{ ton-in.}$$

$$\text{Modulus of section required}=\frac{6{,}930}{7\cdot5}=925 \text{ (in.)}^3$$

Plate III.—Deck Plate Girder Bridge.

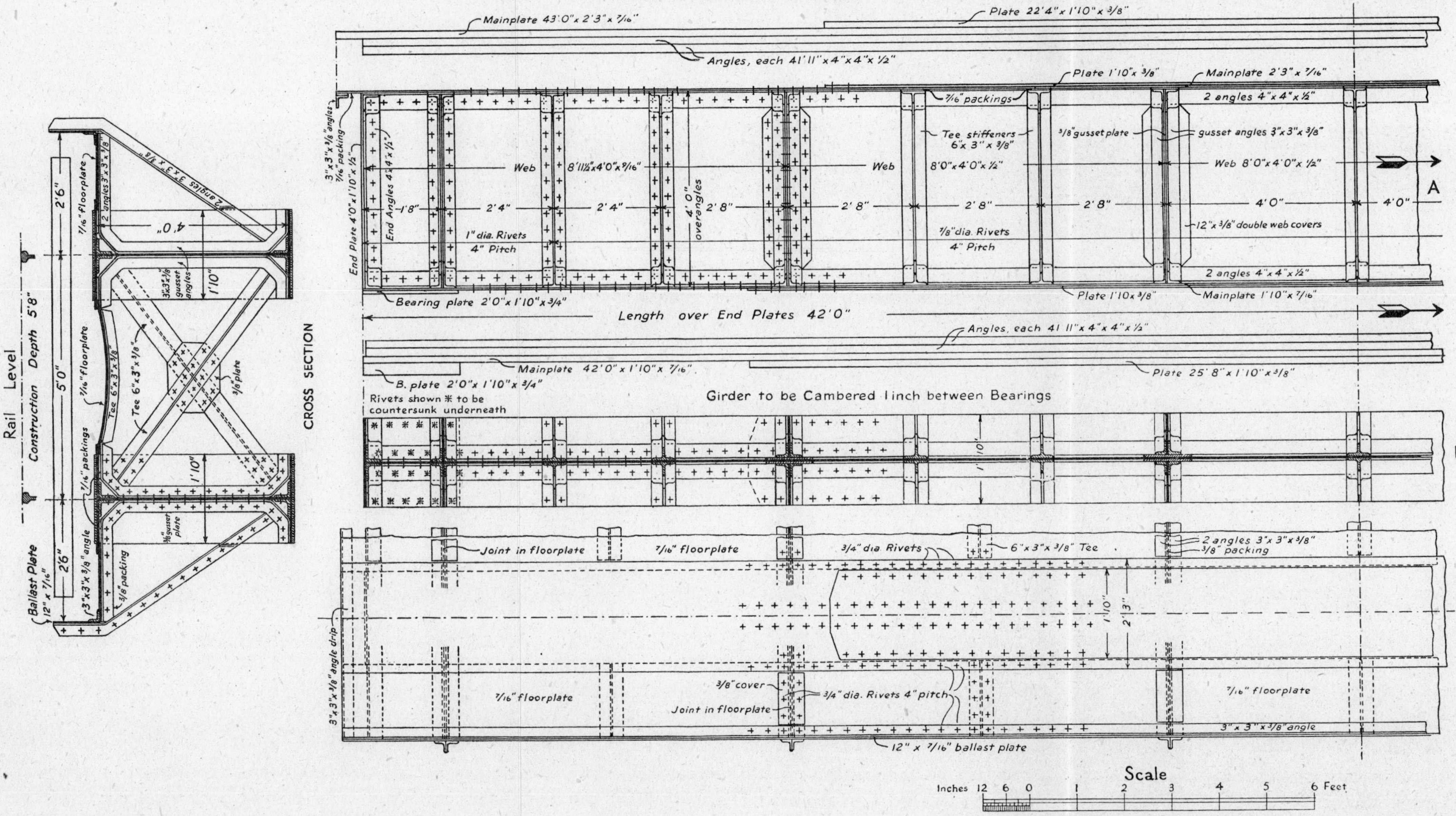

[To face p. 500.

Flange area required with effective depth 48 in. $= \frac{925}{48} = 19.25$ sq. in. The flanges are taken rather broad at 22 in. The main plate is extended by $2\frac{1}{2}$ in. overlap on each side to allow attachment of floor plating, giving a total breadth of 27 in.

Top Flange. Two angle bars $4 \times 4 \times \frac{1}{2}$ in. (see Table V, Appendix) less four rivet holes, taken $\frac{1}{16}$ in. over the rivet diameter (see Art. 50) gives 5·625 sq. in., leaving $19.25 - 5.625 = 13.625$ sq. in. Taking a $\frac{7}{16}$ in. main plate (the minimum suitable thickness for a flange-plate which stands alone) $27 \times \frac{7}{16}$ in. allowing for rivet holes, gives 9·461 sq. in., leaving $13.625 - 9.461 = 4.164$ sq. in.

Thickness required for second plate 22 in. wide, deducting four rivet holes is $\frac{4.164}{18.25} = 0.227$ in., hence $\frac{3}{8}$-in. plate is used. The full area provided is then

2 angles bars less 4 rivet holes $\frac{15}{16}$ in. diameter . . . 5·925 sq. in.
1 main plate less 4 holes $\frac{15}{16}$ in. and 2 holes $\frac{13}{16}$ in. diameter 9·461 ,,
1 outer plate less 4 holes $\frac{15}{16}$ in. diameter . . . . . 6·844 ,,

$$\text{Total} \quad . \quad . \quad . \quad 22.230 \text{ ,,}$$

Bottom Flange—

2 angles as above . . . . 5·625 sq. in.
$\frac{7}{16}$ in. main plate 22 in. less 4 holes $\frac{15}{16}$ in. 7·984 ,,
$\frac{3}{8}$-in. plate 22 in. less 4 holes $\frac{15}{16}$ in. . 6·844 ,,

$$20.453$$

Resistance of $22 \times \frac{3}{8}$ in. plate at 7·5 tons per sq. in.
$$22 \times \tfrac{3}{8} \times 7.5 = 61.875 \text{ tons.}$$
Resistance of $\frac{7}{8}$-in. rivet in single shear $= 0.61 \times 5 = 3.01$ tons.
Number of rivets equal to resistance to outer plate

$$= \frac{61.875}{3.01} = 21 \text{ rivets.}$$

The outer plates are (empirically) prolonged at each end sufficiently to contain 21 rivets beyond its length given by the flange diagrams (Fig. 255).

Moments of Resistance for Flange Diagrams.
Top flange:

2 angles give $5.625 \times 7.5 \times 4 = 168.75$ ton-ft.
Main plate $9.461 \times 7.5 \times 4 = 283.83$,,
Outer plate $6.844 \times 7.5 \times 4 = 205.32$,,

$$\text{Total} \quad . \quad . \quad . \quad 657.90 \quad \text{,,}$$

Central ordinate of parabola 577·5 ton-ft.

Bottom flange:

$$2 \text{ angles, as before} = 168 \cdot 75 \text{ ton-ft.}$$
$$\tfrac{7}{16} \text{ in. main plate } 7 \cdot 984 \times 7 \cdot 5 \times 4 = 239 \cdot 52 \quad ,,$$
$$\tfrac{3}{8} \text{ in. outer plate, as before} = 205 \cdot 32 \quad ,,$$

$$\text{Total . . } 613 \cdot 59 \quad ,,$$

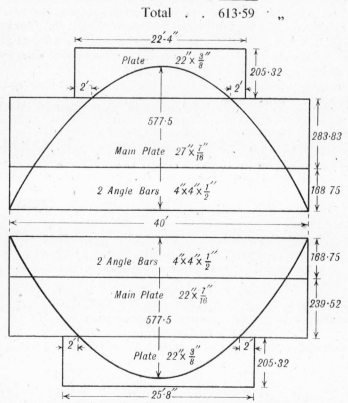

FIG. 255.—Flange resistance diagram (units ton-feet)

The moments of resistance of the various parts and the bending moment are shown in Fig. 255. The lengths of the outer plates prolonged to contain 21 rivets are shown in Fig. 255 and in Plate III.

Web and Stiffeners.

$$\text{End shear for dead load } 19 \cdot 5/2 = 9 \cdot 75 \text{ tons.}$$
$$\text{Equivalent uniform live load for shear } 1 \cdot 15 \times 48 = 55 \cdot 2 \text{ tons.}$$
$$\text{End shear for live load} = 27 \cdot 6 \text{ tons.}$$

Equivalent dead-load shear for any section in the left half of the span (negative shearing force) = dead-load shear + maximum live-load shear+range of shear. The range of shear without regard to sign is the sum of the extreme opposite shears. Hence the equivalent dead-load shear equals the dead-load shear+2(maximum live-load shear)+minimum live-load shear (*i.e.* the maximum value of opposite sign), all three parts taken with like signs. In Fig. 256 the extreme vertical ordinates across the diagram give for the left-hand half of the span the dynamically increased or equivalent dead-load shearing forces: AM=(27·6×2); and the parabola MKA′ is drawn on the base AA′ having ordinates proportional to twice the negative shearing force. The ordinates of the curve EHL from the sloping

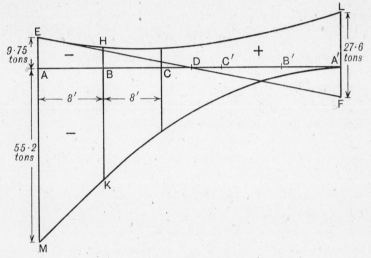

Fig. 256 —Diagram of equivalent dead-load (or dynamically increased)
shearing force on left-hand half of span

base-line EF represent the positive shearing forces, while ordinates of the line ED represent the dead-load shears.

Web lengths of 8 ft. are taken as convenient lengths with about 12 in. extra on the end sections to cover the bearing plates, the full length of girder being about 42 ft., the effective span for calculation 40 ft., and the clear span between the bearing plates about 38 ft. Placing a stiffener over the inner end of the bearing plate leaves 7 ft. 4 in. to the first joint; one intermediate stiffener would give too wide a spacing, so two may be used with spacings of 28 in., 28 in., 32 in., as shown; these distances being exact multiples of the rivet pitch.

The end shear is 27·6+9·75+27·6=64·95 tons. If we allow for the first pair of intermediate stiffeners to take $\frac{2}{3}$ of this at the full allowance of 7·5 tons per sq. in., the total area required would be

$\frac{2}{3} \times 64.95 \div 7.5 = 5.8$ sq. in. Two tees $6 \times 3 \times \frac{3}{8}$ in. (see Appendix) give 6·52 sq. in., and these sections may be used throughout for the intermediate stiffeners. The stiffeners over the end plates and at the web joints are of much more ample strength, consisting of pairs of angles with $\frac{3}{8}$-in. gusset-plates the full width of the flanges; these gusset-plates serve for attachment of the cross-bracing. The maximum unsupported distance between stiffeners at the ends $= 28 - 6 = 22$ in.

Assuming $\frac{9}{16}$-in. web

$$\text{shear stress} = \frac{64.95 \times 16}{48 \times 9} = 2.41 \text{ tons per sq. in.}$$

$$\text{Allowable shear stress} = \frac{6}{1 + \frac{1}{1600}(22/\frac{9}{16})^2} = 3.07 \text{ tons per sq. in.}$$

which is further limited to 3 tons per sq. in. by the specified conditions.

Assuming 1-in. rivets, resistance per rivet in double shear

$$= 0.785 \times 1.75 \times 5 = 6.85 \text{ tons.}$$

Resistance per rivet in bearing

$$= 1 \times \tfrac{9}{16} \times 10 = 5.625 \text{ tons.}$$

Hence from (2), Art. 179, pitch of flange rivets

$$= \frac{5.625 \times 48}{64.95} = 4.16, \text{ say 4 in.}$$

Bearing resistance of a $\frac{7}{8}$-in. rivet

$$= \tfrac{7}{7} \times \tfrac{9}{16} \times 10 = 4.92 \text{ tons.}$$

Shear resistance in 48 in. depth at 4-in. pitch of $\frac{7}{8}$-in. rivets, from (2), Art. 179

$$= \frac{4.92 \times 48}{4} = 59.04 \text{ tons}$$

which is greater than the shear (from Fig. 256) 2 ft. from the end. The rivets are therefore changed to $\frac{7}{8}$-in. at the next stiffener. Shear at joint B (Fig. 256) scales 42·3 tons, or, calculating from the parabolic and straight-line equations

$$(\tfrac{4}{5})^2 + 55.2 + 0.6 \times 9.75 + (\tfrac{1}{5})^2 \times 27.6 = 42.3 \text{ tons.}$$

Assuming $\frac{1}{2}$-in. webs

$$\text{shear stress} = \frac{42.3}{48 \times 0.5} = 1.764 \text{ tons per sq. in.}$$

Allowable stress with stiffeners spaced $\frac{1}{3}$ of 8 ft., *i.e.* 2 ft. 8 in. centres, or 2 ft. 2 in. apart

$$6 \div \left\{ 1 + \tfrac{1}{1600} \times \left(\frac{26}{0.5}\right)^2 \right\} = 6 \div 2.69 = 2.23 \text{ tons per sq. in.}$$

Assuming $\frac{7}{8}$-in. rivets, resistance in bearing

$$=0{\cdot}875\times0{\cdot}5\times10=4{\cdot}375 \text{ tons.}$$

$$p=\frac{4{\cdot}375\times48}{42{\cdot}3}=4{\cdot}96 \text{ in., say 4-in. pitch.}$$

Number of rivets required (for shear alone) in web joint $42{\cdot}3/$ $4{\cdot}375=9{\cdot}7$. Nine rivets are provided, but the stiffener has surplus rivets. Shear at joint C (Fig. 256) scales $26{\cdot}3$ tons or

$$(\tfrac{3}{5})^2\times55{\cdot}2+0{\cdot}2\times9{\cdot}75+(\tfrac{2}{5})^2\times27{\cdot}6=26{\cdot}3 \text{ tons.}$$

With $\frac{1}{2}$-in. web, shear stress $=\dfrac{26{\cdot}3}{48\times0{\cdot}5}=1{\cdot}10$ tons per sq. in.

Allowable stress with stiffeners spaced 4-in. centres, *i.e.* 42 in. apart

$$6\div\left\{1+\tfrac{1}{1600}\left(\frac{42}{0{\cdot}5}\right)^2\right\}=6\div5{\cdot}4=1{\cdot}11 \text{ tons per sq. in.}$$

The 4-in. pitch for $\frac{7}{8}$-in. rivets is continued to the centre.

Other Details. The cross-bracing of the two main girders, the floor plating, ballast plate and its supports are sufficiently shown in Plate III. The side clearances and lack of parapet girders at the outside of the track take this design outside the usual British railway practice.

On the other hand, the provision of a steel-plate floor, low unit stresses (taking account of the high allowance for dynamic increment of live-load stress) and ample scantlings and rivets for stiffeners and webs are typical of the practice of first-class British railways which design bridges with a view to long endurance under proper maintenance. It has been remarked that the plate girder bridge ranks next to the brick or masonry arch as a durable structure, and with proper facilities for painting and effective drainage it is probably economical to allow some provision for a long working life. A feature which might cause comment is the attachment of the floor plating *underneath* the main flange-plate, thereby putting the rivets in tension; this is sometimes done for more effective drainage and the prevention of leakage at the joint. But in many cases the flooring is placed *over* the main flanges; the matter is one of opinion based on practical experience rather than of theory.

The following Table (overleaf) shows an estimate of weights to check the assumed weight of girder. Had there been any serious under-estimate the design would have required modification accordingly.

Example. Estimate the possible maximum stress on any rivet of the web joint nearest the abutments in the above design, assuming the joint to resist bending moment as well as shear.

Bending moment at 0·2 of the span from the end $=6{,}930\times0{\cdot}2\times$ $0{\cdot}8\div(0{\cdot}5)^2=4{,}440$ ton-in. $\frac{1}{6}$ of the web area $=\frac{1}{6}\times48\times0{\cdot}5=4$ sq.

WEIGHTS OF MAIN GIRDERS AND FLOORING

Piece	Number required	Length	Total length	Weight per ft.	Weight in lb.
			ft.	lb.	
Flange . . $1' 10'' \times \frac{3}{8}''$	1 1	$22' 4''$ } $25' 8''$ }	48	28·05	1,346
,, . . . $2' 3'' \times \frac{7}{16}''$	1	$43' 0''$	43	40·16	1,727
,, . . $4'' \times 4'' \times \frac{1}{2}''$	4	$41' 11''$	167·67	12·75	2,138
,, . . . $1' 10'' \times \frac{7}{16}''$	1	$42' 0''$	42	32·72	1,374
Bearing pl. . $1' 10'' \times \frac{3}{4}''$	2	$2' 0''$	4	56·1	224
Web . . . $4' 0'' \times \frac{9}{16}''$	2	$8' 11\frac{1}{2}''$	17·92	91·8	1,645
,, . . . $4' 0'' \times \frac{1}{2}''$	4	$8' 0''$	32	81·6	2,611
Covers . . $12'' \times \frac{3}{8}''$	8	$3' 4''$	26·67	15·3	408
End pls. . . $1' 10'' \times \frac{1}{2}''$	2	$4' 0''$	8	37·4	299
End angles . $4'' \times 4'' \times \frac{1}{2}''$	2 2	$5' 4''$ } $5' 1\frac{1}{2}''$ }	20·92	12·75	267
Tees . . . $6'' \times 3'' \times \frac{3}{8}''$	9 9	$5' 4''$ } $5' 1\frac{1}{2}''$ }	94·12	11·08	1,043
Gusset pls. . $10\frac{1}{2}'' \times \frac{3}{8}''$	12	$3' 11\frac{1}{2}''$	47·5	13·39	636
Gusset angles $3'' \times 3'' \times \frac{3}{8}''$	12 12	$5' 4''$ } $5' 1\frac{1}{2}''$ }	125·5	7·18	901
Packings . $6\frac{1}{2}'' \times \frac{1}{2}''$	18	$6''$ }			
,, ,,	12	$6\frac{1}{2}''$ }	16·83	11·05	186
,, ,,	4	$4''$ }			
					14,805
			Add 5%	rivets	740
					15,545 =6t. 18c. 3q. 5lb.
Flooring—					
Plate . . $1' 6\frac{1}{2}'' \times \frac{7}{16}''$	2	$43' 0''$	86	27·52	2,367
,, . . . $3' 3'' \times \frac{7}{16}''$	1	$43' 0''$	43	58·01	2,494
Covers. . $6'' \times \frac{3}{8}''$	12 6	$1' 1''$ } $2' 10''$ }	30	7·65	230
Tees . $6'' \times 3'' \times \frac{3}{8}''$	5 10	$2' 10''$ } $1' 1''$ }	25	11·08	277
Angles . $3'' \times 3'' \times \frac{3}{8}''$	12 24	$2' 10''$ } $1' 6''$ }	70	7·18	503
Bracing tees $6'' \times 3'' \times \frac{3}{8}''$	12	$5' 4''$	64	11·08	709
pls. . . $1' 5'' \times \frac{3}{8}''$	6	$1' 1\frac{1}{2}''$	6·75	21·68	146
Ballast pls. $12'' \times \frac{7}{16}''$	2	$43' 0''$	86	17·85	1,535
Ballast angle bars . $3'' \times 3'' \times \frac{3}{8}''$	2	$43' 0''$ }			
Angles . ,,	24	$5' 3''$ }	232	7·18	1,666
Drips . . ,,	2	$10' 0''$ }			
Packings . $3'' \times \frac{7}{16}''$	4	$1' 10''$	7·33	4·46	33
					9,960
			Add 5%	rivets	498
Or 5,229 lb. per girder.					10,458 =4 t. 13c. 1q. 14lb.

Ballast 9 in. deep—200 sq. ft. at 120 lb. per cu. ft. gives 18,000 lb. per girder. Asphalt 1 in. thick, 2,600 lb. and permanent way, say $87·5 \times 40 = 3,500$ lb. Total dead load$= 15,545 + 5,229 + 18,000 + 2,600 + 3,500 = 44,874$ lb.$= 20$ tons per girder instead of 19·5 tons as used in the calculations.

in. equivalent area at the depth of the flange. Total equivalent flange area approximately $=21+4=25$ sq. in. Upper limit to moment of resistance of the web $=\frac{4}{25}\times4,440=710\cdot4$ ton-in.

For the group of 19 rivets on one side of the joint $\Sigma(r^2)$ approximately $=2(4^2+8^2+12^2+16^2+2^2+6^2+10^2+14^2+18^2)=2,280$. Hence from Art. 172 (2) approximately (neglecting the distance between the two rows of rivets) the stress on the outermost rivet is

$$710\times18/2,280=5\cdot60 \text{ tons.}$$

Force per rivet due to vertical shear stress $=42\cdot3/19=2\cdot23$ tons. Total on the outer rivet taking these components as perpendicular,

$$\sqrt{\{(5\cdot6)^2+(2\cdot23)^2\}}=6\cdot03 \text{ tons.}$$

Probably no such amount of stress would be developed, because either the joint would yield and locally relieve the web of its share of bending stress or the friction of the joint would offer a great resistance to bending moment. Allowing for the resistance of bending moment by the joint rivets, to keep the force per rivet down to the specified 4·375 tons would require an extra row of rivets and correspondingly wider cover plates.

182. Plate Girder Through-Bridge. Plate IV represents a through-bridge for a single railway track with a floor consisting of rail-bearers or stringers supported on cross-girders, the whole being covered by plating.

Data. Effective span 40 ft. Construction depth limited to 3 ft. Moving loads uniformly distributed, on 40 ft., 105 tons for central section flange area computation, 113 tons for estimating the curtailment of flange-plates (allowing for overlap), 130 tons for shearing force. Cross-girder centres 8 ft. apart, for which length of rail-bearer allow uniformly distributed 44 tons for flange areas and 58 tons for shearing force. Maximum pressure per rail on cross-girder 14 tons. Working unit stresses for dead loads, 6·5 tons per sq. in. for tension, 5 tons per sq. in. for shear, 10 tons per sq. in. for bearing. For web stress

$$6/\{1+d^2/(1,500t^2)\} \text{ tons per sq. in.}$$

where $t=$ thickness and $d=$ distance between stiffeners which are to be placed at all points of concentrated loading, and elsewhere with centres not further apart than the depth of the web if the ratio of depth to thickness of web exceeds 40. For varying stresses the dynamic formula to be used or impact stress equal to the range of stress to be added to the maximum stress for use with the dead load unit stresses.

Rail-bearers or Stringers. (See separate elevation, Plate IV.)

Flanges.—Estimated dead load on 8-ft. length, including ballast 10 in. deep, asphalt, rail, chairs, $\frac{7}{16}$-in. floor plating, Tee stiffeners and weight of rail-bearer (1,000 lb.) $=2\cdot8$ tons.

Live load per rail, $\frac{1}{2}$ of $44=22$ tons.

Equivalent dead load $2\cdot8+2\times22=46\cdot8$,,

Central bending moment $\dfrac{46\cdot8\times8\times12}{8}=561\cdot6$ ton-in.

Modulus of section required $561\cdot6\div6\cdot5=86\cdot3$ (in.)^3.

Taking the depth over the angles as 14 in., and effective depth 13·5 in., say,

Flange area for central section $86\cdot3\div13\cdot5=6\cdot40$ in.

Assuming $\frac{7}{8}$-in. rivets for flanges and $\frac{3}{4}$-in. for flooring attachment, the width required to get in angle and flooring rivets (see (A), Fig. 257) is about 13 in.; net width, allowing 4 rivet holes, about 9·5 in.

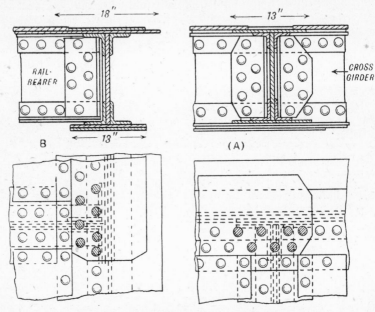

FIG. 257.—Junction of rail-bearer and cross-girder

Two angles $3\times3\times\frac{3}{8}$ in. (see Appendix), less 4 rivet holes, give 2·81 sq. in., leaving $6\cdot40-2\cdot81=3\cdot59$ sq. in.

Thickness $3\cdot59/9\cdot5\ =0\cdot38$ in., say $\frac{7}{16}$-in. plate.

Rail-bearer Rivets and Web.   Assume $\frac{5}{8}$-in. web.

Dead-load shear at the ends $\frac{1}{2}\times2\cdot8=1\cdot4$ ton.

Live-load shear at the ends $\frac{29}{2}=14\cdot5$ tons.

Equivalent dead-load shear at the ends$=1\cdot4+29=30\cdot4$ tons.

Assuming 1-in. rivets, resistance (in bearing)$=10\times0\cdot625=6\cdot25$ tons.

Pitch $p=6\cdot25\times14/30\cdot4=3$-in. pitch.

Plate IV.—Plate Girder Through-Bridge.

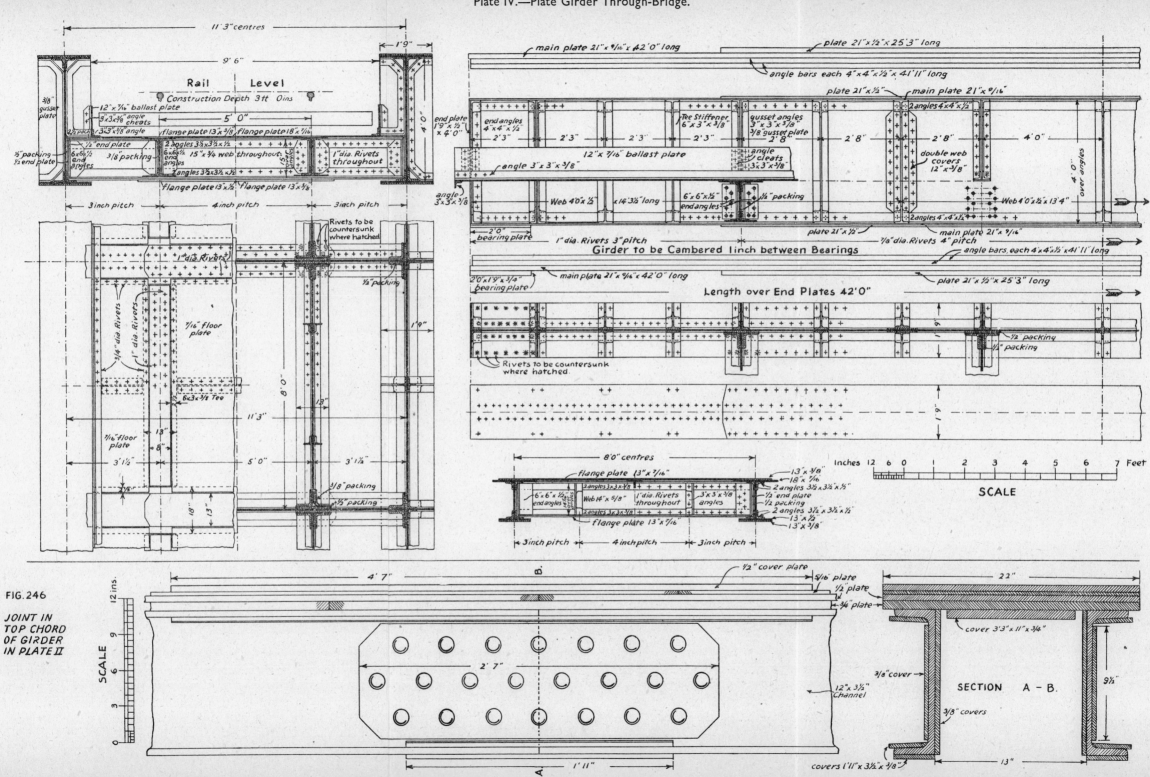

FIG. 246

JOINT IN
TOP CHORD
OF GIRDER
IN PLATE II

SECTION A - B.

To begin 4-in. pitch, try 2 ft. from the ends

Dead-load shear $=\frac{1}{2}\times 1\cdot4=0\cdot70$ ton.

[1] Live-load shear $=(\frac{3}{4})^2\times 14\cdot5=8\cdot16$ tons.

[1] Range of shear $=\{(\frac{3}{4})^2+(\frac{1}{4})^2\}\times 14\cdot5=9\cdot07$ tons.

Equivalent dead-load shear $=17\cdot93$ tons.

$$\text{pitch } p=6\cdot25\times 14/17\cdot93=4\cdot9 \text{ in.}$$

Hence 4-in. pitch may begin at the stiffeners, which are placed 2 ft. from the ends.

Rivets required to transfer the whole end load to the cross-girders

$$30\cdot4\div6\cdot25=5 \text{ rivets.}$$

Shear stress in web $\dfrac{30\cdot4}{14\times0\cdot625}=3\cdot47$ tons per sq. in.

Unsupported distance 24 in. -7 in. $=17$ in., allowable stress

$$=6\div\left\{1+\tfrac{1}{1500}\left(\frac{17}{0\cdot625}\right)^2\right\}=4\cdot0 \text{ tons per sq. in.}$$

but even more would be allowable on account of the small depth between the flange angles.

Cross-Girders. The effective span is taken as the distance between the main girder centres $=11$ ft. 3 in.

Flange Areas. The estimated weight of a cross-girder, together with ballast plate and angles, is equivalent to 1 ton, all uniformly distributed.

Dead load at each rail from stringers, as above, $2\cdot8$ tons.

Live load at each rail (given) 14 tons.

Equivalent dead load at each rail $2\cdot8+2\times14=30\cdot8$ tons.

Central bending moment (see Example 3, Art. 40) $=97\cdot7$ ton-ft.

$$=1,172 \text{ ton-in.}$$

Modulus of section required $1,172/6\cdot5=180\cdot3$ (in.)^3.

Taking the depth over the angles as 15 in. and effective depth $14\cdot75$ in.,

$$\text{Area required}=180\cdot3/14\cdot75=12\cdot23 \text{ sq. in.}$$

Two angles $3\frac{1}{2}\times3\frac{1}{2}\times\frac{1}{2}$ in., less 4 rivet holes, give $4\cdot63$ sq. in., leaving $7\cdot60$ sq. in.

Bottom Flange. Width required for rivets 13 in. (see (B), Fig. 257), net width $9\cdot25$ in.

$$\text{Thickness } 7\cdot60/9\cdot25=0\cdot82 \text{ in.}$$

say $\frac{7}{8}$ in. consisting of $\frac{1}{2}$-in. main plate and $\frac{3}{8}$-in. outer plate (see cross-section in Plate IV).

---

[1] As the load on 8-ft. lengths is considerably concentrated, if $14\cdot5$ tons is a proper amount for the maximum end shears, the intermediate maximum shears will be greater than those given which are the ordinates of a parabola, but will be less than the ordinates of a straight line (see Arts. 61, 62, 65).

Top Flange. Main plate to take the flooring requires $13 + 5 = 18$ in. width (see (B), Fig. 257). The main plate must be $\frac{7}{16}$ in. to lie even with the rail-bearer without packing. Main plate $18 \times \frac{7}{16}$ in., less 4 holes $\frac{15}{16}$ in. and 2 holes $\frac{13}{16}$ in., gives 5·52 sq. in., leaving $7·60 - 5·52 = 2·08$ sq. in. for the outer plate; this being 13 in. wide requires a thickness

$$2·08/9·5 = 0·22 \text{ in.}$$

and $\frac{3}{8}$-in. plate is used.

The flange diagram is shown in Fig. 258, in which the weight of cross-girders, etc., being a small proportion of the whole load, is

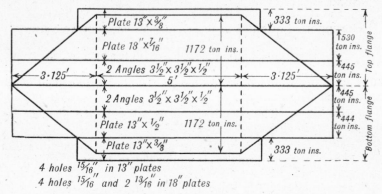

4 holes $\frac{15}{16}''$ in 13" plates
4 holes $\frac{15}{16}''$ and 2 $\frac{13}{16}''$ in 18" plates

Fig. 258.—Flange-resistance diagram for cross-girder

taken as acting at the rail-bearers, at each of which the total equivalent dead load is then $2·8 + 0·5 + 14 \times 2 = 31·3$ tons. Bending moment at and between the stringers, $31·3 \times 3·125 \times 12 = 1,173·8$ ton-in. (Compare with 1,172 with distributed load.)

Each square inch of metal in the section represents a working moment of resistance of $6·51 \times 4·75 = 96$ ton-in. Hence the total provided is

Angles, 4·63 sq. in. equivalent to $4·63 \times 96 = 445$ ton-in.
18-in. by $\frac{7}{16}$-in. plate 5·52 sq. in. equivalent to $5·52 \times 96 = 530$ ton-in.
13-in. by $\frac{3}{8}$-in. plate 3·47 sq. in. equivalent to $3·47 \times 96 = 333$ ton-in.
13-in. by $\frac{1}{2}$-in. plate 4·625 sq. in. equivalent to $4·625 \times 96 = 444$ ton-in.

The curtailment of the outer plates might easily be calculated, for if x is its distance from one end, $31·3x = 445 + 530$, hence $x = 31$ in. for the top flange, and $31·3x = 445 + 444$, $x = 28·4$ in. for the bottom flange.

The live load of 14 tons per rail is a sufficient allowance to give gross lengths, including riveting to the main plate.

Cross-Girder Rivets and Web.   Assuming $\frac{3}{4}$-in. web and 1-in. rivets.

Dead-load end shear, $2\cdot8+0\cdot5=3\cdot3$ tons.

Equivalent dead-load end shear $3\cdot3+28=31\cdot3$ tons.

Resistance of 1-in. rivets in double shear $0\cdot785\times1\cdot75\times5=6\cdot87$ tons.

Pitch $p=6\cdot87\times15/31\cdot3=3\cdot3$, say 3-in. pitch.

The rivets are changed to $\frac{7}{8}$-in. with 4-in. pitch between the stringers where the shearing force is very small.

Shear stress in web $31\cdot3/(15\times0\cdot75)=2\cdot78$ tons.

Connection to Main Girder.

1-in. rivet in single shear, $0\cdot785\times5=3\cdot93$ tons.

Number required to transmit all the end shear $31\cdot3/3\cdot93=8$.

Main Girder.   Take the depth over the angles 4 ft. and flanges 21 in. wide.   Length over all 42 ft.   Estimated weight of girder 7 tons, $\frac{7}{42}=0\cdot167$ ton per foot run, or $1\cdot333$ ton for 8-ft. lengths. This weight may be taken as concentrated like the other loads at the cross-girders without any material error.

Dead Load.   Pressure at cross-girder ends $2\cdot8+0\cdot5=3\cdot3$ tons. Total dead load at each cross-girder $3\cdot3+1\cdot333=4\cdot633$ tons.

Live Load.   For central section flange area, $\frac{105}{2}=52\cdot5$ tons per girder.   The central section is worked out in Example 5, Art. 50.

Flange Diagram.   Fig. 259.

Live load per cross-girder $56\cdot5\times\frac{8}{40}=11\cdot3$ tons.

Equivalent dead load per cross-girder $=(11\cdot3\times2)+4\cdot633=27\cdot233$ tons.

Equivalent bending moment at a and a'

$$8\times2\times27\cdot233=435\cdot7 \text{ ton-ft.}=5,228 \text{ ton-in.}$$

Equivalent bending moment at b and b'

$$24\times27\cdot233=654 \text{ ton-ft.}=7,848 \text{ ton-in.}$$

One square inch of flange section represents a moment of resistance of $48\times6\cdot5=312$ ton-in.   Taking the section from Example 5, Art. 50

Angle bars give $5\cdot62\times312$	$=1,754$ ton-in.
Main plate $\frac{9}{16}$ in. $\times17\cdot25$ in. gives $9\cdot71\times312$	$=3,030$,,
Outer plate $\frac{1}{2}\times17\cdot25$ in. gives $8\cdot625\times312$	$=2,690$,,

Total at central section $=7,474$,,

As shown in Fig. 359, the total moment of resistance at the centre is less than 7,848 ton-in., the value between b and b'; but this is only the value of the bending moment for the flange diagram, reckoned on the $56\cdot5$ tons load.   On the $52\cdot5$ tons load used for the central section design, Example 5, Art. 50, the central bending moment is $615 \times 12 = 7,380$ ton-in.

Main Girder Web and Rivets.

Live load per cross-girder, $65 \times \frac{8}{40} = 13$ tons.

Equivalent dead load per cross-girder $= (13 \times 2) + 4 \cdot 633 = 30 \cdot 6$ tons.

Equivalent dead-load end shear $= 2 \times 30 \cdot 6 = 61 \cdot 2$ tons.

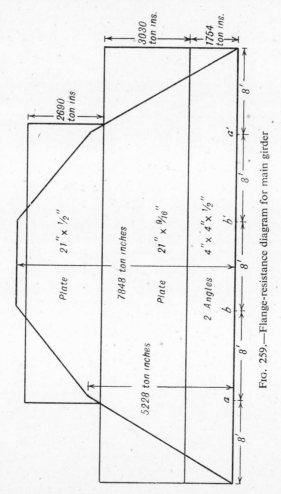

Fig. 259.—Flange-resistance diagram for main girder

Assuming $\frac{1}{2}$-in. web and 1-in. rivets, the resistance per rivet in bearing being $0 \cdot 5 \times 10 = 5$ tons,

rivet pitch for flanges $p = 5 \times 48/61 \cdot 2 = 3 \cdot 92$ in.

hence 3-in. pitch is used at the ends.

The web length for the first panel is 8 ft. $+1$ ft., hence stiffeners are conveniently placed at $\frac{1}{4}$ of 9 ft.$=$2 ft. 3 in. centres (exact multiple of pitch). Over the end plate and at cross-girders and at the web splice two angles and a gusset-plate are used, but for intermediate stiffeners $6 \times 3 \times \frac{3}{8}$ in. Tee sections are used.

$$\text{Shear stress in web} = \frac{61 \cdot 2}{48 \times 0 \cdot 5} = 2 \cdot 55 \text{ tons per sq. in.}$$

Allowable shear stress at 27-in. centres, *i.e.* 21 in. unsupported length

$$6 \div \left\{ 1 + \tfrac{1}{1500} \left(\frac{21}{0 \cdot 5} \right)^2 \right\} = 2 \cdot 75 \text{ tons per sq. in.}$$

Using the conventional method of Art. 132 for the shear in the second panel both for the maximum value and the range, the equivalent dead-load shearing force

$$= 4 \cdot 6 + \tfrac{2}{5} \times 3 \times 13 + \tfrac{1}{5} \times 13 + \tfrac{2}{5} \times 3 \times 13 = 38 \cdot 4 \text{ tons.}$$

Assuming $\frac{7}{8}$-in. rivets and $\frac{1}{2}$-in. web, resistance per rivet being (for bearing)

$$10 \times 0 \cdot 875 \times 0 \cdot 5 = 4 \cdot 375 \text{ tons}$$
$$\text{pitch } p = 4 \cdot 375 \times 48/38 \cdot 4 = 5 \cdot 47 \text{ in.}$$

hence 4-in. pitch is used.

$$\text{Shear stress in web} \ \frac{38 \cdot 4}{48 \times 0 \cdot 5} = 1 \cdot 60 \text{ tons per sq. in.}$$

Using two intermediate stiffeners in the second panel gives centres 2 ft. 8 in., or 26 in. unsupported.

$$\text{Allowable stress, } 6 \div \left\{ 1 + \tfrac{1}{1500} \left(\frac{26}{0 \cdot 5} \right)^2 \right\} = 2 \cdot 13 \text{ tons per sq. in.}$$

$$\text{Rivets required for shear only in web joint} \ \frac{38 \cdot 4}{4 \cdot 375} = 9.$$

The shear in the middle panel is small although changing in sign; $\frac{1}{2}$-in. web may be used with stiffeners 4 in. apart, *i.e.* equal to the depth of the web, with $\frac{7}{8}$-in. rivets at 4-in. pitch. Dead-load shear nil.

$$\text{Live-load shear} = (\tfrac{1}{5} + \tfrac{2}{5}) \ 13 = 7 \cdot 8 \text{ tons.}$$
$$\text{Range} = 15 \cdot 6 \text{ tons.}$$
$$\text{Equivalent dead-load shear} = 7 \cdot 8 + 15 \cdot 6 = 23 \cdot 4 \text{ tons.}$$
$$\text{Shear stress} = \frac{23 \cdot 4}{48 \times 0 \cdot 5} = 0 \cdot 977 \text{ tons per sq. in.}$$

$$\text{Allowable stress} = 6 \div \left\{ 1 + \tfrac{1}{1500} \left(\frac{42}{0 \cdot 5} \right)^2 \right\} = 1 \cdot 05 \text{ ton per sq. in.}$$

Other Details. The comments under this heading relating to stress allowance at the end of Art. 181 are again applicable to the design in the present article.

183. Other Types of Bridge Floors. Bridge Bearings. Steel troughing placed longitudinally over cross-girders, or transversely

s

in lieu of cross-girders, is widely used for bridge floors. Particulars
of the various sections with their modulii are given in steelmaker's
handbooks. Messrs. Dorman, Long & Co.'s *Pocket Companion*
contains several illustrations of its use for both rail and road bridges,
with examples of the calculations which are very instructive.

Bridge floors are also constructed on short-span brick and cement
arches called " Jack arches " spanning from one cross-girder to the

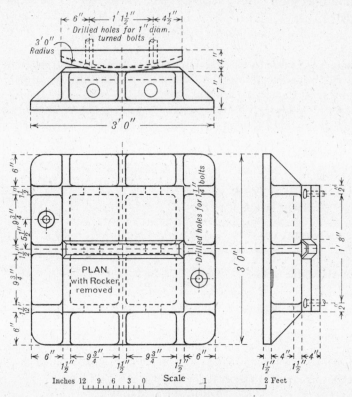

FIG. 260.—Rocker bridge bearing

next in lieu of rail-bearers, or in road bridges sometimes from one
main girder to the next, thus replacing cross-girders.

Various types of bearings are used for bridges; sometimes a
simple bearing or sliding plate attached to the lower flange of the
girder rests on a bed-plate (see Plate II), bolted to the bedstone of
the abutment; such a bearing has freedom to slide, guided by
grooves, to take up expansion, if not prevented by friction.

Roller and pin bearings are also used with the same object, but a
very general type of bearing is illustrated in Fig. 260, which repre-

sents a rocker bearing.   A cast-iron rocker rests on a cast-iron bed-plate bolted to the bedstone, a projection on the bed-plate working in a corresponding groove in the rocker.   The function of the rocker is to transmit the pressure centrally to the bedstone, thereby fixing the effective span and preventing pressure concentration at the face edge of the bedstone.   When expansion of the girder takes place the rocker may either slide or tilt (with increase of camber of the bridge).

The allowable pressure on bedstone is about 12 tons per sq. ft. gritstone, and 18 tons for granite, reckoned on the equivalent dead load in both cases; from this and the end reactions the area required may be calculated.

184. Skew Bridges.   When the main girders of a bridge are not perpendicular to the abutments, as in Plate II, and the cross-girders are placed perpendicular to the main girders, some of the cross-girders near the end of the span rest with one end on the abutment, and are shorter than those which span the full distance between the main girders.   Consequently such cross-girders (which may be lighter than those of full length) transfer less than the full allowance of load to the panel points at their ends on the main girders.   The effect on the main girder bending-moment diagram is to make the ordinates less where the acute angle between the girder and abutment falls inside the bridge than at the other end.   Whether such diminution is worth taking into account depends upon the angle of skew, and the ratio of length of span to the breadth between the main girders.   The bending-moment diagram being not symmetrical with regard to the two abutments, the curtailment of the flange-plates is also unsymmetrical.   In calculating the sections for such a bridge no new principle is involved.

EXAMPLES XVIII

1. Find the lengths of the two outer plates in the girder in Problem No. 17, Examples V, without any end allowances for riveting to the inner plates.

2. Find the length exclusive of attachment allowance, for the outer $\frac{3}{8}$-in. plate of the girder in Problem No. 18, Examples V.

3. A plate girder of 50-ft. span has a web 38 in. deep and 0·5 in. thick, and carries a uniformly distributed load of 144 tons.   Find the necessary thickness of flange plates 16 in. wide at the central section if $6 \times 6 \times \frac{5}{8}$ in. angles are used and the working unit stress is 7·5 tons per sq. in.   If three plates are used, the two outer ones being each $\frac{3}{8}$ in. thick, find their lengths, allowing 18 in. at each end for attachment.

4. Find the pitch and diameter of rivets for double riveting, attaching the web to the flanges in Problem No. 3, allowing 5 tons per sq. in. in shear and 10 tons per sq. in. in bearing.

5. Find a suitable pitch for the stiffeners near the ends of the girder in Problem No. 3.

6. Calculate the weight from the dimensions in Plate IV of (*a*) the main girder, (*b*) a cross-girder, (*c*) a rail-bearer.

CHAPTER XIX

SUSPENSION BRIDGES AND METAL ARCHES

185. Hanging Cable and Relation to Linear Arch. If we may assume perfect flexibility, *i.e.* no resistance to bending, the form of the centre-line of a hanging chain or cable carrying vertical loads, is that of the funicular or link polygon for the loads and end supporting forces, the horizontal pole distance from the vertical load line being that representing the horizontal tension in the cable. Thus if in Fig. 261 a cable of negligible weight is suspended from P and Q and carries the four vertical loads shown, a funicular polygon for

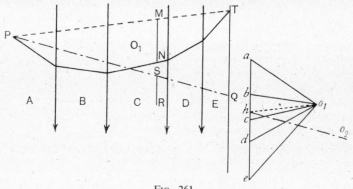

Fig. 261

the loading can be drawn to pass through P and Q and to satisfy one other condition such as that it shall pass through a point R, say, or that it shall have a given pole distance corresponding to a given horizontal tension in the cable. Let the funicular polygon shown in Fig. 261 be drawn starting from P for *any* pole o, and terminating at T on a vertical line through Q. A line o_1h, from the pole o_1 parallel to PQ, determines h. Then the moment of all forces to right or left of a point in a vertical line through R is represented by MN, the height of the closed polygon in this vertical line, which is inversely proportional to the horizontal distance of o_1 from $abcde$. But in the polygon required passing through P, Q, and R the height in the same vertical line must be SR, *i.e.* the vertical distance of R from the line PQ. Hence the horizontal distance of the required pole o_2 from $abcde$ is MN/SR times the horizontal distance of o_1 from $abcde$. And if the line ho_2 is determined as before, the required pole o_2 is completely determined by the intersection of ho_2 with a vertical at the above distance from *abcde*. If the horizontal tension is given instead of the position of a point R on the link polygon, o_2 is found by marking off on the line ho_2 a horizontal distance from *abcde* which represents the given horizontal tension. In all cases each vertical load is balanced by the tensions in the two segments of cable meeting on its line of action. The horizontal tension, which evidently cannot vary throughout the cable since no forces having any horizontal component are applied except at the ends, fixes the precise outline of the cable centre line and supplies the remaining condition to fix the pole position in the line ho_2. For the horizontal distance of the pole from the line *ae* represents the horizontal tension to scale or the constant horizontal component of the tensions in the various segments represented by the lines joining the pole to *a, b, c, d,* and *e*.

For a given shape of the hanging cable and given loads the horizontal tension and the position of the pole for the funicular polygon is thus determinate, but if all the loads and the horizontal tensions were altered in the same ratio, the same formation of cable would still hold

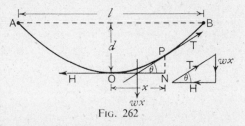

Fig. 262

good. Thus an infinite number of systems of loads having fixed ratios to one another would give a particular formation of cable. Also any given system of loads would give an infinite number of formations, viz. those corresponding to the various poles in the line ho_2, or, in other words, those given by different horizontal tensions. Another simple illustration with uniform loading is given in Fig. 262.

An arch supports vertical loads by material exposed to thrust. The funicular polygon represents the direction of resultant thrust at any section, just as for a suspension cable it represents the direction of resultant pull. The funicular polygon in this case is called the line of thrust or linear arch for the given system of loads. Again, an infinite number of funicular polygons corresponding to any given system of loads may be drawn, and to fix the true line of thrust requires some condition additional to the positions of the end supports. There is an important difference between an arch and a flexible cable in that the line of thrust may pass outside an arch capable of resisting bending, while in the flexible cable the centre line and the line of resistance must coincide. Hence the cable, (1) if free to change shape, will accommodate itself to various loadings; (2) if constrained to a particular shape will take up a corresponding system of stress; if this does not correspond to the loading determinable stresses will be exerted on the constraints.

186. Uniformly Distributed Loads. When the load is uniformly distributed over the span, a case approximately realised in some suspension-bridge cables and in telegraph and trolley wires which are tightly stretched and loaded by their own weight, the form of the curve in which the wire hangs is parabolic.

If the uniform loads are applied at short intervals the funicular polygon would be circumscribed by the parabola corresponding to continuous loading, *i.e.* the points of application of the load would lie on a parabola which the cable would follow if the loading were continuous. When the loading is continuous and easily expressed as a function of some convenient variable, algebraic investigation of the curve is most convenient; the uniformly distributed continuous load is the simplest case of this kind.

Let w be the load per unit length of horizontal span, T the tension at any point P (Fig. 262), and H the constant horizontal component tension. Take the origin at the lowest point O, and the axes of x and y horizontal and vertical respectively. Then the length of wire or chain OP is kept in equilibrium by three forces, viz. T, H, and its weight wx, where $x = $ON, the horizontal projection of OP. Then from the triangle of forces, or moments about P

$$\frac{H}{wx} = \frac{x}{2y} \quad \text{or} \quad y = \frac{wx^2}{2H} \quad . \quad . \quad . \quad . \quad (1)$$

which is the equation to a parabola with its vertex at the origin O. Also

$$H = \frac{wx^2}{2y} = \frac{wl^2}{8d} \quad . \quad . \quad . \quad . \quad . \quad (2)$$

where l is the span AB and d is the total dip.   The tension anywhere is

$$T = \sqrt{(H^2 + w^2 x^2)} \quad . \quad . \quad . \quad . \quad (3)$$

which at the points of support A or B reaches the value

$$T = \sqrt{(H^2 + w^2 l^2/4)} = \frac{wl^2}{8d} \sqrt{(1 + 16d^2/l^2)} . \quad . \quad . \quad (4)$$

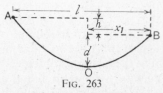

which does not greatly differ from H if d/l is a small fraction. If the points of suspension are at levels differing by h (Fig. 263), and x_1 is the horizontal distance of the vertex of the parabola from the lower support B,

FIG. 263

and d is the dip below that support, from (1)

$$H = \frac{wx^2}{2y} = \frac{wx_1^2}{2d} = \frac{w(l - x_1)^2}{2(d + h)} \quad . \quad . \quad . \quad (5)$$

from which x_1 may be found in terms of d, l, and h.   The intensity of tensile stress in the wire, Fig. 262, is

$$p = \frac{T}{A}$$

where A is the area of cross-section, and neglecting the small variation in T

$$p = \frac{H}{A} = \frac{wl^2}{8Ad} \quad \cdots \cdots \quad (6)$$

Note that for a hanging wire loaded only by its own weight, p is independent of the area of section A, since w is proportional to A. Also that if w is in pounds per *foot* length, l and d in *feet*, p is in pounds per square *inch* if A is in square *inches*.

. The length of such a very flat parabolic arc measured from the origin is approximately [1]

$$x + \tfrac{2}{3}\frac{y^2}{x}$$

hence the total length of cable s is

$$s = l + \tfrac{8}{3}\frac{d^2}{l} \quad \cdots \cdots \quad (7)$$

A change of temperature affects the length of such a hanging wire in two ways: the linear contraction or expansion alters the dip; a change in dip corresponds to a change in tension, but owing to elastic stretch or contraction a change in tension corresponds to a change in length independent of temperature changes.   The change in dip and in tension resulting from a change in temperature is thus jointly dependent on the change of temperature, coefficient of linear expansion, and the elastic properties of the material.

When the dip is *very* small the elastic stretching greatly modifies the influence of the temperature changes.[2]   For such dips as are used in suspension bridges this effect is negligible.

Let s_0 be the initial length of the wire, d_0 the initial dip, p_0 the initial intensity of tensile stress, t the rise in temperature, α the coefficient of linear expansion, w the weight per unit length, A the area of cross-section, w/A is then the weight per unit volume

$$s_0 = l + \tfrac{8}{3}\frac{d_0^2}{l} \qquad p_0 = \frac{wl^2}{8Ad} \quad \cdots \cdots \quad (8)$$

---

[1] If $y = cx^2$, $\dfrac{dy}{dx} = 2cx$ $\dfrac{ds}{dx} = \sqrt{\left\{1 + \left(\dfrac{dy}{dx}\right)^2\right\}} = 1 + \tfrac{1}{2}\left(\dfrac{dy}{dx}\right)^2$

approximately if $\dfrac{dy}{dx}$ is small : $ds = (1 + 2c^2x^2)dx$ $s = x + \tfrac{2}{3}c^2x^3 = x + \tfrac{2}{3}\dfrac{y^2}{x}$.

[2] Numerical examples are given in the author's *Strength of Materials*.

After a change of temperature, neglecting the elastic change in length

$$s = s_0(1 + \alpha t) \quad \text{or} \quad l + \tfrac{8}{3}\frac{d^2}{l} = \left(l + \tfrac{8}{3}\frac{d_0^2}{l}\right)(1 + \alpha t) \quad . \quad . \quad (9)$$

or to a first approximation, reducing

$$d^2 = d_0^2(1 + \alpha t) + \tfrac{3}{8}\alpha t l^2 = d_0^2 + \tfrac{3}{8}\alpha t l^2 \text{ (when } \alpha t \text{ is small)} \quad . \quad (10)$$

or expanding $\qquad\qquad d - d_0 = \tfrac{3}{16}\alpha t \dfrac{l^2}{d_0} \quad . \quad . \quad . \quad . \quad . \quad (11)$

The proportional decrease in stress is

$$\frac{p_0 - p}{p_0} = \frac{(1/d_0 - 1/d)}{1/d_0} = \frac{d - d_0}{d} = \tfrac{3}{16}\alpha t\left(\frac{l}{d_0}\right)^2 \text{ approximately} \quad . \quad (12)$$

Similarly if the cable without a change of temperature is stretched by an additional distribution load w the fractional stretch is

$$\frac{p}{E} = \frac{T}{AE} = \frac{H}{AE} \text{ (constant) nearly, when the dip is small,}$$

hence we may write $\dfrac{H}{AE}$ in place of αt, and the change of dip is approximately

$$d - d_0 = \tfrac{3}{16} \cdot \frac{H}{AE} \cdot \frac{l^2}{d_0} \quad \text{or} \quad \tfrac{3}{128} \cdot \frac{wl^4}{AEd^2} \quad . \quad . \quad (13)$$

Example. A steel cable has a span of 100 ft. and a dip of 10 ft. Find the tension due to a load of 20 tons uniformly distributed horizontally over the span, and also find the length of the cable and the increase of tension due to a fall of temperature of 50° F. if the coefficient of expansion is 0·0000062.

Taking moments about a terminal of the cable

$$H = \tfrac{1}{10} \times 25 \times 10 = 25 \text{ tons.}$$
$$T = \sqrt{(25^2 + 10^2)} = \sqrt{725} = 26 \cdot 9 \text{ tons}$$
$$\text{total length from (7)} = 100 + \tfrac{8}{3} \times \tfrac{100}{100} = 102 \cdot 6 \text{ ft.}$$
$$= 102 \text{ ft. 8 in.}$$

fractional decrease in length $= 0 \cdot 0000062 \times 50 = 0 \cdot 00031$

Hence $\qquad\qquad \tfrac{8}{3} \cdot \dfrac{d^2}{100} = 102 \cdot 6(1 - 0 \cdot 00031) - 100$

$$= \tfrac{8}{3} \times \tfrac{100}{100} - 0 \cdot 0318$$
$$d^2 = 100 - 1 \cdot 19 = 100(1 - 0 \cdot 0119)$$

fractional increase in stress $= \tfrac{1}{2} \times 0 \cdot 0119 = 0 \cdot 00595$

total increase in stress $= 25 \times 0 \cdot 00595 = 0 \cdot 1487$ ton

which may be checked by (12).

187. Simple Suspension Bridge.—In the case of a chain carrying a horizontally uniformly distributed load by uniformly spaced hangers as shown in Fig. 264 by the funicular and force polygons, the shape of the chain is a polygon inscribed in a parabola, *i.e.* having vertices on a parabolic curve.   It may be noted that concentration of loads at the end of a panel (giving nine concentrated loads for ten panels) with two half loads carried directly at the supports, gives funicular ordinates within the parabola except at panel points, whereas concentration at the centre of segments giving as many concentrated loads as panels, as described in Art. 41, gives ordinates outside the parabola except at junctions of segments.

In Fig. 264 the tensions DO and OC balance the vertical load CD, the triangle of forces for the point CDO being *cdo*.

In a suspension bridge the cable is made either of strands of wire which has high tensile strength, or of eyebars pinned at the panel points forming links in a chain.

In a simple unstiffened suspension bridge the load is carried by a

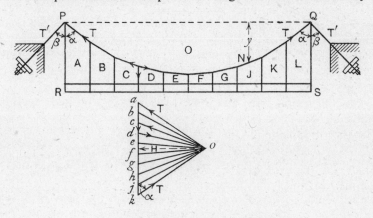

FIG. 264.—Simple suspension bridge

relatively flexible platform or roadway, RS (Fig. 264).   If the dead loads being fairly uniformly distributed give initially a parabolic form to the cable, a relatively heavy moving load for different positions would, by giving very unequal pulls on different hangers, cause the cable to take up shapes varying greatly during the passage of the load.   Such variations would cause variations in the shape and gradient of the platform and would be obviously an impossible condition for heavy traffic such as a railway.   Such simple unstiffened suspension bridges are, in fact, only used for footbridges and similar light loads for which the dead load is sufficient to prevent great variation in the shape of the bridge.   Under uniformly distributed load, in addition to the dead load, the cable would be in the form of the arcs of two or three parabolas.

s*

Relation of a Suspension Cable to Girder carrying the Same Load.
If we resolve the end tension T at Q into vertical and horizontal
components V and H, then taking any section of the cable as at N,
and considering the portion to the right of N, the moment of the
external force is the same as the bending moment on the corresponding section of a rigid girder simply supported at P and Q.   In the
girder the bending moment (here contra-clockwise) is balanced by
the clockwise moment of resistance.   In the cable the same clockwise moment is supplied by the horizontal tension at Q, viz. H . y,
where y is the depth of N below Q.

Stresses in Anchorage Cables and on Piers.   Occasionally suspension bridges have side spans between the piers and the shore in
which the anchorage cables will form approximately arcs of parabolas
similar to that in the centre span.   Frequently, however, the cables
pass in a straight line (neglecting the sag due to their own weight)
from the tops of the piers to anchorages in masonry.   If the cable
passes over a fixed pulley or fixed rollers at the top of the piers, the
tension in the cable is unaltered at those points except for friction
of the pulleys.   If T is the tension (Fig. 264), then T=H cosec α,
and the horizontal (inward) pressure at the top of the piers is

$$H-T . \sin \beta = H(1 - \sin \beta \operatorname{cosec} \alpha) \quad . \quad . \quad . \quad (1)$$

This horizontal force at the top of a pier will produce bending
moments on the pier which will have to be allowed for in the design.
The vertical pressure on the pier is

$$T(\cos \alpha + \cos \beta) = H(\cot \alpha + \cos \beta \operatorname{cosec} \alpha) \quad . \quad . \quad (2)$$

where half the load may be substituted for T cos α if the loading is
symmetrical and P on the same level as Q.

Frequently to avoid horizontal pressure on the piers the cable
passes over saddles free to run on rollers on the tops of the piers.
In this case the horizontal pressure is limited to the frictional
resistance to the movement of the saddle, and neglecting this the
horizontal components of the tensions are the same for the anchorage cables as at the ends of the central span.   If T′=tension of
anchorage cables,

$$H=T' \sin \beta = T . \sin \alpha \quad \text{or} \quad T' = H . \operatorname{cosec} \beta \quad . \quad (3)$$

The vertical pressure on the pier

$$=T . \cos \alpha + T' . \cos \beta$$
$$=T (\cos \alpha + \sin \alpha \cot \beta) \quad \text{or} \quad H (\cot \alpha + \cot \beta) \quad . \quad (4)$$

Bridges with Stiffening Rods.   Sloping stiffening rods from the top
of the piers to the feet of the hangers have been used; these rods do
not carry much of the load on the platform but reduce oscillations
set up by change in shape of the cable due to alteration in position
or amount of the load.

Example. If the cable in the example of Art. 186 passes over a saddle on rollers at a tower and then to an anchorage at an angle of 45° to the horizontal, neglecting friction, find the tension in these backstays and the pressure on the pier.

The slope of the cable at the pier is easily found from the fact that for a parabolic cable it is twice the average slope between the vertex and the point considered (verify by differentiation), viz. the slope is $2 \times \frac{10}{50} = 0.4 = \cot \alpha$. Hence, using the previous result,

$$\text{tension in the backstay} = 25 \times \sqrt{2} = 35.35 \text{ tons}$$
$$\text{pressure on pier} = 25(0.4 + 1) = 35 \text{ tons}$$

188. Stiffened Suspension Bridges. To make a suspension bridge suitable for heavy traffic, it requires stiffening to resist changes of shape in the roadway. This is accomplished mainly in three ways: (*a*) by carrying the roadway on a girder hinged at the two ends of the span, see Fig. 268; (*b*) by two girders each taking half the span, hinged at the piers and hinged together midway between the piers, see Fig. 265; (*c*) by replacing the cable by two stiff suspension girders hinged together midway between the piers; these virtually form an inverted three-hinged arch, see Figs. 271–274. The first two produce statically indeterminate structures, but the third is statically determinate.

In suspension bridges carrying the roadway on stiffening girders the moment of the external forces to either side of a vertical section is balanced in part by the moment of resistance of the girder, and in part by the moment of the tension of the cable at the section. The distribution of resistance between the two depends upon their stiffnesses or elasticities, viz. of the cable and hangers in tension, and of the girder in flexure, and is in accordance with the principles dealt with in Chapter xiv. A treatment on such lines is necessarily lengthy and is outside the scope of this volume. The bending moments and cable stresses are usually estimated on certain simple assumptions as to distribution, but in any given case the results should be used with caution, as their validity will depend upon the relative proportions of cable and girder.

189. Three-hinged Stiffening Girder. It is assumed that whatever the live load on the girders the chain retains its parabolic form which it assumes under the uniformly distributed dead load; such form and the carrying of all the dead load by the cable can be secured by adjustment of the length and tension of the hangers during erection. If the cable remains parabolic, the pull of the hangers, downwards on the cable and upwards on the girders, must be uniformly distributed along the span for all loadings. The function of the stiffening girders is to so distribute the load. The assumed conditions would be approached by very stiff girders and hangers which are equally elastic, *i.e.* the cross-sections proportional to the lengths. Temperature stresses will be to a considerable extent reduced by the central hinge, but the structure is not really statically determinate on account of the hangers.

Let Fig. 265 represent such a bridge, the cable suspended from A and B, and the girders hinged to F and E and together at C. Then taking A as origin, and measuring y downwards, ACB being a parabola with vertex at C,

$$y = 4dx(l-x)/l^2 \quad \cdots \cdots \quad (1)$$

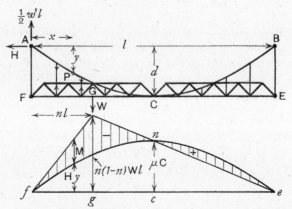

FIG. 265.—Suspension bridge with three-hinged stiffening girder

Then for any live load let M be the bending moment on the girder at the vertical section through any point P on the cable. Let μ be the bending moment for a girder simply supported at its ends on the span FE with the same loading. Let w' be the load per foot run transferred to the cable by the hangers, giving an upward vertical reaction $\tfrac{1}{2}w'l$ at A, the upward vertical reaction at F due to the load on the beam FE being relieved by an equal amount. Then taking moments, say, to the left of a vertical section through P, and ignoring the equal and opposite forces w' and their reactions,

$$M = \mu + H \cdot y \quad \cdots \cdots \quad (2)$$

where μ will be a negative quantity according to the convention of Art. 42 for downward loads, and M may be positive or negative. The value of H, and hence of w', is determined from the fact that M = 0 at the hinge C where $y = d$, for

$$0 = \mu_C + Hd \quad \text{or} \quad H = -\mu_C/d \quad \cdots \cdots \quad (3)$$

and as in Art. 186 by moments of forces on the cable,

$$H = \frac{w'l^2}{8d} \quad \text{hence} \quad w' = -\frac{8\mu_C}{l^2} \quad \cdots \cdots \quad (4)$$

hence from (2),

$$M = \mu - \frac{y}{d}\mu_C \qquad \cdots \cdots \cdots \quad (5)$$

Hence to draw the bending-moment diagram for the girder it is only necessary to draw the diagram of bending moments (μ) as for a beam simply supported at F and E, and subtract from each ordinate a quantity equal to the central value cn of μ reduced in the ratio of the cable depth to the central dip, which is done by drawing a parabola with vertex at n, passing through the ends f and e. The case illustrated in Fig. 265 is that of a single concentrated weight at W distant nl horizontally from F and A.

The graphical aspect of the matter is that the funicular polygon, whether parabolic or otherwise, which shows the form of cable also represents to scale the diminution of bending moment, $H \cdot y$, *i.e.* the upward-convexity bending moment on the girder due to the hanger tensions. The bending-moment diagram (μ) for a beam FE with any loading may be drawn by a funicular polygon (see Art. 41) with any pole distance, but to use this polygon for superposition on the cable polygon it must be to the same scale, *i.e.* have the same pole distance representing H. This may be found by calculation or a trial polygon may be drawn and the central ordinate reduced to the depth d to pass through C, the pole distance being altered in the inverse ratio of the central ordinates; the ordinates measured from the cable polygon to the polygon for the bending moments on a simply supported beam, then give the bending moments on the stiffening girders. Or since from (2) and (3),

$$M = H\left(\frac{\mu}{H} + y\right) = -H\left(\frac{d}{\mu_C} \cdot \mu - y\right) \qquad \cdots \quad (6)$$

the negative bending moment at any section is equal to the horizontal thrust multiplied by the length represented to scale by the excess of the load polygon ordinate over the cable polygon ordinate.

Bending Moments for Simple Loads. Consider the bending moment on the girder at any section G distant nl, say, less than $\frac{1}{2}l$ from the end F (Fig. 265), due to a load W in all positions. Let $x =$ distance of the load W from A; we may find the bending moment M on the girder from (2), remembering that from (3) $H = Wx/(2d)$, and using the value (1),

$$Hy = 2Wn(1-n)x \qquad \cdots \cdots \quad (7)$$

Then for values of x less than nl,

$$M = -W(1-n)x + 2Wn(1-n)x = -W(1-n)(-2n)x \qquad (8)$$

For values of x greater than nl,

$$M = -Wn(l-x) + 2Wn(1-n)x = Wn\{(3-2n)x - l\} \qquad (9)$$

If x is greater than $\frac{1}{2}l$,

$$H = W(l-x)/2d \quad \text{and} \quad Hy = 2Wn(1-n)(l-x) \quad . \quad (10)$$

hence from (2),

$$M = -Wn(l-x) + 2Wn(1-n)(l-x) = +Wn(1-2n)(l-x) \quad . \quad (11)$$

Since (8) is proportional to x, and (11) to $(l-x)$, and (9) is linear in x, we may easily draw the influence line *fpqse* (Fig. 266). Writing $x = nl$ in (8) or (9) gives the ordinate

$$-Wln(1-n)(1-2n) \quad . \quad . \quad . \quad . \quad (12)$$

at g, and writing $x = \frac{1}{2}l$ in (9) or (11) gives the ordinate

$$+\tfrac{1}{2}Wln(1-2n) \quad . \quad . \quad . \quad . \quad . \quad (13)$$

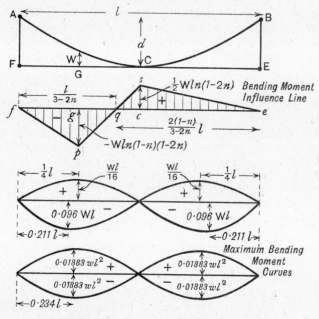

FIG. 266.—For three-hinged stiffening girder

at c. Thus gp and cs differ numerically only in the factors $1-n$ and $\frac{1}{2}$, and as n is less than $\frac{1}{2}$, $1-n$ is greater than $\frac{1}{2}$, and the ordinate gp is numerically the greatest, *i.e.* the maximum bending moment at any section occurs when the load is over the section.

Maximum Moments for Concentrated Loads. The maximum negative bending moment is found by differentiating (12) with respect to n and equating to zero, giving

$$6n^2 - 6n + 1 = 0 \quad \text{or} \quad n = 0.5 \pm 0.289, \text{ i.e. } nl = 0.211l \text{ or } 0.789l \quad . \quad (14)$$

distant $0·211l$ from F and E.   And substituting in (12) the maximum negative bending moment anywhere is found to be

$$0·096Wl \quad \ldots \quad \ldots \quad (15)$$

The positive bending moment for all sections, from (11), reaches a maximum for $x = \frac{1}{2}l$, viz. $\frac{1}{2}Wln(1-2n)$, which is the greatest for $n = \frac{1}{4}$ and has the value

$$\tfrac{1}{16} \cdot Wl \quad \ldots \quad \ldots \quad (16)$$

This is apparent also from Fig. 265, for the maximum positive ordinate is midway between c and e for all values of n, and on the cable diagram is $\frac{3}{4}d - \frac{1}{2}d = \frac{1}{4}d$, which multiplied by the maximum value of H for W at C is $\frac{1}{4}d \times Wl/4d = \frac{1}{16}Wl$. The maximum bending moment curves from (12) and (13) are shown in Fig. 266.

Maximum Moments for Uniformly Distributed Load.   As in Art. 88, we may apply the influence line (Fig. 266) to a uniformly distributed load w per foot by writing $W = 1$ and taking the area between the line and the base line.   From (9), for $M = 0$, $x = l/(3-2n)$, the length to be loaded for maximum negative bending moment at G. Then maximum negative bending moment at G

$$= w \times \text{area } fpq = -\frac{w}{2} \cdot \frac{l}{3-2n} \times \frac{ln(1-n)(1-2n)}{1}$$

$$= -\frac{wl^2}{2} \cdot \frac{n(1-n)(1-2n)}{3-2n} \quad \ldots \ldots \quad (17)$$

Differentiating this with respect to n and equating to zero gives

$$8n^3 - 24n^2 + 18n - 3 = 0 \quad \text{hence} \quad n = 0·234 \quad . \quad . \quad (18)$$

And substituting in (17) the maximum negative bending moment anywhere is

$-0·01883wl^2$ or $-\frac{1}{53}wl^2$ (approx.) at $0·234l$ from the ends . (19)

the loaded length being $0·395l$.

For maximum positive moment the loaded length qe is

$$l - fq = \frac{2(1-n)}{3-2n} \cdot l,$$

and the maximum positive bending moment at G is

$$w \times \text{area } qse = \frac{w}{2} \cdot \frac{2(1-n)l}{3-2n} \cdot \frac{ln(1-2n)}{2} = \frac{wl^2n(1-n)(1-2n)}{2(3-2n)} \quad . \quad (20)$$

which is the same as (17) except in sign, hence as before the maximum positive bending moment anywhere is

$+0·01833wl^2$ or $+\frac{1}{53}wl^2$ approx. $0·234l$ from the ends . (21)

the loaded length in this case being $qe = 0·605l$.   The maximum bending-moment curves from (17) and (20) are shown in Fig. 266.

Shear Influence Line and Maximum Shears. For a single rolling load the positive shearing force (as defined in Art. 42), on the girder is increased by the vertical component of the cable tension, which, if a vertical section be supposed, is additional vertical force on the girder section, hence since the tangent of cable slope is dy/dx, the shearing force

$$F = f + H\,dy/dx \quad . \quad . \quad . \quad . \quad . \quad (22)$$

where f is the shearing force for a simply supported beam on a span l. And at nl from the end F, differentiating (1) for dy/dx and putting $x = nl$

$$F = f + H\frac{4d}{l}(1 - 2n) \quad . \quad . \quad . \quad . \quad (23)$$

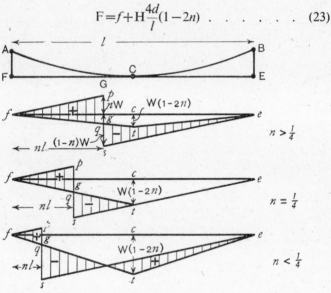

FIG. 267.—Influence lines for shearing force in three-hinged stiffening girder

For a rolling load W, since for the two halves of the span $H = \dfrac{Wx}{2d}$

and $\dfrac{W(l-x)}{2d}$

$$F = f + 2W(1 - 2n)\frac{x}{l} \quad \text{and} \quad f + 2W(1 - 2n)\frac{l-x}{l} \quad . \quad (24)$$

These consist of two terms, the first, f, is the influence line shown in Fig. 102, and also by *fpse*, Fig. 267, and the second is the line *fte* discontinuous at t shown in Fig. 267.   The two parts being superposed, the influence line ordinates are measured from the line *fte* across the shaded area to the line *fpse*.   The diagram takes the different shapes according to the value of n.

The maximum shearing force curves for a single rolling load may be deduced from Fig. 267.

The maximum shearing force curves for a uniformly distributed load may be easily found, also from the areas in the influence diagram, the loaded lengths for the different maximum values being the projections of the areas of like sign in Fig. 267. The positive and negative areas are equal for any value of n, and, consequently, the positive and negative maximum curves are similar. The most important value is the end shear ($n=0$), a particular case of the diagram showing n less than $\frac{1}{4}$ in Fig. 267; then $qs=W=1$, the loaded lengths are $\frac{1}{3}l$ from f for maximum negative shear at f, and $\frac{2}{3}l$ from e for maximum positive shear at f, both values being $\frac{1}{2} \times \frac{1}{3}l$. $w=\frac{1}{6}wl$.

At the centre of the span dy/dx being zero it follows from (22) that the maximum shearing force is as in Fig. 85, viz. $\frac{1}{8}wl$. The complete curves are left as an exercise to the reader.

190. Two-hinged Stiffening Girder. (Fig. 268.) The girder is hinged to the piers at each end. It is usually assumed that the cable remains in the form of a parabola to which it is adjusted by the hangers so as to carry the whole dead load. Such an assumption may be approximate for light loads on a stiff girder, but is not a very reliable assumption without investigation of the proportions of the cable and girder. If the girder were very flexible the parabolic form of the cable would not be retained, and the load would not be uniformly distributed; on the other hand, if the girder were infinitely stiff it would transfer the whole load to the end supports. The assumption is that the hangers carry the whole load, and that the end reactions for unsymmetrical loading are equal and opposite.

Adopting the notation of the previous article (189) for a single load W distant x from F, taking moments about the hinges,

$$R_E=W(x-\tfrac{1}{2}l)/l=-R_F \quad . \quad . \quad . \quad . \quad (1)$$

Also $\qquad\qquad w' . l=W \quad . \quad . \quad . \quad . \quad . \quad . \quad . \quad (2)$

Then as before, $\qquad M=\mu+Hy \quad . \quad . \quad . \quad . \quad . \quad . \quad (3)$

but $H=\dfrac{w'l^2}{8d}=\dfrac{Wl}{8d}$ (a constant, independent of the load position) (4)

Hence the bending-moment diagram (not shown) is found by the difference of the ordinates of the bending-moment diagram (triangular in this case) for a load W on a simple beam span FE and those of a parabola Hy the central ordinate of which is $\frac{1}{8}$Wl (when $y=d$). The triangle will intersect the parabola and give some positive ordinates for all positions except the central one, for which it is tangential at the ends.

For other types of loading the same principles hold, the μ

diagram for a simple span is reduced by parabolic ordinates $\dfrac{w'l^2}{8d}y$ or $\dfrac{Wl}{8d} \cdot y$ where W = total load on the span.

Influence Line for Bending Moment. At a distance nl from F the bending moment due to a load distant x from F is from (3),

$$\mu + Hy = \mu + \frac{Wl}{8d}y = \mu + \frac{Wl}{8d}4dn(1-n) = \mu + \tfrac{1}{2}Wln(1-n) \quad . \quad (5)$$

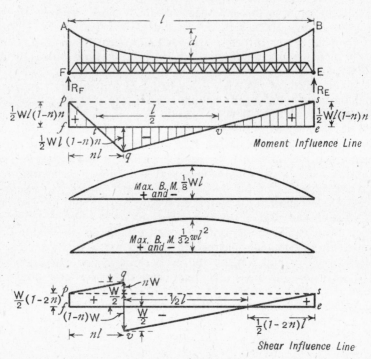

FIG. 268

the first term μ represents the (negative) ordinate of the influence line for the simple span (Fig. 100), while the second term, $\tfrac{1}{2}Wln(1-n)$, is constant for all values of x, hence the influence line is as shown in Fig. 268; it may be looked upon as the triangle *pqs* with the rectangle *pfes* superposed.

Maximum Bending Moment. Due to a single load W, it follows from the influence line diagram that the maximum bending moment, both positive and negative at nl from f, is $\tfrac{1}{2}Wln(1-n)$. For different values of n this gives ordinates of a parabola, the central maximum ordinate being $\tfrac{1}{8}Wl$ (for $n=\tfrac{1}{2}$). The diagram is shown in Fig. 268.

For a uniformly distributed load w per foot it is evident from the influence line that the load must extend over a length *tv* for maximum negative bending moment, and over lengths *ft* and *ve* for maximum positive bending moment; in either case writing $W=1$ the magnitude is $w \times \text{area} = \frac{1}{2}w \cdot \frac{1}{2}l \cdot \frac{1}{2}l(1-n)n = \frac{1}{8}wl^2(1-n)n$, the ordinate of a parabola reaching a maximum value $\frac{1}{32}wl^2$ at the middle of the span where $n=\frac{1}{2}$.

Influence Line for Shear; and Maximum Shear. As in the previous article adding the vertical pull of the cable to the shearing force for a simple beam,

$$F=f+H\frac{dy}{dx}=f+\frac{Wl}{8d} \cdot \frac{4d}{l}(1-2n)=f+\frac{1}{2}W(1-2n) \quad . \quad (6)$$

The influence line (see Fig. 268) is as in Fig. 102 with the ordinates $\frac{1}{2}W(1-2n)$ added, or the base line lowered from *ps* to *fe*.

The maximum positive shearing force for a single load is, for a distance *nl* from F, $nW+\frac{1}{2}W(1-2n)=\frac{1}{2}W$, and the maximum negative shearing force has the same magnitude. The maximum shearing forces are therefore the same for all sections. For a uniform load *w* per foot the maximum positive shearing force is

$$w\{\tfrac{1}{2}n^2l+\tfrac{1}{2}nl(1-2n)+\tfrac{1}{2} \times \tfrac{1}{4}(1-2n)^2l\}=wl/8$$

which is independent of *n* and therefore the same for all sections. It has been pointed out in Art. 188 that the actual stresses depend upon the relative sections of the cable and the girder; the above theory is only a rough approximation. Obviously the bending moment and shears *pf* and *se* in the influence lines of Fig. 268 should be zero. The superposed rectangles *pfes* should in fact be curves on the bases *ps*, the ordinates depending upon the relative sections of the cable and girder. The assumptions and results of the previous article for the centrally hinged girder will be more reliable than those for the girder without the intermediate hinge.

191. Temperature Stresses in Stiffening Girder. If the resistance of the girder is small compared to the cable resistance so that the cable remains parabolic, the girder must sag or rise with the cable due to temperature variations in such a way as to take a uniformly distributed *change of load*. Hence we can calculate the change in chord stress in the girder due to changes in dip of the cable. This change is estimated to a first approximation in Art. 186 (11) as $\frac{3}{16}$ $\alpha t \, l^2/d_0$, which will be increase of dip for an increase $t°$ and decrease dip for a fall of temperature $t°$. But from (16), Art. 79, writing D for the depth of the girder, the change of bending stress is $f=\frac{24}{5} \cdot ED/l^2 \times$ central deflection. Hence,

$$f=\tfrac{24}{5} \cdot \frac{ED}{l^2} \cdot \tfrac{3}{16}\alpha t\frac{l^2}{d_0} =\tfrac{9}{10} \cdot \frac{D}{d_0} \cdot E\alpha t \quad . \quad . \quad . \quad (1)$$

where *f* is in the same units as Young's modulus E, the sag d_0 being in the same units as the girder depth D.   It is interesting to note that this is independent of the length of span and the section of the girder chords, and is proportional to the depth of the stiffening girder.

The temperature stresses in the centrally hinged girder are of about equal magnitude.   For from (1) Art. 189, putting $x=\frac{1}{4}l$, the depth of cable is $\frac{3}{4}d$.   Hence the change of sag is about three-quarters of the change at the centre; but due to turning about the central hinge the change in level is half the change of sag at the centre, hence the central change of level producing stress is *one-quarter* of that in the case of the girder not hinged at the centre; hence for the half-span length $\frac{1}{2}l$, (1) becomes

$$f=\frac{1}{4}\times\frac{24}{5}\cdot\frac{ED}{(\frac{1}{2}l)^2}\times\frac{3}{16}\alpha t\frac{l^2}{d_0}=\frac{9}{10}\cdot\frac{D}{d_0}\cdot E\alpha t \quad . \quad . \quad . \quad (2)$$

In either type of girder a fall of temperature reduces the sag and causes positive bending moment, *i.e.* tension in the top chord and thrust in the lower chord, while a rise in temperature causes moments and stresses of opposite signs.

Example.   A steel suspension bridge has a span of 100 ft., dip 10 ft., and the stiffening girder is 4 ft. deep.   Find the change in chord stress due to a change of temperature of 50° F.; take E= 13,000 tons per sq. in., coefficient of expansion 0·0000062.

From (1) or (2) $f=\frac{9}{10}\cdot\frac{4}{10}\times\dfrac{13,000\times62\times50}{10^7}=1\cdot45$ tons per sq. in.

192. Stiffened Cables.   The suspension bridge in which the cable is replaced by two braced girders hinged together at the centre of the span forms a statically determinate structure.   It has great possibilities of economy for long spans.   The determination of reactions and stresses is exactly analogous to those in the three-hinged arch treated in Art. 194.

193. The Metal Arch and Arched Rib.   An arch may be looked upon as a curved girder, either a solid rib or braced, supported at its ends and carrying transverse loads which are frequently all vertical; the arch as a whole is subjected to thrust.   The *line of resultant thrust* or *linear arch* for an arch carrying vertical loads can easily be drawn when in addition to the vertical loads we know the horizontal component of the thrust of the abutments.   The vertical components of the reactions at the abutments are determined algebraically or graphically as for a straight beam and are not affected by the horizontal thrust if the abutments are on the same level, as is evident if we consider moments about an abutment.

Thus in Fig. 269, representing an abutment of an arch with vertical loads AB, BC, CD, if the horizontal thrust H is known, and the vertical reaction V has been determined algebraically or graphically, and the vertical loads *ab*, *bc*, *cd*, etc., and the reaction $oa=oh+ha$

are set off as shown, the line of thrust AO, BO, CO, etc., can be drawn by starting from the centre of the abutment and drawing lines parallel to *oa*, *ob*, *oc*, etc., terminated by the force lines AB, BC, CD, respectively. At the section shown the resultant thrust of the remainder of the arch on the portion shown is DO represented by *do*. The first step to the solution of the stresses in an arch is to determine the horizontal thrust. In one type—the three-hinged arch—the horizontal thrust is statically determinate, but with the two-hinged and not-hinged types the horizontal thrust is statically indeterminate and the structure is subject to indeterminate initial stresses and stresses due to changes of temperature.

The arch may also be compared with a girder with a curved loaded top chord; when the bending moment curve ordinates are propor-

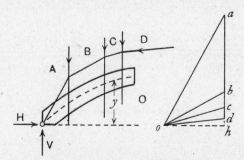

FIG. 269.—Line of thrust

tional to the heights of the girder (see Art. 127) there is no stress in the diagonals, and the vertical shear is carried by the curved top chord in thrust. In the arch the external thrust of the abutments replaces the tension of the lower chord of the girder. If the loading alters, the curved arch has to withstand not the whole bending moments which would arise in a straight girder, but a relatively small difference between them and bending moments of generally about the same average amount over the span. The possible economy of material in the superstructure is obvious; on the other hand, the cost of abutments to withstand the thrust of the arch may more than neutralise this. Steel arch construction is very frequently adopted to span steep gorges, the sides of which provide natural abutments of ample resistance.

The straining actions at any normal cross-section are conveniently resolved into a bending moment and a shearing force, as in the case of a straight beam carrying transverse loads, with the addition in the arched rib of a thrust perpendicular to the section; for, unlike the case of the straight beam, the loads not being all perpendicular to the axis of the rib, the resultant force perpendicular to a radial cross-section is not zero.   Thus, at a section AB (Fig. 270) of an arched

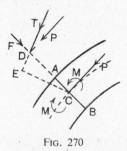

rib the external forces give rise to (1) a thrust normal P through the centroid C, (2) a radial shearing force F on the transverse section AB, and (3) a bending moment M. These three actions are statically equivalent to a single thrust T through a point D, in the section AB produced, where T is the resultant of all the external forces to the right of a section through C, *i.e.* the resultant of

Fig. 270

the rectangular components F and P of the force exerted by the right-hand on the left-hand portion of the structure.   The distance CD=M/P.   For continuous loading the linear arch will be a curve having the directions of resultant thrust as tangents.   The straining action may thus be specified by the normal thrust, the radial shearing force, and the bending moment, or simply by the linear arch, and when the straining actions are known, the stress intensities in the rib can be calculated.   As in straight beams, the shearing force may often be neglected as producing little effect on the stresses.   The curvature of the rib not being great, it is usually sufficient to calculate the bending stresses as for a straight beam, as in Art. 46.   The uniform compression arising from the thrust P is added algebraically to the bending stress, as in Arts. 99 and 100, and the radial and circumferential shearing stress arising from the radial shearing force may be calculated as in Art. 53, and, if necessary, combined with the bending and other direct stress to find the principal stresses, as in Arts. 18 and 54.

In all types, if y is the height of the axis of the arch at any section, and μ is the bending moment calculated as for a straight horizontal beam under the vertical forces only, the actual bending moment M at this section of the arch (conforming to the convention of Art. 42 as to sign) is the algebraic sum of μ and the effect $H \cdot y$ of the horizontal thrust, or

$$M = \mu + H \cdot y \quad . \quad . \quad . \quad . \quad . \quad (1)$$

where μ will always have a negative value for downward loads.

194. Three-hinged Arch. .   In this statically determinate structure, having a hinge at each abutment or springing, and also at the crown, the horizontal thrust H, and hence the line of thrust or linear arch, are found from the fact that the bending moment at the crown hinge as well as at the springings is zero, *i.e.* the line of thrust passes through this hinge.

Graphically.   In Fig. 271 let ACB represent the axis of the arch and W or EF a single load; then since there is no load on the por-

tion CB, the thrust at B must pass through C and be in the direction
BC. Hence if BC meets the vertical line EF in Z and the line *ef* is
set off to represent W, then completing the triangle *efo* by drawing
fo parallel to BZ and *eo* parallel to AZ (since Z is the point of con-

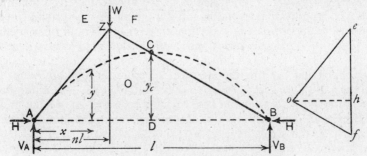

FIG. 271.—Three-hinged arch: single load

currency of the three forces), the reactions *oe* and *fo* are completely
determined, and the horizontal thrust H is their common horizontal
component *oh*.

The graphical problem for the case of several loads is to draw a
funicular polygon through the three given points A, B, and C. In

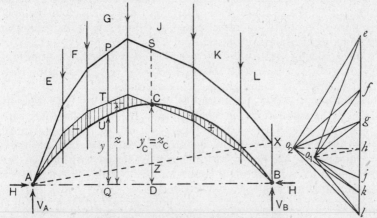

FIG. 272.—Three-hinged arch: several loads

Fig. 272 a trial funicular polygon APSXZA is drawn for any pole o_1,
and then taking a pole distance $o_2h = SZ/CD \times$ horizontal distance
of o_1 from *efgkl*, a line of thrust which is the funicular polygon for
the pole o_2 if started from A will pass through C and B.

Algebraically. In Figs. 271 and 272, if $\mu_0 =$ bending moment for
vertical forces, at the centre D of a span AB, since the bending

moment at C is zero

$$\mu_C + H \cdot y_C = 0 \quad \text{or} \quad H = -\mu_C/y_C$$

Hence for any other section

$$M = \mu + Hy = \mu - \mu_C \times y/y_C$$

Eddy's Theorem. All ordinates of the linear arch from the base AB are proportional to the bending moment of the vertical forces alone, and the ordinate at C is equal to H . y_C or H multiplied by the ordinate of the linear arch; hence the value of μ everywhere is $-H \times$ ordinate (z) of the linear arch (QT representing z to scale); and the actual bending moment for a section through any point U on the axis of the arch is $-Hz + Hy = -H(z-y)$, *i.e.* $-H$ multiplied by the height $(z-y)$ of the linear arch above the axis of the arch. If the linear arch lies below the axis of the arch the bending moment is positive, the signs being as in Art. 42. (Positive moments tend to produce increased convexity of the axis upwards.) The intercepts between the arch axis and the linear arch represent the bending moment to the same scale on which CD represents H . y_C, viz. $p \cdot q \cdot o_2 h$ lb.-ft. to 1 in., where the other scales are p lb. to 1 in., q ft. to 1 in., and $o_2 h$ is measured in inches (see Art. 33).

The normal thrust at U, say, may be obtained by multiplying the resultant thrust (represented by go_2) by the cosine of the angle between the tangent to the arch axis at U, and the direction of thrust GO (or go_2); the transverse or radial shearing force may be obtained by multiplying the resultant thrust (go_2) by the sine of its inclination to the tangent of the arch axis at U.

Algebraically the resultant thrust may be obtained by compounding the constant horizontal thrust H with the *vertical* shearing force determined as for a straight horizontal beam.

It is evident that if the centre line of the arched rib is of the same form as the curve of μ, the bending moment M is everywhere zero, *e.g.* in the case of an arched rib carrying a load uniformly spread over the length of span the bending-moment diagram of μ is a parabola (Art. 40, Fig. 49) symmetrically placed with its axis perpendicular to and bisecting the span; if the rib is also such a parabola the bending moment is everywhere zero.

Example 1. A symmetrical parabolic arched rib has a span of 40 ft. and a rise of 8 ft., and is hinged at the springings and crown. If it carries a uniformly spread load of $\frac{1}{2}$ ton per foot run over the left-hand half of the span, find the bending moment, normal thrust, and radial shearing force at the hinges and at $\frac{1}{4}$ span from each end.

Taking the origin at D, Fig. 272, say, the equation to the curved axis or parabolic curve of the centroids is

$$x^2 = c(8-y) \quad \text{and at A, } x = 20 \quad y = 0 \quad \text{hence } c = 50$$

and $\quad x^2 = 50(8-y) \quad \text{or} \quad y = 8 - x^2/50; \quad dy/dx = -x/25$

which gives the tangent of slope anywhere on the rib.

The vertical components of the reactions are evidently

$$V_A = \tfrac{3}{4} \times 20 \times \tfrac{1}{2} = 7 \cdot 5 \text{ tons} \qquad V_B = 2 \cdot 5 \text{ tons}$$

Taking moments about C

$$7 \cdot 5 \times 20 - 10 \times 20 \times \tfrac{1}{2} - H \times 8 = 0 \qquad H = 6 \cdot 25 \text{ tons}$$

Normal Thrust at A.

Resultant thrust $R_A = \sqrt{\{(7 \cdot 5)^2 + (6 \cdot 25)^2\}} = 9 \cdot 763$ tons

Tangent of inclination to horizontal $= \dfrac{V_A}{H} = \dfrac{7 \cdot 5}{6 \cdot 25} = 1 \cdot 2 = \tan 50 \cdot 20°$

Tangent of slope of rib from dy/dx is

$$20/25 = 0 \cdot 8 = \tan 38 \cdot 67°$$

Inclination of R_A to centre line of rib $= 50 \cdot 20 - 38 \cdot 67 = 11 \cdot 53°$.

Normal thrust at $A = 9 \cdot 763 \times \cos 11 \cdot 53° = 9 \cdot 56$ tons
Shearing force at $A = 9 \cdot 763 \times \sin 11 \cdot 53° = 1 \cdot 95$ tons

Between A and C at x ft. horizontally from D

$$M = -7 \cdot 5(20 - x) + \tfrac{1}{4}(20 - x)^2 + 6 \cdot 25y = -2 \cdot 5x + \tfrac{1}{8}x^2$$

This reaches a (negative) maximum for $x = 10$ when $M = -12 \cdot 5$ ton-ft. The vertical shearing force is then $7 \cdot 5 - 10 \times \tfrac{1}{2} = 2 \cdot 5$ tons (upward external force to the left), the slopes of the rib and the thrust are the same, viz. $\tan^{-1} 0 \cdot 4$, and the normal thrust is equal to the resultant thrust, viz.

$$\sqrt{\{(6 \cdot 25)^2 + (2 \cdot 5)^2\}} = 6 \cdot 73 \text{ tons}$$

At the crown, *vertical* shearing force $= -7 \cdot 5 + 10 = 2 \cdot 5$ tons (downward to the left).

$$\text{Thrust } T_C = \sqrt{\{(6 \cdot 25)^2 + (2 \cdot 5)^2\}} = 6 \cdot 73 \text{ tons}$$

The direction and magnitude of the thrust on all the right-hand side of the rib is constant, being in the line BC (as in Fig. 271).

At 10 ft. from B the bending moment, which is evidently the maximum value on BC, is

$$-2 \cdot 5 \times 10 + 6 \cdot 25 \times 6 = +12 \cdot 5 \text{ ton-ft.}$$

i.e. 12·5 ton-ft. tending to produce greater curvature of the rib.

At B, tangent of inclination of thrust $= \dfrac{2 \cdot 5}{6 \cdot 25} = 0 \cdot 4 = \tan 21 \cdot 8°$

and tangent of inclination of rib (as at A) is

$$0 \cdot 8 = \tan 38 \cdot 67°$$

Inclination of reaction at B to centre line of rib $= 38 \cdot 67 - 21 \cdot 8 = 16 \cdot 87°$

Normal thrust at $B = 6 \cdot 73 \cos 16 \cdot 87° = 6 \cdot 44$ tons
Shearing force at $B = 6 \cdot 73 \sin 16 \cdot 87° = 1 \cdot 95$ tons

195. Three-hinged Spandrel-braced Arch. When the reactions have been obtained algebraically or graphically, as described in the previous article, the determination of the dead load stresses in the members of this structure, illustrated in Fig. 273, gives rise to no special point.   The stresses may be found by the method of sections or by a stress diagram, half of which for uniform panel loads is shown at (*a*) in Fig. 273.

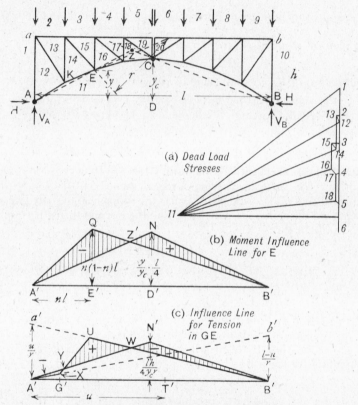

(a) *Dead Load Stresses*

(b) *Moment Influence Line for E*

(c) *Influence Line for Tension in* GE

FIG. 273.—Three-hinged spandrel-braced arch

The use of influence lines will make the determination of the moving load stresses clear.   Taking a vertical section through the panel GF, the stress in GF is found from moments about E.   Now from (1), Art. 193, the bending moment at $E = M_E = \mu + Hy$.   Hence taking unit load, say, the influence line for E is found by super-posing the influence line A′QB′(*b*), Fig. 273, for a beam of span *l* (see Fig. 100), and that for the terms H*y* in which *y* is a constant (height of E above AB) and $H = -\mu_C/y_C$, so that $Hy = -\mu_C y/y_C$.

The influence line for μ_C is a particular case of that in Fig. 100, and has a central ordinate when the load is at C of $-l/4$; hence the influence line for Hy has a central ordinate $ND' = +yl/(4y_C)$. The complete influence line is shown at (*b*), Fig. 273, the base line being A'NB'.

The projections of the shaded triangular areas (see Art. 73) show the portions to be loaded with uniform moving load for maximum negative and positive bending moments at E, corresponding to maximum thrust and tension respectively in GF. And if expressions be written for these areas they give the extreme bending moments at E for unit load per foot, and hence the stress in GF for any uniform load w per foot by multiplying by w and dividing by FE. The projection of the intersection Z' gives the section at which a concentrated load would give zero bending moment at E. This is also shown at Z, the intersection of AE and BC, for a load over Z has a reaction in the line AE which is the only external force to the left of E, and has zero moment about E. If the load moves to the left or right of Z, the reaction line moves above or below E, giving a negative or positive moment at E.

The influence line for the point F, say, will be the same as regards the line A'QB', but will differ in having the point N raised above A'B' in the ratio that F is higher than E above the line AB.

If all the panel points on the curved rib AECB lie on a parabola, it follows that with uniformly distributed load the maximum opposite (positive and negative) bending moments at any of these points are of equal magnitude, for they arise from loadings on complementary portions of the span, and if both these portions are loaded simultaneously, the linear arch is a parabola passing through these panel points and causing zero bending moment at them.

For the moving load stress in the diagonal GE, take moments about T the intersection of GF and KE. Let $r =$ the perpendicular distance of T from GE, and let $u = a$T, $l-u = b$T. Then for unit load moving from a to G for the structure to the right of a vertical section we find

$$\text{Tension on GE} = \{V_B(l-u)/r - Hh\} = V_B(l-u)/r - H \cdot h/r$$

where $h =$ height Aa = Bb.

The first term is represented by the line A'X, a part of A'b', in Fig. 273 (c), reaching a value $(l-u)/r$ (for unit load) at b. The second term is represented by the line A'N'B'. For loads from F to b the first term becomes $V_A \cdot u/r$, and is represented by the line B'U, a part of B'a', reaching u/r for unit load at a. The variation in tension arising from vertical loads passing over GF is evidently linear, hence joining UX completes the influence line for the first term. Superposing the negative ordinates of A'N'B' on the positive ordinates of A'XUB' gives the resultant influence line for tension in GE measured from A'N'B' as a base. The areas give the magnitudes for the tensions for unit load per foot with loads over the portions of the span projected vertically from the shaded areas. The distance along the span to the change point W might also be found by the intersection of AT with BC produced.

The influence line for stress in a vertical member may be deduced in a similar manner.

The uniformly distributed load equivalent to any given train load will not be that for a simply supported girder; the effect of load concentration will be very strongly marked in its effect on the extreme stresses.

Approximate Method. The foregoing stress calculations for uniform loads from influence line areas may be described as exact, but as in Chapter XIII, a conventional calculation may be made by assuming full panel loads. Thus for the maximum negative moment at E, instead of taking a load from *a* to a point over Z and Z', full panel loads at *a*, G, F, and S may be assumed. And for maximum positive bending moment at E, full panel loads from the centre to *b*. Or again, for maximum live load tension in GE, instead of load over the horizontal length between the change points Y and W, full panel loads at F and S only, may be assumed, and for maximum live load thrust, full panel loads at *a* and G and from the centre to *b*. When the stresses in all the members are required, it is convenient to tabulate stress coefficients, *i.e.* stresses for unit loads at each panel point in succession. The dead load and maximum and minimum moving load stresses are then easily selected by adding the appropriate coefficients and multiplying the results by the actual panel loads.

Example. Fig. 274. Find the dead load and extreme moving load coefficients for stress in members FG and FQ.

The coefficients are given in tabular form, and the reader is left to work out the results for other members. The position of the moment centre and their distances from the members may be scaled from a drawing or calculated.

The points A, P, Q, S, etc., lie on a parabola, hence the full live load and the dead-load bending moment and top-chord stresses are zero, and the (complementary) extreme live-load stresses in the top chord are equal and opposite. And, considering the top joints, the diagonals evidently carry the horizontal components of the top-chord stresses; hence they also have zero full-load stresses and equal and opposite maximum and minimum stresses. Also at full loads the verticals must just carry the panel loads, and the arched lower chord must have a constant horizontal component throughout, and vertical components just equal to the vertical shearing force. These tests form satisfactory checks for the tabulated stresses in any member of the structure. It is instructive to check the calculations by the more exact method, using the influence-line areas.

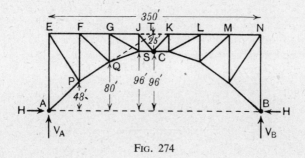

FIG. 274

TABLE OF COEFFICIENTS OF TENSILE STRESS FOR UNIT PANEL LOADS IN FIG. 274

For member FQ, T is in PQ produced, FT$=\frac{73}{32}\times50=114$ ft.   FQ$=\sqrt{(50^2+41^2)}=$ 64·65 ft. Distance of FQ from T$=114\times\dfrac{41}{64.65}=72.3$ ft., which may also be obtained by drawing to scale.

Unit load at	V_A	H	Member FG, moment centre Q, arm GQ=41 ft.	Member FQ, moment centre T, arm 72·3 ft.
F	$\frac{6}{7}$	$\frac{25}{96}$	$-\frac{1}{41}(\frac{1}{7}\times250-\frac{25}{96}\times80)=-0.363$	$\frac{1}{72.3}(\frac{1}{7}\times186-\frac{25}{96}\times121)=-0.0683$
G	$\frac{5}{7}$	$\frac{25}{48}$	$-0.363\times2=-0.726$	$\frac{1}{72.3}(\frac{5}{7}\times164-\frac{25}{48}\times121)=+0.7487$
J	$\frac{4}{7}$	$\frac{25}{32}$	$-\frac{1}{41}(\frac{4}{7}\times100-\frac{25}{32}\times80)=+0.131$	$\frac{1}{72.3}(\frac{4}{7}\times164-\frac{25}{32}\times121)=-0.0113$
K	$\frac{3}{7}$	$\frac{25}{32}$	$\frac{1}{41}(\frac{25}{32}\times80-\frac{3}{7}\times100)=+0.480$	$\frac{1}{72.3}(\frac{3}{7}\times164-\frac{25}{32}\times121)=-0.3350$
L	$\frac{2}{7}$	$\frac{25}{48}$	$\frac{2}{3}\times0.480=+0.320$	$-\frac{2}{3}\times0.3350=-0.2233$
M	$\frac{1}{7}$	$\frac{25}{96}$	$\frac{1}{3}\times0.480=+0.160$	$-\frac{1}{3}\times0.3350=-0.1117$
F, G, J, K, L, M	3	$\frac{25}{8}$	0	0 (approximately)
F, G			-1.089	—
J, K, L, M			$+1.091$	—
G			—	$+0.7487$
F, J, K, L, M			—	-0.7492

Deflection. The deflection of the central hinge C and all other points may be found as described in Arts. 145–147. Adopting the graphical method of Art. 147, the two halves of Fig. 273 may be treated separately as if A*a* and B*b* remained vertical, say, and their lower ends fixed. The changes in length in AC and BC are thus found, and hence, applying the graphical method again to the triangle ABC, A and B remaining fixed, the deflection of C is found, and, if desired, the deflection of all other points may be drawn in.

196. Flexural Deformation of a Curved Rib.   The bending of a curved rib results in an alteration in the shape, and in particular, chords joining points on the original centre line may be considerably altered in length.   Let ACB (Fig. 275) represent the centre line of a curved rib which is subjected to a variable bending moment. To find the alteration in the length AB, consider the effect of the bending of an element of length *ds*; if the remaining part of the bar were unchanged while the element *ds* turned through an angle *di*

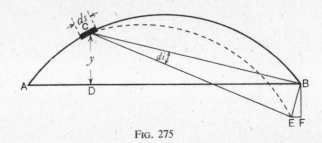

FIG. 275

the rib at A being supposed fixed in position and direction, B would move to E, the horizontal projection of this displacement being

$$EF = EB \cos B\hat{E}F = CB \, . \, di \, . \, \cos B\hat{E}F = di \, . \, CB \cos B\hat{C}D = DC \, . \, di$$
   or $y \, . \, di$.

And from Art. 78 the change of curvature

$$di/ds = M/(EI) \quad \text{or} \quad di = (M/EI)ds$$

where I is the moment of inertia of cross-section, and E is the modulus of direct elasticity.

   Hence the alteration EF in the chord AB resulting from the bending of the element *ds* is $(M/EI)y \, . \, ds$; and the total alteration due to bending is

$$\int (My/EI)ds \quad . \quad . \quad . \quad . \quad . \quad (1)$$

the integral or sum being taken between limits corresponding to the ends A and B.   Bending moments producing greater curvature evidently cause decrease of length of the chord, and those producing decrease of curvature cause increase in length.

   Similarly, the displacement of B perpendicular to AB is

$$\int (Mx/EI)ds \quad . \quad . \quad . \quad . \quad . \quad (2)$$

where *x* is measured along BA from B.

   If A represents a hinge fixed in position about which the rib can

freely turn, and if B instead of being free is constrained to move in
any given locus, the position of B after strain may be found by finding its displaced position, say, B′, by components (1) and (2) as if
the rib were fixed at A, and then striking an arc with centre A and
radius AB′ to intersect the given locus.   For small strains, as in
Art. 147, the arc will be a straight line perpendicular to the original
chord AB.   Hence the actual strained position of B is found by projecting perpendicularly to AB.   Hence, taking A fixed in position
and B constrained to remain in the line AB the shortening of the
chord AB due to flexure is as given by (1).

If the strain due to a variable thrust T along a rib of cross-section
A is taken into account, an arc ds is shortened by an amount
$T ds/(AE)$, and if θ is the inclination of the rib to the chord, the
corresponding shortening of the chord element dx is $T ds \cos \theta/(AE)$
or $T dx/(AE)$.   Hence the additional shortening of the chord is

$$\int \frac{T \cos \theta}{AE} ds \quad \text{or} \quad \int_0^l \frac{T}{AE} dx \quad \cdot \quad \cdot \quad \cdot \quad (3)$$

where l = total length of chord.

In a vertically loaded arch rib the constant horizontal thrust
$H = T \cos \theta$, hence the decrease in the chord is

$$H \int \frac{ds}{AE} \quad \text{or} \quad \frac{HS}{AE} \quad \cdot \quad \cdot \quad \cdot \quad \cdot \quad \cdot \quad (4)$$

where S = total length of arch rib along the axis.

The correction (4) is small and is only important for very flat
arches or deep ribs; it omits a correction due to the change in curvature which is itself only important for arches of great curvature.
Thus for very approximate results correction (4) may be added to
(1) for flat arches and omitted in other cases.

Deflection of the Crown Hinge of a Three-hinged Arch Rib.   The
deflection of C in Fig. 272 may be found by calculating the changes
in AC and BC by (1) corrected by (4) if necessary, and then proceeding as in Art. 147 (Figs. 212 and 216).   The integrals in (1) may not
be easily calculable algebraically; in such a case they may be found
by approximate methods, dividing the arcs into a number of short
lengths δs and taking for M the values at the centres of the short
lengths.

197. Arched Rib hinged at the Ends.   A rib hinged at the ends
differs from one having three hinges, in that bending stress may
result from expansion or contraction of the rib if the hinges at the
ends are rigidly fixed in position.   The stresses in such a rib are
statically indeterminate unless some condition beyond the zero
bending moment at the two hinges is assumed.   It is usual to suppose that before loading the rib is free from stress, and that after the

load is applied the hinged ends remain at the same distance apart as previously, *i.e.* the span remains unchanged. This condition allows

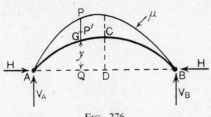

of the horizontal thrust being calculated from the principle of displacement. With the notation of Arts. 193 and 194, let M be the bending moment at any cross-section of which G, Fig. 276, is the centroid; then

$$M = \mu + H \cdot y \quad . \quad (1)$$

FIG. 276

and from Art. 196 (1), the total decrease of span, neglecting the effect of the normal thrust, is

$$\int_A^B \frac{M \cdot y}{EI} ds = \int_A^B \frac{(\mu + Hy) y \, ds}{EI}$$

where I is the moment of inertia of cross-section and *ds* represents an element of the arc AGCB; and by the assumption that the hinges remain in the same position

$$\int \frac{(\mu + Hy)y}{EI} \cdot ds = 0 \quad . \quad . \quad . \quad . \quad (2)$$

or $\quad -\int \frac{\mu}{EI} \cdot y \, ds = H \int \frac{y^2}{EI} ds \quad$ and $\quad H = \dfrac{-\int \dfrac{\mu y}{EI} ds}{\int \dfrac{y^2}{EI} ds} \quad . \quad (3)$

the summations being taken over the whole length of the rib. In a large built-up arched rib I will generally be variable, but if not, and E is constant, (3) reduces to

$$H = -\frac{\int \mu \cdot y \, ds}{\int y^2 ds} \quad . \quad . \quad . \quad . \quad . \quad (4)$$

If y, μ, and *ds* can be expressed as functions of a common variable this value of H may be found by ordinary integration, and in any case it may be found approximately when the curve of μ has been drawn by dividing the arc AGCB into short lengths δs and taking the sums of the products $\mu \cdot y \cdot \delta s$ and $y^2 \cdot \delta s$, using values of μ and y corresponding to the middle of the length δs. If I varies, products $(\mu/I)y \cdot \delta s$ and $(y^2/I) \cdot \delta s$ must be used in the summations.

In a circular arch y, *ds* and horizontal distances can easily be expressed as functions of the angle at the centre of curvature, and if the moment μ can be expressed as in Chapter IV as a function of horizontal distances along the span, the integrals in (4) can easily be found.   In the case of concentrated loads the integral containing μ can be split into ranges over which μ varies continuously.   When H has been found, M and the normal thrust P may be found from (1) as in the previous article, or graphically from the linear arch drawn by a funicular polygon with a pole distance proportional to H.   For a very flat arch the correction (4), Art. 196, may be added to the left side of (2), which adds a term S/AE to the denominator in (3) and a term IS/A or k^2S to the denominator of (4).

Alternative Method.   As an alternative, to find H we may adopt the principle of minimum strain energy (Art. 96).   Again neglecting the deformation due to normal thrust, from ((5), Art. 96), the total strain energy U is

$$U=\tfrac{1}{2}\int M di=\tfrac{1}{2}\int\frac{M^2}{EI}ds=\tfrac{1}{2}\int\frac{(\mu+Hy)^2}{EI}ds=\tfrac{1}{2}\int(\mu^2+2\mu Hy+H^2y^2)\frac{1}{EI}ds$$

and since

$$\frac{dU}{dH}=0,\ \int\frac{\mu y}{EI}ds=H\int\frac{y^2}{EI}ds\ \text{ or }\ H=-\int\frac{\mu y}{EI}ds\div\int\frac{y^2}{EI}ds\quad . \quad(3\text{A})$$

Movement of Supports.   If the two hinges instead of remaining a constant distance apart are forced a distance δx apart by the thrust, δx must be added to the right-hand side of equation (2) and to the numerator of (3), or EI . δx to the numerator of (4).

Graphical Method.   If the force scale is *p* lb. to 1 in., the correct pole distance for drawing the linear arch is $h=H/p$, and if the linear scale is *q* in. to 1 in., P' (Fig. 276) being a point on the linear arch or line of thrust

$$-\mu=P'Q\times p\ .\ q\ .\ h\ \text{ (Art. 41) and }\ y=q\ .\ GQ$$

hence from (3) $$H=ph=\frac{\displaystyle\int\frac{P'Q\times GQ}{EI}ds\times p\ .\ hq^2}{\displaystyle\int\frac{GQ^2}{EI}ds\times q^2}$$

therefore $$\frac{\displaystyle\int\frac{P'Q\times GQ}{EI}\ .\ ds}{\displaystyle\int\frac{GQ^2}{EI}ds}=1$$

If the diagram of bending moments μ be drawn to *any* scale, the ordinates PQ being *n* times the true ordinates P'Q

$$\frac{\displaystyle\int\frac{PQ\ .\ GQ}{EI}\ .\ ds}{\displaystyle\int\frac{GQ^2}{EI}\ .\ ds}=n$$

T

To get the true ordinates P'Q of the linear arch, each ordinate such as PQ must be altered in the ratio 1 to n or multiplied by $1/n$, *i.e.* by

$$\frac{\int \dfrac{GQ^2}{EI}ds}{\int \dfrac{PQ \cdot GQ}{EI}ds}$$

a ratio which can be found for any case graphically, by approximate summation after subdivision of the curve into a number of equal lengths.

Reaction Locus; Single Load W. In dealing graphically with the effect of concentrated loads, such as live panel loads on a two-hinged arch, it is sometimes convenient to construct a locus of the intersections of the reactions. Let Fig. 271 represent a two-hinged arch, in which BZ does *not* necessarily pass through C, and let z be the height of Z above AB, then if the horizontal distance of W from A is nl, by similar triangles

$$\frac{z}{nl}=\frac{eh}{oh}=\frac{V_A}{H}=\frac{(1-n)W}{H}$$

and $\qquad\qquad z=n(1-n)l \cdot \dfrac{W}{H}$ the locus required . . (5)

Parabolic Rib; Single Load W. The case of a parabolic rib is much simplified if we make the reasonable supposition that the value of I varies proportionally to the secant of the angle of slope of the rib, which is unity at C (Fig. 276), $I=I_0$ say. Then elsewhere $I=I_0\dfrac{ds}{dx}$, and substituting this value in (3), E being constant gives

$$H = -\int \mu y dx \div \int y^2 dx \quad . \quad . \quad . \quad . \quad (6)$$

Then in Fig. 271, for a *two*-hinged arch, with single load W, nl from A, $y=4y_C x(l-x)/l^2$, splitting the integration into two ranges,

$$-\int_0^l \mu y dx = \frac{y_C 4W(1-n)}{l^2}\int_0^{nl} x^2(l-x)dx + \frac{4Wny_C}{l^2}\int_{nl}^l x(l-x)^2 dx$$

hence from (6)

$$H=\tfrac{5}{8}\frac{Wl}{y_C}n(1-n)(1+n-n^2) \quad . \quad . \quad . \quad . \quad (7)$$

and substituting this in (5), we get the locus

$$z=y_C \cdot \frac{8}{5(1+n-n^2)} \quad \text{and} \quad z_e=1\cdot28y_C \quad . \quad . \quad (8)$$

Circular Rib; Single Load W. Using the notation of Fig. 271, 277 or 301, but taking the rib as *hinged* at both ends, the load being in the angular position $\theta=\beta$, *i.e.* R sin β to the left of the centre of the span, the value of H is easily found by taking half the value for two loads, W, symmetrically placed at angular positions, β and $-\beta$. From $x=0$ or $\theta=\alpha$ to $x=a$ or $\theta=\beta$, $\mu=Wx=WR$ (sin $\alpha-$sin θ), and from $x=a$ or $\theta=\beta$ to $x=\frac{1}{2}l$ or $\theta=0$, $\mu=Wa=W$(sin $\alpha-$sin β), and writing $y=R$(cos $\theta-$cos α) and $ds=-Rd\theta$, equation (4) gives

$$H=\frac{1}{2}\frac{-\int_0^{2\alpha}\mu yRd\theta}{-\int_0^{2\alpha}y^2Rd\theta}=\frac{1}{2}\frac{\int_0^{\alpha}\mu yd\theta}{\int_0^{\alpha}y^2d\theta}$$

$$=\frac{W}{2}\cdot\frac{R^2\int_{\beta}^{\alpha}(\sin\alpha-\sin\theta)(\cos\theta-\cos\alpha)d\theta+R^2(\sin\alpha-sin\beta)\int_0^{\beta}(\cos\theta-\cos\alpha)d\theta}{R^2\int_0^{\alpha}(\cos\theta-\cos\alpha)^2d\theta}$$

$$=W\cdot\frac{\frac{1}{2}(\sin^2\alpha-\sin^2\beta)+\cos\beta(\cos\beta-\cos\alpha-\alpha\sin\alpha+\beta\sin\beta)}{\alpha-3\sin\alpha\cos\alpha+2a\cos^2\alpha}\ .\ \ (9)$$

which takes the simple form $(W/\pi)\cos^2\beta$ for a semicircular arch when $\alpha=90°$.

198. Temperature Stresses in Two-hinged Rib.

If an arched rib were free to take up any position it would expand, due to increase of temperature, and remain of the same shape. But if the ends are hinged to fixed abutments the span cannot increase, and in consequence the rib exerts an outward thrust on the hinges, and the hinges exert an equal and opposite thrust on the rib; a fall in temperature would cause forces opposite to those called into play by an increase. In either case the horizontal reactions arising from temperature change produce a bending moment as well as a direct thrust or pull in the rib. The change in span arising from these bending moments and that arising from temperature change neutralise one another or have a sum zero.

Let α be the coefficient of linear expansion (see Art. 27), and t be the *increase* of temperature of the rib; then the horizontal expansion, being prevented by the hinges, is

$$\alpha t\ .\ l$$

where l is the length of span. Hence if M is the bending moment produced at any section of the rib, the centroid of which is at a height y above the horizontal line joining the hinges, and ds is an element of length of the curved centre line of the rib, from Art. 196 (1)

$$\alpha tl-\int\frac{M}{EI}\ .\ y\ .\ ds=0\ .\ \ .\ \ .\ \ .\ \ .\ \ .\ \ (1)$$

and since M arises from the horizontal thrust H

$$M = Hy \quad \ldots \ldots \ldots \quad (2)$$

hence

$$\alpha t l - H \int \frac{y^2}{EI} ds = 0 \quad \text{or} \quad H = \frac{\alpha t l}{\int \frac{y^2}{EI} ds} \quad \ldots \quad (3)$$

and if E and I are constant, this becomes

$$H = \frac{EI \alpha t l}{\int y^2 ds} \quad \ldots \ldots \ldots \quad (4)$$

the integrals being taken in either case over the whole span.

The bending moment anywhere, H . y, being proportional to y, the ordinates of the centre line of the rib measured from the horizontal line joining the hinge centres are proportional to the bending moment, thus giving a bending-moment diagram; the straight line joining the hinges is the line of thrust or " linear arch " for the temperature effects. The stresses at any section due to bending, and due to direct thrust or pull, may be calculated separately and added, the former being the more important. If h is the rise of the rib above the hinges at the highest point or crown,

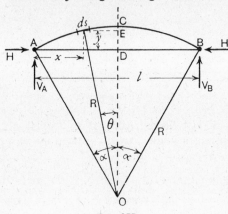

FIG. 277

and d is the depth of the section, taken as constant and symmetrical about a central axis, the maximum bending moment due to temperature change is

$$H . h = \frac{EI \alpha t l h}{\int y^2 ds}$$

and the resulting change of bending stress at outside edges of this section is

$$f = \frac{Hh}{I} \times \frac{d}{2} = \frac{E \alpha t l h d}{2 \int y^2 ds} \quad \ldots \ldots \quad (5)$$

In the case of a circular rib the term $\int_{\theta = \alpha}^{\theta = -\alpha} y^2 ds$ in the notation of Fig. 277 may be replaced by $R^3(\alpha - 3 \sin \alpha \cos \alpha + 2\alpha \cos^2 \alpha)$ as in (9), Art. 197. In the parabolic rib, if $\dfrac{ds}{I} = \dfrac{dx}{I_0}$, using $\int_0^l y^2 dx$, the value is $\frac{16}{15}h^2 l$.

Example. A circular arched rib of radius equal to the span is hinged at each end. Find the horizontal thrust resulting from a rise of temperature of 50° F., the coefficient of expansion being 0·0000062 per degree Fahrenheit. If the depth of the rib is $\frac{1}{40}$ of the span, and E=13,000 tons per sq. in., find the extreme change in the bending stresses.

From Fig. 277

$$l=R \qquad \sin \alpha=\tfrac{1}{2} \qquad \alpha=\frac{\pi}{6} \qquad \cos \alpha=\frac{\sqrt{3}}{2} \qquad ds=-Rd\theta$$

$$y=R(\cos \theta - \sqrt{3}/2)$$

$$\int_{\theta=\alpha}^{\theta=-\alpha} y^2 ds=2\int_0^\alpha R^3(\cos^2 \theta - \sqrt{3}\cos \theta+\tfrac{3}{4})d\theta - R^3 \cdot \frac{5\pi-9\sqrt{3}}{12}$$

$$=0·00996R^3$$

hence, from (4), the horizontal thrust

$$H=\frac{EI\alpha tR}{0·00996R^3}=\frac{50 \times 0·0000062EI}{0·00996R^2}=0·03112\frac{EI}{R^2}$$

The bending moment at the crown is

$$HR(1-\sqrt{3}/2)=0·03112 \times 0·134EI/R=0·00417EI/R$$

hence the extreme change of bending stress is

$$0·00417\frac{EI}{R} \times \frac{R}{80I}=0·0000521 \times 13,000=0·677 \text{ ton per sq. in.}$$

199. Two-hinged Spandrel-braced Arch. This is a statically indeterminate frame of the kind dealt with in Art. 149. A preliminary design may be based on a known structure or on calculations from reactions deduced from (3) or (4), Art. 197, taking the braced arch as a rib having a constant value of I. The stresses in the members of such a design may then be calculated after the horizontal thrusts H have been determined for each position of the load by (6), Art. 149, assuming an infinitely stiff member between the hinges to take all the horizontal force. This will necessarily be tedious for all the live loads, but the work is much facilitated by determining the locus of the reaction lines with the panel load lines. This may be done by determining the intersections for say three points on the half-span (including the centre) and drawing a smooth curve through them. Tabulation from conventional whole-panel loads, as in Art. 195, or influence lines, may be used.

200. Arched Rib fixed at the Ends.[1] The arched rib fixed or clamped in direction at both ends is statically indeterminate, and

---

[1] For a method of solution applicable to a braced arch with fixed ends, including a worked-out example, see Paper No. 4037, by Mason, in the *Proc. Inst. C.E.*, vol. cxciii, 1912–13, part iii.

bears to the rib virtually hinged at each end much the same relation as that of the straight built-in beam to the beam simply supported at each end. The principles of Chapter VIII hold good for the built-in arched rib. In order to draw the linear arch or otherwise find the bending moment at any section X of such a rib (Fig. 278), it is necessary to know the fixing couples applied at the built-in ends and the horizontal thrust, or three other quantities which make the problem determinate from the simple principles of statics.

First Method. We may write, as in Arts. 87 to 91, allowing for the effect of horizontal thrust

$$M = \mu + M_A + (M_B - M_A)\frac{x}{l} + Hy \quad . \quad . \quad . \quad . \quad (1)$$

where μ is the bending moment on a straight horizontal freely supported beam carrying the same vertical loads, M_A and M_B are the

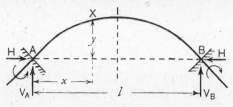

FIG. 278

fixing couples at the ends A and B respectively, H is the constant horizontal thrust, and y is the height of the rib at X above the supports A and B. Bending moments being reckoned positive if tending to increase *convexity upwards* as in Art. 194, the fixing couples M_A and M_B will generally be positive quantities, as in Chapter VIII.

The three unknown quantities M_A, M_B, and H may be found from the following three conditions:

(1) The assumption that A and B remain fixed leads, as in Art. 197, from (1), Art. 196, to the equation

$$\int \frac{My}{EI} \cdot ds = \int \frac{\mu y}{EI} ds + M_A \int \frac{yds}{EI} + \frac{M_B - M_A}{l} \int \frac{xyds}{EI} + H \int \frac{y^2}{EI} ds = 0 . \quad (2)$$

the integrals being taken over the complete length of the curved centre line of the rib; if E and I are constant they may be omitted from each term.

(2) The assumption, as in Art. 88, that the total bending or change from original direction over the whole length of an arch is zero when the ends are firmly fixed gives

$$\int \frac{M}{EI} ds = \int \frac{\mu}{EI} ds + M_A \int \frac{ds}{EI} + \frac{M_B - M_A}{l} \int \frac{xds}{EI} + H \int \frac{yds}{EI} = 0 . \quad (3)$$

the integrals being over the whole length of the curve, and EI being omitted when constant.

(3) If the ends A and B remain at the same level, as in Arts. 88 and 196 (2),

$$\int \frac{Mx}{EI}ds = \int \frac{\mu x}{EI}ds + \dot{M}_A \int \frac{xds}{EI} + \frac{M_B - M_A}{l} \int \frac{x^2 ds}{EI} + H \int \frac{xy}{EI}ds = 0 \quad . \quad (4)$$

the integrals being over the whole length of curve between A and B, and EI being omitted when constant.

The three equations (2), (3), and (4) are sufficient to determine the three unknown quantities M_A, M_B, and H. If all the variables entering into the integrals can easily be expressed in terms of a single variable, ordinary methods of integration may be used. If not, some approximate form of summation by division of the arch AB into short lengths δs, or graphical methods such as are explained in Art. 88, may be used.

In the case of symmetrical loading, $M_A = M_B$ and equation (4) becomes unnecessary; in that case equations (2) and (3) reduce to

$$\int \frac{\mu y}{EI}ds + M_A \int \frac{yds}{EI} + H \int \frac{y^2 ds}{EI} = 0 \quad . \quad . \quad . \quad . \quad (5)$$

$$\int \frac{\mu}{EI}ds + M_A \int \frac{ds}{EI} + H \int \frac{yds}{EI} = 0 \quad . \quad . \quad . \quad . \quad (6)$$

which are still further simplified if E and I are constants.

Second Method. Just as (1) represents a modification in the bending moment μ for a simply supported beam, we may, as in Art. 88 and Fig. 148, look upon the rib fixed at both ends as a curved cantilever fixed at A (Fig. 278) and carrying certain loads, and in addition the otherwise free end B subjected to (1) a vertical supporting force V_B, (2) a horizontal thrust H, and (3) a fixing couple M_B. Let m be the bending moment produced at any section if the rib at B were free. Then

$$M = m - V_B(l - x) + M_B + H \cdot y \quad . \quad . \quad . \quad (7)$$

The conditions stated for equations (2), (3), and (4), taking EI as constant, give

$$\int Myds = \int myds - V_B \int (l-x)yds + M_B \int yds + H \int y^2 ds = 0 \quad . \quad (8)$$

$$\int Mds = \int m \cdot ds - V_B \int (l-x)ds + M_B \int ds + H \int yds = 0 \quad . \quad (9)$$

$$\int Mxds = \int mxds - V_B \int (l-x)xds + M_B \int xds + H \int xyds = 0 \quad . \quad (10)$$

In the case of symmetrical loading V_B = half the load, and (10) may be omitted.

As in Art. 197, the equations (2) to (10) inclusive may easily be deduced from the principle of minimum strain energy by writing the strain energy

$$U = \tfrac{1}{2} \int \frac{M^2}{EI} ds$$

and substituting for M from (1) and then putting

$$\frac{dU}{dH} = 0, \quad \frac{dU}{dM_A} = 0, \quad \frac{dU}{dM_B} = 0$$

Symmetrical Arches. In the (usual) case of symmetry of the curved centre line about the vertical centre line, we may simplify the equations. For writing for the whole length $\int ds = S$, $\int y ds = \bar{y} \cdot S$, where $\bar{y}$ is the mean height

$$\int (l-x)y ds = \int xy ds = \tfrac{1}{2}l \int y ds = \tfrac{1}{2}l \cdot \bar{y} \int ds = \tfrac{1}{2}l \cdot \bar{y} \cdot S$$

$$\int (l-x) ds = \int x ds = \tfrac{1}{2}l \int ds = \tfrac{1}{2}l \cdot S. \quad \text{Also} \int_0^S y^2 ds = 2 \int_0^{\frac{1}{2}S} y^2 ds$$

Inserting these, equations (8), (9), and (10) become

$$\int my ds - \tfrac{1}{2}l \cdot \bar{y} \cdot S \cdot V_B + M_B \cdot \bar{y} \cdot S + H \int y^2 ds = 0 \quad . \quad (8A)$$

$$\int m ds - \tfrac{1}{2}l \cdot S \cdot V_B + M_B \cdot S + \bar{y} \cdot S \cdot H = 0 \quad . \quad (9A)$$

$$\int mx ds - (\tfrac{1}{2}l^2 \cdot S - \int x^2 ds)V_B + M_B \cdot \tfrac{1}{2}lS + \tfrac{1}{2}ly \cdot SH = 0 \quad . \quad (10A)$$

H is independent of the third condition, for from (8A) and (9A)

$$H = \frac{\bar{y} \int_0^S m ds - \int_0^S my ds}{2 \int_0^{\frac{1}{2}S} y^2 ds - (\bar{y})^2 S} \quad \text{or} \quad \frac{\int_0^S m(\bar{y}-y) ds}{2 \int_0^{\frac{1}{2}S} y^2 ds - (\bar{y})^2 \cdot S} \quad . \quad . \quad (11)$$

V_B is independent of the first condition, for from (9A) and (10A)

$$V_B = \frac{\tfrac{1}{2}l \int_0^S m ds - \int_0^S mx ds}{\int_0^S x^2 ds - \tfrac{1}{4}l^2 S} \quad . \quad . \quad . \quad . \quad (12)$$

and from the symmetry

$$\int_0^S x^2 ds = 2 \int_0^{\frac{1}{2}S} (\tfrac{1}{2}l - x)^2 ds + \left(\frac{l}{2}\right)^2 S \quad \text{(see Theorem 1, Art. 34)}$$

hence (12) becomes

$$V_B = \frac{\int_0^S m(\tfrac{1}{2}l - x) ds}{2 \int_0^{\frac{1}{2}S} (\tfrac{1}{2}l - x)^2 ds} \quad . \quad . \quad . \quad . \quad (12A)$$

And from (9A)

$$M_B = \tfrac{1}{2}lV_B - H \cdot \bar{y} - \frac{\displaystyle\int_0^S mds}{S} \quad \ldots \quad (13)$$

Also from moments about the crown the bending moment there is

$$M_C = H(h - \bar{y}) - \frac{1}{S}\int_0^S mds + m_C \quad \ldots \quad (13\text{A})$$

Approximate Summations. If the above integrals cannot be easily calculated algebraically, approximate summations may be made. If the whole length S be divided into $2n$ *equal* parts, it is only necessary to write Σ for $\int$, δs for ds, $2n \cdot \delta s$ for S, $\Sigma y \delta s / n$ for $\bar{y}$, and divide out the factor δs common to the numerators of (11), (12), (12A), and (13).

Varying Moment of Inertia. If the moment of inertia (I) of cross-sections of the rib is variable, the factor $1/I$ will be retained in each of the equations (8), (9), and (10), and the subsequent summations.

It may happen that $I = I_0 ds/dx$ approximately, where $ds/dx =$ secant of inclination of the rib, and $I = I_0$ at the crown. In this case the common factor I_0 disappears, and ds is replaced by dx and the limit S by l, and $\bar{y}$ becomes the mean height of the enclosed area instead of that of the curved boundary. In approximate solutions the lengths δs must not be equal but inversely proportional to the value of I at the centre of each length δs, *i.e.* so that $\delta s \div I = $ constant for each length chosen. The factor $\delta s \div I$ then may be divided out from the expressions for H, M_B, and V_B.

Single Concentrated Load. For a single concentrated load W distant a horizontally from A (Fig. 278 or Fig. 301), from A to the load $m = W(a - x)$, and beyond the load $m = 0$; hence, writing equations (11), (12A), and (13) for ordinary integration or for approximate summation when the centre line is divided into $2n$ *equal* parts, remembering that $\bar{y} = \dfrac{1}{2n}\Sigma(y)$ for the whole length or $\dfrac{1}{n}\Sigma(y)$ for the half-span

$$H = W \cdot \frac{\bar{y}\displaystyle\int_0^{x=a}(a-x)ds - \int_0^{x=a}(a-x)yds}{2\displaystyle\int_0^{\frac{1}{2}S}y^2ds - (\bar{y})^2S}$$

or

$$\frac{W}{2} \cdot \frac{\displaystyle\sum_0^{\frac{1}{2}l}(y) \times \sum_0^{a}(a-x) - n\sum_0^{a}\{(a-x)y\}}{n\displaystyle\sum_0^{\frac{1}{2}l}(y^2) - \left\{\sum_0^{\frac{1}{2}l}(y)\right\}^2} \quad \ldots \quad (14)$$

T*

$$V_{B} = \tfrac{1}{2}W \cdot \frac{\tfrac{1}{2}l \int_0^{x=a}(a-x)ds - \int_0^{x=a} x(a-x)ds}{\int_0^{\frac{1}{2}S}(\tfrac{1}{2}l-x)^2 ds}$$

or

$$\frac{W}{2} \cdot \frac{\sum_0^a \{(a-x)(\tfrac{1}{2}l-x)\}}{\sum_0^{\frac{1}{2}l}(\tfrac{1}{2}l-x)^2} \qquad \ldots \quad (15)$$

which is equal to V_C, the vertical shearing force at the crown, if there is no change between B and the crown, *i.e.* if a is less than $\tfrac{1}{2}l$; and for a load W similarly placed on the right-hand half of the arch V_C is merely changed in sign, V being equal to the vertical upward external force to the right (or downward to the left) of any section in accordance with the convention for F in straight beams (Art. 42).

$$M_B = \tfrac{1}{2}l \cdot V_B - H\bar{y} - \frac{W}{S}\int_{x=0}^{x=a}(a-x)ds$$

or

$$\tfrac{1}{2}l \cdot V_B - \frac{H}{n}\sum_0^{\frac{1}{2}l}(y) - \frac{W}{2n}\sum_0^a(a-x) \quad \ldots \quad (16)$$

Also

$$M_C = H(h-y) - \frac{W}{S}\int_{x=0}^{x=a}(a-x)ds$$

or

$$H\left\{h - \frac{1}{n}\sum_0^{\frac{1}{2}l}(y)\right\} - \frac{W}{2n}\sum_0^a(a-x) \quad \ldots \quad (17)$$

The advantage of these forms of H, V_B, and M_B is that the limits over which the summations are to be taken are short; consequently in tabulating numerical values there are few terms. The values derived from (2), (3), and (4) involve more terms in the summations since μ is not anywhere zero, although some reduction is obtained by taking the value of H for two loads $\tfrac{1}{2}W$ symmetrically placed apart from the crown.

Movement of Supports. If the support B moves relatively to A, the movement can be taken into account by adding suitable terms to the fundamental equations. If B moves δx horizontally from A, δy downwards below A, and rotates δi clockwise, the terms δx, δi, and δy will have to be added to the right-hand sides of equations (2), (3), and (4) respectively, or EI times these terms to the right-hand sides of equations (8), (9), and (10) respectively.

Correction due to Shortening of Rib by Normal Thrust. As for the rib hinged at both ends, approximately for very flat ribs the correction (4), Art. 196, may be added to the left side of equation (2) or EI times this amount to the left side of equation (8).

Stresses, etc. When H, V_B, and M_B are determined, the bending moment anywhere is obtained from (7), and the normal thrust as explained in Arts. 193 and 194. If it is desired to draw the linear arch, the vertical line is drawn and the pole set off from V_B and H. A starting-point is found either at a distance M_B/H vertically below B or M_B/V_B horizontally to the left of B, or M_C/H below the crown.

Example 1. Find the unknown quantities for a parabolic arch, rise of centre line *h*, and distance between centres of fixed ends *l*, carrying a load W distant *a* horizontally from the left-hand support centre, taking $I = I_0 ds/dx$.

It is only necessary to write *dx* instead of *ds* in (14), (15), and (16). The equation of the centre line is

$$y = \frac{4h}{l^2} x(l-x) \quad \text{and} \quad \bar{y} = \tfrac{2}{3}h.$$

$$\int_0^a (a-x)dx = \tfrac{1}{2}a^2, \quad \int_0^a (a-x)ydx = \frac{4h}{l^2}\int_0^a x(a-x)(l-x)dx = \frac{a^3h(2l-a)}{3l^2}$$

$$\int_0^{\frac{1}{2}l} y^2 dx = \frac{16h^2}{l^4}\int_0^{\frac{1}{2}l}(l^2x^2 - 2lx^3 + x^4)dx = \tfrac{4}{15}h^2l. \quad l(\bar{y})^2 = \tfrac{4}{9}h^2l$$

$$\int_0^a x(a-x)dx = \tfrac{1}{6}a^3, \quad \int_0^{\frac{1}{2}l}(\tfrac{1}{2}l-x)^2dx = \tfrac{1}{24}l^3$$

Substituting these in (14), (15), (16), and (17) with *dx* for *ds*, we find

$$H = \frac{15W}{4} \cdot \frac{a^2(l-a)^2}{l^3h} \qquad V_B = V_C = W\frac{a^2(3l-2a)}{l^3}$$

$$M_B = -\frac{Wa^2}{2l^3}(3l-5a)(l-a) \qquad M_C = \frac{Wa^2}{4l^3}\{5(l-a)^2 - 2l^2\}$$

Example 2. Find the horizontal thrust in a symmetrical circular arch, radius R, fixed at the ends, and carrying a single load W. The arch subtends an angle 2α at the centre of curvature, and the arc between the crown and the load subtends an angle β. Notation as in Fig. 277 or Fig. 301, $s = R(\alpha - \theta)$, $ds = -Rd\theta$.

$$S = 2R\alpha \qquad y = R(\cos\theta - \cos\alpha) \qquad (a-x) = R(\sin\theta - \sin\beta)$$

$$\tfrac{1}{2}l - x = R\sin\theta \qquad \bar{y} = R\int_0^a yd\theta \div R\alpha = \frac{R}{\alpha}(\sin\alpha - \alpha\cos\alpha)$$

$$\int_{x=0}^{x=a}(a-x)(\bar{y}-y)ds = R^3\int_\beta^a (\sin\theta - \sin\beta)\left(\frac{\sin\alpha}{\alpha} - \cos\theta\right)d$$

The remaining integrals in (11) are simple, and the result is

$$H = \frac{W}{2} \cdot \frac{\sin\alpha(2\cos\beta + 2\beta\sin\beta - 2\cos\alpha - \alpha\sin\alpha) - \alpha\sin^2\beta}{\alpha^2 + \alpha\sin\alpha\cos\alpha - 2\sin^2\alpha}$$

The calculations of V_B and M_B offer no difficulty.

$$V_B = \frac{W}{2} \cdot \frac{2(\alpha-\beta)-\sin 2\alpha+4\cos\alpha\sin\beta-\sin 2\beta}{2\alpha-\sin 2\alpha}$$

$$M_C = M_B - \tfrac{1}{2} \cdot V_B \cdot l + HR(1-\cos\alpha)$$

$$= HR\left(1 - \frac{\sin\alpha}{\alpha}\right) + \tfrac{1}{2}WR \cdot \frac{\cos\alpha-\cos\beta+(\alpha-\beta)\sin\beta}{\alpha}$$

For a numerical example of the approximate method, see Art. 207.

201. Temperature Stresses in Fixed Rib. With the same notation as in Art. 198, for the direction AB (Fig. 278), in which expansion is prevented as for the two-hinged rib

$$\alpha t l - \int \frac{My}{EI} \cdot ds = 0 \quad \ldots \ldots \quad (1)$$

Also, as in (3), Art. 199

$$\int \frac{M ds}{EI} = 0 \quad \ldots \ldots \quad (2)$$

and as in (4), Art. 199

$$\int \frac{Mx}{EI} ds = 0 \quad \ldots \ldots \quad (3)$$

Let H and V be the vertical and horizontal thrusts at either end of the span resulting from a temperature change of t degrees (V is equal and opposite at the two ends and is taken positive when upwards at A), and let M_A be the fixing couple at the supports due to the temperature change; then

$$M = M_A - V \cdot x + H \cdot y \quad \ldots \ldots \quad (4)$$

This value of M substituted in the three equations (1), (2), and (3), gives the necessary equations to find M_A, V, and H. The bending moment anywhere in the rib then follows from (4).

If the rib is symmetrical about a vertical axis through the middle of the span, V is zero, and the two equations (2) and (3) reduce to one, and equation (4) becomes

$$M = M_A + Hy \quad \ldots \ldots \quad (5)$$

which, being substituted in (1) and (2), gives

$$M_A \int \frac{y}{EI} \cdot ds + H \int \frac{y^2}{EI} \cdot ds - \alpha t l = 0 \quad \ldots \quad (6)$$

and

$$M_A \int \frac{ds}{EI} + H \int \frac{y}{EI} ds = 0 \quad \ldots \ldots \quad (7)$$

from which M_A and H may be found.

The " line of thrust " in this case is a straight horizontal line the distance of which above AB (Fig. 278) is

$$-\frac{M_A}{H} = \frac{\int y ds}{\int ds} = \text{mean height of centre line (if EI = constant)}$$

In the uncommon case of an unsymmetrical rib the line of thrust would be inclined to the line AB, passing at distances M_A/T and M_B/T respectively from A and B, where T is the thrust the components of which are H and V, and M_B is the fixing moment at B, viz. $M_A - V . l$.

The necessary integrals for equations (6) and (7) have been given in the preceding articles for the circular rib and for the parabolic rib in which $ds/I = dx/I_0$.

Example. Solve the problem at the end of Art. 198, in the case of an arched rib rigidly fixed in direction at both ends. Find also the points of zero bending moment.

In this case

$$\int_{\theta=\pi/6}^{\theta=-\theta/6} y\,ds = 2R^2 \int_0^{\pi/6} \left(\cos\theta - \frac{\sqrt{3}}{2}\right) d\theta = R^2\left(1 - \frac{\sqrt{3}\pi}{6}\right) = 0{\cdot}0931R^2$$

$$\int_{\theta=\pi/6}^{\theta=-\pi/6} y^2\,ds = 0{\cdot}00996R^3 \text{ (see Art. 198)}, \quad \int_{\theta=\pi/6}^{\theta=-\pi/6} ds = \frac{\pi}{3}R = 1{\cdot}0472R$$

Substituting these values in (6) and (7)

$$0{\cdot}0931M_A . R^2 + 0{\cdot}00996R^3 . H - 0{\cdot}00031EIR = 0$$
$$1{\cdot}0472M_A . H + 0{\cdot}09310R^2H = 0$$

$$-M_A = \frac{0{\cdot}09310}{1{\cdot}0472}HR = 0{\cdot}08890HR$$

hence $\quad H = 0{\cdot}1845EI/R^2 \quad M_A = -0{\cdot}0164EI/R$

At the crown (Fig. 277) $\quad y = (1 - \sqrt{3}/2)R = 0{\cdot}134R$

and $\quad M_C = -0{\cdot}0164EI/R + 0{\cdot}1845 \times 0{\cdot}134EI/R = +0{\cdot}0083EI/R$

The maximum bending moment is M_A at the supports, and at those sections the extreme change in bending stress is

$$f = \frac{-M_A \times d}{2I} = \frac{0{\cdot}0164EI}{2RI} \times \frac{R}{40} = 0{\cdot}000205 \times 13{,}000$$
$$= 2{\cdot}665 \text{ tons per sq. in.}$$

which is nearly four times the value for the similar hinged arch in Art. 198.

The points of zero bending moment occur when $Hy = -M_A$.

$$y = -M_A/H = 0{\cdot}0889R = R(\cos\theta - \sqrt{3}/2)$$
$$\cos\theta = 0{\cdot}0889 + \sqrt{3}/2 = 0{\cdot}9549 \quad \theta = 17{\cdot}3°$$

Distance from support $= x = R(\tfrac{1}{2} - \sin\theta) = 0{\cdot}2026R$ or $0{\cdot}2026$ of the span.

EXAMPLES XIX

1. Limiting the dip to one-tenth of the span, find the greatest span which a uniform steel wire may have without exceeding a stress of 7·5 tons per sq. in. due to its own weight—viz. 0·28 lb. per cu. in.

2. A suspension bridge cable of 80-ft. span has to support a total load of $\frac{1}{2}$ ton per foot of span, and its dip is 8 ft. Find the maximum pull in the steel cables, and their cross-sectional area and length if the working stress is to be 5 tons per sq. in. If the cable passes over a saddle and the backstay is inclined 30° to the horizontal, find the tension in the backstay and the pressure on the pier. If the cable passes over a pulley, find the horizontal and vertical pressures on the pier, and draw triangles of forces for both cases.

3. A chain consisting of eyebar links has a span of 99 ft., and 10 hangers which divide the span into 11 equal parts, and each hanger carries a load of 2 tons. The right-hand end is 16 ft. and the left-hand end is 4 ft. above the lowest point in the centre line of the chain. Draw the form of the chain, and write down the tension in the successive links from the left-hand end.

4. A suspension cable of 100-ft. span and 10-ft. dip is stiffened by a three-hinged girder. The dead load is $\frac{1}{4}$ ton per foot run. Determine the maximum tension in the cable and the maximum bending moment in the girder due to a concentrated load of 5 tons crossing the span, assuming that the whole dead load is carried by the cable without stressing the girder. Find the bending moment in the girder at one-tenth of the span from either pier when the concentrated load is 25 ft. from the left-hand pier.

5. If the girder in Problem No. 4 is traversed by a uniform load of $\frac{1}{10}$ ton per ft., find the maximum positive or negative bending moment in the left-hand half of the girder due to live load and the lengths covered by the load when these maxima occur.

6. Find the maximum shearing forces at $\frac{1}{8}$, $\frac{1}{4}$, $\frac{3}{8}$ of the span with the data in Problem No. 4.

7. Solve Problem No. 6, but using the loads of No. 5.

8. Solve Problem No. 4 if the central hinge is omitted.

9. Solve Problem No. 5 if the central hinge is omitted.

10. Solve Problem No. 6 if the central hinge is omitted.

11. Solve Problem No. 7 if the central hinge is omitted.

12. Find the change in the stress in the chords of a two- or three-hinged stiffening girder of a suspension bridge due to a change of 60° F. in temperature if the dip is 20 ft. and the depth of the girder 7 ft. (E = 13,000 tons per sq. in. Coefficient of expansion 62×10^{-7}.)

13. A symmetrical three-hinged arch rib is of circular form, has a span of 50 ft. and a rise of 10 ft. If the uniformly distributed load is 1 ton per foot of span, find the horizontal thrust and the bending moment at $\frac{1}{4}$ span (horizontally) from one end.

14. A parabolic arched rib, hinged at the springings and crown, has a span of 50 ft. and a rise of 10 ft.; if the load varies uniformly with the horizontal distance from the crown from $\frac{1}{2}$ ton per foot of span at the crown to 1 ton per foot run at the springings, find the horizontal thrust and the bending moment at $\frac{1}{4}$ span. What is the normal thrust and the shearing force 5 ft. from one of the abutments?

15. If the rib in Problem No. 14 has a concentrated load of 5 tons, 12·5 ft. from one support, find the horizontal thrust and the bending moments on the rib at the $\frac{1}{4}$-span points; also if it has 5-ton loads at 12·5 ft. from *each* end support.

16. Find approximately in terms of the panel loads W, say, the extreme live-load stresses in EF and EP (Fig. 274).

17. Find by the exact method the extreme moving load stresses in FG (Fig. 274) for a uniform load w per ft.

18. Find the horizontal thrust for the arch in Problem No. 14 if it is hinged at the ends only.

19. A parabolic two-hinged arched rib has a span of 40 ft. and a rise of

8 ft., and carries a load of 10 tons at the crown. The moment of inertia of the cross-section of the rib is everywhere proportional to the secant of the angle of slope of the rib. Find the horizontal thrust and the bending moment at the crown.

20. Solve Problem No. 19 if the load is at (*a*) $\frac{1}{4}$ span, (*b*) $\frac{1}{5}$ span.

21. A circular arched rib 40-ft. radius hinged at both ends and subtending an angle of 90° at the centre carries a load of 1 ton at a horizontal distance of 20 ft. from midspan. Find what horizontal thrust is caused by this load.

22. Find the maximum intensity of bending stress in a circular arched rib 50-ft. span and 10-ft. rise, hinged at each end, due to a rise in temperature of 60° F., the constant depth of the rib being 12 in. (Coefficient of expansion $\frac{2}{3} \times 10^{-5}$. E = 12,500 tons per sq. in.)

23. Solve Problem No. 19 if the rib is fixed at both ends.

24. A semicircular arched rib of span *l*, and fixed at both ends, carries a load W at the crown. Find the bending moment, normal thrust, and shearing force at the ends and crown.

25. Solve Problem No. 21 if the rib is fixed at both ends.

26. A piece of steel 1 in. square is bent into a semicircle of 20 in. mean radius, and both ends are firmly clamped. Find the maximum bending stress resulting from a change in temperature of 100° F. in the steel. What is the angular distance of the points of zero-bending moment from the crown of the semicircle? (Coefficient of expansion 62×10^{-7}. $E = 30 \times 10^6$ lb. per sq. in.)

27. Solve Problem No. 22 if the rib is fixed at both ends.

CHAPTER XX

EARTH PRESSURE, FOUNDATIONS, MASONRY STRUCTURES

202. Earth Pressure. In order to compute the forces to which various foundations and masonry structures, etc., such as retaining walls, are subjected, the pressures exerted by and on plane faces of earth are required. There are numerous theories as to the pressure exerted, differing somewhat in the assumptions made and the expressions deduced. Most theories are based upon the supposition that earth is a granular mass entirely lacking in cohesion and having for each kind of earth a definite angle of repose or natural slope which it will assume if left unsupported for a sufficient time. The various theories give results which in most practical cases do not materially differ from one another. There is very little experimental evidence that the calculated pressures form a reliable guide to the actual conditions which vary with many circumstances. The cohesion in moist, well-rammed earth is often very considerable, and in consequence many structures are able to withstand earth pressure which, if the granular earth theories gave correct values, would be quite unsafe.

It is well to recognise that earth pressures cannot be calculated with anything approaching the accuracy usually possible in say stress computations for a simple steel framework or a simply supported steel beam. One theory is here given in some detail, and for others the reader is referred to books specially devoted to such matters.

Rankine's Theory of Earth Pressure. This postulates dry granular particles of earth free from cohesion but held in place by friction and indefinite in extent. It follows that at any plane surface within a mass of earth the pressure cannot be inclined to the normal at a greater angle than the angle of repose of such earth, without slipping taking place. Notation: φ = angle of repose of earth = maximum angle which any resultant force across any internal face can make to the normal without slipping occurring. w = weight of unit volume of earth (say pounds per cubic foot).

(*a*) *Vertical Wall Face: Horizontal Earth Surface.* When slipping is about to take place downwards across the plane where the resultant force is most oblique to the normal, it follows from (8), Art. 15, that the smaller principal stress is

$$p_y = p_x \cdot \frac{1 - \sin \varphi}{1 + \sin \varphi} \qquad \qquad (1)$$

where p_x is the intensity of the maximum principal stress.

At a depth h in the earth the maximum principal stress will be vertical, *i.e.* perpendicular to a horizontal face and equal to wh, since 1 sq. ft., say, supports a column of earth h ft. high, having contents h cu. ft. and weight wh lb. Hence the horizontal pressure in pounds per square foot is

$$p_y = wh \cdot \frac{1-\sin \varphi}{1+\sin \varphi} \quad \ldots \ldots \quad (2)$$

which is proportional to h. Hence the total pressure per foot length of a vertical face is (average intensity × area)

$$P = \tfrac{1}{2}wh \cdot \frac{1-\sin \varphi}{1+\sin \varphi} \cdot h = \tfrac{1}{2}wh^2\frac{1-\sin \varphi}{1+\sin \varphi} \text{ or } \tfrac{1}{2}w \cdot h^2 \tan^2(45° - \tfrac{1}{2}\varphi) \, . \, (3)$$

or　$\rho \times \dfrac{1-\sin \varphi}{1+\sin \varphi}$ times that of water pressure on the same wall face,

where ρ is the specific gravity of the earth. The force P acts as shown in Fig. 279 at a depth of $\tfrac{2}{3}$ of h from the horizontal earth surface.[1]

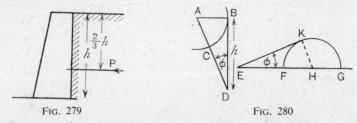

FIG. 279　　　　　　　　　　FIG. 280

It will be noticed from (2) and (3) that the magnitudes are those for the pressure of a liquid of density w per unit volume multiplied by the coefficient $\dfrac{1-\sin \varphi}{1+\sin \varphi}$, which is unity for a liquid, which may be defined by the static property $\varphi = 0$.

Simple graphical constructions for P and for $wh\dfrac{1-\sin \varphi}{1+\sin \varphi}$ are shown in Fig. 280; $AC = AB$, $BD = h$, angle $A\hat{D}B = \varphi$, then $P = \tfrac{1}{2} \cdot w \cdot CD^2$. And if $EG = wh$ to scale and the semicircle FKG is drawn to touch EK inclined φ to EG, $EF = wh\dfrac{1-\sin \varphi}{1+\sin \varphi}$.

(*b*) *Sloping Wall Face : Horizontal Earth Face.* Let the slope be θ to the vertical (see Fig. 281). Then the intensity of pressure across the face at a depth h by (3), Art. 15, is

$$p = \sqrt{(p_x{}^2 \sin^2 \theta + p_y{}^2 \cos^2 \theta)} = \sqrt{(p_n{}^2 + p_t{}^2)} \quad . \quad . \quad (4)$$

---

[1] For the depth of the centre of pressure see any book dealing with the mechanics of fluids, such as the author's *Mechanics for Engineers*.

where $p_x = wh$ and p_y as before is $wh \cdot \dfrac{1-\sin\varphi}{1+\sin\varphi}$, hence p is proportional to h. The total pressure per foot length of wall face is $\frac{1}{2}p \times$ area or substituting

$$P = p \cdot \tfrac{1}{2}h \cdot \sec\theta = \tfrac{1}{2}wh^2\sqrt{\{\tan^2\theta + \tan^4(45 - \tfrac{1}{2}\varphi)\}} \quad (5)$$

and this pressure acts in the direction given by (5), Art. 15.

Graphical Construction. The value of p may be found graphically, the principal stresses p_x and p_y being known as above. The graphical construction is shown in Fig. 282, where p_x is across a horizontal

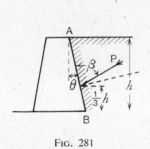

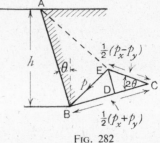

FIG. 281   FIG. 282

plane. The proof, with the notation of Art. 15 is as follows:

$$ED = \tfrac{1}{2}(p_x - p_y)\sin 2\theta = p$$
$$BD = \tfrac{1}{2}(p_x + p_y) - \tfrac{1}{2}(p_x - p_y)\cos 2\theta$$
$$= \tfrac{1}{2}p_x(1 - \cos 2\theta) + \tfrac{1}{2}p_y(1 + \cos 2\theta)$$
$$= p_x\sin^2\theta + p_y\cos^2\theta = p_n$$
$$BE = \sqrt{(BD^2 + ED^2)} = \sqrt{(p_n^2 + p^2)} = p.$$

$$P = \tfrac{1}{2}ph\sec\theta \text{ or } \tfrac{1}{2}p \cdot AB \quad\quad\quad (6)$$

acting parallel to BE through a point in AB, $\frac{2}{3}$ of AB from A.

(c) *Vertical Wall surcharged at Slope* α. Rankine assumed that the pressure on a vertical face was parallel to the earth slope, *i.e.* inclined α to the horizontal. Then at any depth h the vertical pressure p_1 on a plane face inclined α to the horizontal, forms with the resultant pressure intensity p_2 on a vertical face a pair of conjugate stresses, *i.e.* p_1 is parallel to the face across which p_2 acts, and p_2 is parallel to the face across which p_1 acts. Now referring to Fig. 283,

$$p_1 = \frac{wh}{\sec\alpha} = wh\cos\alpha \text{ (not a principal stress)} \quad . \quad (7)$$

The stresses p_1 and p_2 may be looked upon as resultants of principal stresses p_x and p_y (in directions unknown), and therefore of a normal stress $\frac{1}{2}(p_x + p_y)$ added geometrically to a stress $\frac{1}{2}(p_x - p_y)$

acting at an unknown angle 2θ to the normals of the faces giving resultants inclined α to the normals. Fig. 284 represents the vector diagram, AC being proportional to $\frac{1}{2}(p_x + p_y)$ and BC ($=$CD) to $\frac{1}{2}(p_x - p_y)$. The two stresses inclined α to the normals are represented by AB and AD, so that

$$\frac{p_2}{p_1} = \frac{AB}{AD} \quad \cdot \quad \cdot \quad \cdot \quad \cdot \quad \cdot \quad \cdot \quad (8)$$

and substituting in terms of AC and BC and writing from (9),

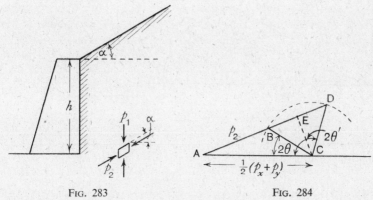

FIG. 283   FIG. 284

Art. 15 or (5), Art. 17, when slipping is about to take place, $\dfrac{p_x - p_y}{p_x + p_y} = \sin \varphi$, and using (7) we get

$$p_2 = wh \cdot \cos \alpha \cdot \frac{\cos \alpha - \surd(\cos^2 \alpha - \cos^2 \varphi)}{\cos \alpha + \surd(\cos^2 \alpha - \cos^2 \varphi)} \quad \cdot \quad (9)$$

which reduces to (1) when $\alpha = 0$.

The total pressure per foot length of face is

$$P = \tfrac{1}{2}p_2 \cdot h = \tfrac{1}{2}wh^2 \cdot \cos \alpha \cdot \frac{\cos \alpha - \surd(\cos^2 \alpha - \cos^2 \varphi)}{\cos \alpha + \surd(\cos^2 \alpha - \cos^2 \varphi)} \quad \cdot \quad (10)$$

If the surcharge reaches the maximum possible angle φ (10) becomes the maximum possible pressure on a vertical wall, viz.

$$P = \tfrac{1}{2}wh^2 \cdot \cos \varphi \quad \cdot \quad \cdot \quad \cdot \quad \cdot \quad (11)$$

Graphical Constructions. The value p_2 is easily found graphically as shown in Fig. 285, by drawing a semicircle BEC centred at O, and from E a tangent AE to meet the circumference in E, and from A drawing AC inclined α to AD cutting the semicircle in B and C, and then drawing CD perpendicular to AC. Then AB represents p_2 and AC represents p_1 on the scale that AD represents wh. The point E is the limiting position of both B and C for maximum surcharge.

P may be represented by the weight of a triangular prism of earth XYZ (Fig. 286), 1 ft. long, perpendicular to the figure if YZ = $h \cdot AB/AC$ (Fig. 285), or $h \cdot AB/AD$ (Fig. 284).

(*d*) *Sloping Surcharged Wall* (Fig. 287). The resultant pressure on a sloping face AB may be found by finding that on BC as in the previous case, and adding geometrically the weight of a triangular prism of earth ABC. The algebra involved is quite simple but occupies much space, so is not set forth here. It should be noticed

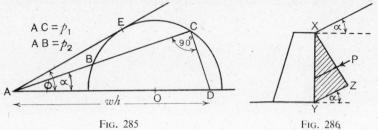

$$AC = p_1$$
$$AB = p_2$$

FIG. 285   FIG. 286

that BC is equal to $h(1 + \tan \theta \cdot \tan \alpha)$ or $h\{\cos (\alpha - \theta) \sec \alpha \cdot \sec \theta\}$. The final result, which the reader may verify for himself, is

$$P = \tfrac{1}{2}wh^2 \cos (\alpha - \theta) \sec^2 \theta \sec \alpha$$
$$\times \sqrt{\{\sin^2 \theta + 2K \tan \alpha \sin \theta \cos (\alpha - \theta) + K^2 \cos^2 (\alpha - \theta) \sec^2 \alpha\}}. \quad (12)$$

where K is the ratio $\cos \alpha \cdot \dfrac{\cos \alpha - \sqrt{(\cos^2 \alpha - \cos^2 \varphi)}}{\cos \alpha + \sqrt{(\cos^2 \alpha - \cos^2 \varphi)}}$

The inclination of P to the horizontal is β where

$$\tan \beta = \frac{1}{K} \sin \theta \sec (\alpha - \theta) + \tan \alpha \quad . \quad . \quad . \quad (13)$$

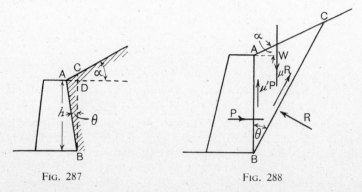

FIG. 287   FIG. 288

Wedge Theories. Another method of estimating the pressure on say a vertical face AB is to consider it as supporting a wedge or triangular prism of earth ABC (Fig. 288), which would slip away if the face were removed. This involves the *assumption* that the surface of rupture would be a *plane* of rupture such as BC, inclined say θ to the vertical. From the principles of statics the value of the normal component pressure P exerted by the wall on the wedge may be written in terms of θ and constants. To find the maximum value of P this expression may be differentiated with respect to θ and the result equated to zero, and hence θ obtained. By substituting this value of θ the maximum value of P may be found. Various assumptions may be made with respect to the angle of friction β, say between the earth and the wall. The commonest is to make $\tan \beta = \mu' = \tan \varphi = \mu$. If we put $\beta = 0$ (*i.e.* $\mu' = 0$), equivalent to neglecting wall friction as Coulomb did, and $\alpha = 0$, $\theta = 45 - \frac{1}{2}\varphi$, and we obtain Rankine's value (3), which may also be written $\frac{1}{2}wh^2\{\sqrt{(1+\mu^2)} - \mu\}^2$. If we put $\mu' = \mu$, resolving horizontally and vertically and eliminating R,

$$P = \tfrac{1}{2}wh^2 \cdot \frac{1 - \mu \tan \theta}{(2\mu \cot \theta + 1 - \mu^2)(1 - \tan \alpha \tan \theta)} \qquad . \quad (14)$$

and differentiating this with respect to θ and equating to zero to find the conditions which give a maximum normal thrust P, we find

$$\tan \theta = \frac{2\mu^2 - \sqrt{\{2\mu(1+\mu^2)(\mu - \tan \alpha)\}}}{(1+\mu^2)\tan \alpha - \mu(1 - \mu^2)} \qquad . \quad . \quad (15)$$

which when substituted in (14) gives the maximum value of P. The actual thrust on the face AB according to this theory is the resultant of $\mu'P$ downward and P horizontally.

Taking the particular case of level earth, *i.e.* $\alpha = 0$, and substituting in (15) and (14), we find

$$\tan \theta = \frac{\sqrt{\{2(1+\mu^2)\}} - 2\mu}{1 - \mu^2} \qquad . \quad . \quad . \quad . \quad . \quad (16)$$

and

$$P = \tfrac{1}{2}wh^2 \frac{1 + 3\mu^2 - 2\mu\sqrt{\{2(1+\mu^2)\}}}{(1 - \mu^2)^2} \qquad . \quad . \quad (17)$$

In the more general case of pressure exerted by and on a sloping wall when the earth is surcharged let Fig. 289 represent the wall face AB inclined β to the vertical (or having a batter β) and surcharged with earth to an angle α to the horizontal. The upper surface of the earth is BC: the plane of rupture giving a maximum pressure on AB is AD inclined θ to the vertical. The line AC from A represents a plane at φ_1 to the horizontal where φ_1 is the angle of repose of the earth. The angle of friction of the earth on the wall face is φ_2. The forces exerted upon the wedge of earth ABD are: (*a*) its weight W acting through its c.g., (*b*) the reaction R_1 of the earth below the plane of rupture AD acting at an angle φ_1 to AD, and (*c*) the reaction R_2 of the wall, inclined φ_2 to the normal to the face AB. These three forces must be in equilibrium; they are represented on the vector force triangle *adf* on the right-hand side of Fig. 289. We might state the value of R_2 in terms of W and the variable θ as before and find by equating $dR_2/d\theta$ to zero the conditions to give a maximum R_2 and its magnitude. But the same results can be found by a simple graphical construction shown in Fig. 289. From B a line BE, at an angle $\widehat{ABE} = \varphi_1 + \varphi_2$ to AB, is drawn to meet AC in E and from E a line EK perpendicular to AC is drawn to meet a semicircle AKC described on AC in K. A distance AF equal to AK is marked off along AC. From F a

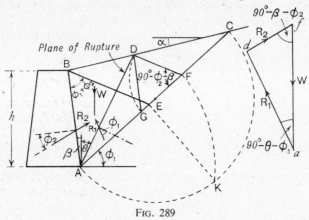

Fig. 289

line FD is drawn parallel to BE, meeting BC in D. Then AD represents the plane of rupture for a maximum thrust R_2 on AB (and equal reaction of the wall on the wedge ABD). The weight W, say per foot perpendicular to the diagram can easily be calculated in terms of *w* and the dimensions of the triangle ABD. Finally, if from F along FA a length FG be set off equal to FD the (maximum) value of R_2 is equal to the weight of a triangular prism of earth of the section FDG and 1 ft. long perpendicular to the figure or $R_2 = w \times (\text{area FGD})$.

To prove this it is convenient to change the variable from θ and adopt one of the lengths which is dependent on the value of θ. Let EF = *x*, a variable the magnitude of which depends on the fixed data *h*, φ_1, φ_2, α, β and the variable angle θ. Let AE = *a*, AC = *b*, BE = *d*, all constants independent of θ. From the foregoing construction it follows that EK is a mean proportional between AE and EC, *i.e.* $EK^2 = AE \times EC = a(b-a)$. Also $AF^2 = AK^2 = AE^2 + EK^2 = a^2 + a(b-a) = ab$; therefore $AF = \sqrt{(ab)}$, *i.e.* AF is a mean proportional between *a* and *b*.

The triangle FAD is similar to the vector triangle *fad*, hence

$$R_2 = W \times DF/AF = \tfrac{1}{2}wBD \times BA \sin \hat{ABD} \times (DF/AF) \atop = W \times \text{area } ABD \times (DF/AF) \quad\Bigr\} \quad . \quad (18)$$

Since the triangles BCE and DCF are similar,

$$BD/BC = EF/EC \quad \text{or} \quad BD = BC(EF/EC) \quad . \quad . \quad (19)$$

and, substituting this in (18),

$$R_2 = \tfrac{1}{2}wBC \, . \, BA \sin \hat{ABD} \times (EF/EC)(DF/AF) \atop = w\varDelta(EF/EC)(DF/AF) \quad\Bigr\} \quad . \quad (20)$$

where $\varDelta$ = area of the triangle ABC (a constant).

From the similarity of triangles DFC and BEC, $DF/BE = CF/CE$ and $DF/AF = (BE/AF) \times (CF/CE)$, hence from (20)

$$\left. \begin{aligned} R_2 &= w\varDelta \times \frac{EF}{EC} \times \frac{BE}{AF} \times \frac{CF}{EC} \\ &= w\varDelta \times \frac{d}{(b-a)^2} \cdot \frac{x(b-a-x)}{(x+a)} \end{aligned} \right\} \quad . \quad . \quad . \quad (21)$$

differentiating with respect to x and putting $dR_2/dx = 0$ we find $x = \sqrt{(ab)} - a$ as the condition for a maximum value of R_2. But this was the basis of the foregoing construction which made $AF = \sqrt{(ab)}$ and therefore $EF = \sqrt{(ab)} - a$, hence the construction gives the value of R_2. It only remains to prove that the maximum value is represented by the area of the triangle DFG.

The ratio of the triangles

$$BDA/ADC = BD/DC = EF/FC = x/(b-a-x) = \sqrt{(a/b)} \quad . \quad (22)$$

the value $\sqrt{(ab)} - a$ being substituted for x.

Also $\quad\quad DFA/ADC = AF/AC = (a+x)/b = \sqrt{(a/b)} \quad . \quad . \quad (23)$

and from the equality of (22) and (23) the triangle BDA is equal in area to the triangle DFA and the magnitude of W, for 1 ft. length of wall, is $w \times BDA$ or $w \times DFA$.

From (18)

$$R_2 = W \times DF/FA = W \times FG/FA$$

since FG was made equal to FD and since W is equal to $w \times$ area ADF, and the ratio FG/FA is equal to the ratio of the area FGD to area ADF

$$R_2 = w \times \text{area } FGD \quad . \quad . \quad . \quad . \quad . \quad (24)$$

The wedge theory has been fairly widely adopted as a working basis of calculating earth pressure and experiments by Jenkin [1] on dry sand give it some confirmation for that material. On the basis

[1] " The Pressure on Retaining Walls," by C. F. Jenkin, *Proc. Inst. C.E.*, vol. 234, p. 103 (1931–32).

of his experiments Jenkin has put forward a Revised Wedge Theory. The application of it is rather complicated but is somewhat simplified by the use of special tables, and reference must be made to the paper cited or to " Earth Pressure Tables."[1]

Important conclusions from Jenkin's experiments are that there are in many cases *two* planes of rupture and that the centre of pressure is not in all cases at one-third of the height from the base of the retaining wall. The second plane of rupture may coincide with the face of the wall or may be inclined to it, the two planes of rupture meeting at the foot of the wall. The centre of pressure on the wall was commonly from 0·4 to 0·55 of the height above the base of the wall.

203. Resistance and Stability of Masonry, Brickwork, etc.
Masonry and similar structures are usually employed (without steel reinforcement) mainly to resist compressive forces. This, of course (Art. 7), causes shear stress on surfaces oblique to that which withstands thrust.

(1) Owing to eccentricity of the resultant thrust (Arts. 99 and 100) bending stresses arise which unless the eccentricity is suitably limited will involve tensile stress. It is a general practice to disregard any tensile resistance which such structures are capable of exerting in virtue of the adhesion of the mortar or cementing material, and to attempt to limit the possible eccentricity of thrust so as to prevent tensile stress.

(2) The shearing resistance of joints is likewise taken as negligible, and consequently the obliquity of thrust across any joint should be limited to the angle of friction (Fig. 290), *i.e.* the tangential stress on a joint should not exceed the frictional resistance to sliding. The main function of mortar is not adhesive resistance, but uniform distribution of thrust across joints.

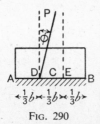

FIG. 290

(3) The resistance to thrust (really dependent on the shearing resistance on oblique planes) is limited by the strength of the stone or brick or concrete. To allow for concentration of pressure due to uneven bedding a high factor of safety is usually adopted.

Middle Third Rule. The majority of masonry and brickwork joints are of rectangular section, and from Art. 100 and Fig. 146 it is evident that to avoid tension the eccentricity of thrust must be limited to $\frac{1}{6}$ of the breadth of the joint, *i.e.* the thrust must fall *within the middle third* of the joint. In Fig. 290, to avoid tension at B, the resultant thrust P must not fall outside DE. If it falls to the left of D, tension at B may open the joint. The result is a smaller

---

[1] *Building Research Special Report No.* 24, D.S.I.R. (H.M. Stationery Office).

bearing surface, giving increased intensity of compressive stress at A. In many cases with the ample margins allowed no serious consequences may ensue, but too great an opening of the joint may result in failure by shearing associated with compression in the neighbourhood of A.

Stresses in Masonry and Brickwork. Stone and brick are in general much less homogeneous than say steel, and further they are often not even approximately isotropic; they have different strengths and elasticities in different directions. A masonry or brickwork structure varies in properties even more than does a single piece of the component material, hence the application of the principles previously deduced for ideal homogeneous and perfectly elastic material must be regarded as conventional to a considerable degree. For many such structures strength considerations are not the primary ones, but where considerable loads are to be carried the principles already dealt with, allowing ample margins, form the basis of calculation.

204. Foundations. Provided that the earth is sufficiently firm to support a structure without piles or other form of reinforcement, the area of a foundation is found by dividing the total weight borne by the known allowable unit pressure, which will not cause a serious amount of compression. The allowable unit pressure in loose earths is about from 1 to 2 tons per sq. ft., rising to say 10 tons on good rock. In loose ground to prevent the earth being squeezed out laterally, the horizontal pressure intensity at the depth of the foundation must be a certain amount. If W=total weight on a foundation in tons, and A=its area in square feet, the unit pressure is $p = W/A$. According to Rankine's theory of earth pressure, Art. 202, (1), the least lateral pressure to prevent movement must be $p(1 - \sin \varphi)/(1 + \sin \varphi)$. Again, to support this horizontal pressure at the outside of the base, there must similarly be a vertical unit pressure $(1 - \sin \varphi)/(1 + \sin \varphi)$ times the horizontal pressure, or $p\left(\dfrac{1 - \sin \varphi}{1 + \sin \varphi}\right)^2$; if this pressure is supplied by sinking the horizontal surface its intensity is wh, where w=weight of earth in tons per cubic foot, and h=depth in feet, hence the minimum depth of a foundation for stability is given by

$$wh = \frac{W}{A}\left(\frac{1 - \sin \varphi}{1 + \sin \varphi}\right)^2 \quad \text{or} \quad h = \frac{W}{Aw}\left(\frac{1 - \sin \varphi}{1 + \sin \varphi}\right)^2 \quad . \quad . \quad (1)$$

Example 1. Find the necessary depth of a concrete foundation 6 ft. wide carrying a wall which supports 8 tons per lineal foot, including its own weight. The weight of concrete foundation is $1\frac{1}{4}$ cwt. per cu. ft.; weight of earth, 1 cwt. per cu. ft.; angle of repose 30°.

$$\text{Total load per foot run} = 8 + \frac{1 \cdot 25 \times 6 \times h}{20} = 8 + 0 \cdot 375h$$

$$\left(\frac{1 - \sin 30°}{1 + \sin 30°}\right)^2 = \tfrac{1}{9}, \text{ hence from (1)}$$

$$h = \frac{8 + 0 \cdot 375h}{0 \cdot 05 \times 6} \times \tfrac{1}{9} \quad \text{hence } h = 2 \cdot 6 \text{ ft.}$$

Footings. The steps in which the area of the base of a wall or pier is increased to the full area of the base are called footings (Fig. 291)

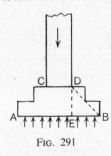

Due to the upward pressure at the foundation, there is bending action on the overhanging portion EB, which may be treated as a cantilever uniformly loaded, giving a maximum bending moment at ED. It is desirable to keep the tensile bending stress at E within safe limits, and also to see that the shear stress on ED is within safe limits, remembering Art. 53 that the maximum value may be about 1·5 times the mean value. Actually the thickness DE for a given type of masonry or brickwork structure and the projections of successive courses are determined by empirical rules, which allow ample margins in these respects.

Fig. 291

Grillage Foundations. The necessity of deep excavations to secure a wide base for a foundation to carry a heavy load, such as that carried by a large stanchion, may be obviated by the use of two or more tiers of steel joists set in concrete. In poor bearing soils a single layer of steel joists may even be used in the concrete of a heavy wall foundation. The practical requirements are that all joists of a tier should be spaced sufficiently far apart to allow of concrete being well rammed between them, say 4 in. or 5 in. between flanges. The joists are kept in proper position by cast-iron separators, or by bolts passing through steel tubes about 1 in. diameter. Fig. 292 shows such a stanchion foundation having two layers of joists. At least 12 in. depth of concrete below the joists is generally allowed. The resistance of the joists to both bending and shearing must be considered in designing such a foundation, and the joists must not be placed too far apart to provide sufficient shearing resistance in their webs. For a given stanchion base as many (usually 3 or 4) joists are placed in the first tier as can be spaced sufficiently far apart as to allow of proper ramming.

The calculation of bending moment in the joists under a stanchion base is a conventional one, for it depends upon what assumption is made as to the distribution of the pressure exerted by the base on the grill.

Let Fig. 293 represent a stanchion base resting on a single layer of steel beams; if they are embedded in concrete the upward pressure may be taken as uniformly distributed, say W/L per ft., where W = total load and L = length of beam in feet. Then if the beams are so flexible in comparison with the (shorter) stanchion base that

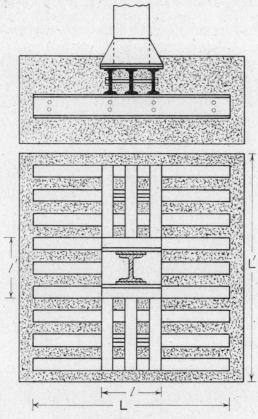

FIG. 292.—Grillage foundation

they bend so as to rest on the edges of the base, the diagram of bending moments is of the type shown (for different proportions) in Fig. 52, and as shown by the curve ADFEB (Fig. 293). In this case the maximum bending moment at D is as for a cantilever of length $\frac{1}{2}(L - l)$ equal to the overhang, and loaded W/L per ft., viz.

$$\frac{1}{8}\frac{W}{L}(L - l)^2 \qquad . \quad . \quad . \quad . \quad . \quad . \quad (1)$$

If, on the other hand, the stanchion base is so flexible as to bend with the beam, the downward pressure might be taken as a uniformly distributed load W/l per ft., giving the bending moment diagram ADCEB where DEC is a parabola, and the maximum OC is

$$\tfrac{1}{2}W \cdot \tfrac{1}{4}L - \tfrac{1}{2}W \cdot \tfrac{1}{4}l = \tfrac{1}{8}W(L-l) \quad . \quad . \quad . \quad (2)$$

or $L/(L-l)$ times as great as (1). The actual distribution of pressure, and therefore the bending moment, depends upon the relative flexural stiffness of the parts, and is statically indeterminate: both values (1) and (2) are conventional. If the base were *very* flexible, the pressure might be more concentrated towards the centre of the base, giving some such ordinates as indicated by DGE (Fig. 293).

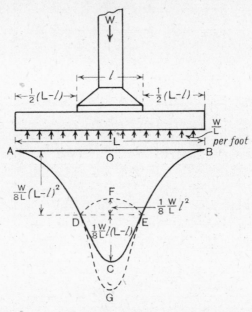

FIG. 293

In the case of the lower tier of joints the downward load is necessarily partially distributed by the upper tier.

Frequently both grillage and stanchion base will be made exactly square; if not, however, appropriate values of L or L' and l or l' in (1) and (2) must be adopted.

The maximum shearing force, whatever the distribution of pressure, will be practically at the edge of the stanchion base and will be

$$\tfrac{1}{2}W(L-l)/L \quad . \quad . \quad . \quad . \quad (3)$$

Example 2. A stanchion designed to stand a direct load of 120 tons has a base 30 in. square. Arrange a suitable grillage for the foundation to give a pressure of not more than 2 tons per sq. ft. Use British Standard Beams, and limit the bending stress in the flanges to $7\frac{1}{2}$ tons per sq. in. and the mean shearing stress to 4 tons per sq. in., taking the web area as the thickness multiplied by the depth of joist.

Area required $=\frac{120}{2}=60$ sq. ft.; concrete, say 8 ft. by 8 ft.; joists, 7 ft. long and 6 in. from edges. For the lower tier use 8 joists spaced 12 in. apart, the outside ones being 6 in. from the edges.

$$L-l=84-30=54 \text{ in.}$$

Then from (2), maximum bending moment $=\frac{1}{8}\times 120\times 54=810$ ton-in.

Modulus of section per beam $=\frac{1}{8}\times 810/7\cdot5=13\cdot6$ (in.)^3.

Referring to Table I, Appendix, the B.S.B. 12, 8 ×4 in., with a modulus of 13·92, will suit.

The shearing force (3), is $\frac{1}{2}\times 120\times\frac{54}{84}=38\cdot6$ tons
$$=4\cdot82 \text{ tons per beam.}$$

The allowable shearing force per beam is $0\cdot28\times 8\times 4=9\cdot3$ tons, which is ample.

The clear spaces between flanges is 12 in. -4 in. $=8$ in.

For the upper tier, taking three joists, the modulus required is
$$\tfrac{1}{3}\times 810/7\cdot5=36 \text{ (in.)}^3.$$

And Table I gives for B.S.B. 20, 12 ×5 in., modulus 36·66 (in.)^3.

Shearing force per beam $38\cdot7/3=12\cdot9$ tons.

Allowable shearing force per beam $0\cdot35\times 12\times 4=16\cdot8$ tons, which allows a margin.

The three flanges occupy $5\times 3=15$ in., leaving 15 in. for two spaces or 7·5 in. clear between flanges.

205. Resistance of Retaining Walls. It has already been indicated that neither the earth pressure on a retaining wall nor the stress caused in masonry by given forces can be accurately calculated. The following conditions with which a retaining wall is made to comply must therefore be regarded as more or less empirical. Let P (Fig. 294) be the estimated earth pressure per foot run from one of the theories given in Art. 202; let W be the weight of masonry in the wall per foot run, and G be the position of the centre of gravity of this piece of the

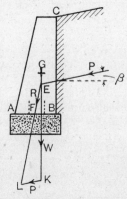

Fig. 294

wall. Then combining W and P by the triangle of forces EKL drawn to scale (or by trigonometrical calculation), the resultant pressure R on the base AB is ascertained in magnitude and direction. It is then necessary that

(1) R shall cut AB in a point F within the middle third to avoid a vertical component tension at the inner toe B.

(2) That the intensity of vertical compressive stress at A calculated by (2), Art. 100 (taking a normal thrust $W+P \sin \beta$), shall be within the working limits suitable to the masonry used.

(3) The inclination of R to the normal to the base of the wall shall be less than the safe angle of friction between the masonry and the foundation.

The wall should also satisfy the same conditions for all horizontal sections. The position of F may easily be found by equating the opposite moments about, say, A or B, of the forces acting on the wall including the reaction of the foundation which is equal and opposite to R.

Practical Proportions. The above conditions, in conjunction with the commoner rules for earth pressure, often lead to retaining-wall proportions which are unnecessarily wasteful. The late Sir Benjamin Baker stated that as a result of his experience he made the width of the bases of retaining walls for average ground equal to $\frac{1}{3}$ of the height from the footings to the top. Also, that a thickness of $\frac{1}{4}$ of the height with a batter of 1 or 2 in. per foot on the face was sufficient with favourable backing and foundation, while with a solid foundation the thickness need *never* exceed $\frac{1}{2}$ of the height. He also stated that good filling gives a thrust equivalent to that of a fluid weighing 10 lb. per cu. ft.; hence, allowing a factor of safety of 2, the wall should be capable of sustaining the pressure exerted by a fluid weighing 20 lb. per cu. ft. (see also end of Art. 206).

Example. A trapezoidal retaining wall is 24 ft. high, the base is 8 ft. wide, and the top 6 ft. If the earth weighs 110 lb. per cu. ft. and its angle of repose is 50°, and if it stands level with the top of the wall, find, according to Rankine's rule, the centre of pressure on the base of the wall, and the extreme intensities of normal stress on the base assuming that the intensity varies uniformly and the masonry weighs 150 lb. per cu. ft.

The total horizontal force on the wall per foot, by Rankine's rule, is

$$\tfrac{1}{2} \times 110 \times 24^2 \times \frac{1-0.766}{1+0.766} = 4,200 \text{ lb.}$$

Weight of masonry per lineal foot is $\frac{1}{2}(8+6)24 \times 150 = 25,200$ lb.

Horizontal distance of centre of gravity from the inner side of the wall $= \{(6 \times 24 \times 3) + (\frac{1}{2} \times 24 \times 2 \times 6\frac{2}{3})\} \div 168 = 3.5236$ ft.

Taking moments about the inner toe of the wall

Distance of centre of pressure $\times 25{,}200 = 25{,}200 \times 3{\cdot}5236 + 4{,}200 \times \frac{24}{3}$.

Distance of centre of pressure $= 3{\cdot}5236 + 1{\cdot}3333 = 4{\cdot}8569$ ft.;

i.e. 0·8569 ft. from the centre of the base, and therefore well within the middle third, which extends $\frac{8}{6}$ ft. $= 1$ ft. -4 in. from the centre.

206. Masonry Dams. The thrust on the face of a masonry dam being, unlike that on a retaining wall, due to water pressure, is calculable with considerable exactness. But there is not, and cannot well be, any exact computation of the state of internal stresses in dams. They form, however, such large, costly, and important structures that much attention has been paid to the estimation of such stresses.

Most existing dams have been designed so far as strength and stability are concerned with a view to fulfilling the three conditions laid down in Art. 205 for retaining walls for earth. It may be pointed out, however, that the fall of the resultant within the middle third of the horizontal section only ensures that, *assuming a uniformly varying distribution* of normal stress across the section, there is no tensile component across this section.

The dam may be regarded as a vertical cantilever of cross-sectional dimensions (breadth) comparable with its height. To apply the theory of long uniform beams to such a case is at best a rough approximation. The normal stresses across the horizontal sections will not generally be principal stresses, and there will be tangential components or shearing stress on such sections, which may involve tensile stress across some other plane. Most recent theories of stresses in dams have been supported by some experimental approximations (deduced from models) as to the distribution of horizontal shearing stress in the dam. Such data and theories as representing anything like actual conditions in a masonry dam must for the present be regarded as tentative, and are here only given by references at the end of this article.

Water Pressure. The water face of a dam is usually so little curved in its vertical section that the water pressures on either part or the whole may be taken as if the face were plane. The pressures per foot run of the dam for whole or part of the depth are then easily estimated by the rules of hydrostatics applicable to immersed rectangles. Thus if Fig. 295 represents a section of a dam with water up to the sill at A, the pressure per foot run on the curved face AB may be taken as that on a rectangle of length AB and breadth 1 ft., the mean intensity being that at E midway between the ends A and B, *i.e.* at half the vertical depth of B. Further,

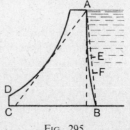

Fig. 295

this pressure is perpendicular to AB, and acts through a point F in AB distant one-third of AB from B. Strictly, the weight of water within the space between the straight and curved faces AB should be added geometrically to this pressure, but it is usually negligible, and such approximation is on the safe side. A still closer approximation would be obtained by dividing AB into a number of straight faces, and summing geometrically the partial pressures, and finding the position of the resultant by a funicular polygon.

Middle Third Rule and Lines of Thrust or Resistance. If the main criterion as to stability is accepted as being that the line of resultant thrust shall pass within the middle third of horizontal sections, it becomes desirable to test a vertical section of a given design by drawing lines called *lines of resistance*, or lines of thrust which give the direction and position of the resultant thrust on all horizontal

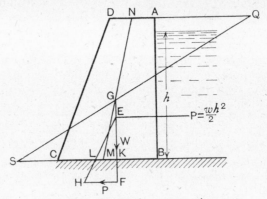

FIG. 296.—Centre of pressure on base

sections under the extreme conditions of no water pressure and full water pressure. Fig. 296 shows how to determine graphically a single point in the lines of resistance for the reservoir full and the reservoir empty. The section chosen is at the floor-level of the reservoir, but the construction is the same for any other horizontal section. Taking 1 ft. perpendicular to the figure, the centre of gravity G of the masonry ABCD is found by the well-known trapezoidal rule of joining NM, the middle points of AD and BC, and finding the intersection G with SQ, where AQ=CB and CS= AD. The weight of masonry W acts through G, and its line of action cuts the base CB in K, which is a point in the line of resistance for the reservoir empty. With the reservoir full the line of action of the pressure $P=\frac{1}{2}wh^2$ (where w=weight of 1 cu. ft. of water, say 62·4 lb.) is $\frac{1}{3}$ of h above B and cuts GK in E. A triangle of forces EFH gives the direction of the resultant thrust EH, which cuts CB in L, which is a point in the line of resistance for the full reservoir. Then L and K and similarly determined points for all other horizontal sections are required to fall within the middle third of the various horizontal sections.

Forms of Section. Actual dams are rarely trapezoidal, but have the flank hollowed, and the base widened by a rake of the flank, and just so much on the face as will keep the thrust well within the middle third when the reservoir is empty.

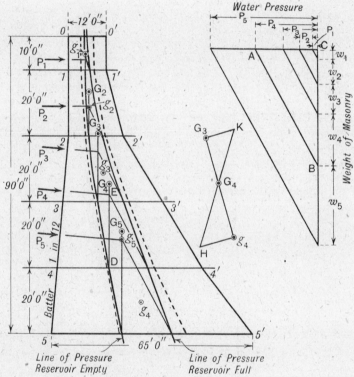

FIG. 297.—Lines of pressure

Complete curves between dotted lines marking the middle third boundaries are shown in Fig. 297 for a typical reservoir dam section. The vector-force triangles for the five horizontal sections are set out to the right-hand side of the diagram. It will be sufficient to indicate in detail the method of finding two sample points, say D and F, for the section 44′. The weight w_4 of the masonry 433′4′ is calculated, and its centre of gravity g_4 found by calculation or graphically as in Fig. 296. The weight of masonry 300′3′ $(w_1+w_2+w_3)$ having been previously calculated and its centre of gravity G_3

U

determined, the centre of gravity G_4 of all the masonry above 44′ is found, as indicated for clearness just to the right of the dam section, by dividing the line $G_3 g_4$ inversely as the weights $w_1 + w_2 + w_3$ to w_4. This is accomplished by drawing a line G_3K proportional to w_4 and a parallel line g_4H proportional to $w_1 + w_2 + w_3$, and joining HK; then the intersection of HK with $G_3 g_4$ gives the centre of gravity of the masonry 432100′1′2′3′4′ at G_4. By dropping a perpendicular G_4D on 44′ the point D in the line of pressure for the empty reservoir is obtained.

The water pressure P_4 on the face 01234 is taken as perpendicular to the line 04 and $\frac{2}{3}$ of its length from 0, *i.e.* 140/3 ft. vertically below the water surface. The mean pressure is taken as that at a depth of $\frac{1}{2}$ of 70=35 ft. below the surface, viz. $35 \times 62 \cdot 5$ lb. per sq. ft., and the area per foot length of dam is equal to the number of feet in the straight line 04. The line of action of P_4 intersects G_4D at E. The direction of the resultant of $w_1 + w_2 + w_3 + w_4$ and P_4 is given by the line AB in the vector diagram. Hence, drawing EF parallel to AB to meet 44′ gives the point F in the line of pressure for the reservoir full to the sill 00′. The other points are similarly obtained. The pressure vectors P_2, P_3, P_4, P_5 radiating from C are so nearly parallel that they cannot all be drawn separately. In obtaining P the effect of the weight of the prism of water shown in profile by the triangle 024 is neglected. Its effect would be to slightly lower E and slightly increase the steepness of EF, thus bringing F very slightly closer to the middle of 44′. Alternatively, P_4 might be found by calculating the true pressure on 01, 12, 23, 34 and obtaining their vector sum and true position of their resultant by vector and link polygons or by calculation.

Trapezoidal Retaining Wall or Dam. The limiting dimensions for a trapezoidal wall with vertical face subject to normal pressure due to level filling calculated by Rankine's rule, so that the thrust on the base just remains in the middle third, may easily be estimated by moments. Thus in Fig. 298 if the ratio of the weight of 1 cu. ft.

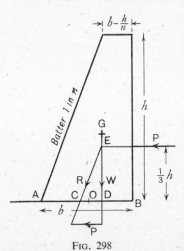

FIG. 298

of masonry to $\dfrac{1 - \sin \varphi}{1 + \sin \varphi}$ times that of 1 cu. ft. of filling is s, where

φ = angle of repose (so that for water on the face $\varphi = 0$, s = specific gravity of the masonry), we have

$$P/W = \tfrac{1}{2}h^2 \div sh(b - \tfrac{1}{2}h/n) = \frac{h}{s(2b - h/n)}$$

and by moments of areas

$$BD = \frac{3b^2 - (3bh/n) + h^2/n^2}{3(2b - h/n)}, \quad CD = \tfrac{1}{3}h \times \frac{P}{W} = \frac{h^2}{3s(2b - h/n)}$$

If the intersection C falls at the limit of the middle third, equating $BD + CD = \tfrac{2}{3}b$, we find

$$b^2 + bh/n - h^2\{(1/n^2) + (1/s)\} = 0 \quad . \quad . \quad . \quad (1)$$

a quadratic equation for b with a given batter one in n or a quadratic in n for a given width of base b.

In the particular case of a triangular section $b = h/n$ this reduces to

$$b = h\sqrt{(1/s)} \quad . \quad . \quad . \quad . \quad . \quad (2)$$

which also holds for a rectangular section, n being infinite. If for a reservoir we put, say, $s = 2$, then $b = 0.7h$, while for $s = 2.5$, $b = 0.63h$. If we take Baker's suggestion of allowing for a fluid of density 20 lb. per cu. ft., and take masonry at 150 lb. per cu. ft., $s = 7.5$, (2) gives $b = 0.365h$, while if we put $n = 12$ in (1) we get $b = 0.336h$.

REFERENCES TO STABILITY OF DAMS, ETC.

" On some Disregarded Points in the Stability of Masonry Dams," by L. W. Atcherly and Karl Pearson (Dulau).

" An Experimental Study of the Stresses in Masonry Dams," by Karl Pearson and A. F. C. Pollard (Dulau).

" Stresses in Masonry Dams," by Sir J. W. Ottley and A. W. Brightmore, *Proc. Inst. C.E.*, 1907–1908.

Letters and Articles in *Engineering*, vols. 79 and 80, and in the *Engineer*, 1907–1908.

207. Masonry Arches. The mechanics of masonry (including brickwork) arches presents considerable difficulty, and there is no theory dealing with this point which is both simple and satisfactory. The arch ring supporting the load is made of material such as brick, or stone and mortar, which is more or less perfectly elastic. The names used in connection with this ring and the adjacent parts are shown in Fig. 299. The ring may be of uniform radial depth, or it may gradually thicken from the crown to the haunches.

Such a structure is, in any case, statically indeterminate, and the true line of thrust or linear arch for any given loading cannot be drawn with great certainty. For, in the first place, the incidence of the loading on the ring, when the force is transmitted through the spandrel, filled, it may be, with more or less loose material, is indeterminate. The pressure of granular material will not be wholly vertical, but will have a horizontal component dependent on the angle of repose. It is usual to take the loading as vertical, any error resulting being on the safe side. In some cases open spandrels are used, the load from the roadway being transmitted by vertical masonry columns connected under the roadway by short arches; in such a case the loading of the arch ring is fairly definitely vertical.

Then of all the possible reactions at the skewbacks which would satisfy the statical conditions of equilibrium, the correct values will depend upon the relative elasticities of the ring and the abutments (including heavy semi-rigid backing over the haunches and piers). It is interesting to record that in Germany attempts have been made

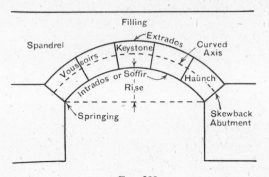

Fig. 299

to localise the line of thrust at three sections in the arch by the insertion of blocks of lead near the curved axis between voussoirs at those sections, thus forming quasi hinges. Masonry arches have also been constructed with actual metal pin hinges.

If we treat the arch ring as an elastic rib fixed at both ends, we may apply to it the theory of Art. 200. Experiments made by the Austrian Society of Engineers and Architects showed that masonry arches behaved very nearly as elastic arches with fixed ends.[1] This is, of course, equivalent to taking the rigidity of the abutments as infinite in comparison with the flexibility of the arch ring.

Winkler's Criterion of Stability. Neglecting the strain from normal thrust and considering the strain energy due to bending moment, (6), Art. 96, the principle of minimum strain energy, Arts. 148 and 150, indicates that the average square of the bending moments will be as small as possible. And as for vertical loads the bending moment is everywhere proportional to the vertical distance of the arch axis from the line of thrust (Art. 194) the average square of the

---

[1] For a brief account of these experiments, see Howe's *Treatise on Arches*, which, with *Symmetrical Masonry Arches*, by the same writer, contains much valuable information.

vertical distance must be as small as possible, *i.e.* the correct horizontal thrust will be such as to give minimum deviation of the line of thrust from the axis as measured by the square of the vertical deviations. If the corresponding funicular polygon or linear arch is wholly within the middle third of the arch ring, and if the maximum compressive stress is within the safe allowance for the material, the arch may be considered stable. If, therefore, any funicular polygon can be drawn for the particular system of loads such as to lie wholly within the middle third of the arch ring, the ring is stable for that system of loads. To ensure stability under all systems, the polygons for different positions of the movable load would have to be drawn, or their effect investigated. This is somewhat beyond the scope of this brief treatment of the subject, but it is usually sufficient to apply the criterion to the arch under (1) Dead load only, (2) Full load, (3) Dead load, and full movable load on half of the span only.

In an arch the dead load is a considerable proportion of the whole load, and minimises the deviation of the linear arch from the curved axis, and if it is sufficiently great will keep it within the required limits, provided the axis follows the linear arch for the dead load. In designing an arch, the ring may be made to an empirical formula, the curved axis following, say, the linear arch for the dead load, and then its stability tested by the above criterion. Or the depth of the ring, say, at the crown, and the intrados curve may be assigned, and then the lines of thrust may be drawn in by the elastic method of Art. 200 (estimating roughly the weight of ring) and then the extrados drawn so as to form a ring of variable radial depth, the middle third of which lies entirely outside the extreme limits of the line of thrust.

The elastic method offers the most direct method of design and gives the most probable line of thrust, according to Winkler's criterion, for in Art. 200 it was shown that (neglecting strain due to thrust) the solution given, follows from the principle of minimum strain energy. If, however, an entirely empirical design is made the criterion may be applied by trial, either graphically, by drawing various trial lines of thrust, or algebraically by calculating the moments, and hence the deviation of the linear arch from the curved axis. In either case three conditions have to be assumed for any trial line of thrust. These three conditions may be three points in the linear arch (say at the crown and the abutments) or two points and one direction, or any three which make the funicular polygon determinate; these three assumptions correspond to the three quantities actually computed in Art. 200.

The application of the criterion graphically by trial is much facilitated by a device due to Fuller, which is illustrated in Fig. 300, which represents an arch ring, the boundaries of the middle third

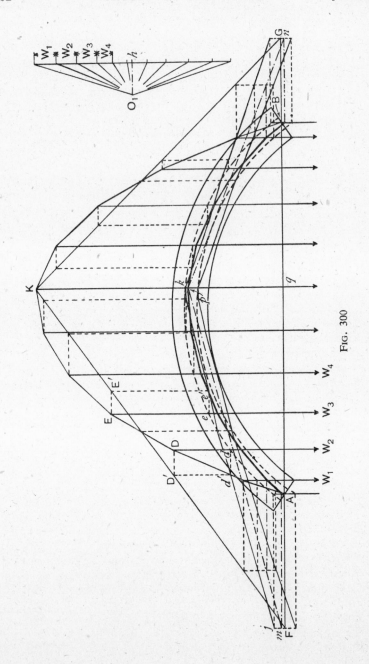

Fig. 300

being shown dotted. The funicular polygon ADEKB is drawn with any pole distance, $o_1 h$ corresponding to any horizontal thrust, for the loads W_1, W_2, W_3, W_4, etc., on a horizontal base AB the points A and B being the intersection of the curved axis with the skewbacks. Any length FG on the line AB is then chosen, and the highest point K of the funicular polygon is joined to F and G. Then FKG represents the funicular polygon " straightened out." The next step is to correspondingly modify the region between the middle third boundaries. This is accomplished by projecting horizontally the vertices such as D and E of the funicular polygon on to FK and KG, giving such points as D′ and E′. Vertical lines through D and E intersect the upper boundary of the middle third region at d and e; horizontal lines through d and e intersect vertical lines through D′ and E′ in $d′$ and $e′$, giving points in the modified or derived upper boundary of the middle third region; other points are similarly obtained, and both upper and lower boundaries are drawn in through the points j, $d′$, $e′$, k, etc. If now two intersecting straight lines, mpn, can be drawn to meet in p on the vertical through K and k, and lie wholly within the modified middle third region, corresponding funicular polygons can be drawn within the original middle third region. Such a funicular polygon may be drawn by projecting horizontally the intersections of the lines mp and pn, with the verticals through D′ and E′, etc., on to the verticals through D and E, etc., or by taking a pole distance equal to $o_1 h \times \dfrac{Kq}{\text{height of } p \text{ above } m}$ and starting the polygon through p, or through the horizontal projection of m, say, on the vertical through A. If several polygons are possible, a good approximation to the most probable one could be obtained by drawing in the centre line of the modified middle third region, and drawing by inspection a pair of intersecting straight lines, such as mp and pn, deviating as little as possible from the centre line, which is the axis, as modified.

Elastic Method. The application of the elastic method to the determination of the line of thrust in a masonry arch may best be explained by an example. A segmental or circular arch is chosen and the approximate methods for the summations given in Art. 200 are used, although, after dividing the continuous load into several concentrated loads the exact formulae given in Example 2, Art. 200, might have been employed. The purpose is, however, to illustrate the method, and with that object the data have been simplified as far as possible. See Fig. 301.

Data. Radius of centre line of symmetrical arch ring 40 ft. Angle at centre of arc 80° ($\alpha = 40°$). Uniform radial depth of ring 2 ft. Filling to stand level 3 ft. above the top of the ring at the crown. Average weight of filling to include roadway, 120 lb. per cu. ft.;

weight of masonry in ring 160 lb. per cu. ft. Moving load 150 lb. per foot run per foot of width of roadway.

The arch is considered per foot width of roadway throughout. The arc is divided into 10 parts of 8° each, and both dead and live load are taken as that vertically above the 8° length of the curved axis, and acting vertically through points 1, 2, 3, 4, 5, 5', 4', 3', 2', 1', in the centre of the 8° arcs. Thus at point 4 the dead load is that of the spandrel filling and the arch ring shown cross-hatched in Fig. 301. The estimation of the dead and moving loads assigned to these points is simple mensuration and is not shown in detail, any

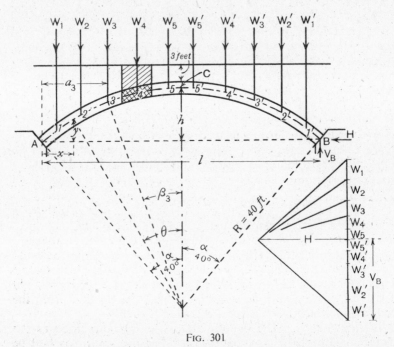

Fig. 301

reasonable approximation being satisfactory. The three unknown quantities H, V_B, and M_C, as given in (14), (15), and (17), Art. 200, are first calculated for unit loads at points 2, 3, 4, and 5, the values for point 1 being zero according to the approximation. The following values are first tabulated (Table A), the notation being given in Fig. 301. The number of significant figures used may be in excess of that warranted by the assumptions, but will assist the reader in tracing the work clearly.

Half span of centre line $= 40 \sin 40° = 25 \cdot 7116$ ft.
Rise of centre line $40 (1 - \cos 40°) = 9 \cdot 3582$ ft.

TABLE A

1	2	3	4	5	6	7	8	9	10	11	12	13	14	15	16	17	18
						(By differences of column 3) $(a-x)=40(\sin\theta-\sin\beta)$ for load at				$y(a-x)$ for load at				$(a-x)(\tfrac{1}{2}l-x)$ for load at			
Point	$\theta°$	$\tfrac{1}{2}l-x=$ $40\sin\theta$ (ft.)	$y=40$ $(\cos\theta-\cos40)$	y^2	$(\tfrac{1}{2}l-x)^2$	2	3	4	5	2	3	4	5	2	3	4	5
1	36	23·5112	1·7192	2·9556	552·78	4·7324	9·8304	15·1948	20·7208	8·1359	16·9004	26·1229	35·6232	111·3	231·1	357·2	487·2
2	28	18·7788	4·6764	21·8687	352·64	—	5·0980	10·4624	15·9884	—	23·8403	48·9264	74·7682	—	95·7	196·2	300·2
3	20	13·6808	6·9460	48·2469	187·16	—	—	5·3644	10·8904	—	—	37·2611	75·6447	—	—	73·4	149·0
4	12	8·3164	8·4844	71·9850	69·16	—	—	—	5·5260	—	—	—	46·8848	—	—	—	46·0
5	4	2·7904	9·2608	85·7624	7·79	—	—	—	—	—	—	—	—	—	—	—	—
Sums		31·0868		230·82	1169·53	4·7324	14·9284	31·0216	53·1256	8·1359	40·7407	112·3104	232·9209	111·3	326·8	627·1	982·4

From Table A the summations required for the expressions (14), (15), and (17), Art. 200, are taken. Some of these are independent of the load position and magnitude. For example, the denominator for (14) is (n being 5)

$$n \Sigma(y^2) - \{\Sigma(y)\}^2 = 5 \times 230 \cdot 82 - (31 \cdot 087)^2 = 187 \cdot 7$$

The denominator for (15) is

$$\Sigma\{(\tfrac{1}{2}l - x)^2\} = 1,170.$$

And for (17), the coefficient

$$\{h - \Sigma(y)/n\} = 9 \cdot 35822 - \frac{31 \cdot 0868}{5} = 3 \cdot 14086 \text{ ft.}$$

The values of H, V_B, and M_C for unit load at the various points are next calculated. Sample calculations are as follows:
For unit load at 3 or 3', from Table A, columns 4 and 8,

$$\Sigma(y) \times \Sigma(a - x) - n \Sigma\{(a - x)y\}$$
$$= 31 \cdot 0868 \times 14 \cdot 9284 - 5 \times 40 \cdot 7407 = 260 \cdot 4$$

hence from (14), Art. 200,

$$H = \tfrac{1}{2} \times 260 \cdot 4/187 \cdot 7 = 0 \cdot 6935.$$

For unit load at point 3, from (15), Art. 200, taking the value from Table A, columns 16 and 6, $V_C = V_B = \tfrac{1}{2} \times 326 \cdot 8/1,170 = 0 \cdot 1398$, and for load at 3' V_C would be $-0 \cdot 1398$, and V_B would be $1 - 0 \cdot 1398$.

Also for unit load at 3 or 3', using the above values and column (8), Table A in (17), Art. 200

$$M_C = 0 \cdot 6935 \times 3 \cdot 14086 - \tfrac{1}{10} \times 14 \cdot 9284 = +0 \cdot 6854.$$

The other quantities similarly calculated are entered in columns 2, 9, and 5 of Table C. They may be checked by the exact formulae given in Example 2, Art. 200, and show the nearness of the method of approximate summation.

We investigate one type of loading only, viz. movable load covering the left-hand half of the arch only. Then by simple mensuration we find approximately the loads in Table B.

TABLE B

Point	Weight of filling (lb.)	Weight of arch ring (lb.)	Total dead load (lb.)	Total live load
1	5,640	1,790	7,430	680
2	4,460	1,790	6,250	740
3	3,360	1,790	5,150	790
4	2,520	1,790	4,310	820
5	2,070	1,790	3,860	840

TABLE C

1	2	3	4	5	6	7	8	9	10
Points	H for unit load at either point	H for dead load at either point	H for live load at either point	M_C for unit load at either point	M_C for dead load at either point	M_C for live load at either point	V_B for dead load on *both* points	$V_B=V_C$ for unit load on left point only	$V_B=V_C$ for live load left point only
1, 1'	0	0	0	0	0	0	7,430	0	0
2, 2'	0·2835	1,772	210	+0·4172	2,608	309	6,250	0·0476	35
3, 3'	0·6935	3,572	546	+0·6854	3,530	539	5,150	0·1398	110
4, 4'	1·0730	4,625	880	+0·2680	1,155	220	4,310	0·2681	220
5, 5'	1·2972	5,007	1,085	−1·2382	−4,780	−1,036	3,860	0·4199	351
Totals	—	14,976	2,721	—	2,513	+32	27,000	—	716

Total H for arch, $2 \times 14{,}976 + 2{,}721 = 32{,}673$ lb.

Total M_C for arch, $2 \times 2{,}513 + 32 =$ say 5,060 lb.-ft.

Total V_B for arch $27{,}000 + 716 =$ say 27,720 lb.

$V_C = 716$, say 720 lb.

The loads in Table B are used with the unit load coefficients to find the contribution of each load to the totals as shown in Table C. Thus at point 3 we have for H $0·6935 \times 5{,}150 = 3{,}572$, and $0·6935 \times 790 = 546$.

The three unknown quantities H, M_C, and V_B or V_C, being now known, the funicular polygon which is the linear arch may be drawn by setting off the load line, and V_B and H, as shown to the right of Fig. 301, and starting at a point $5{,}060 \div 32{,}673 = 0·155$ ft. vertically below C. On account of the difficulty of obtaining an accurate result in the thin ring graphically, the work may be completed arithmetically by calculating the bending moments. If V is the vertical shearing force, that is the external downward force to the left of any section (or upward to the right), δV the increase of V on passing any load is equal to that load, hence after entering column 3, Table D, column 4 is easily obtained by addition or subtraction, since we know starting-points V_C or V_B.

Also the increase δM in bending moment between two consecutive loads is easily found by taking moments about the second of the two to be

$$\delta M = H . \delta y + V \delta x,$$

which is also evident by differentiating (7), Art. 200, thus

$$dM/dx = dm/dx + V_B + H dy/dx$$

and since

$$dm/dx + V_B = V, \quad \delta M = V . \delta x + H \delta v.$$

TABLE D

1	2	3	4	5	6	7	8	9	10	11	12
Point	Angle	Load = δV lb.	V to right of point (lb.)	δx to right of point (ft.)	δy (ft.) to next point	δM to next point (lb.-ft.)	M (lb.-ft.)	P to right of points (lb.)	Eccentricity towards intrados = M/P (ft.)	Maximum unit thrust f_c lb. per sq. ft.	Maximum unit tension f_t lb. per sq. ft.
A	40	—	−30,150	2·2004	1·7192	−10170	+15,520	44,400	0·350	45,500	1,100
1	36	8,110	−22,040	4·7324	2·9572	−7,690	+5,350	39,400	0·136		—
2	28	6,990	−15,050	5·0980	2·2696	−2,560	−2,340	35,900	−0·065		—
3	20	5,940	−9,110	5·3644	1·5384	+1,400	−4,900	33,800	−0·145		—
4	12	5,130	−3,980	5·5260	0·7764	+3,370	−3,500				—
5	4	4,700	+720	2·7904	0·0974	+5,190	−130				—
C	0	0	+720	2·7904	−0·0974	−1,170	+5,060	32,670	+0·155		—
5'	−4	3,860	+4,580	5·5260	−0·7764	−60	+3,890				—
4'	−12	4,310	+8,890	5·3644	−1·5384	−2,580	+3,830				—
3'	−20	5,150	+14,040	5·0980	−2·2696	−2,590	+1,250				—
2'	−28	6,250	+20,290	4·7324	−2·9572	−600	−1,340	38,300			—
1'	−36	7,430	27,720	2·2004	−1·7192	+4,820	−1,940	42,800	−0·051		—
B	−40	—	—	—	—		+2,880	—	0·067		—

Columns 4 and 5, Table D, follow by subtraction from columns 3 and 4 of Table A, and from the known values of H and V, column 7, Table D, is easily calculated.　Thus from point 3 to point 4

$$\delta M = -9,110 \times 5 \cdot 3644 + 32,673 \times 1 \cdot 5384 = 1,400.$$

Then knowing M_C as a starting-point, column 8, Table D, is completed by additions and subtractions from column 7.　Column 9, Table D, gives the normal thrusts on the ring sections, viz.

$$P = H \cos \theta - V \sin \theta.$$

The radial eccentricity of thrust at any cross-section is $M \div P$. Line 1, column 10, shows that the eccentricity at the abutment A is 0·350 ft.　The limits of the middle third of the ring have an eccentricity of $\frac{1}{6}$ of 2 ft. = 0·333 ft., so the linear arch is just outside those limits by 0·017 ft. or less than $\frac{1}{4}$ of an inch.

The values of the extreme stresses are calculated on the assumptions and by the formulae of Art. 100, *e.g.*

$$f_c = \frac{M}{\frac{1}{6} \times 1 \times 2^2} + \frac{P}{2 \times 1} = 1 \cdot 5M + 0 \cdot 5P \text{ lb. per sq. ft.}$$

and at point A

$$f_c = 1 \cdot 5 \times 15,520 + 0 \cdot 5 \times 44,400 = 45,500 \text{ lb. per sq. ft.}$$
$$f_t = 1 \cdot 5 \times 15,520 - 0 \cdot 5 \times 44,400 = 1,100 \text{ lb. per sq. ft.}$$

It will be observed from the changes in sign of M in column 8, Table D, that the line of thrust crosses the axis of the arch ring four times.

To complete the investigation it would be necessary to find the live-load positions to give maximum bending moment at every section.　For example, if point A be chosen, for each unit load to the left of C, taking a section at C and moments about A, $M_A = M_C - Hh - \frac{1}{2}V_C l + 1 \times a$, where M_C, H and V_C may be taken from columns 5, 2 and 9 respectively, of Table C.　For each unit load to the right of C the corresponding values from the left are modified by the omission of the term $Wa = a$ (since $W = 1$) and reversal of the sign of V_C.　When all the coefficients for unit loads are obtained, live load may be taken at points which give like signs for M_A, and M_A then calculated for the extreme variations in conditions.　Influence lines for M, V, H, P, etc., may also be plotted approximately by setting up ordinates at the load points 1, 2, 3, 4, 5, etc.

EXAMPLES XX

1. A concrete foundation has to be provided for a wall to carry 6 tons per linear foot at 1·5 ton per sq. ft. bearing pressure.　Estimate the necessary depth of foundation, according to Rankine's rule, if the angle of repose of the earth is 35°, and its weight 110 lb. per cu. ft.

2. Using British Standard Beams, find suitable dimensions for a two-tier grillage foundation to carry a stanchion designed to carry 100 tons, the base being 2 ft. square. The earth is to be limited to a pressure of 1·75 ton per sq. ft. and the tensile and shear unit stresses in the joists to 7·5 and 4 tons per sq. in. respectively.

3. A retaining wall, trapezoidal in cross-section, 24 ft. high and 8 ft. wide at the base, has a vertical face and a batter of 1 in 12 at the back. Find, according to Rankine's rule, how far from the centre of the base the resultant thrust passes (*a*) for horizontal filling to the level of the top of the wall, (*b*) for the maximum surcharge of earth if the angle of repose is 45°, weights of earth filling 120 lb., masonry 150 lb. per cu. ft. Assuming uniformly varying intensity of stress in each case, find the extreme values of the normal unit stress across the base of the wall.

4. For the same height, batter and constants as in Problem No. 3, find the minimum width of base to prevent the resultant passing outside the middle third of the base.

5. Assuming uniformly varying normal stress across the base, find the limit of height of a triangular masonry dam with water up to the vertical face in order that the vertical compressive stress across the base shall not exceed 6 tons per sq. ft. if the masonry weighs 150 lb. per cu. ft.

6. Assuming uniform variation in the intensity of vertical stress across the base of the dam in Fig. 297, find the extreme unit stresses at the upstream and downstream toes 5 and 5′, given that the widths at the levels 0, 1, 2, 3, 4, 5, are 12 ft., 12 ft., 18 ft., 32 ft., 47 ft. and 65 ft. respectively, and the masonry weighs 160 lb. per cu. ft.

DIMENSIONS AND PROPERTIES OF BRITISH STANDARD SECTIONS

THESE Tables are based on *Report No.* 6 of the British Standards Institution and are published by permission of the Institution. Some of the tables are slightly modified in form, and some contain the properties of sections of thicknesses not given in the above *Report*. All the tables have been taken by permission of Messrs. Dorman, Long & Co., Ltd., from their " Pocket Companion."

Changes, mainly of a minor character, take place from time to time in such tables and reference marks in particular have been changed since the first edition of this book was published. The designer will use the current tables of the British Steelwork Association, the handbooks of the manufacturers and the specifications of the British Standards Institution.

TABLE I

DIMENSIONS AND PROPERTIES OF

Reference mark	Size D×B in.	Weight per foot lb.	Web t	Flange T	Radius R1	Radius R2
1	2	3	4	5	6	7
B S B 30	24×7½	100	0·6	1·07	0·7	0·35
,, 29	20×7½	89	0·6	1·01	0·7	0·35
,, 28	18×7	75	0·55	0·928	0·65	0·325
,, 27	16×6	62	0·55	0·847	0·65	0·325
,, 26	15×6	59	0·5	0·88	0·6	0·3
,, 25	15×5	42	0·42	0·647	0·52	0·26
,, 24	14×6	57	0·5	0·873	0·6	0·3
,, 23	14×6	46	0·4	0·698	0·5	0·25
,, 22	12×6	54	0·5	0·883	0·6	0·3
,, 21	12×6	44	0·4	0·717	0·5	0·25
,, 20	12×5	32	0·35	0·55	0·45	0·225
,, 19	10×8	70	0·6	0·97	0·7	0·35
,, 18	10×6	42	0·4	0·736	0·5	0·25
,, 17	10×5	30	0·36	0·552	0·46	0·23
,, 16	9×7	58	0·55	0·924	0·65	0·325
,, 15	9×4	21	0·3	0·46	0·4	0·2
,, 14	8×6	35	0·44	0·597	0·54	0·27
,, 13	8×5	28	0·35	0·575	0·45	0·225
,, 12	8×4	18	0·28	0·402	0·38	0·19
,, 11	7×4	16	0·25	0·387	0·35	0·175
,, 10	6×5	25	0·41	0·52	0·51	0·255
,, 9	6×4½	20	0·37	0·431	0·47	0·235
,, 8	6×3	12	0·26	0·348	0·36	0·18
,, 7	5×4½	18	0·29	0·448	0·39	0·195
,, 6	5×3	11	0·22	0·376	0·32	0·16
,, 5	4¾×1¾	6·5	0·18	0·325	0·28	0·14
,, 4	4×3	9·5	0·22	0·336	0·32	0·16
,, 3	4×1¾	5	0·17	0·24	0·27	0·135
,, 2	3×3	8·5	0·2	0·332	0·3	0·15
,, 1	3×1½	4	0·16	0·248	0·26	0·13

BRITISH STANDARD **I** BEAMS

Area sq. in.	Moments of inertia		Radii of gyration in.		Section modulus	Reference mark
	About X—X	About Y—Y	About X—X	About Y—Y	About X—X	
8	9	10	11	12	13	14
29·4	2654	66·92	9·5	1·5	221·1	B S B 30
26·17	1670	62·63	7·99	1·54	167·0	,, 29
22·06	1149	47·04	7·21	1·46	127·6	,, 28
18·23	725·7	27·08	6·31	1·21	90·71	,, 27
17·35	628·9	28·22	6·02	1·27	83·85	,, 26
12·35	428	11·81	5·88	0·978	57·06	,, 25
16·76	532·9	27·96	5·63	1·29	76·12	,, 24
13·53	440·5	21·6	5·7	1·26	62·92	,, 23
15·88	375·5	28·3	4·86	1·33	62·58	,, 22
12·94	315·3	22·27	4·93	1·31	52·55	,, 21
9·41	220	9·753	4·83	1·01	36·66	,, 20
20·6	344·9	71·67	4·09	1·86	68·98	,, 19
12·35	211·5	22·95	4·13	1·36	42·3	,, 18
8·82	145·6	9·79	4·06	1·05	29·12	,, 17
17·06	229·5	46·3	3·66	1·64	51·0	,, 16
6·176	81·1	4·2	3·62	0·824	18·02	,, 15
10·29	110·5	17·95	3·27	1·32	27·62	,, 14
8·24	89·32	10·26	3·29	1·11	22·33	,, 13
5·294	55·69	3·578	3·24	0·822	13·92	,, 12
4·706	39·21	3·414	2·88	0·851	11·2	,, 11
7·35	43·61	9·116	2·43	1·11	14·53	,, 10
5·88	34·62	5·415	2·42	0·959	11·54	,, 9
3·53	20·21	1·339	2·39	0·616	6·736	,, 8
5·29	22·69	5·664	2·07	1·03	9·076	,, 7
3·235	13·61	1·462	2·05	0·672	5·444	,, 6
1·912	6·73	0·263	1·87	0·37	2·833	,, 5
2·794	7·52	1·281	1·64	0·677	3·76	,, 4
1·47	3·668	0·186	1·58	0·355	1·834	,, 3
2·5	3·787	1·262	1·23	0·71	2·524	,, 2
1·176	1·659	0·124	1·18	0·324	1·106	,, 1

TABLE II

DIMENSIONS AND PROPERTIES OF

Reference mark	Size A × B	Standard thicknesses		Radii		Weight per ft. lb.
		t	T	R	r	
1	2	3	4	5	6	7
B S C 27	15 × 4	0·525	0·630	0·630	0·440	41·94
,, 26	12 × 4	0·525	0·625	0·625	0·425	36·47
,, 25	12 × 3½	0·500	0·600	0·600	0·425	32·88
,, 24	12 × 3½	0·375	0·500	0·500	0·350	26·10
,, 22	11 × 3½	0·475	0·575	0·575	0·400	29·82
,, 21	10 × 4	0·475	0·575	0·575	0·400	30·16
,, 20	10 × 3½	0·475	0·575	0·575	0·400	28·21
,, 19	10 × 3½	0·375	0·500	0·500	0·350	23·55
,, 17	9 × 3½	0·450	0·550	0·550	0·375	25·39
,, 16	9 × 3½	0·375	0·500	0·500	0·350	22·27
,, 15	9 × 3	0·375	0·437	0·437	0·350	19·37
,, 13	8 × 3½	0·425	0·525	0·525	0·375	22·72
,, 12	8 × 3	0·375	0·500	0·500	0·350	19·30
,, 10	7 × 3½	0·400	0·500	0·500	0·350	20·23
,, 9	7 × 3	0·375	0·475	0·475	0·325	17·56
,, 8	6 × 3½	0·375	0·475	0·475	0·325	17·9
,, 6	6 × 3	0·312	0·437	0·437	0·300	14·49

TABLE III

DIMENSIONS AND PROPERTIES OF

Reference mark	Size A × B	Standard thicknesses		Area sq. in.	Weight per ft. lb.
		t	T		
1	2	3	4	5	6
B S Z 8	10 × 3½	0·475	0·575	8·283	28·16
,, 7	9 × 3½	0·450	0·550	7·449	25·33
,, 6	8 × 3½	0·425	0·525	6·670	22·68
,, 5	7 × 3½	0·400	0·500	5·948	20·22
,, 4	6 × 3½	0·375	0·475	5·258	17·88
,, 3	5 × 3	0·350	0·450	4·169	14·17

BRITISH STANDARD CHANNELS

Area sq. in.	Dimension P	Moments of inertia		Section moduli		Radii of gyration in.		Reference mark
		About XX	About YY	About XX	About YY	About XX	About YY	
8	**9**	**10**	**11**	**12**	**13**	**14**	**15**	**16**
12·334	0·935	377·0	14·55	50·27	4·748	5·53	1·09	B S C 27
10·727	1·031	218·2	13·65	36·36	4·599	4·51	1·13	,, 26
9·671	0·867	190·7	8·922	31·79	3·389	4·44	0·960	,, 25
7·675	0·860	158·6	7·572	26·44	2·868	4·55	0·993	,, 24
8·771	0·896	148·6	8·421	27·02	3·234	4·12	0·980	,, 22
8·871	1·102	130·7	12·02	26·14	4·147	3·84	1·16	,, 21
8·296	0·933	117·9	8·194	23·59	3·192	3·77	0·994	,, 20
6·925	0·933	102·6	7·187	20·52	2·800	3·85	1·02	,, 19
7·469	0·971	88·07	7·660	19·57	3·029	3·43	1·01	,, 17
6·550	0·976	79·90	6·963	17·76	2·759	3·49	1·03	,, 16
5·696	0·754	65·18	4·021	14·48	1·790	3·38	0·840	,, 15
6·682	1·011	63·76	7·067	15·94	2·839	3·09	1·03	,, 13
5·675	0·844	53·43	4·329	13·36	2·008	3·07	0·873	,, 12*
5·950	1·061	44·55	6·498	12·73	2·664	2·74	1·04	,, 10
5·166	0·874	37·63	4·017	10·75	1·889	2·70	0·882	,, 9
5·266	1·119	29·66	5·907	9·885	2·481	2·36	1·06	,, 8
4·261	0·938	24·01	3·503	8·003	1·699	2·37	0·907	,, 6

BRITISH STANDARD ZED BARS

Radii—in.		Moments of inertia		Section moduli		Angle α degrees	Least radius of gyration in.	Reference mark
R	r	About XX	About YY	About XX	About YY			
7	**8**	**9**	**10**	**11**	**12**	**13**	**14**	**15**
0·500	0·350	117·865	12·876	23·573	3·947	14	0·839	B S Z 8
0·475	0·350	87·889	12·418	19·531	3·792	16½	0·843	,, 7
0·450	0·325	63·729	12·024	15·932	3·657	19½	0·845	,, 6
0·450	0·300	44·609	11·618	12·745	3·521	23	0·840	,, 5
0·425	0·300	29·660	11·134	9·887	3·361	28½	0·821	,, 4
0·375	0·250	16·145	6·578	6·458	2·328	29½	0·698	,, 3

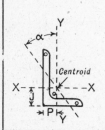

TABLE IV

DIMENSIONS AND PROPERTIES OF BRITISH STANDARD UNEQUAL ANGLES

Reference mark	Size and thickness	Area square inches	Weight per foot lb.	Radii		Dimensions		Moments of inertia		Section moduli		Angle α degrees	Least radius of gyration
				Root	Toe	J	P	About XX	About YY	About XX	About XX		
1	2	3	4	5	6	7	8	9	10	11	12	13	14
B S U A													
25	7 ×3½× ½	5·0	17·00	0·425	0·300	2·50	0·764	25·1	4·28	5·58	1·56	14½	0·74
25	,, ,, ⅝	6·172	20·98	0·425	0·300	2·55	0·814	30·55	5·15	6·86	1·92	14½	0·74
25	,, ,, ¾	7·313	24·86	0·425	0·300	2·60	0·862	35·68	5·95	8·11	2·26	14	0·73
24	6½×4½× ½	5·248	17·84	0·45	0·325	2·08	1·09	22·2	8·75	5·02	2·57	25	0·97
24	,, ,, ⅝	6·482	22·04	0·45	0·325	2·13	1·14	27·09	10·60	6·20	3·15	25	0·96
24	,, ,, ¾	7·686	26·13	0·45	0·325	2·18	1·19	31·66	12·32	7·33	3·72	25	0·96
22	6½×3½× ⅜	3·610	12·27	0·425	0·300	2·22	0·741	15·7	3·27	3·67	1·18	16½	0·75
22	,, ,, ½	4·750	16·15	0·425	0·300	2·28	0·792	20·4	4·20	4·83	1·55	16½	0·75
22	,, ,, ⅝	5·860	19·92	0·425	0·300	2·33	0·841	24·83	5·06	5·95	1·90	16	0·74
21	6 ×4 × ⅜	3·610	12·27	0·425	0·300	1·91	0·923	13·2	4·73	3·23	1·54	23½	0·87
21	,, ,, ½	4·750	16·15	0·425	0·300	1·96	0·974	17·1	6·10	4·23	2·02	23½	0·86
21	,, ,, ⅝	5·860	19·92	0·425	0·300	2·02	1·02	20·8	7·36	5·23	2·47	23½	0·86
20	6 ×3½× ⅜	3·424	11·64	0·40	0·275	2·01	0·773	12·6	3·22	3·16	1·18	19	0·76
20	,, ,, ½	4·502	15·31	0·40	0·275	2·06	0·823	16·4	4·14	4·16	1·55	19	0·75
20	,, ,, ⅝	5·549	18·87	0·40	0·275	2·11	0·872	19·88	4·97	5·11	1·89	18½	0·75
19	5½×3½× ⅜	3·236	11·00	0·40	0·275	1·80	0·807	9·93	3·15	2·68	1·17	22	0·76
19	,, ,, ½	4·252	14·46	0·40	0·275	1·85	0·857	12·80	4·05	3·51	1·53	22	0·75
19	,, ,, ⅝	5·236	17·80	0·40	0·275	1·90	0·905	15·6	4·86	4·33	1·87	21½	0·75
18	5½×3 × ⅜	3·050	10·37	0·375	0·250	1·90	0·662	9·45	2·02	2·62	0·86	17	0·64
18	,, ,, ½	4·003	13·61	0·375	0·250	1·95	0·711	12·2	2·58	3·44	1·13	16½	0·64
18	,, ,, ⅝	4·925	16·74	0·375	0·250	2·00	0·759	14·7	3·08	4·20	1·37	16½	0·63
17	5 ×4 × ⅜	3·236	11·00	0·40	0·275	1·51	1·01	7·96	4·53	2·28	1·52	32	0·85
17	,, ,, ½	4·252	14·46	0·40	0·275	1·56	1·06	10·3	5·82	2·99	1·98	32	0·84
17	,, ,, ⅝	5·236	17·80	0·40	0·275	1·60	1·11	12·4	7·01	3·66	2·43	32	0·83
16	5 ×3½× ⅜	3·050	10·37	0·375	0·250	1·59	0·848	7·64	3·09	2·24	1·17	25½	0·75
16	,, ,, ½	4·003	13·61	0·375	0·250	1·64	0·897	9·86	3·96	2·93	1·52	25½	0·75
16	,, ,, ⅝	4·925	16·74	0·375	0·250	1·69	0·944	11·9	4·75	3·60	1·86	25	0·74

TABLE IV—continued

DIMENSIONS AND PROPERTIES OF BRITISH STANDARD UNEQUAL ANGLES

Reference mark	Size and thickness	Area square inches	Weight per foot lb.	Radii		Dimensions		Moments of inertia		Section moduli		Angle α degrees	Least radius of gyration
				Root	Toe	J	P	About XX	About YY	About XX	About YY		
1	2	3	4	5	6	7	8	9	10	11	12	13	14
BSUA													
15	5 ×3 ×5/16	2·402	8·17	0·350	0·250	1·66	0·667	6·14	1·68	1·84	0·72	20	0·65
15	,, ,, 3/8	2·859	9·72	0·350	0·250	1·68	0·693	7·24	1·97	2·18	0·85	19½	0·65
15	,, ,, 1/2	3·749	12·75	0·350	0·250	1·73	0·742	9·33	2·51	2·85	1·11	19½	0·64
15	,, ,, 5/8	4·609	15·67	0·350	0·250	1·78	0·789	11·25	3·00	3·49	1·36	19	0·64
14	4½×3½×5/16	2·402	8·17	0·350	0·250	1·36	0·866	4·82	2·55	1·54	0·97	30½	0·74
14	,, ,, 3/8	2·859	9·72	0·350	0·250	1·39	0·891	5·69	3·00	1·83	1·15	30½	0·74
14	,, ,, 1/2	3·749	12·75	0·350	0·250	1·44	0·940	7·31	3·84	2·39	1·5	30	0·74
14	,, x,, 5/8	4·609	15·67	0·350	0·250	1·48	0·987	8·81	4·61	2·92	1·83	30	0·74
12	4 ×3½×5/16	2·246	7·64	0·350	0·250	1·16	0·915	3·46	2·47	1·22	0·96	37	0·72
12	,, ,, 3/8	2·671	9·08	0·350	0·250	1·19	0·941	4·08	2·90	1·45	1·13	37	0·72
12	,, ,, 1/2	3·499	11·90	0·350	0·250	1·24	0·990	5·23	3·71	1·89	1·48	37	0·71
12	,, ,, 5/8	4·296	14·61	0·350	0·250	1·28	1·04	6·28	4·44	2·31	1·80	36½	0·71
11	4 ×3 ×5/16	2·091	7·11	0·325	0·225	1·24	0·746	3·31	1·59	1·20	0·71	28½	0·64
11	,, ,, 3/8	2·485	8·45	0·325	0·225	1·27	0·771	3·89	1·87	1·42	0·84	28½	0·64
11	,, ,, 1/2	3·251	11·05	0·325	0·225	1·31	0·819	4·98	2·37	1·85	1·09	28½	0·63
11	,, ,, 5/8	3·985	13·55	0·325	0·225	1·36	0·865	5·96	2·83	2·26	1·33	28	0·63
9	3½×3 ×5/16	1·934	6·58	0·325	0·225	1·04	0·792	2·27	1·53	0·92	0·69	35½	0·62
9	,, ,, 3/8	2·298	7·81	0·325	0·225	1·07	0·819	2·67	1·80	1·10	0·83	35½	0·62
9	,, ,, 1/2	3·001	10·20	0·325	0·225	1·11	0·867	3·40	2·28	1·42	1·07	35½	0·61
9	,, ,, 5/8	3·673	12·49	0·325	0·225	1·16	0·912	4·05	2·71	1·73	1·30	35	0·61
8	3½×2½×5/16	1·779	6·05	0·30	0·20	1·12	0·627	2·15	0·910	0·90	0·49	26½	0·54
8	,, ,, 3/8	2·111	7·18	0·30	0·20	1·15	0·652	2·52	1·06	1·07	0·57	26	0·53
8	,, ,, 1/2	2·752	9·36	0·30	0·20	1·20	0·699	3·20	1·34	1·39	0·74	26	0·53
7	3 ×2½× 1/4	1·312	4·46	0·275	0·20	0·895	0·648	1·14	0·716	0·54	0·39	34	0·52
7	,, ,, 3/8	1·921	6·53	0·275	0·20	0·945	0·697	1·62	1·02	0·79	0·57	34	0·52
7	,, ,, 1/2	2·499	8·50	0·275	0·20	0·992	0·744	2·05	1·28	1·02	0·73	33½	0·52
6	3 ×2 × 1/4	1·187	4·04	0·275	0·20	0·976	0·482	1·06	0·373	0·52	0·25	23½	0·43
6	,, ,, 3/8	1·733	5·89	0·275	0·20	1·03	0·532	1·50	0·525	0·76	0·36	23	0·42
6	,, ,, 1/2	2·249	7·65	0·275	0·20	1·07	0·578	1·89	0·656	0·98	0·46	22½	0·42
5	2½×2 × 1/4	1·063	3·61	0·250	0·175	0·774	0·527	0·636	0·359	0·37	0·24	32	0·42
5	,, ,, 5/16	1·309	4·45	0·250	0·175	0·799	0·552	0·770	0·433	0·45	0·30	31½	0·42
5	,, ,, 3/8	1·547	5·26	0·250	0·175	0·823	0·575	0·895	0·502	0·53	0·35	31½	0·42
4	2 ×1½× 3/16	0·622	2·11	0·225	0·150	0·627	0·381	0·240	0·115	0·17	0·10	28½	0·32
4	,, ,, 1/4	0·814	2·77	0·225	0·150	0·653	0·407	0·308	0·146	0·23	0·13	28	0·31
4	,, ,, 5/16	0·997	3·39	0·225	0·150	0·678	0·431	0·369	0·174	0·28	0·16	28	0·31

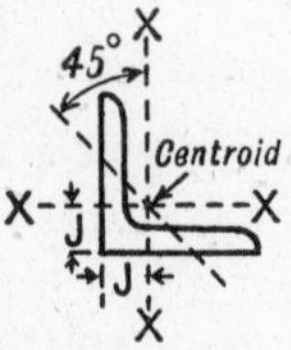

TABLE V

DIMENSIONS AND PROPERTIES OF BRITISH STANDARD EQUAL ANGLES

Reference mark	Size and thickness	Area sq. in.	Weight per ft. lb.	Radii		Dimension J	Moment of inertia XX	Section modulus XX	Least radius of gyr't'n
				Root	Toe				
1	2	3	4	5	6	7	8	9	10
BSEA									
16	8 ×8 × ½	7·75	26·35	0·600	0·425	2·15	47·4	8·10	1·58
16	,, ,, ⅝	9·609	32·67	0·600	0·425	2·20	58·2	10·03	1·57
16	,, ,, ¾	11·437	38·89	0·600	0·425	2·25	68·5	11·91	1·56
14	6 ×6 × 7/16	5·062	17·21	0·475	0·325	1·64	17·3	3·97	1·18
14	,, ,, ⅝	7·112	24·18	0·475	0·325	1·71	23·8	5·55	1·18
14	,, ,, ¾	8·441	28·70	0·475	0·325	1·76	27·8	6·56	1·17
13	5 ×5 × ⅜	3·610	12·27	0·425	0·300	1·37	8·51	2·34	0·98
13	,, ,, ½	4·750	16·15	0·425	0·300	1·42	11·0	3·07	0·98
13	,, ,, ⅝	5·860	19·92	0·425	0·300	1·47	13·4	3·80	0·98
12	4½×4½× ⅜	3·236	11·00	0·400	0·275	1·22	6·14	1·87	0·88
12	,, ,, ½	4·252	14·46	0·400	0·275	1·29	7·92	2·47	0·87
12	,, ,, ⅝	5·236	17·80	0·400	0·275	1·34	9·56	3·03	0·87
11	4 ×4 × ⅜	2·859	9·72	0·350	0·250	1·12	4·26	1·48	0·78
11	,, ,, ½	3·749	12·75	0·350	0·250	1·17	5·46	1·93	0·77
11	,, ,, ⅝	4·609	15·67	0·350	0·250	1·22	6·56	2·36	0·77
10	3½×3½× 5/16	2·091	7·11	0·325	0·225	0·975	2·39	0·95	0·68
10	,, ,, ⅜	2·485	8·45	0·325	0·225	1·00	2·80	1·12	0·68
10	,, ,, ½	3·251	11·05	0·325	0·225	1·05	3·57	1·46	0·68
10	,, ,, ⅝	3·985	13·55	0·325	0·225	1·09	4·27	1·77	0·68
9	3 ×3 × ¼	1·44	4·90	0·300	0·200	0·827	1·21	0·56	0·59
9	,, ,, ⅜	2·111	7·18	0·300	0·200	0·877	1·72	0·81	0·58
9	,, ,, ½	2·752	9·36	0·300	0·200	0·924	2·19	1·05	0·58
9	,, ,, ⅝	3·362	11·43	0·300	0·200	0·970	2·59	1·28	0·58
7	2½×2½× ¼	1·187	4·04	0·275	0·200	0·703	0·677	0·38	0·48
7	,, ,, 5/16	1·464	4·98	0·275	0·200	0·728	0·822	0·46	0·48
7	,, ,, ⅜	1·733	5·89	0·275	0·200	0·752	0·962	0·55	0·48
7	,, ,, ½	2·249	7·65	0·275	0·200	0·799	1·21	0·71	0·48
6	2¼×2¼× 3/16	0·809	2·75	0·250	0·175	0·616	0·378	0·23	0·44
6	,, ,, ¼	1·063	3·61	0·250	0·175	0·643	0·489	0·30	0·44
6	,, ,, 5/16	1·309	4·45	0·250	0·175	0·668	0·592	0·37	0·43
6	,, ,, ⅜	1·547	5·26	0·250	0·175	0·692	0·686	0·44	0·43
5	2 ×2 × 3/16	0·715	2·43	0·250	0·175	0·554	0·260	0·18	0·39
5	,, ,, ¼	0·938	3·19	0·250	0·175	0·581	0·336	0·24	0·39
5	,, ,, 5/16	1·153	3·92	0·250	0·175	0·605	0·401	0·29	0·38
5	,, ,, ⅜	1·36	4·62	0·250	0·175	0·629	0·467	0·34	0·38
4	1¾×1¾× 3/16	0·622	2·11	0·225	0·150	0·495	0·172	0·14	0·34
4	,, ,, ¼	0·814	2·77	0·225	0·150	0·520	0·220	0·18	0·34
4	,, ,,	0·997	3·39	0·225	0·150	0·544	0·264	0·22	0·34
3	1½×1½× 5/16	0·526	1·79	0·200	0·150	0·434	0·105	0·10	0·29
3	,, ,, ¼	0·686	2·33	0·200	0·150	0·458	0·134	0·13	0·29
3	,, ,, 5/16	0·839	2·85	0·200	0·150	0·482	0·159	0·16	0·29
2	1¼×1¼× 3/16	0·433	1·47	0·200	0·150	0·371	0·058	0·07	0·24
2	,, ,, ¼	0·561	1·91	0·200	0·150	0·396	0·073	0·09	0·23

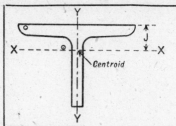

TABLE VI

DIMENSIONS AND PROPERTIES OF
BRITISH STANDARD TEES

Reference mark	Size and thickness	Area square inches	Weight per foot lb.	Radii		Dimension J	Moments of inertia		Section moduli		Radii of gyration	
				Table root	Table toe		About XX	About YY	About XX	About YY	About XX	About YY
1	2	3	4	5	6	7	8	9	10	11	12	13
B S T												
21	6 ×4 × $\frac{3}{8}$	3·634	12·36	0·425	0·300	0·915	4·700	6·344	1·52	2·11	1·137	1·321
21	,, ,, $\frac{1}{2}$	4·771	16·22	0·425	0·300	0·968	6·070	8·621	2·00	2·87	1·128	1·344
21	,, ,, $\frac{5}{8}$	5·878	19·99	0·425	0·300	1·02	7·350	10·912	2·47	3·64	1·118	1·362
20	6 ×3 × $\frac{3}{8}$	3·260	11·08	0·400	0·275	0·633	2·062	6·389	0·87	2·13	0·795	1·400
20	,, ,, $\frac{1}{2}$	4·272	14·53	0·400	0·275	0·684	2·635	8·649	1·14	2·88	0·785	1·423
20	,, ,, $\frac{5}{8}$	5·256	17·87	0·400	0·275	0·732	3·144	10·938	1·39	3·65	0·773	1·443
19	5 ×4 × $\frac{3}{8}$	3·257	11·07	0·400	0·275	0·998	4·471	3·691	1·49	1·48	1·172	1·065
19	,, ,, $\frac{1}{2}$	4·268	14·51	0·400	0·275	1·05	5·772	5·017	1·96	2·01	1·163	1·084
17	5 ×3 × $\frac{3}{8}$	2·875	9·78	0·350	0·250	0·691	1·973	3·716	0·85	1·49	0·828	1·137
17	,, ,, $\frac{1}{2}$	3·762	12·79	0·350	0·250	0·741	2·516	5·031	1·11	2·01	0·818	1·156
15	4 ×4 × $\frac{3}{8}$	2·872	9·77	0·350	0·250	1·11	1·901	1·901	1·45	0·95	1·208	0·814
15	,, ,, $\frac{1}{2}$	3·758	12·78	0·350	0·250	1·16	5·402	2·590	1·90	1·29	1·199	0·830
14	4 ×3 × $\frac{3}{8}$	2·498	8·49	0·325	0·225	0·767	1·860	1·914	0·83	0·96	0·863	0·875
14	,, ,, $\frac{1}{2}$	3·262	11·08	0·325	0·225	0·816	2·365	2·599	1·08	1·30	0·851	0·893
13	3½ ×3½ × $\frac{3}{8}$	2·496	8·49	0·325	0·225	0·988	2·768	1·284	1·10	0·73	1·053	0·717
13	,, ,, $\frac{1}{2}$	3·259	11·08	0·325	0·225	1·04	3·543	1·752	1·44	1·00	1·043	0·733
11	3 ×3 × $\frac{3}{8}$	2·121	7·21	0·300	0·200	0·868	1·708	0·816	0·80	0·54	0·897	0·620
11	,, ,, $\frac{1}{2}$	2·76	9·38	0·300	0·200	0·918	2·165	1·115	1·04	0·74	0·886	0·636
10	3 ×2½ × $\frac{3}{8}$	1·929	6·56	0·275	0·200	0·695	1·015	0·814	0·56	0·54	0·725	0·650
10	,, ,, $\frac{1}{2}$	2·506	8·52	0·275	0·200	0·742	1·275	1·109	0·73	0·74	0·713	0·665
8	2½ ×2½ × $\frac{1}{4}$	1·197	4·07	0·275	0·200	0·697	0·677	0·302	0·38	0·24	0·752	0·502
8	,, ,, $\frac{5}{16}$	1·474	5·01	0·275	0·200	0·724	0·823	0·387	0·46	0·31	0·747	0·512
8	,, ,, $\frac{3}{8}$	1·742	5·92	0·275	0·200	0·750	0·959	0·473	0·55	0·38	0·742	0·521
7	2¼ ×2¼ × $\frac{1}{4}$	1·071	3·64	0·250	0·175	0·638	0·488	0·224	0·30	0·20	0·675	0·457
7	,, ,, $\frac{3}{8}$	1·554	5·28	0·250	0·175	0·689	0·685	0·349	0·44	0·31	0·664	0·474
6	2 ×2 × $\frac{1}{4}$	0·947	3·22	0·250	0·175	0·579	0·337	0·157	0·24	0·16	0·597	0·407
6	,, ,, $\frac{3}{8}$	1·367	4·64	0·250	0·175	0·628	0·469	0·246	0·34	0·25	0·586	0·424
5	1½ ×2 × $\frac{1}{4}$	0·820	2·79	0·225	0·150	0·648	0·307	0·068	0·23	0·09	0·612	0·288
5	,, ,, $\frac{5}{16}$	1·003	3·41	0·225	0·150	0·674	0·369	0·088	0·28	0·12	0·607	0·296
4	1¾ ×1¾ × $\frac{1}{4}$	0·820	2·79	0·225	0·150	0·519	0·221	0·107	0·18	0·12	0·520	0·361
4	,, ,, $\frac{5}{16}$	0·999	3·40	0·225	0·150	0·544	0·265	0·137	0·22	0·16	0·515	0·370
3	1½ ×1½ × $\frac{3}{16}$	0·531	1·81	0·200	0·150	0·435	0·106	0·048	0·10	0·06	0·447	0·301
3	,, ,, $\frac{1}{4}$	0·692	2·35	0·200	0·150	0·460	0·135	0·067	0·13	0·09	0·442	0·312

	0	1	2	3	4	5	6	7	8	9	1	2	3	4	5	6	7	8	9
10	0000	0043	0086	0128	0170						4	9	13	17	21	26	30	34	38
						0212	0253	0294	0334	0374	4	8	12	16	20	24	28	32	37
11	0414	0453	0492	0531	0569						4	8	12	15	19	23	27	31	35
						0607	0645	0682	0719	0755	4	7	11	15	19	22	26	30	33
12	0792	0828	0864	0899	0934						3	7	11	14	18	21	25	28	32
						0969	1004	1038	1072	1106	3	7	10	14	17	20	24	27	31
13	1139	1173	1206	1239	1271						3	7	10	13	16	20	23	26	30
						1303	1335	1367	1399	1430	3	7	10	12	16	19	22	25	29
14	1461	1492	1523	1553							3	6	9	12	15	18	21	24	28
					1584	1614	1644	1673	1703	1732	3	6	9	12	15	17	20	23	26
15	1761	1790	1818	1847	1875	1903					3	6	9	11	14	17	20	23	26
							1931	1959	1987	2014	3	5	8	11	14	16	19	22	25
16	2041	2068	2095	2122	2148						3	5	8	11	14	16	19	22	24
						2175	2201	2227	2253	2279	3	5	8	10	13	15	18	21	23
17	2304	2330	2355	2380	2405	2430					3	5	8	10	13	15	18	20	23
							2455	2480	2504	2529	2	5	7	10	12	15	17	19	22
18	2553	2577	2601	2625	2648						2	5	7	9	12	14	16	19	21
						2672	2695	2718	2742	2765	2	5	7	9	11	14	16	18	21
19	2788	2810	2833	2856	2878						2	4	7	9	11	13	16	18	20
						2900	2923	2945	2967	2989	2	4	6	8	11	13	15	17	19
20	3010	3032	3054	3075	3096	3118	3139	3160	3181	3201	2	4	6	8	11	13	15	17	19
21	3222	3243	3263	3284	3304	3324	3345	3365	3385	3404	2	4	6	8	10	12	14	16	18
22	3424	3444	3464	3483	3502	3522	3541	3560	3579	3598	2	4	6	8	10	12	14	15	17
23	3617	3636	3655	3674	3692	3711	3729	3747	3766	3784	2	4	6	7	9	11	13	15	17
24	3802	3820	3838	3856	3874	3892	3909	3927	3945	3962	2	4	5	7	9	11	12	14	16
25	3979	3997	4014	4031	4048	4065	4082	4099	4116	4133	2	3	5	7	9	10	12	14	15
26	4150	4166	4183	4200	4216	4232	4249	4265	4281	4298	2	3	5	7	8	10	11	13	15
27	4314	4330	4346	4362	4378	4393	4409	4425	4440	4456	2	3	5	6	8	9	11	13	14
28	4472	4487	4502	4518	4533	4548	4564	4579	4594	4609	2	3	5	6	8	9	11	12	14
29	4624	4639	4654	4669	4683	4698	4713	4728	4742	4757	1	3	4	6	7	9	10	12	13
30	4771	4786	4800	4814	4829	4843	4857	4871	4886	4900	1	3	4	6	7	9	10	11	13
31	4914	4928	4942	4955	4969	4983	4997	5011	5024	5038	1	3	4	6	7	8	10	11	12
32	5051	5065	5079	5092	5105	5119	5132	5145	5159	5172	1	3	4	5	7	8	9	11	12
33	5185	5198	5211	5224	5237	5250	5263	5276	5289	5302	1	3	4	5	6	8	9	10	12
34	5315	5328	5340	5353	5366	5378	5391	5403	5416	5428	1	3	4	5	6	8	9	10	11
35	5441	5453	5465	5478	5490	5502	5514	5527	5539	5551	1	2	4	5	6	7	9	10	11
36	5563	5575	5587	5599	5611	5623	5635	5647	5658	5670	1	2	4	5	6	7	8	10	11
37	5682	5694	5705	5717	5729	5740	5752	5763	5775	5786	1	2	3	5	6	7	8	9	10
38	5798	5809	5821	5832	5843	5855	5866	5877	5888	5899	1	2	3	5	6	7	8	9	10
39	5911	5922	5933	5944	5955	5966	5977	5988	5999	6010	1	2	3	4	5	7	8	9	10
40	6021	6031	6042	6053	6064	6075	6085	6096	6107	6117	1	2	3	4	5	6	8	9	10
41	6128	6138	6149	6160	6170	6180	6191	6201	6212	6222	1	2	3	4	5	6	7	8	9
42	6232	6243	6253	6263	6274	6284	6294	6304	6314	6325	1	2	3	4	5	6	7	8	9
43	6335	6345	6355	6365	6375	6385	6395	6405	6415	6425	1	2	3	4	5	6	7	8	9
44	6435	6444	6454	6464	6474	6484	6493	6503	6513	6522	1	2	3	4	5	6	7	8	9
45	6532	6542	6551	6561	6571	6580	6590	6599	6609	6618	1	2	3	4	5	6	7	8	9
46	6628	6637	6646	6656	6665	6675	6684	6693	6702	6712	1	2	3	4	5	6	7	7	8
47	6721	6730	6739	6749	6758	6767	6776	6785	6794	6803	1	2	3	4	5	5	6	7	8
48	6812	6821	6830	6839	6848	6857	6866	6875	6884	6893	1	2	3	4	4	5	6	7	8
49	6902	6911	6920	6928	6937	6946	6955	6964	6972	6981	1	2	3	4	4	5	6	7	8
50	6990	6998	7007	7016	7024	7033	7042	7050	7059	7067	1	2	3	3	4	5	6	7	8

	0	1	2	3	4	5	6	7	8	9	1	2	3	4	5	6	7	8	9
51	7076	7084	7093	7101	7110	7118	7126	7135	7143	7152	1	2	3	3	4	5	6	7	8
52	7160	7168	7177	7185	7193	7202	7210	7218	7226	7235	1	2	2	3	4	5	6	7	7
53	7243	7251	7259	7267	7275	7284	7292	7300	7308	7316	1	2	2	3	4	5	6	6	7
54	7324	7332	7340	7348	7356	7364	7372	7380	7388	7396	1	2	2	3	4	5	6	6	7
55	7404	7412	7419	7427	7435	7443	7451	7459	7466	7474	1	2	2	3	4	5	5	6	7
56	7482	7490	7497	7505	7513	7520	7528	7536	7543	7551	1	2	2	3	4	5	5	6	7
57	7559	7566	7574	7582	7589	7597	7604	7612	7619	7627	1	2	2	3	4	5	5	6	7
58	7634	7642	7649	7657	7664	7672	7679	7686	7694	7701	1	1	2	3	4	4	5	6	7
59	7709	7716	7723	7731	7738	7745	7752	7760	7767	7774	1	1	2	3	4	4	5	6	7
60	7782	7789	7796	7803	7810	7818	7825	7832	7839	7846	1	1	2	3	4	4	5	6	6
61	7853	7860	7868	7875	7882	7889	7896	7903	7910	7917	1	1	2	3	4	4	5	6	6
62	7924	7931	7938	7945	7952	7959	7966	7973	7980	7987	1	1	2	3	3	4	5	6	6
63	7993	8000	8007	8014	8021	8028	8035	8041	8048	8055	1	1	2	3	3	4	5	5	6
64	8062	8069	8075	8082	8089	8096	8102	8109	8116	8122	1	1	2	3	3	4	5	5	6
65	8129	8136	8142	8149	8156	8162	8169	8176	8182	8189	1	1	2	3	3	4	5	6	6
66	8195	8202	8209	8215	8222	8228	8235	8241	8248	8254	1	1	2	3	3	4	5	5	6
67	8261	8267	8274	8280	8287	8293	8299	8306	8312	8319	1	1	2	3	3	4	5	5	6
68	8325	8331	8338	8344	8351	8357	8363	8370	8376	8382	1	1	2	3	3	4	4	5	6
69	8388	8395	8401	8407	8414	8420	8426	8432	8439	8445	1	1	2	2	3	4	4	5	6
70	8451	8457	8463	8470	8476	8482	8488	8494	8500	8506	1	1	2	3	3	4	4	5	6
71	8513	8519	8525	8531	8537	8543	8549	8555	8561	8567	1	1	2	2	3	4	4	5	5
72	8573	8579	8585	8591	8597	8603	8609	8615	8621	8627	1	1	2	2	3	4	4	5	5
73	8633	8639	8645	8651	8657	8663	8669	8675	8681	8686	1	1	2	2	3	4	4	5	5
74	8692	8698	8704	8710	8716	8722	8727	8733	8739	8745	1	1	2	2	3	4	4	5	5
75	8751	8756	8762	8768	8774	8779	8785	8791	8797	8802	1	1	2	2	3	3	4	5	5
76	8808	8814	8820	8825	8831	8837	8842	8848	8854	8859	1	1	2	2	3	3	4	5	5
77	8865	8871	8876	8882	8887	8893	8899	8904	8910	8915	1	1	2	2	3	3	4	4	5
78	8921	8927	8932	8938	8943	8949	8954	8960	8965	8971	1	1	2	2	3	3	4	4	5
79	8976	8982	8987	8993	8998	9004	9009	9015	9020	9025	1	1	2	2	3	3	4	4	5
80	9031	9036	9042	9047	9053	9058	9063	9069	9074	9079	1	1	2	2	3	3	4	4	5
81	9085	9090	9096	9101	9106	9112	9117	9122	9128	9133	1	1	2	2	3	3	4	4	5
82	9138	9143	9149	9154	9159	9165	9170	9175	9180	9186	1	1	2	2	3	3	4	4	5
83	9191	9196	9201	9206	9212	9217	9222	9227	9232	9238	1	1	2	2	3	3	4	4	5
84	9243	9248	9253	9258	9263	9269	9274	9279	9284	9289	1	1	2	2	3	3	4	4	5
85	9294	9299	9304	9309	9315	9320	9325	9330	9335	9340	1	1	2	2	3	3	4	4	5
86	9345	9350	9355	9360	9365	9370	9375	9380	9385	9390	1	1	2	2	3	3	4	4	5
87	9395	9400	9405	9410	9415	9420	9425	9430	9435	9440	0	1	1	2	2	3	3	4	4
88	9445	9450	9455	9460	9465	9469	9474	9479	9484	9489	0	1	1	2	2	3	3	4	4
89	9494	9499	9504	9509	9513	9518	9523	9528	9533	9538	0	1	1	2	2	3	3	4	4
90	9542	9547	9552	9557	9562	9566	9571	9576	9581	9586	0	1	1	2	2	3	3	4	4
91	9590	9595	9600	9605	9609	9614	9619	9624	9628	9633	0	1	1	2	2	3	3	4	4
92	9638	9643	9647	9652	9657	9661	9666	9671	9675	9680	0	1	1	2	2	3	3	4	4
93	9685	9689	9694	9699	9703	9708	9713	9717	9722	9727	0	1	1	2	2	3	3	4	4
94	9731	9736	9741	9745	9750	9754	9759	9763	9768	9773	0	1	1	2	2	3	3	4	4
95	9777	9782	9786	9791	9795	9800	9805	9809	9814	9818	0	1	1	2	2	3	3	4	4
96	9823	9827	9832	9836	9841	9845	9850	9854	9859	9863	0	1	1	2	2	3	3	4	4
97	9868	9872	9877	9881	9886	9890	9894	9899	9903	9908	0	1	1	2	2	3	3	4	4
98	9912	9917	9921	9926	9930	9934	9939	9943	9948	9952	0	1	1	2	2	3	3	4	4
99	9956	9961	9965	9969	9974	9978	9983	9987	9991	9996	0	1	1	2	2	3	3	3	4

	0	1	2	3	4	5	6	7	8	9	1	2	3	4	5	6	7	8	9
·00	1000	1002	1005	1007	1009	1012	1014	1016	1019	1021	0	0	1	1	1	1	2	2	2
·01	1023	1026	1028	1030	1033	1035	1038	1040	1042	1045	0	0	1	1	1	1	2	2	2
·02	1047	1050	1052	1054	1057	1059	1062	1064	1067	1069	0	0	1	1	1	1	2	2	2
·03	1072	1074	1076	1079	1081	1084	1086	1089	1091	1094	0	0	1	1	1	1	2	2	2
·04	1096	1099	1102	1104	1107	1109	1112	1114	1117	1119	0	1	1	1	1	2	2	2	2
·05	1122	1125	1127	1130	1132	1135	1138	1140	1143	1146	0	1	1	1	1	2	2	2	2
·06	1148	1151	1153	1156	1159	1161	1164	1167	1169	1172	0	1	1	1	1	2	2	2	2
·07	1175	1178	1180	1183	1186	1189	1191	1194	1197	1199	0	1	1	1	1	2	2	2	2
·08	1202	1205	1208	1211	1213	1216	1219	1222	1225	1227	0	1	1	1	1	2	2	2	3
·09	1230	1233	1236	1239	1242	1245	1247	1250	1253	1256	0	1	1	1	1	2	2	2	3
·10	1259	1262	1265	1268	1271	1274	1276	1279	1282	1285	0	1	1	1	1	2	2	2	3
·11	1288	1291	1294	1297	1300	1303	1306	1309	1312	1315	0	1	1	1	2	2	2	2	3
·12	1318	1321	1324	1327	1330	1334	1337	1340	1343	1346	0	1	1	1	2	2	2	2	3
·13	1349	1352	1355	1358	1361	1365	1368	1371	1374	1377	0	1	1	1	2	2	2	3	3
·14	1380	1384	1387	1390	1393	1396	1400	1403	1406	1409	0	1	1	1	2	2	2	3	3
·15	1413	1416	1419	1422	1426	1429	1432	1435	1439	1442	0	1	1	1	2	2	2	3	3
·16	1445	1449	1452	1455	1459	1462	1466	1469	1472	1476	0	1	1	1	2	2	2	3	3
·17	1479	1483	1486	1489	1493	1496	1500	1503	1507	1510	0	1	1	1	2	2	2	3	3
·18	1514	1517	1521	1524	1528	1531	1535	1538	1542	1545	0	1	1	1	2	2	2	3	3
·19	1549	1552	1556	1560	1563	1567	1570	1574	1578	1581	0	1	1	1	2	2	3	3	3
·20	1585	1589	1592	1596	1600	1603	1607	1611	1614	1618	0	1	1	1	2	2	3	3	3
·21	1622	1626	1629	1633	1637	1641	1644	1648	1652	1656	0	1	1	2	2	2	3	3	3
·22	1660	1663	1667	1671	1675	1679	1683	1687	1690	1694	0	1	1	2	2	2	3	3	3
·23	1698	1702	1706	1710	1714	1718	1722	1726	1730	1734	0	1	1	2	2	2	3	3	4
·24	1738	1742	1746	1750	1754	1758	1762	1766	1770	1774	0	1	1	2	2	2	3	3	4
·25	1778	1782	1786	1791	1795	1799	1803	1807	1811	1816	0	1	1	2	2	2	3	3	4
·26	1820	1824	1828	1832	1837	1841	1845	1849	1854	1858	0	1	1	2	2	3	3	3	4
·27	1862	1866	1871	1875	1879	1884	1888	1892	1897	1901	0	1	1	2	2	3	3	3	4
·28	1905	1910	1914	1919	1923	1928	1932	1936	1941	1945	0	1	1	2	2	3	3	4	4
·29	1950	1954	1959	1963	1968	1972	1977	1982	1986	1991	0	1	1	2	2	3	3	4	4
·30	1995	2000	2004	2009	2014	2018	2023	2028	2032	2037	0	1	1	2	2	3	3	4	4
·31	2042	2046	2051	2056	2061	2065	2070	2075	2080	2084	0	1	1	2	2	3	3	4	4
·32	2089	2094	2099	2104	2109	2113	2118	2123	2128	2133	0	1	1	2	2	3	3	4	4
·33	2138	2143	2148	2153	2158	2163	2168	2173	2178	2183	0	1	1	2	2	3	3	4	4
·34	2188	2193	2198	2203	2208	2213	2218	2223	2228	2234	1	1	2	2	3	3	4	4	5
·35	2239	2244	2249	2254	2259	2265	2270	2275	2280	2286	1	1	2	2	3	3	4	4	5
·36	2291	2296	2301	2307	2312	2317	2323	2328	2333	2339	1	1	2	2	3	3	4	4	5
·37	2344	2350	2355	2360	2366	2371	2377	2382	2388	2393	1	1	2	2	3	3	4	4	5
·38	2399	2404	2410	2415	2421	2427	2432	2438	2443	2449	1	1	2	2	3	3	4	4	5
·39	2455	2460	2466	2472	2477	2483	2489	2495	2500	2506	1	1	2	2	3	3	4	5	5
·40	2512	2518	2523	2529	2535	2541	2547	2553	2559	2564	1	1	2	2	3	4	4	5	5
·41	2570	2576	2582	2588	2594	2600	2606	2612	2618	2624	1	1	2	2	3	4	4	5	5
·42	2630	2636	2642	2649	2655	2661	2667	2673	2679	2685	1	1	2	2	3	4	4	5	6
·43	2692	2698	2704	2710	2716	2723	2729	2735	2742	2748	1	1	2	2	3	4	4	5	6
·44	2754	2761	2767	2773	2780	2786	2793	2799	2805	2812	1	1	2	3	3	4	4	5	6
·45	2818	2825	2831	2838	2844	2851	2858	2864	2871	2877	1	1	2	3	3	4	5	5	6
·46	2884	2891	2897	2904	2911	2917	2924	2931	2938	2944	1	1	2	3	3	4	5	5	6
·47	2951	2958	2965	2972	2979	2985	2992	2999	3006	3013	1	1	2	3	3	4	5	5	6
·48	3020	3027	3034	3041	3048	3055	3062	3069	3076	3083	1	1	2	3	4	4	5	6	6
·49	3090	3097	3105	3112	3119	3126	3133	3141	3148	3155	1	1	2	3	4	4	5	6	6

	0	1	2	3	4	5	6	7	8	9	1	2	3	4	5	6	7	8	9
·50	3162	3170	3177	3184	3192	3199	3206	3214	3221	3228	1	1	2	3	4	4	5	6	7
·51	3236	3243	3251	3258	3266	3273	3281	3289	3296	3304	1	2	2	3	4	5	5	6	7
·52	3311	3319	3327	3334	3342	3350	3357	3365	3373	3381	1	2	2	3	4	5	5	6	7
·53	3388	3396	3404	3412	3420	3428	3436	3443	3451	3459	1	2	2	3	4	5	6	6	7
·54	3467	3475	3483	3491	3499	3508	3516	3524	3532	3540	1	2	2	3	4	5	6	6	7
·55	3548	3556	3565	3573	3581	3589	3597	3606	3614	3622	1	2	2	3	4	5	6	7	7
·56	3631	3639	3648	3656	3664	3673	3681	3690	3698	3707	1	2	3	3	4	5	6	7	8
·57	3715	3724	3733	3741	3750	3758	3767	3776	3784	3793	1	2	3	3	4	5	6	7	8
·58	3802	3811	3819	3828	3837	3846	3855	3864	3873	3882	1	2	3	4	4	5	6	7	8
·59	3890	3899	3908	3917	3926	3936	3945	3954	3963	3972	1	2	3	4	5	5	6	7	8
·60	3981	3990	3999	4009	4018	4027	4036	4046	4055	4064	1	2	3	4	5	6	6	7	9
·61	4074	4083	4093	4102	4111	4121	4130	4140	4150	4159	1	2	3	4	5	6	7	8	9
·62	4169	4178	4188	4198	4207	4217	4227	4236	4246	4256	1	2	3	4	5	6	7	8	9
·63	4266	4276	4285	4295	4305	4315	4325	4335	4345	4355	1	2	3	4	5	6	7	8	9
·64	4365	4375	4385	4395	4406	4416	4426	4436	4446	4457	1	2	3	4	5	6	7	8	9
·65	4467	4477	4487	4498	4508	4519	4529	4539	4550	4560	1	2	3	4	5	6	7	8	9
·66	4571	4581	4592	4603	4613	4624	4634	4645	4656	4667	1	2	3	4	5	6	7	9	10
·67	4677	4688	4699	4710	4721	4732	4742	4753	4764	4775	1	2	3	4	5	7	8	9	10
·68	4786	4797	4808	4819	4831	4842	4853	4864	4875	4887	1	2	3	4	6	7	8	9	10
·69	4898	4909	4920	4932	4943	4955	4966	4977	4989	5000	1	2	3	5	6	7	8	9	10
·70	5012	5023	5035	5047	5058	5070	5082	5093	5105	5117	1	2	4	5	6	7	8	9	11
·71	5129	5140	5152	5164	5176	5188	5200	5212	5224	5236	1	2	4	5	6	7	8	10	11
·72	5248	5260	5272	5284	5297	5309	5321	5333	5346	5358	1	2	4	5	6	7	9	10	11
·73	5370	5383	5395	5408	5420	5433	5445	5458	5470	5483	1	3	4	5	6	8	9	10	11
·74	5495	5508	5521	5534	5546	5559	5572	5585	5598	5610	1	3	4	5	6	8	9	10	12
·75	5623	5636	5649	5662	5675	5689	5702	5715	5728	5741	1	3	4	5	7	8	9	10	12
·76	5754	5768	5781	5794	5808	5821	5834	5848	5861	5875	1	3	4	5	7	8	9	11	12
·77	5888	5902	5916	5929	5943	5957	5970	5984	5998	6012	1	3	4	5	7	8	10	11	12
·78	6026	6039	6053	6067	6081	6095	6109	6124	6138	6152	1	3	4	6	7	8	10	11	13
·79	6166	6180	6194	6209	6223	6237	6252	6266	6281	6295	1	3	4	6	7	9	10	11	13
·80	6310	6324	6339	6353	6368	6383	6397	6412	6427	6442	1	3	4	6	7	9	10	12	13
·81	6457	6471	6486	6501	6516	6531	6546	6561	6577	6592	2	3	5	6	8	9	11	12	14
·82	6607	6622	6637	6653	6668	6683	6699	6714	6730	6745	2	3	5	6	8	9	11	12	14
·83	6761	6776	6792	6808	6823	6839	6855	6871	6887	6902	2	3	5	6	8	9	11	13	14
·84	6918	6934	6950	6966	6982	6998	7015	7031	7047	7063	2	3	5	6	8	10	11	13	15
·85	7079	7096	7112	7129	7145	7161	7178	7194	7211	7228	2	3	5	7	8	10	12	13	15
·86	7244	7261	7278	7295	7311	7328	7345	7362	7379	7396	2	3	5	7	8	10	12	13	15
·87	7413	7430	7447	7464	7482	7499	7516	7534	7551	7568	2	3	5	7	9	10	12	14	16
·88	7586	7603	7621	7638	7656	7674	7691	7709	7727	7745	2	4	5	7	9	11	12	14	16
·89	7762	7780	7798	7816	7834	7852	7870	7889	7907	7925	2	4	5	7	9	11	13	14	16
·90	7943	7962	7980	7998	8017	8035	8054	8072	8091	8110	2	4	6	7	9	11	13	15	17
·91	8128	8147	8166	8185	8204	8222	8241	8260	8279	8299	2	4	6	8	9	11	13	15	17
·92	8318	8337	8356	8375	8395	8414	8433	8453	8472	8492	2	4	6	8	10	12	14	15	17
·93	8511	8531	8551	8570	8590	8610	8630	8650	8670	8690	2	4	6	8	10	12	14	16	18
·94	8710	8730	8750	8770	8790	8810	8831	8851	8872	8892	2	4	6	8	10	12	14	16	18
·95	8913	8933	8954	8974	8995	9016	9036	9057	9078	9099	2	4	6	8	10	12	15	17	19
·96	9120	9141	9162	9183	9204	9226	9247	9268	9290	9311	2	4	6	8	11	13	15	17	19
·97	9333	9354	9376	9397	9419	9441	9462	9484	9506	9528	2	4	7	9	11	13	15	17	20
·98	9550	9572	9594	9616	9638	9661	9683	9705	9727	9750	2	4	7	9	11	13	16	18	20
·99	9772	9795	9817	9840	9863	9886	9908	9931	9954	9977	2	5	7	9	11	14	16	18	20

Degrees.	Radians	Chord	Sine	Tangent	Cotangent	Cosine			
0°	0	0	0	0	∞	1	1·414	1·5708	90°
1	·0175	·017	·0175	·0175	57·2900	·9998	1·402	1·5533	89
2	·0349	·035	·0348	·0349	28·6363	·9994	1·389	1·5359	88
3	·0524	·052	·0523	·0524	19·0811	·9986	1·377	1·5184	87
4	·0698	·070	·0698	·0699	14·3007	·9976	1·364	1·5010	86
5	·0873	·087	·0872	·0875	11·4301	·9962	1·351	1·4835	85
6	·1047	·105	·1045	·1051	9·5144	·9945	1·338	1·4661	84
7	·1222	·122	·1219	·1228	8·1443	·9925	1·325	1·4486	83
8	·1396	·140	·1392	·1405	7·1154	·9903	1·312	1·4312	82
9	·1571	·157	·1564	·1584	6·3138	·9877	1·299	1·4137	81
10	·1745	·174	·1736	·1763	5·6713	·9848	1·286	1·3963	80
11	·1920	·192	·1908	·1944	5·1446	·9816	1·272	1·3788	79
12	·2094	·209	·2079	·2126	4·7046	·9781	1·259	1·3614	78
13	·2269	·226	·2250	·2309	4·3315	·9744	1·245	1·3439	77
14	·2443	·244	·2419	·2493	4·0108	·9703	1·231	1·3265	76
15	·2618	·261	·2588	·2679	3·7321	·9659	1·218	1·3090	75
16	·2793	·278	·2756	·2867	3·4874	·9613	1·204	1·2915	74
17	·2967	·296	·2924	·3057	3·2709	·9563	1·190	1·2741	73
18	·3142	·313	·3090	·3249	3·0777	·9511	1·176	1·2566	72
19	·3316	·330	·3256	·3443	2·9042	·9455	1·161	1·2392	71
20	·3491	·347	·3420	·3640	2·7475	·9397	1·147	1·2217	70
21	·3665	·364	·3584	·3839	2·6051	·9336	1·133	1·2043	69
22	·3840	·382	·3746	·4040	2·4751	·9272	1·118	1·1868	68
23	·4014	·399	·3907	·4245	2·3559	·9205	1·104	1·1694	67
24	·4189	·416	·4067	·4452	2·2460	·9135	1·089	1·1519	66
25	·4363	·433	·4226	·4663	2·1445	·9063	1·075	1·1345	65
26	·4538	·450	·4384	·4877	2·0503	·8988	1·060	1·1170	64
27	·4712	·467	·4540	·5095	1·9626	·8910	1·045	1·0996	63
28	·4887	·484	·4695	·5317	1·8807	·8829	1·030	1·0821	62
29	·5061	·501	·4848	·5543	1·8040	·8746	1·015	1·0647	61
30	·5236	·518	·5000	·5774	1·7321	·8660	1·000	1·0472	60
31	·5411	·534	·5150	·6009	1·6643	·8572	·985	1·0297	59
32	·5585	·551	·5299	·6249	1·6003	·8480	·970	1·0123	58
33	·5760	·568	·5446	·6494	1·5399	·8387	·954	·9948	57
34	·5934	·585	·5592	·6745	1·4826	·8290	·939	·9774	56
35	·6109	·601	·5736	·7002	1·4281	·8192	·923	·9599	55
36	·6283	·618	·5878	·7265	1·3764	·8090	·908	·9425	54
37	·6458	·625	·6018	·7536	1·3270	·7986	·892	·9250	53
38	·6632	·651	·6157	·7813	1·2799	·7880	·877	·9076	52
39	·6807	·668	·6293	·8098	1·2349	·7771	·861	·8901	51
40	·6981	·684	·6428	·8391	1·1918	·7660	·845	·8727	50
41	·7156	·700	·6561	·8693	1·1504	·7547	·829	·8552	49
42	·7330	·717	·6691	·9004	1·1106	·7431	·813	·8378	48
43	7505	·733	·6820	·9325	1·0724	·7314	·797	·8203	47
44	·7679	·749	·6947	·9657	1·0355	·7193	·781	·8029	46
45°	·7854	·765	·7071	1·0000	1·0000	·7071	·765	·7854	45°
			Cosine	Cotangent	Tangent	Sine	Chord	Radians	Degrees

Angle.

TABLE OF ULTIMATE COMPRESSION OR CRUSHING STRENGTH

Material	Breaking strength in tons per sq. in.
Cast iron	40 to 50
Brass	5
Copper (cast)	20
Brick	1 to 3
Granite	10
Sandstone	3 to 4
Oak	2 to 4 ⎫
Ash	4 ⎪ Along
Yellow pine	2 to 2½ ⎬ the
Red pine	4 to 5 ⎭ grain

TABLE OF COEFFICIENTS OF ELASTICITY

Material	Stretch, direct, or Young's modulus (E) in tons per sq. in.	Transverse or shearing modulus or modulus of rigidity (N, C, or G) in tons per sq. in.
Wrought iron	12,000 to 13,000	5,000 to 6,000
Steel	13,000 to 14,000	5,500 to 6,500
Cast iron	6,000 to 9,000	2,500 to 3,500
Copper	6,000 to 7,000	2,000 to 3,000
Brass	5,000 to 6,000	2,000 to 3,000
Gun-metal	5,000 to 6,000	2,000 to 3,000
Aluminium	4,000 to 5,000	—
Aluminium-bronze	7,500	—
Oak	—	650
Ash	—	700
Elm	—	500
Teak	—	1,000
Yellow pine	—	700
Red pine	—	700
Spruce	—	700

TABLE OF APPROXIMATE WORKING STRESSES FOR DEAD LOADS

Material	Kind of stress	Magnitude of allowable stress
Structural steel (Board of Trade allowance)	Tension	6·5 tons per sq. in.
Structural steel (Board of Trade allowance)	Compression	6·5 ,, ,,
Rivet steel	Shearing	5 ,, ,,
Wrought iron (Board of Trade)	Tension	5 ,, ,,
,, ,, ,, ,,	Compression	5 ,, ,,
,, ,, ,, ,,	Shearing	4 ,, ,,
Cast iron	Tension	2 ,, ,,
,, ,,	Compression	4 ,, ,,
,, ,,	Shearing	1·5 ,, ,,
Portland cement concrete, 5 to 1	Compression	15 tons per sq. ft.
Bricks in mortar	Compression	4 ,, ,,
Granite	Compression	70 ,, ,,
Sandstone	Compression	35 ,, ,,

ANSWERS TO EXAMPLES

EXAMPLES I

(1) 3·96 tons per sq. in.; 13,700 tons per sq. in.; 1·98 tons per sq. in.

(2) 20° 54½′; 2·62 tons per sq. in.; 2·80 tons per sq. in.

(3) 3·27 tons per sq. in.; 3·60 tons per sq. in.

(4) 0·0318 in.

(5) 23,200,000 lb. per sq. in.; 3·385.

(6) 3·5 tons per sq. in.; 0·866 ton per sq. in.; 3·60 tons per sq. in. inclined 76° 5′ to the plane.

(7) 32·5° and 3·54 tons per sq. in., or 72° and 2·27 tons per sq. in.

(8) 4·58 tons per sq. in. 40·9° to plane; 4 tons per sq. in.

(9) 8·12 tons per sq. in.; normal of plane inclined 38° to axis of 5-ton stress.

(11) 6·65 tons per sq. in.; normal of plane inclined 22½° to axis of 5-ton stress.

(10) 4·828 tons per sq. in. tensile on plane inclined 22½° to cross-section. 0·828 ton per sq. in. compressive on plane inclined 67½° to cross-section.

(12) 4·16 and 3·16 tons per sq. in.

(13) 4·375 tons per sq. in.

(14) $\dfrac{m^2-m-1}{m(m-1)}$.

(15) 19,556 lb. per sq. in. (steel); 10,222 lb. per sq. in. (brass); 48·89 per cent.

EXAMPLES II

(1) 32·4 and 21·6 tons per sq. in.; 23·5 per cent.; 13,120 tons per sq. in.

(2) (a) 15·77 tons; (b) 69·1 tons.

(3) 7·03 in.-tons.

(4) 620 in.-lb.

(5) 2,760 and 16·26 in.-lb.

(6) 8 tons per sq. in.; 0·0738 in.; 4·06 tons.

(7) (a) 55 tons; 4·07 sq. in.; (b) 25 tons; 1·85 sq. in.

(8) 5·46 tons per sq. in.

(9) 3·50 in.

(10) 4·17 tons per sq. in. (Launhardt); 3·33 tons per sq. in. (Dynamic).

(11) 1·56 sq. in. (Launhardt); 1·71 sq. in. (Dynamic).

EXAMPLES III

(1) 3·55 in.

(2) 2·52 in. from outside of flange.

(3) 312 (in.)⁴.

(4) 74·1 (in.)⁴, 2·47 in.

EXAMPLES IV

(1) 158 ton-ft.; 20 tons; 50 ton-ft.; 14 tons.

(2) 2,650 ton-ft.

(3) 8 ton-ft.; 6 ft. from left end; 9·75 ton-ft.

(4) 10·958 ft. from left support; 88·1 ton-ft.; 87 ton-ft.

(5) $\dfrac{1}{\sqrt{3}}l$ ft.; $\dfrac{wl^2}{9\sqrt{3}}$ ton-ft.; 10·4 ft.; 41·5 ton-ft.

(6) 11·76 ft. from A.

(7) 13·1 ft. from A.

(8) 32 and 40 ton-ft.; 3·05 ft. from supports.

(9) 0·207l and 0·293l from ends.

(10) 4·6 ton-ft.; 0·5 ton-ft.; 4·9 ft. from left support; 4·74 ft. from right support.

(11) 13 ton-ft.; 2·89 ft. from left support; 1·46 ft. from right support.

(12) 27·5 ton-ft.; 52 ton-ft.; 16 ton-ft.; 4·15 ft. (left) and 1·41 ft. (right).

(13) (a) $\tfrac{1}{8}Wl$; (b) $\tfrac{1}{8}Wl\left(1-\dfrac{1}{n^2}\right)$.

(14) (a) $\tfrac{1}{8}Wl$; (b) $\tfrac{1}{8}Wl\left(1+\dfrac{1}{n^2}\right)$.

Examples V

(1) 4·8 tons per sq. in.

(2) 217·5 ton-in.

(3) 15·625 tons; 7·812 tons.

(4) 937·5 ft.; 253·2 ton-in.

(5) 1,470 lb. per sq. in.; 609·5 ft.

(6) $3\tfrac{1}{3}$ in.

(7) 13·1 in.

(8) 1·414.

(9) 12 ft.

(10) 3·27 to 1.

(11) 7 tons per sq. in.

(12) 21,750 lb.-in.

(13) 5·96 (in.)^4.

(14) 4·57 in.; 930 (in.)^4; 1·36 ton; 1·95 ton per sq. in.

(15) 30·7 ft.

(16) 7·15 tons per sq. in.

(17) 16 in.

(18) $\tfrac{7}{8}$ in.

(19) 5·80 tons per sq. in.; 3·93.

(21) 4·68 tons per sq. in. tension inclined 53° 44′ to section; 2·60 tons per sq. in. inclined 36° 46′ to section.

(22) 351,900 lb.-in.; 18,000 lb. per sq. in.

(23) 1,437 lb.; 6,930 lb. per sq. in.

(24) 0·63 sq. in.; 386 lb.

(25) 4·67 sq. in.

(26) 0·565 sq. in.; 14,580 lb. per sq. in.

(27) 3 sq. in.; 18,000 lb. per sq. in.

(28) 9,580 lb. per sq. in.; 1,040,000 lb.-in.

Examples VI

(1) 1·875 tons; −16·875 tons; ±7·5 tons; 337·5 and 450 ton-ft.

(2) Positive, 0·33, 0·67, and 1 ton; negative, 1·67, 1·33 and 1 ton; 8·33 ton-ft.; 13·33 ton-ft.; 15 ton-ft.

(3) 1·125, 3·75 and 5·25 tons; 162·5, 306 and 318·75 ton-ft.; 0·255 ton per ft.

(4) 243 ton-ft.; 2·5 ft. from centre; 240 ton-ft.

(5) 100 ton-ft. at centre; 27·24 ft.

(6) 31·2 ft. from an abutment; 779 ton-ft.

(7) 3,238,500 lb.-ft.; 615,000 lb.-ft.

(8) 137,700 lb.

(9) 5,500 lb. per ft.; 4,400,000 lb.-ft.; 4,320,000 lb.-ft.

(10) 12·52 ft.

(11) 612 ton-ft.; 7·5 tons; 13·5 tons.

EXAMPLES VII

(1) 4·96 tons; 4·74 tons per sq. in.; 7·94 tons; 3·79 tons per sq. in.

(2) $\frac{1}{384}\frac{Wl^3}{EI}$; $\dfrac{\dfrac{W}{2}}{1+\dfrac{48EI}{el^3}}$.

(3) 3 in. (nearly) from centre of span; 0·262 in.

(4) $\frac{5}{2}W$; $\frac{7}{96}\frac{Wl^3}{EI}$.

(5) $\frac{5}{16}W$; $\frac{5}{32}Wl$; $\frac{3}{16}Wl$; $\frac{1}{\sqrt{5}}l$ from free end; $\frac{1}{48\sqrt{5}}\frac{Wl^3}{EI}$; 0·2038 W.

(6) $\frac{19}{32}$.

(7) $\frac{1}{30}\frac{wl^4}{EI}$.

(8) 0·134 in.; 0·148 in.; 9·25 in. from centre; 0·148 in.

(9) 9·18 tons; 3·3 tons.

(10) 8·8 in. from centre; 0·342 in.

(11) 12·083 tons (centre); 3·958 tons (ends).

(12) 0·414; 0·68.

(13) 0·29; 0·337; 0·644.

(14) $\frac{4}{5}$; $\frac{12}{19}$.

(15) 0·0186 in.; 0·224 in.; 0·0181 in. (upward); 9·87 ft.

(16) 0·0988; 0·073 in. (upward); 0·409 in.; 4·63 ft. to left of D.

(17) $0·544\frac{Wl^3}{EI_0}$.

(18) 2·98 in.

(19) $0·0241\frac{Wl^3}{EI_0}$.

(20) $0·0153\frac{Wl^3}{EI_0}$.

EXAMPLES VIII

(1) 6·55 tons per sq. in.; 0·152 in.

(2) $\frac{1}{30}wl^2$; $\frac{1}{20}wl^2$; $\frac{9}{30}wl$; $\frac{3}{20}wl$; 0·025l from centre.

(3) $\frac{2}{9}Wl$; $\frac{1}{9}Wl$; $\frac{5}{648}Wl^3/EI$; $\frac{1}{162}Wl^3/EI$; $\frac{2}{9}l$ from ends.

(4) $\frac{2}{27}Wl$; $\frac{4}{27}Wl$; $\frac{7}{27}W$; $\frac{20}{27}W$; $\frac{5}{1296}Wl^3/EI$; $\frac{8}{2187}Wl^3/EI$; $\frac{4}{7}l$ from light end; $\frac{16}{3969}Wl^3/EI$; $\frac{2}{7}l$ and $\frac{4}{5}l$ from light end.

(5) 22·025 ton-ft. (left); 19·475 ton-ft. (right).

(6) $\frac{11}{192}wl^2$ and $\frac{5}{192}wl^2$; 0·182l and $\frac{13}{18}l$ from heavy end; 0·443 from heavy end; 0·00134 wl^4/EI.

(7) 0·1108Wl; 0·1392Wl; 0·007 $\dfrac{Wl^3}{EI}$.

(8) 0·0759Wl; 0·0491Wl; 0·0037$\dfrac{Wl^3}{EI}$.

(9) 0, $\frac{1}{10}wl^2$, $\frac{1}{10}wl^2$, 0; $\frac{4}{10}wl$, $1\frac{1}{10}wl$, $1\frac{1}{10}wl$, $\frac{4}{10}wl$.

(10) 0, 175 ton-ft., 125 ton-ft., 0; 24·16 tons, 57·083 tons, 55 tons, 23·75 tons.

(11) 7·429 ton-ft. at B, 4·913 ton-ft. at C; in order A, B, C, D, 3·45, 7·34, 6·39, 3·82 tons.

(12) (a) From fixed end, $\frac{9}{104}wl^2$, $\frac{1}{13}wl^2$, $\frac{11}{104}wl^2$, 0; $\frac{53}{104}wl$, $\frac{25}{26}wl$, $\frac{59}{52}wl$, $\frac{41}{104}wl$. (b) $\frac{1}{12}wl^2$ at each; $\dfrac{wl}{2}$ at ends, wl at inner supports.

(13) In order A, B, C, D, 6·193, 5·661, 5·486, 0 ton-ft.; 4·441, 6·03, 6·843, 3·703 tons.

(14) 2·94 and 8·65 ton-ft.; 4·01, 5·60, 8·32, 3·07 tons.

EXAMPLES IX

(1) 3·2 to 1, 1 to 3.
(2) 7·4 per cent.

EXAMPLES X

(1) 1·936 and 0·844 tons per sq. in.
(2) 5·6 and 2·4 tons per sq. in.
(3) 7·417 and 6·583 tons per sq. in.
(4) 14·85 ft.
(5) 72·8 tons.
(6) 4 ft. 6·6 in.
(7) 989 tons.

(8) 354 tons.
(9) 324 tons.
(10) 36·6 tons.
(11) 121·3 tons.
(12) 0·48 in.
(13) 9·5 in.
(14) 3·43 in.

(15) 2·441 and 0·339 tons per sq. in.
(16) 0·309 in.
(17) 46·3 in.; 0·34 ton per sq. in.
(18) 770 tons.
(19) 19·06 tons; 5·42 tons per sq. in.
(20) 2·275 in.
(21) 13·2 tons; 4·06 tons per sq. in.
(22) 4,571 and 521 lb. per sq. in. compression
(23) 0·0308 in.; 3,173 lb. per sq. in.
(24) 87,150 lb.; 10,333 lb. per sq. in. compressive; 3,000 lb. per sq. in. tensile.
(25) 93,500 lb.; 10,270 lb. per sq. in. compressive; 3,540 lb. per sq. in. tensile.

EXAMPLES XI

(1) At bearings 392 lb. at apex and struts 784 lb., at bearings and apex 940 lb., at strut 1,880 lb.
(2) 7,390 lb.
(3) At shoe and apex 1,155 lb.; at intermediate joints 2,310 lb.

X

Examples XII

(1) *Dead loads.* Main rafters and short strut 2,630, 2,280 and 700 lb. thrust. Main ties and inclined ties 2,350, 1,568 and 786 lb. tension. *Wind loads.* Main rafters and short strut 3,290, 3,290 and 1,880 lb. thrust. Main ties and inclined tie 3,680, 1,575 and 2,100 lb. tension.

(2) Main rafters 7,700, 6,060, 7,700 lb. thrust, short struts 3,980 lb. thrust, main ties 8,610 and 3,100 lb. tension, inclined tie 5,510 lb. tension.

(3) Main rafters 14,680, 13,830, 13,000, 12,300 lb. thrust; truss struts 1,680, 3,360, 1,680 lb. thrust; main ties 13,130, 11,250, 7,500 lb., second truss ties 3,750 and 5,625 lb., sub-truss tie 1,875 lb.

(4) Add to No. 3 answers in order, 11,140, 11,140, 11,140, 11,140 lb., 2,475, 4,950, 2,475 lb., 12,440, 9,680, 4,150 lb., 5,530, 8,300 lb., 3,760 lb.

(5) From left end, $+$ for tension, $-$ for thrust. Diagonals $-16\cdot96$, $+16\cdot96$, $-11\cdot19$, $+11\cdot19$, $-5\cdot089$, $+5\cdot089$, $+0\cdot36$, $-0\cdot36$, $+6\cdot135$, $-6\cdot135$, $+9\cdot02$, $-9\cdot02$, $+9\cdot02$, $-9\cdot02$, $+9\cdot02$, $-9\cdot02$ tons. Top chord thrusts $16\cdot96$, $28\cdot16$, $33\cdot26$, $32\cdot90$, $26\cdot78$, $17\cdot78$, $8\cdot78$ tons. Lower chord tensions $8\cdot48$, $22\cdot56$, $30\cdot71$, $33\cdot08$, $29\cdot84$, $22\cdot28$, $13\cdot28$, $4\cdot28$ tons.

(6) Coefficients of W from left end. Diagonals (tension) $\frac{95}{28}$, $\frac{15}{7}$, $\frac{25}{28}$, (0), $\frac{5}{14}$, $\frac{45}{28}$, $\frac{125}{56}$, $\frac{125}{56}$. Verticals (thrust) $\frac{19}{7}$, $\frac{12}{7}$, $\frac{5}{7}$, 0, $\frac{2}{7}$, $\frac{9}{7}$, $\frac{25}{14}$, $\frac{25}{14}$. Top chord (thrust), $\frac{57}{28}$, $\frac{93}{28}$, $\frac{27}{7}$, $\frac{27}{7}$, $\frac{51}{14}$, $\frac{75}{28}$, $\frac{75}{56}$. Lower chord (tension) 0, $\frac{57}{28}$, $\frac{93}{28}$, $\frac{51}{14}$, $\frac{75}{28}$, $\frac{75}{56}$, 0.

(7) $\dfrac{l^2}{h} \dfrac{(n-1)(n+1)}{6n} \cdot$ W.

(8) $\frac{21}{16} \cdot \dfrac{l}{h} \cdot$ W.

(9) Top chord thrusts firm support to centre 1,294, 1,230, 1,295, 1,423, 1,402, 1,378 tons. Lower chord tensions, 915, 915, 931, 1,290, 1,290, 1,444, 1,444, 1,422 tons.

Examples XIII

(1) From support to centre (in tons): lower chord maximum tensions, $44\cdot1$, $44\cdot1$, $75\cdot6$, $94\cdot5$; minimum tensions, $12\cdot6$, $12\cdot6$, $21\cdot6$, $27\cdot0$; top chord maximum thrusts, $75\cdot6$, $94\cdot5$, $100\cdot8$; minimum thrusts, $21\cdot6$, $27\cdot0$, $28\cdot8$.

(2) $+$ tension, $-$thrust (in tons). End posts, $-73\cdot5$, -21. Diagonals, support to centre first, $+54\cdot4$, $+13\cdot1$, second $+37\cdot1$, $+3\cdot4$, third $+21\cdot8$, $-8\cdot3$. More exactly diagonals: first $+53\cdot7$, $+13\cdot9$, second $+35\cdot8$, $+4\cdot8$, third $+20\cdot1$, $-6\cdot6$.

(3) From support to centre (in tons): lower chord tensions (max.) $23\cdot3$, $60\cdot3$, $78\cdot7$, (min.) $6\cdot03$, $15\cdot3$, $19\cdot9$; upper chord thrusts (max.) $46\cdot1$, $73\cdot9$, $83\cdot1$, (min.) $11\cdot5$, $18\cdot5$, $20\cdot8$; extreme stresses in diagonals, end to centre (tension $+$) max. $-46\cdot8$, $+45\cdot65$, $-29\cdot65$, $+28\cdot50$, $-15\cdot35$, $+14\cdot20$, min. $-12\cdot1$, $+10\cdot95$, $-6\cdot11$, $+4\cdot96$, $+2\cdot66$, $-3\cdot81$.

(4) $2\cdot8$ tons per ft.
From end to centre (in tons): lower chord maximum tensions 0, 30, $42\cdot86$; top chord maximum thrusts $30\cdot9$, $43\cdot3$, $48\cdot2$; diagonals maximum tensions $42\cdot1$, $23\cdot3$, $12\cdot6$; verticals maximum thrusts $37\cdot5$, $17\cdot8$, $9\cdot7$, 0.

Examples XIV

(1) $-1,250w$, $+3,750w$ and $+2,500w$ ton-ft.

(2) Maximum tension $115\cdot8$ tons; maximum thrust $26\cdot1$ ton-ft.

(3) Bay QE; $67\cdot0$ tons; $12\cdot1$ tons.

(4) MF and FG.

(5) 111·4 and 13·5 tons (tension).

(6) 104 and 12·6 tons.

(7) 49·3 tons thrust; 216·4 tons tension.

(8) 62·8 and 21·2 tons tension.

(9) 185,600 and 66,900 lb. tension.

(10) Thrusts 14 tons; tension 17·4 tons.

(11) Thrusts 14 tons; tension 9·9 tons.

(12) Stresses in lb.; tension +; tie, +1,000; jib −1,732; shear legs (a) +650 each, (b) +1,060 and +170, (c) +1,154 and 0; post (a) −370, (b) −310, (c) −260; strut RS, (a) −485, (b) −785, (c) −870; strut RT (a) −485, (b) −125, (c) 0.

(13) AB 1,450 lb., AD 1,280 lb., AC 800 lb.

Examples XV

(1) 0·0252 in., 0·00762 in.

(2) 0·2124 in.

(3) 0·2395 in.

(4) AC, 2·40 tons; BC 5·49 tons, DC 5·25 tons.

(5) Sides 207 lb.; vertical diagonal 707 lb. tension; horizontal diagonal 293 lb. thrust.

(6) 0·387W and 0·467W.

(7) 1,540 lb. tension, 2,180 lb. thrust.

(8) 25·98 tons, (a) 40 tons, (b) 38 tons.

Examples XVI

(1) 242 lb.; 6·03 tons per sq. in.; 1·33 ton per square inch.

(2) 59,130 lb.-ft.

(3) 56,318 lb.-ft.

(4) 2·625 ton-ft.; 1·125 ton-ft.

(5) 0·393 in.

(6) 2·5 ton-ft.; 1·25 ton-ft.

(7) 0·357 in.

(8) 12·455; 10·446 and 21·797 tons-in.

(9) 0·1148 in.

Examples XVII

(1) to (5) Indefinite; refer to Plate II.

(6) 4·91 tons.

(7) 2·749 tons.

(8) 2·943 tons.

Examples XVIII

(1) 6 ft. 8 in. and 12 ft. 10 in.

(2) 16 ft. 1 in.

(3) 1·25 in.; 23 ft. 6 in.; 32 ft.

(4) $\frac{7}{8}$-in. rivets, pitch 5·8 in. theoretical, 4 in. actual; or 1-in. rivets, 6-in. pitch changing to $\frac{7}{8}$-in. rivets at first stiffener.

(5) 24 in. or 21 in. according to 4-in. or 6-in. pitch.

(6) (a) 6 tons 12 cwt. 1 qr. 13 lb.; (b) 17 cwt. 2 qrs. 22 lb.; (c) 8 cwt. 3 qrs. 17 lb.

x*

EXAMPLES XIX

(1) 3,710 ft.

(2) 53·85 tons; 10·77 sq. in.; 82·13 ft., 57·7 tons; 48·85 tons; 3·36 tons; 46·9 tons.

(3) (by calculation) left end 30·79, right end 31·10 tons.

(4) 47·3 tons; 48 ton-ft.; left −15 ton-ft., right +10 ton-ft.

(5) +18·83 tons-ft.; −18·83 tons-ft. at 23·4 ft. from left, 60·5 ft. from right and 39·5 ft. from left loaded.

(6) +1·5625 and −3·4375 tons; +2·5 and −2·5 tons; +2·8125 and −2·1875 tons.

(7) + and − 0·9450, 0·625, 1·055 tons.

(8) 40·39 tons + and −62·5 ton-ft.; −15 ton-ft., +10 ton-ft.

(9) + and − 31·25 ton-ft.; for + value, 25 ft. from each end; for − value 50 ft. central.

(10) + and − 2·5 tons for all sections.

(11) + and − 1·25 tons for all sections.

(12) 1·523 tons per sq. in.

(13) 31·25 tons; 8·4 ton-ft.

(14) 20·83 tons; 6·51 ton-ft.; 25·1 ton-ft.; 25·1 tons; 0·57 ton.

(15) 3·125 tons; −23·4375 ton-ft.; +7·8125 ton-ft.; 6·25 tons; −15·625 ton-ft.

(16) + and − 0·563 W and 0·9945 W.

(17) Thrust 1·032 W; tension 1·1628 W; (W=load per 50 ft. panel).

(18) 30·5 tons.

(19) 9·76 tons; 21·9 ton-ft.

(20) 6·96 tons; 5·66 ton-ft.; 5·8 tons; 6·4 ton-ft.

(21) 0·421 ton.

(22) 0·43 ton per sq. in.

(23) 11·72 tons; −18·75 ton-ft.

(24) Ends −0·0553 Wl; −½W; 0·459 W; Crown −0·0757 Wl; 0·459 W; zero.

(25) 0·3103 ton.

(26) 1,990 lb. per sq. in.; 50·5°.

(27) 1·62 tons per sq. in.

EXAMPLES XX

(1) 2·24 ft.

(2) Three 12 × 5 in. beams on eight 8 × 4 in. beams all 7 ft. long in concrete 8 ft. by 8 ft.

(3) (a) 1·405 ft.; 6,468 lb. thrust and 168 lb. tension per sq. ft.; (b) 1·3446 ft.; 10,665 lb. thrust and 45 lb. tension per sq. ft.

(4) (a) 8·17 ft.; (b) 8·04 ft.

(5) 89·6 ft.

(6) Upstream toe 6·22 tons per sq. ft.; downstream toe 4·98 tons per sq. ft.

INDEX

(The numbers refer to pages)